SCHAUM'S OUTLINE OF

THEORY AND PROBLEMS

OF

ADVANCED STRUCTURAL ANALYSIS

•

BY

JAN J. TUMA, Ph.D.

Engineering Consultant
Boulder, Colorado

AND

R. K. MUNSHI, Ph.D.

Assistant Professor of Civil Engineering
Oklahoma State University

SCHAUM'S OUTLINE SERIES

McGRAW-HILL BOOK COMPANY

New York, St. Louis, San Francisco, Düsseldorf, Johannesburg, Kuala Lumpur, London, Mexico, Montreal, New Delhi, Panama, Rio de Janeiro, Singapore, Sydney, and Toronto

07-065426-3

1 2 3 4 5 6 7 8 9 0 SH SH 7 5 4 3 2 1

Preface

This book is the second volume in a series of three, dealing with the static analysis of linear structures. Whereas the first volume dealt with the scalar analysis of simple coplanar systems, the matrix analysis of complex coplanar structures is developed herein. As before, the statements of theory are sufficiently complete, and supported by derivations and proofs, so that the book may be used as a textbook for a formal course in matrix structural analysis or as a supplement to all current standard texts on this subject.

The numerous solved problems illustrate the meaning and the application of the principles and methods presented in the theory parts of each chapter, and with the tables of formulas and coefficients provide the teacher, the student and the practicing engineer with a wealth of ready-made solutions to many important problems.

Since the matrix analysis is only a special form of application of the basic theorems introduced in the first book, a brief summary and a set of review problems are given in the first chapter. Next, two basic concepts, the static vector and the deformation vector, are developed (Chapters 2 and 3), and their linear dependence is given in terms of the respective transport matrices, designated by superscripts (systems) and subscripts (stations), facilitating their correspondence.

With the symbolic logic set, the main part of the book is devoted to the development and applications of the major methods of matrix analysis: the transport method (Chapter 4), the flexibility method (Chapters 5, 6, 7, 8, 9), and the stiffness method (Chapters 10, 11), each applied to the analysis of particular structural systems.

Finally, the matrix analysis of planar trusses is presented in the last chapter as a summary of concepts developed in the preceding chapters. Thus the last chapter is also a review chapter, showing in a simple matrix form the conceptual duality of the flexibility and stiffness methods.

In the organization and preparation of the material presented in this book the authors have been assisted by many individuals. Over one hundred college teachers of structural mechanics participated in three NSF summer institutes directed by the senior author at Oklahoma State University and critically tested this material. Several hundred Oklahoma State University students and engineers attended residence and extension classes dealing with this subject matter. Many of them enthusiastically recorded our lectures and assisted in the preparation of problems, tables of coefficients and special solutions. Although it is impossbile to mention all of them by name, the assistance of the following individuals is acknowledged in the sequence of their participation: R. J. Ungson, A. J. Celis, K. S. Havner, J. F. Hedges, D. E. Morrisset, D. C. Carman, J. W. Gillespie, C. A. Martin, S. E. French, N. G. Simpson, S. L. Chu, R. J. Larkin, T. I. Lassley, E. R. Sturm, J. O. Cobb, C. Heller, J. W. Harvey, H. C. Boecker, J. T. Oden, C. W. Wu, J. W. Exline, H. S. Yu, G. D. Houser, J. D. Ramey, and M. N. Reddy. They all belonged to a team known in their time as the 4B4 class. This volume is dedicated to all 4B4 classes.

Finally, but not least, gratitude is expressed to Daniel Schaum, Thomas Dembofsky, Nicola Monti, David Beckwith, and Henry Hayden for their excellent editorial cooperation, encouragement and continued interest.

J. J. TUMA
R. K. MUNSHI

Boulder, Colorado
Stillwater, Oklahoma
October 1971

CONTENTS

CONTENTS

Chapter 1

Principles of Analysis

1.1 SCOPE

The structures considered in this book are *systems of bars* (straight, bent or curved), forming with their loads and reactions a *coplanar system*. They are classified as *beams, arches, frames and trusses* and their function is to carry *loads* and resist *stresses* (imparted by volume changes and/or displacement of supports).

Whereas the elementary analysis deals with simple structural systems, a *systematic analysis* of *complex linear structures* is developed here. The *linearity* implies that *all governing differential equations are linear* and consequently the *superposition* of causes and effects is admissible (Definitions I-1.1,2).*

1.2 ANALYSIS

The methodical *investigation* of the *stability, strength and rigidity* of structures is known as the structural analysis. The aim is accomplished when the structure was found geometrically stable and the comparison was made of the stresses and deformations developed by the existing causes with the allowable stresses and deformations.

The structure which is analyzed is a *mathematical model* represented by centroidal axes of its members, supported by idealized constraints and acted upon by assumed, symbolic loads.

The following properties assigned to this model are introduced as the *assumptions of the analysis*: (*a*) the model is in a state of static equilibrium, (*b*) all loads have been applied gradually and no kinetic energy is imparted, (*c*) the system is conservative and its performance is independent of time, (*d*) the structural material is homogeneous, isotropic, continuous and follows Hooke's Law, (*e*) all deformations are small, elastic and do not alter (significantly) the initial geometry of the structure, (*f*) the principle of linear superposition of causes and effects is valid.

1.3 FUNCTIONS AND CONSTANTS

For the analysis four types of basic quantities are essential: (*a*) *geometric quantities*, (*b*) *statical quantities*, (*c*) *deformations*, and (*d*) *material constants*.

The *geometric quantities* are the position coordinates (defining the position of the bar axis and the location of statical and deformation vectors) and the properties of the bar cross section, known from the mechanics of solids.

The *statical quantities* are the external forces and moments acting on the structure (loads), the forces and moments developed by these causes at the points of support (reactions), the forces and moments developed at the cross sections of a structural member or at the points or planes of connection of two or more members denoted as the stresses (stress resultants).

The *deformations* are defined as the linear displacements (deflections) and the angular displacements (rotations) of the cross section of the structural member.

---

* In this book definition, equation, table, section and problem numbers preceded by the Roman numeral I refer to "Theory and Problems of Structural Analysis" by Jan Tuma, Schaum's Outline Series, McGraw-Hill Book Company, New York, 1969.

The *material constants* are the moduli of elasticity and rigidity of structural material, spring constants of connections and foundations, and volume change coefficients. These constants are assumed to be known from experiments, independent of time and linearly related to statical and deformation vectors.

1.4 BASIC THEOREMS

Structural analysis developed historically along two distinct paths: (A) *Vectorial mechanics*, based on the principles of static equilibrium and geometry of deformation. (B) *Virtual work mechanics* based on the principle of conservation of energy.

A1. Principle of Static Equilibrium

A planar structural system is in a state of static equilibrium when the resultant of all forces and all moments equals zero (Definition I-1.3).

$$\sum F_x = 0 \qquad \sum F_y = 0 \qquad \sum M = 0 \tag{1.1a}$$

or

$$\sum M_i = 0 \qquad \sum M_j = 0 \qquad \sum M_k = 0 \tag{1.1b}$$

where F_x, F_y are force components along the respective coordinate axis, M is a moment vector normal to the plane of structure and i, j, k are three different moment poles, arbitrarily selected.

A2. Normal Force Area Theorem

The change in length between two cross sections of a straight loaded bar is equal to the area of the normal force diagram between these two cross sections, divided by the axial rigidity EA (Definition I-5.1).

$$\Delta_N = \int_0^l \frac{N\,dx}{EA} \tag{1.2}$$

where N = axial force, E = modulus of elasticity, A = cross-sectional area, l = distance between two cross sections.

A3. Shearing Force Area Theorem

The shearing detrusion between two cross sections of a straight loaded bar is equal to the area of the shearing force diagram between these two cross sections divided by the shearing rigidity GA/β (Definition I-5.2).

$$\Delta_V = \int_0^l \frac{\beta V\,dx}{GA} \tag{1.3}$$

where V = shearing force, G = modulus of rigidity, β = shape factor of the cross section.

A4. Moment Area Theorem I

The change in flexural slope between two points i, j of the elastic curve of a straight loaded bar is equal to the area of the bending moment diagram between these two cross sections, divided by the flexural rigidity EI (Definition I-5.3).

$$\phi_{ij} = \int_{x_i}^{x_j} \frac{M\,dx}{EI} \tag{1.4}$$

where M = bending moment, I = moment of inertia of the cross section.

A5. Moment Area Theorem II

The tangential deviation of one point i of the flexural elastic curve with respect to the tangent drawn to the elastic curve at another point j is equal to the static moment of the area of the bending moment diagram between the verticals drawn through these two points, about the deviation line, divided by the flexural rigidity EI (Definition I-5.4).

$$t_{ij} = \int_{x_i}^{x_j} \frac{M(x - x_i)\,dx}{EI} \tag{1.5}$$

where t_{ij} = tangential deviation at i and x_i, x_j are the coordinates of i, j respectively.

B1. Virtual Displacements Principle—Mechanical System

A mechanical plane system is in a state of equilibrium if the virtual work done by all real forces and/or moments is zero for every virtual displacement consistent with the constraints (Definition I-7.4-1).

$$\sum (P_j\bar{\delta}_j) + \sum (Q_j\bar{\theta}_j) + \sum (R_k\bar{\delta}_k) + \sum (M_k\bar{\theta}_k) = 0 \tag{1.6}$$

where P, Q, R, M = real load and reactions, $\bar{\delta}_x$, $\bar{\delta}_y$, $\bar{\theta}$ = external virtual displacements, and $(P_j\bar{\delta}_j)$, $(Q_j\bar{\theta}_j)$, $(R_k\bar{\delta}_k)$, $(M_k\bar{\theta}_k)$ are scalar products of two vectors.

B2. Virtual Displacements Principle—Deformable System

A deformable plane system is in a state of equilibrium if the total virtual work done by the real external forces and/or moments is equal to the total virtual work done by all real internal stresses for every virtual displacement consistent with the constraints (Definition I-7.4-2).

$$\sum (P_j\bar{\delta}_j) + \sum (Q_j\bar{\theta}_j) + \sum (R_k\bar{\delta}_k) + \sum (M_k\bar{\theta}_k) = \int (\sigma_x\bar{\epsilon}_x + \tau_{xy}\bar{\gamma}_{xy})\,dx\,dy\,dz \tag{1.7}$$

where σ_x, τ_{xy} = real stresses, $\bar{\epsilon}_x$, $\bar{\gamma}_{xy}$ = internal virtual displacements (strains), and $(P_j\bar{\delta}_j)$, $(Q_j\bar{\theta}_j)$, $(R_k\bar{\delta}_k)$, $(M_k\bar{\theta}_k)$ are scalar products of two vectors.

B3. Virtual Forces Principle—Deformable System

A deformable plane system has the real displacements and strains compatible with the external and internal constraints, if the total external virtual work is equal to the total internal virtual work for every system of virtual forces, moments and stresses satisfying equilibrium (Definition I-7.4-3).

$$\sum (\bar{P}_k\delta_k) + \sum (\bar{Q}_j\theta_j) + \sum (\bar{R}_k\delta_k) + \sum (\bar{M}_k\theta_k) = \int (\bar{\sigma}_x\epsilon_x + \bar{\tau}_{xy}\gamma_{xy})\,dx\,dy\,dz \tag{1.8}$$

where $\bar{P}_j$, $\bar{Q}_j$, $\bar{R}_k$, $\bar{M}_k$ = virtual loads and reactions, $\bar{\sigma}_x$, $\bar{\tau}_{xy}$ = virtual stresses and $(\bar{P}_j\delta_j)$, $(\bar{Q}_j\theta_j)$, $(\bar{R}_k\delta_k)$, $(\bar{M}_k\theta_k)$ are scalar products of two vectors.

B4. Castigliano's Theorem I

If a set of loads is applied on a linearly elastic structure and the strain energy U is expressed as a function of the displacements at the points of application and acting in their directions, the partial derivative of U with respect to one of these displacements Δ_j equals the corresponding load (stress) F_j (Definition I-9.1).

$$\frac{\partial U}{\partial \Delta_j} = F_j \tag{1.9}$$

B5. Engesser's Theorem I

If a set of loads is applied on a deformable structure and the complementary energy U^* is expressed as a function of these loads, the partial derivative of U^* with respect to one of these loads (stresses) F_j equals the displacement Δ_j at the point of application and in the direction of F_j (Definition I-9.2).

$$\frac{\partial U^*}{\partial F_j} = \Delta_j \tag{1.10}$$

For linear structures, $U = U^*$.

1.5 RECIPROCAL AND INFLUENCE THEOREMS

C1. Maxwell-Mohr's Reciprocal Theorem

For an elastic structure subjected to two unit causes at points i and j respectively, the displacement at i in the i' direction due to the cause at j acting in the j' direction is equal to the displacement at j in the j' direction due to the cause at i acting in the i' direction (Definition I-7.9).

$$\Delta_{ij} = \Delta_{ji} \tag{1.11}$$

C2. Virtual Work Mechanism as Influence Line

By removing the constraint of a statically determinate structure at i where the effect is desired and replacing it by the corresponding reaction or stress, the mechanism thus formed, if in the state of virtual displacement compatible with the remaining constraints, produces a configuration which is to some scale the desired influence line, representing the variation of the respective effect at i due to a unit force moving across the structure (Definition I-11.4).

C3. Müller–Breslau Principle

The influence line for reaction or stress at i in a statically indeterminate elastic structure is to some scale its elastic curve which is obtained by removing the constraint corresponding to that reaction or stress and introducing in its place the corresponding displacement compatible with the remaining constraints (Definition I-11.5).

C4. Influence Lines for Deflection

The influence line for deflection at i in the i' direction in an elastic structure due to a unit moving force, normal to the path of motion in all conceivable positions, is the elastic curve of that structure produced by a unit force applied at i in the i' direction (Definition I-11.6).

C5. Influence Lines for Slope

The influence line for slope of the elastic curve at i in an elastic structure due to a unit moving force, normal to the path of motion in all conceivable positions, is the elastic curve of that structure produced by a unit moment applied at i (Definition I-11.7).

1.6 METHODS

These fifteen theorems presented in three separate groups (A, B, C) form the foundation of the structural analysis, and their applications lead to a large variety of methods.

Regardless of their names, each of these methods belongs to one of the following categories:

(1) *The transport methods* (Chapter I-6).
(2) *The flexibility methods* (Chapter I-8).
(3) *The stiffness methods* (Chapter I-10).

The flexibility and stiffness methods are the most fundamental and universal methods of analysis, applicable to structural systems of all kinds. The systematic development of these methods and their matrix application to the analysis of large structures is presented in the following chapters.

1.7 SIGN CONVENTIONS

Two standard sign conventions are commonly used. They are designated as the flexibility sign convention and the stiffness sign convention.

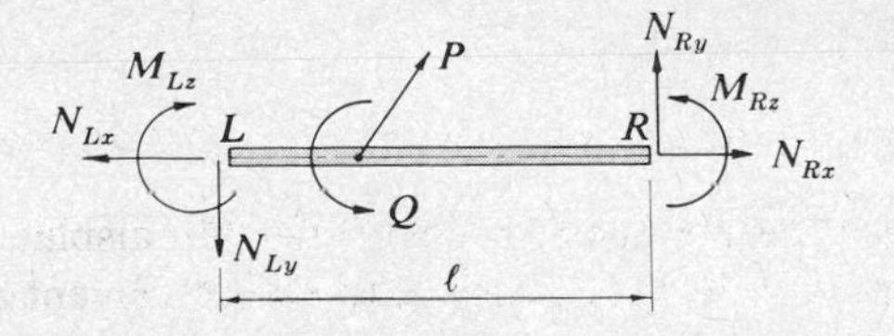

Fig. 1-1. Positive Stresses, Flexibility Method

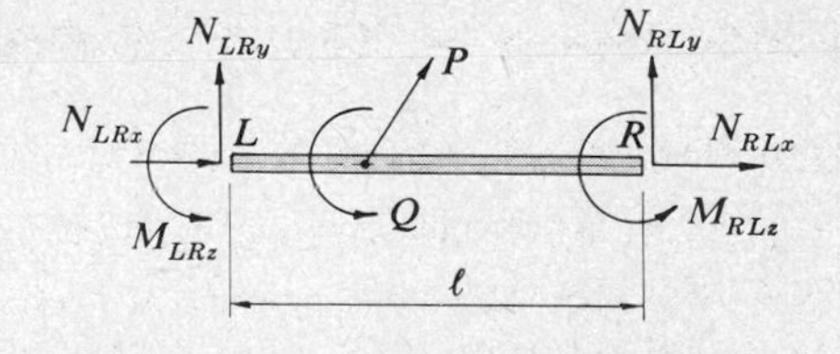

Fig. 1-2. Positive Stresses, Stiffness Method

1. *End Stress Vectors, Flexibility Method*

The positive end stress vectors in the bar LR (Fig. 1-1) are

$$\sigma_L = \{N_{Lx}, N_{Ly}, M_{Lz}\} \qquad \sigma_R = \{N_{Rx}, N_{Ry}, M_{Rz}\} \tag{1.12}$$

where N_x, N_y, M_z are the normal force, the shearing force and the bending moment respectively. The subscripts L and R stand for the left and right end respectively.

2. *End Stress Vectors, Stiffness Method*

The positive end stress vectors in the bar LR (Fig. 1-2) are

$$\sigma_{LR} = \{N_{LRx}, N_{LRy}, M_{LRz}\} \qquad \sigma_{RL} = \{N_{RLx}, N_{RLy}, M_{RLz}\} \tag{1.13}$$

where N_x, N_y, M_z and L, R have the same meaning as in (*1.12*).

3. *End Displacement Vectors, Flexibility Method*

The positive end displacement vectors in the bar LR (Fig. 1–3) are

$$\Delta_{LR} = \{\delta_{LRx}, \delta_{LRy}, \theta_{LRz}\} \qquad \Delta_{RL} = \{\delta_{RLx}, \delta_{RLy}, \theta_{RLz}\} \tag{1.14}$$

where δ, θ are the linear and angular displacements respectively. The subscripts x and y stand for the displacement components parallel to X, Y axes respectively.

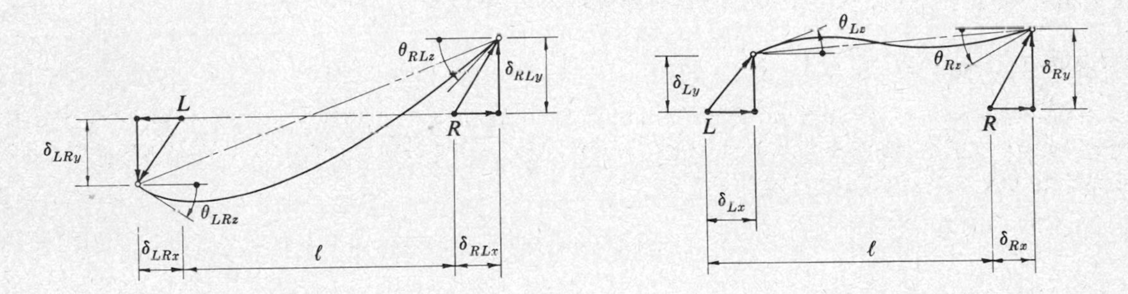

Fig. 1-3. Positive Displacements, Flexibility Method

Fig. 1-4. Positive Displacements, Stiffness Method

4. *End Displacement Vectors, Stiffness Method*

The positive end displacement vectors in the bar LR (Fig. 1-4) are

$$\Delta_L = \{\delta_{Lx}, \delta_{Ly}, \theta_{Lz}\} \qquad \Delta_R = \{\delta_{Rx}, \delta_{Ry}, \theta_{Rz}\} \tag{1.15}$$

where δ, θ and x, y have the same meaning as in (*1.14*).

5. *Relationships*

The comparison of the respective vectors yields the following relationships:

$$\begin{aligned} \sigma_L &= -\sigma_{LR} \qquad & \sigma_R &= \sigma_{RL} \\ \Delta_L &= -\Delta_{LR} \qquad & \Delta_R &= \Delta_{RL} \end{aligned} \tag{1.16}$$

Thus the right side vectors have the same sign in both methods. For the left side vectors the opposite is true.

Review Problems

The following problems represent a concise summary of the most important topics, knowledge of which is prerequisite for the material covered in this book. (See footnote, page 1, about the cross-references in the problems.)

1.1. Static Equilibrium—Beams

Calculate the reactions for the simple beam (Problem I-1.1), cantilever beam (Problem I-1.2), simple beam with overhang (Problem I-1.4) and compound beam (Problem I-1.11).

1.2. Static Equilibrium—Three-hinged Arches and Frames

Calculate the reactions and forces at the internal hinge for the three-hinged arch (Problems I-1.18 and I-1.19) and for the three-hinged frame (Problem I-1.20).

1.3. Stresses in Beams—Basic Concepts

(*a*) State the definition of the normal force, shearing force and bending moment (Definitions I-1.5 to I-1.7).
(*b*) Derive the differential and difference load-stress relationships (Eqs. I-*2.3* to I-*2.5*).
(*c*) Derive the integral load-stress relationships (Eq. I-*2.6*).
(*d*) State the conditions for the location of the extreme value of stress (Eq. I-*2.7* and Definition I-2.5).

1.4. Stresses in Beams—Equations and Diagrams

Write the stress equations and draw the stress diagrams for the statically determinate beams (Problems I-2.7, I-2.19, I-2.33, I-2.40).

1.5. Stresses in Frames and Arches—Equations and Diagrams

Write the stress equations and draw the stress diagrams for the statically determinate frames and arches (Problems I-3.2, I-3.5, I-3.8, I-3.21 and I-3.23).

1.6. Stresses in Trusses—Major Methods

Discuss the method of joints and sections and solve a typical planar truss by both methods (Sections I-4.7 and I-4.8, Problems I-4.1 and I-4.2).

1.7. Elastic Curve—Cantilever Beam

Compute the slope and deflection of the flexural elastic curve at D (Problem I-5.4).

1.8. Elastic Curve—Simple Beam

(*a*) Compute the end slopes of the flexural elastic curve (Problem I-5.12).
(*b*) Compute the location and the magnitude of the maximum flexural deflection (Problem I-P-5.14).
(*c*) Derive the analytical expression for the end angular deviations of the flexural elastic curve in the simple beams loaded as shown in: Table I-P-5.38, Case 1; Table I-P-5.39, Case 4; and Table I-P-5.40, Case 1.

1.9. Virtual Work—Maxwell-Mohr Method

Using the unit dummy load method compute the end displacements of a portal frame (Problem I-7.5).

1.10. Flexibility Method—Concept

Define the following terms related to the flexibility method of analysis: (*a*) Basic structure. (*b*) Complementary structure. (*c*) Compatibility. (*d*) Direct flexibility. (*e*) Indirect flexibility. (*f*) Load flexibility. (Sections I-8.1, I-8.4 to I-8.6)

1.11. Segmental Flexibilities—Straight Bar

Derive the analytical expressions for the segmental flexibilities of a cantilever and simple straight beam of constant cross section (Tables I-8-1 and I-8-3).

1.12. Segmental Flexibilities—Curved Bar

Derive the analytical expressions for the segmental flexibilities of a cantilever and simple curved beam of constant cross section (Tables I-8-2 and I-8-4).

1.13. Properties of Flexibility Matrices

Define the properties common to all flexibility matrices (Definitions I-8.7 to I-8.9).

1.14. Two-hinged Frame and Arch

Write the compatibility equation for the two-hinged frame (Problem I-P-8.4) and two-hinged arch (Problem I-P-8.5).

1.15. Three-moment Equation

Derive the three-moment equation for a continuous beam of constant cross section (Problem I-8.10) and write the flexibility matrix equation for this beam (Problem I-8.11).

1.16. Elasto-static Analogy

Show the analogy between the properties of a plane section and the flexibilities of a fixed frame (Problem I-9.4).

1.17. Column Analogy

Using the elasto-static analogy introduced in the preceding problem, analyze the gable frame (Problem I-9.7).

1.18. Stiffness Method—Concept

Define the following terms related to the stiffness method of analysis: (*a*) Basic structure. (*b*) Complementary structure. (*c*) Direct stiffness. (*d*) Indirect stiffness. (*e*) Load stiffness. (Sections I-10.1 to I-10.3, I-10.5)

1.19. Segmental Stiffnesses—Straight Bar

Derive the analytical expressions for the segmental stiffnesses of a straight bar of constant cross section (Table I-10-1).

1.20. Slope-deflection Equation

Derive the slope-deflection equation for a straight bar of constant cross section (Section I-10.9).

1.21. Properties of Stiffness Matrices

Define the properties common to all stiffness matrices (Definitions I-10.7 to I-10.9).

1.22. Three-slope Equation

Derive the three-slope equation for a continuous beam of constant cross section (Problem I-10.3) and write the stiffness matrix equation for this beam (Problem I-10.4).

1.23. Distribution of Joint Moments

Derive the joint moment distribution constants and discuss the related numerical procedure of successive approximation (Problems I-10.8 and I-10.9).

1.24. Stiffnesses in Terms of Flexibilities

Express the stiffness factors and the fixed end moments of a straight bar of constant cross section in terms of the direct, indirect and load flexibilities of the same bar (Tables I-P-10.15 and I-P-10.16).

1.25. Duality of Flexibility and Stiffness Methods

Show the duality of the flexibility and stiffness methods (Problem I-10.14).

Chapter 2

Static Vector

2.1 GEOMETRY

Two systems of coordinate axes are introduced in the matrix analysis of structures:

(*a*) *Reference System* (Global System), arbitrarily selected set of orthogonal axes X^0, Y^0, Z^0.

(*b*) *Member System* (Local System), given by the principal axes X^i, Y^i, Z^i of the respective member.

The direction of the first system is *fixed* and *common* for all parts of the structure, whereas the second one rotates and translates with the cross section of the member, being *specific* for each station of investigation (Fig. 2-1).

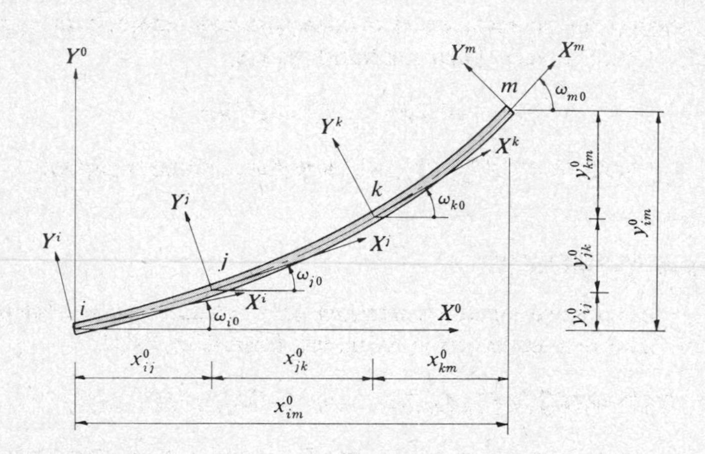

Fig. 2-1. Geometry of Planar Bar

The *position coordinates* of a joint, support or cross section related to these systems are *directed segments*, so that

$$x^0_{ij} = -x^0_{ji} \qquad y^0_{ij} = -y^0_{ji} \qquad z^0_{ij} = -z^0_{ji} = 0$$

and (2.1)

$$x^i_{ij} = -x^i_{ji} \qquad y^i_{ij} = -y^i_{ji} \qquad z^i_{ij} = -z^i_{ji} = 0$$

where the superscript, first subscript and second subscript identify the system, origin and position respectively (Fig. 2-2 below). These relationships stated for i and j are perfectly general and valid for any doublet of points.

The transformation relationships between these two systems are given by the *angular transformation matrices* ω^{i0} and ω^{0i} which are

$$\omega^{i0} = \begin{bmatrix} \cos\omega_{i0} & \sin\omega_{i0} & 0 \\ -\sin\omega_{i0} & \cos\omega_{i0} & 0 \\ 0 & 0 & 1 \end{bmatrix} \qquad \omega^{0i} = \begin{bmatrix} \cos\omega_{i0} & -\sin\omega_{i0} & 0 \\ \sin\omega_{i0} & \cos\omega_{i0} & 0 \\ 0 & 0 & 1 \end{bmatrix} \qquad (2.2)$$

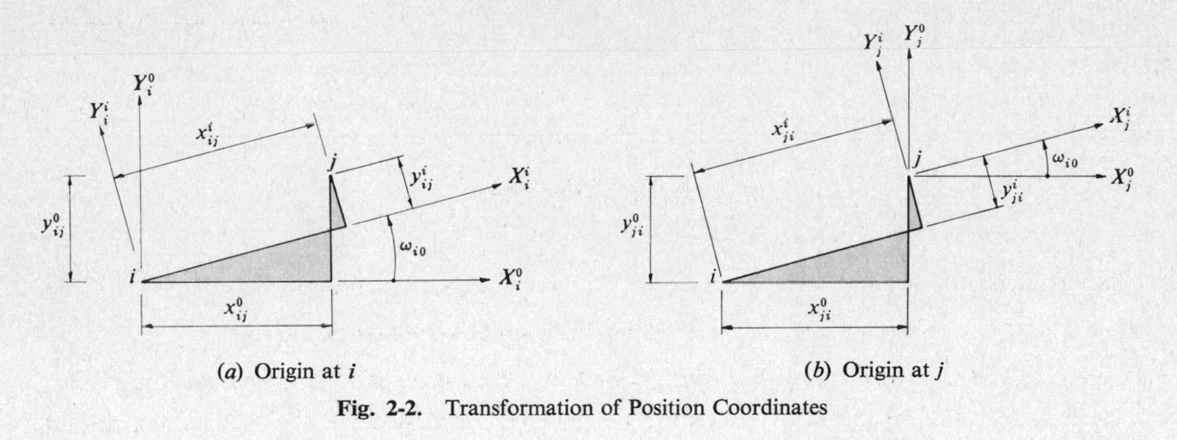

(*a*) Origin at *i* (*b*) Origin at *j*

Fig. 2-2. Transformation of Position Coordinates

Matrices (*2.2*) are orthogonal since

$$\omega^{i0} = \omega^{0i)T} = \omega^{0i)-1} \qquad \text{and} \qquad \omega^{0i} = \omega^{i0)T} = \omega^{i0)-1} \tag{2.3}$$

where $\omega^{0i)T}$, $\omega^{i0)T}$ are the *transposes* of the respective matrices and $\omega^{0i)-1}$, $\omega^{i0)-1}$ are the *inverses* of the same respective matrices.

A vector V_i (any vector) can be resolved into three directed segments in each system, given by column matrices V_i^i and V_i^0 respectively. Their relationships are

$$V_i^i = \omega^{i0} V_i^0 \qquad V_i^0 = \omega^{0i} V_i^i \tag{2.4}$$

where $V_i^i = \{V_{ix}^i, V_{iy}^i, V_{iz}^i\}$ and $V_i^0 = \{V_{ix}^0, V_{iy}^0, V_{iz}^0\}$ are these column matrices.

2.2 STATIC CAUSES AND EFFECTS

Loads acting upon a structure are called the *static causes*, and their *static effect* at the centroid of an arbitrarily selected section is known as the *stress*. In matrix form (Fig. 2-3*a*),

$$W_m{}^m = \{P_{mx}^m, P_{my}^m, Q_{mz}^m\} \qquad \sigma_k{}^k = \{N_{kx}^k, N_{ky}^k, M_{kz}^k\}$$

where $W_m{}^m$ = load vector matrix at m, in m-system, 3×1, and $\sigma_k{}^k$ = stress vector matrix at k, in k-system, 3×1.

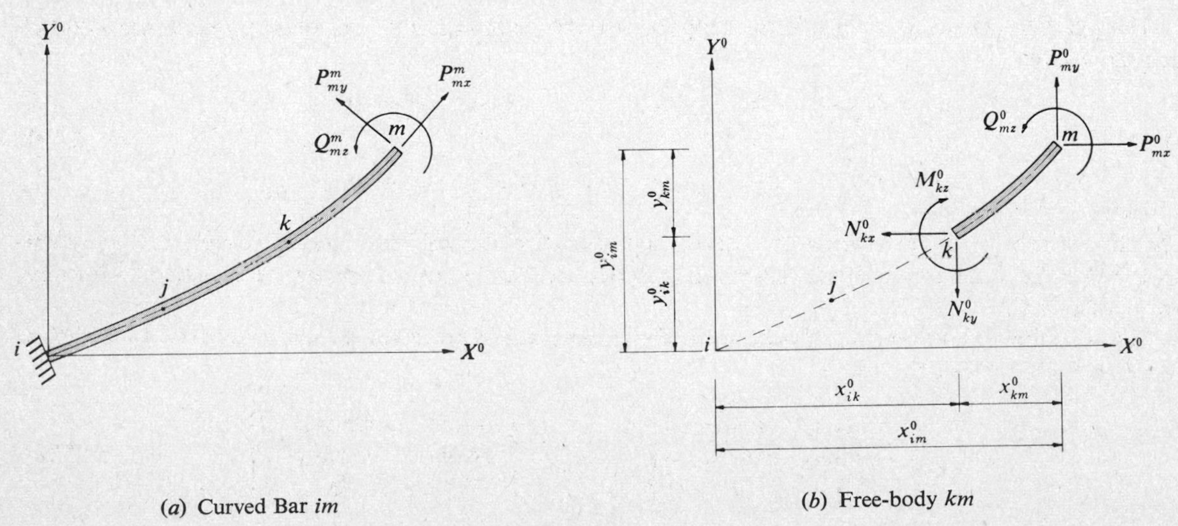

(*a*) Curved Bar *im* (*b*) Free-body *km*

Fig. 2-3

The *load vector* consists of the concentrated load components P_{mx}^{m}, P_{my}^{m} and the applied moment Q_{mz}^{m} normal to the plane of structure. The *stress vector* includes the normal force N_{kx}^{k}, the shearing force N_{ky}^{k} and the bending moment M_{kz}^{k}. The *relationship* between these vectors and their 0-system equivalents is given by (*2.4*) as

$$W_m{}^0 = \omega^{0m} W_m{}^m \qquad \sigma_k{}^0 = \omega^{0k} \sigma_k{}^k \tag{2.5}$$

From the equilibrium of km (Fig. 2-3*b*),

$$\sigma_k{}^0 = r_{km}^0 W_m{}^0 \tag{2.6}$$

where

$$r_{km}^0 = \left[\begin{array}{cc|c} 1 & 0 & 0 \\ 0 & 1 & 0 \\ \hline -y_{km}^0 & x_{km}^0 & 1 \end{array}\right] \tag{2.7}$$

is the *linear transport matrix km* in 0-system.

2.3 LINEAR TRANSPORT

Similarly, the stress vector $\sigma_k{}^0$ acting at the centroid of k as the static cause in jk develops at j the static effect $\sigma_j{}^0$. From the equilibrium of jk,

$$\sigma_j{}^0 = r_{jk}^0 \sigma_k{}^0$$

Inversely,

$$\sigma_k{}^0 = r_{kj}^0 \sigma_j{}^0$$

and so

$$r_{kj}^0 \cdot r_{jk}^0 = I \qquad \text{and} \qquad r_{kj}^0 = r_{jk}^{0)-1} \tag{2.8}$$

Since $x_{jk}^0 = -x_{kj}^0$ and $y_{jk}^0 = -y_{kj}^0$,

$$r_{jk}^0 = \begin{bmatrix} 1 & 0 & 0 \\ 0 & 1 & 0 \\ -y_{jk}^0 & x_{jk}^0 & 1 \end{bmatrix} = r_{kj}^{0)-1} \qquad \text{and} \qquad r_{kj}^0 = \begin{bmatrix} 1 & 0 & 0 \\ 0 & 1 & 0 \\ -y_{kj}^0 & x_{kj}^0 & 1 \end{bmatrix} = r_{jk}^{0)-1} \tag{2.9}$$

2.4 LINEAR TRANSPORT CHAIN

If the effect of $W_m{}^0$ is required at j (Fig. 2-3*a*), two matrix forms are available:

$$\sigma_j{}^0 = r_{jm}^0 W_m{}^0 \qquad \text{or} \qquad \sigma_j{}^0 = r_{jk}^0 r_{km}^0 W_m{}^0$$

The first equation transports $W_m{}^0$ directly to j and the second one carries it to k and from k to j. Similarly,

$$\sigma_i{}^0 = r_{im}^0 W_m{}^0 \qquad \text{or} \qquad \sigma_i{}^0 = r_{ij}^0 r_{jk}^0 r_{km}^0 W_m{}^0$$

This last relationship leads to a perfectly general statement,

$$r_{im}^0 = r_{ij}^0 r_{jk}^0 r_{km}^0 \tag{2.10}$$

known as the *linear transport chain*.

2.5 ANGULAR TRANSPORT CHAIN

If the effect of $\sigma_k{}^0$ is required at k but in 2-direction (Fig. 2-4), two matrix forms are available:

$$\sigma_k{}^2 = \omega^{20} \sigma_k{}^0 \qquad \text{or} \qquad \sigma_k{}^2 = \omega^{21} \omega^{10} \sigma_k{}^0$$

where 0, 1, 2 identify the respective systems.

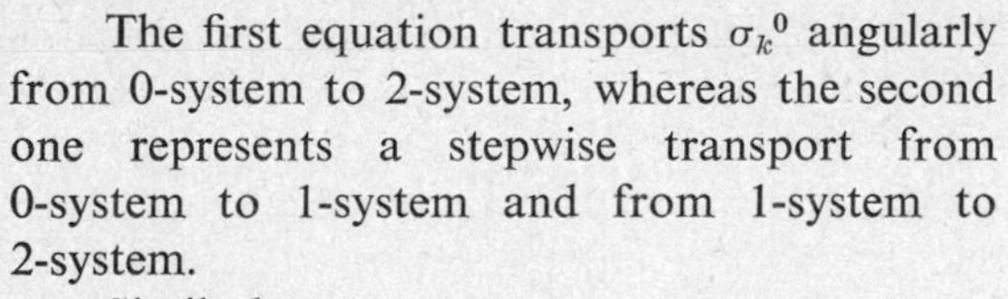

The first equation transports $\sigma_k{}^0$ angularly from 0-system to 2-system, whereas the second one represents a stepwise transport from 0-system to 1-system and from 1-system to 2-system.

Similarly,

$$\sigma_k{}^3 = \omega^{30}\sigma_k{}^0 \qquad \text{or} \qquad \sigma_k{}^3 = \omega^{32}\omega^{21}\omega^{10}\sigma_k{}^0$$

This last relationship leads again to a perfectly general statement,

$$\omega^{30} = \omega^{32}\omega^{21}\omega^{10} \tag{2.11}$$

known as the *angular transport chain.*

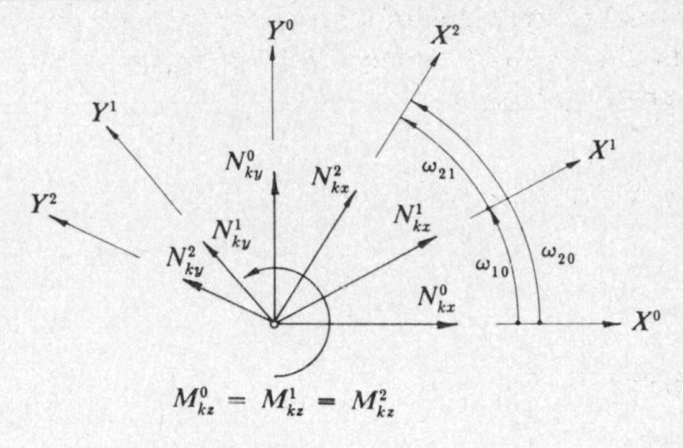

Fig. 2-4. Angular Transport Chain

2.6 GENERAL TRANSPORT

The stress at k acting in k-direction measured at j in j-direction (Fig. 2-1) is

$$\sigma_j{}^j = r^j_{jk}\omega^{jk}\sigma_k{}^k \qquad \text{or} \qquad \sigma_j{}^j = \omega^{jk}r^k_{jk}\sigma_k{}^k$$

where

$$r^j_{jk}\omega^{jk} = \omega^{jk}r^k_{jk} = t^{jk}_{jk} \tag{2.12}$$

is the *general transport matrix.*

The notion of *general transport chain* follows then automatically as

$$t^{ik}_{ik} = r^i_{ij}\omega^{ij}r^j_{jk}\omega^{jk} = \omega^{ij}r^j_{ij}\omega^{jk}r^k_{jk} = t^{ij}_{ij}t^{jk}_{jk} \tag{2.13}$$

The value of the nomenclature is now apparent from the correspondence of superscripts (systems) and subscripts (stations).

2.7 INTERMEDIATE LOADS

If loads enter the transport at the joint and/or within the span, they must be inserted in the transport chain. From Fig. 2-5,

$$\begin{bmatrix} \sigma_m{}^0 \\ \sigma_k{}^0 \\ \sigma_j{}^0 \\ \sigma_i{}^0 \end{bmatrix} = \begin{bmatrix} I & 0 & 0 & 0 \\ r^0_{km} & I & 0 & 0 \\ r^0_{jm} & r^0_{jk} & I & 0 \\ r^0_{im} & r^0_{ik} & r^0_{ij} & I \end{bmatrix} \begin{bmatrix} W_m{}^0 \\ W_k{}^0 \\ W_j{}^0 \\ W_i{}^0 \end{bmatrix} \tag{2.14}$$

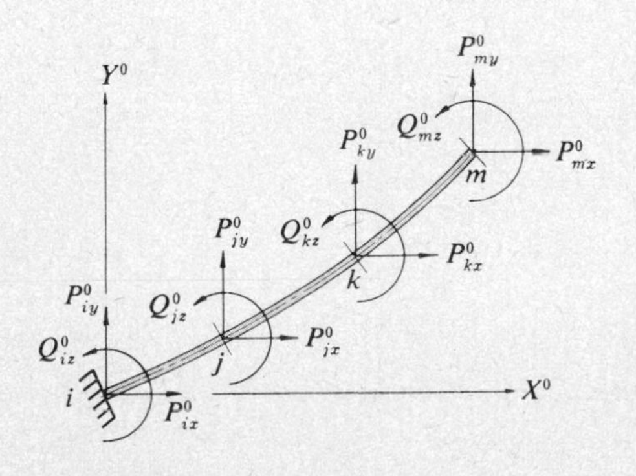

Fig. 2-5. Loads in 0-System

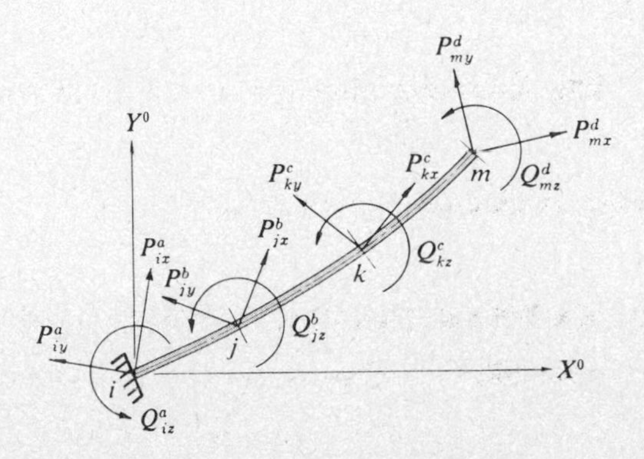

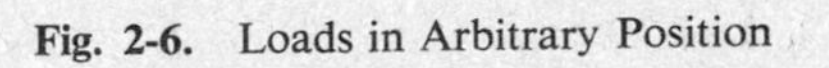

Fig. 2-6. Loads in Arbitrary Position

If the stress vectors are measured in the respective member system and the load vectors are given as shown in Fig. 2-5, then

$$\begin{bmatrix} \sigma_m{}^m \\ \sigma_k{}^k \\ \sigma_j{}^j \\ \sigma_i{}^i \end{bmatrix} = \begin{bmatrix} \omega^{m0} & 0 & 0 & 0 \\ 0 & \omega^{k0} & 0 & 0 \\ 0 & 0 & \omega^{j0} & 0 \\ 0 & 0 & 0 & \omega^{i0} \end{bmatrix} \begin{bmatrix} I & 0 & 0 & 0 \\ r^0_{km} & I & 0 & 0 \\ r^0_{jm} & r^0_{jk} & I & 0 \\ r^0_{im} & r^0_{ik} & r^0_{ij} & I \end{bmatrix} \begin{bmatrix} W_m{}^0 \\ W_k{}^0 \\ W_j{}^0 \\ W_i{}^0 \end{bmatrix}$$

Finally, if the stress vectors and the load vectors are measured and given in prescribed systems (Figs. 2-1 and 2-6 above), then

$$\begin{bmatrix} \sigma_m{}^m \\ \sigma_k{}^k \\ \sigma_j{}^j \\ \sigma_i{}^i \end{bmatrix} = \begin{bmatrix} \omega^{m0} & 0 & 0 & 0 \\ 0 & \omega^{k0} & 0 & 0 \\ 0 & 0 & \omega^{j0} & 0 \\ 0 & 0 & 0 & \omega^{i0} \end{bmatrix} \begin{bmatrix} I & 0 & 0 & 0 \\ r^0_{km} & I & 0 & 0 \\ r^0_{jm} & r^0_{jk} & I & 0 \\ r^0_{im} & r^0_{ik} & r^0_{ij} & I \end{bmatrix} \begin{bmatrix} \omega^{0d} & 0 & 0 & 0 \\ 0 & \omega^{0c} & 0 & 0 \\ 0 & 0 & \omega^{0b} & 0 \\ 0 & 0 & 0 & \omega^{0a} \end{bmatrix} \begin{bmatrix} W_m{}^d \\ W_k{}^c \\ W_j{}^b \\ W_i{}^a \end{bmatrix}$$

which is obviously a general transport equation shown below.

$$\begin{bmatrix} \sigma_m{}^m \\ \sigma_k{}^k \\ \sigma_j{}^j \\ \sigma_i{}^i \end{bmatrix} = \begin{bmatrix} t^{md}_{mm} & 0 & 0 & 0 \\ t^{kd}_{km} & t^{kc}_{kk} & 0 & 0 \\ t^{jd}_{jm} & t^{jc}_{jk} & t^{jb}_{jj} & 0 \\ t^{id}_{im} & t^{ic}_{ik} & t^{ib}_{ij} & t^{ia}_{ii} \end{bmatrix} \begin{bmatrix} W_m{}^d \\ W_k{}^c \\ W_j{}^b \\ W_i{}^a \end{bmatrix} \tag{2.15}$$

These relationships show the versatility of symbols ω, r, t and the correspondence of their indices.

2.8 STATIC EQUILIBRIUM EQUATIONS

The last row of (*2.15*) written for the curved planar bar of Fig. 2-7 as

$$\sigma_L{}^L = t^{Li}_{Li} W_i{}^i + t^{Lj}_{Lj} W_j{}^j + t^{Lk}_{Lk} W_k{}^k + t^{LR}_{LR} \sigma_R{}^R$$

or

$$\sigma_R{}^R = -t^{Rk}_{Rk} W_k{}^k - t^{Rj}_{Rj} W_j{}^j - t^{Ri}_{Ri} W_i{}^i + t^{RL}_{RL} \sigma_L{}^L \tag{2.16}$$

is the *matrix equation of static equilibrium* in the left end and the right end form respectively.

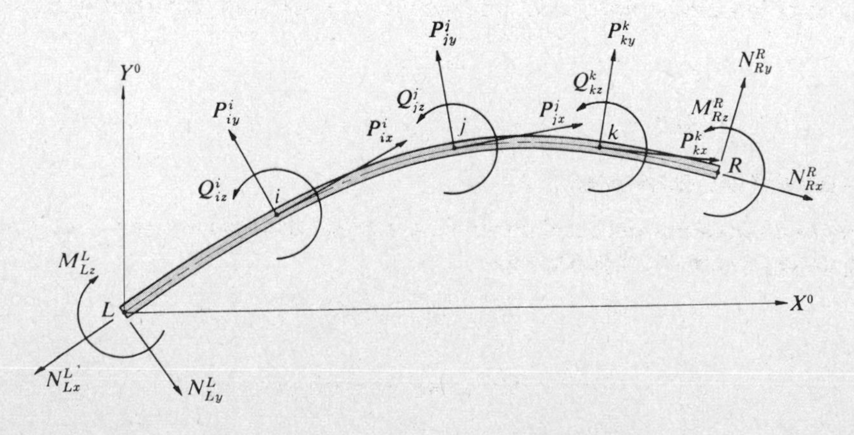

Fig. 2-7. Curved Bar, Free-body

2.9 EQUIVALENT LOADS

If *distributed loads* which may vary over a given segment of the structure are present, it is necessary (to avoid integral expressions) to replace such loads by an *equivalent system of concentrated loads*. For this purpose the load diagram is divided into a certain number of strips of equal or unequal length and each strip is treated as a simple beam. The reactions of these simple beams are then applied as the equivalent concentrated loads on the given structure (joint loads).

For load curves defined by analytical functions this can be done exactly by integration or by various approximations. For irregular load diagrams, only approximate equivalents are available. Two most *common approximations* are shown in Table 2-1.

Table 2-1. Joint Loads

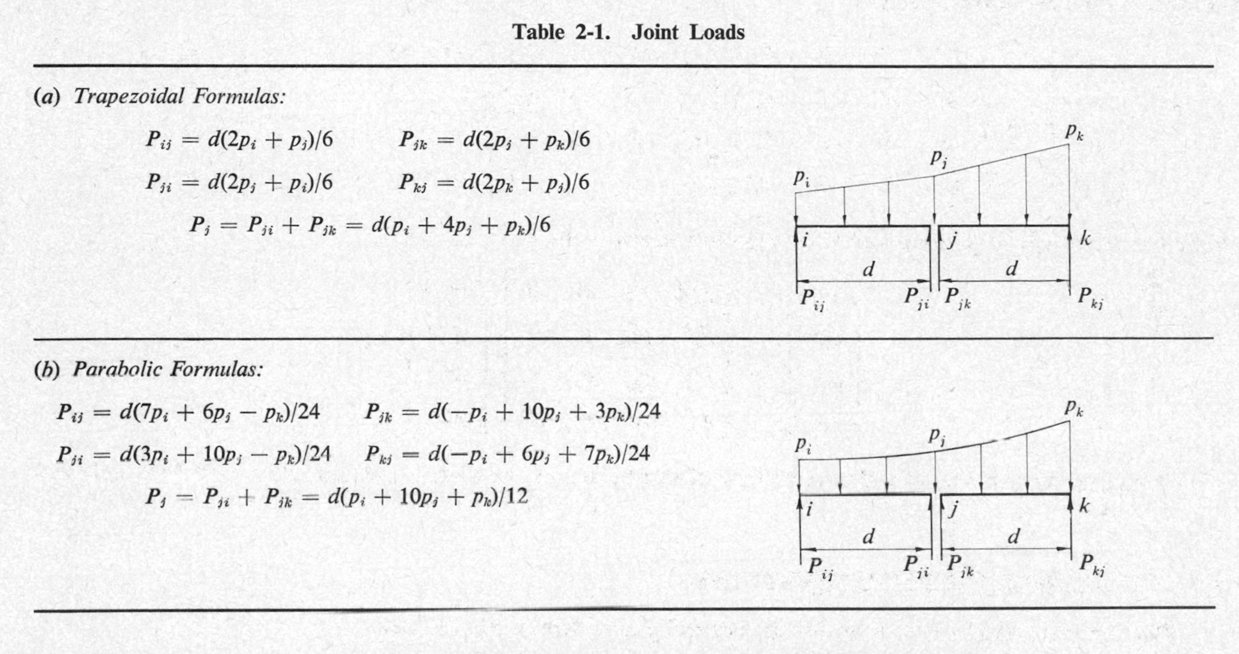

(*a*) *Trapezoidal Formulas:*

$$P_{ij} = d(2p_i + p_j)/6 \qquad P_{jk} = d(2p_j + p_k)/6$$

$$P_{ji} = d(2p_j + p_i)/6 \qquad P_{kj} = d(2p_k + p_j)/6$$

$$P_j = P_{ji} + P_{jk} = d(p_i + 4p_j + p_k)/6$$

(*b*) *Parabolic Formulas:*

$$P_{ij} = d(7p_i + 6p_j - p_k)/24 \qquad P_{jk} = d(-p_i + 10p_j + 3p_k)/24$$

$$P_{ji} = d(3p_i + 10p_j - p_k)/24 \qquad P_{kj} = d(-p_i + 6p_j + 7p_k)/24$$

$$P_j = P_{ji} + P_{jk} = d(p_i + 10p_j + p_k)/12$$

The *joint load expressions* rearranged in matrix form give the following *joint load matrix*,

$$\underbrace{\begin{bmatrix} P_i \\ P_j \\ P_k \end{bmatrix}}_{P} = \underbrace{\begin{bmatrix} c_i & c_{ij} & 0 \\ c_{ji} & c_j & c_{jk} \\ 0 & c_{kj} & c_k \end{bmatrix}}_{\alpha} \underbrace{\begin{bmatrix} p_i \\ p_j \\ p_k \end{bmatrix}}_{p}$$

This matrix equation can be written for any number of joints and expressed symbolically as

$$P = \alpha p \tag{2.17}$$

2.10 NEWMARK'S METHOD, PART I

For straight beams (and trusses) acted upon by equally spaced transverse joint loads (Fig. 2-8 below), the linear transport equation (*2.14*) reduces to

$$\begin{aligned} V_j &= V_k + P_j \\ M_j &= M_k + V_k d \end{aligned} \tag{2.18}$$

where P_j = joint load at j and d = segment length.

P_j, kips		0^k	1^k	2^k	3^k	4^k	5^k	6^k	7^k	8^k	9^k	10^k
d, ft			2′	2′	2′	2′	2′	2′	2′	2′	2′	2′
j		0	1	2	3	4	5	6	7	8	9	10
V_j, kips	−16.5	−16.5	−15.5	−13.5	−10.5	−6.5	−1.5	4.5	11.5	19.5	28.5	38.5
$M_{j/2}$		0	16.5	32.0	45.5	56.0	62.5	64.0	59.5	48.0	28.5	
M_j		0	33	64	91	112	125	128	119	96	57	

Fig. 2-8. Stresses in Simple Beam

Equations (*2.18*) can be used for the successive calculation of shears and bending moments at selected stations as shown in Fig. 2-8.

This procedure, known as Newmark's Method, Part I, offers two numerical controls at the close of transport:

$$V_0 = -R_{0y} \qquad M_0 = 0$$

2.11 MOMENT MATRIX

For a straight bar acted upon by a system of transverse concentrated loads, the bending moment diagram takes the form of a *string polygon*, the *angle change* of which equals the respective joint load (Fig. 2-9):

$$P_j = (-M_i + 2M_j - M_k)/d \qquad (2.19)$$

where M_i, M_j, M_k are the bending moments at i, j, k respectively and d is the spacing of these joints (stations).

For the entire bar of Fig. 2-9,

$$\underbrace{\frac{1}{d}\begin{bmatrix} 2 & -1 & 0 \\ -1 & 2 & -1 \\ 0 & -1 & 2 \end{bmatrix}}_{\beta} \underbrace{\begin{bmatrix} M_i \\ M_j \\ M_k \end{bmatrix}}_{M} = \underbrace{\begin{bmatrix} P_i \\ P_j \\ P_k \end{bmatrix}}_{P}$$

and symbolically

$$\beta M = P \qquad (2.20)$$

Combining (*2.17*) and (*2.20*),

$$\beta M = \alpha p$$

from which

$$M = \beta)^{-1}\alpha p = mp \qquad (2.21)$$

where m is a square matrix of *bending moment influence values*.

Given Load Diagram

Equivalent Loads

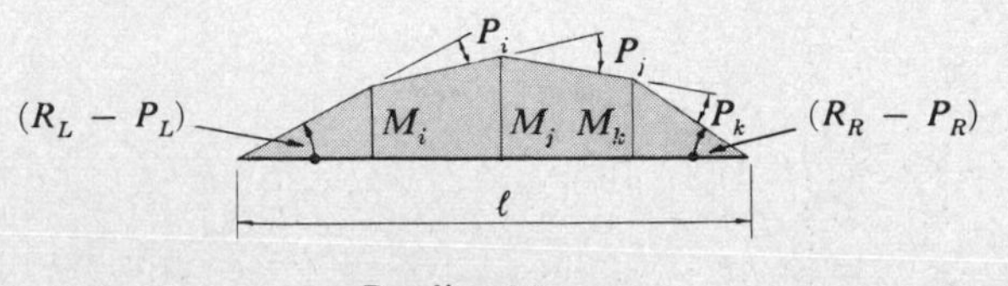

Bending Moment

Fig. 2-9. Bending Moment String Polygon

Solved Problems

LINEAR AND ANGULAR TRANSPORT

2.1. Using the linear transport matrices (*2.7*), compute the stress vectors σ_2^0 and σ_1^0 in the cantilever bar of Fig. P-2.1.

$$\sigma_2^{\,0} = \overset{0}{r}_{23} W_3^{\,0} = \begin{bmatrix} 1 & 0 & 0 \\ 0 & 1 & 0 \\ -5 & 10 & 1 \end{bmatrix} \begin{bmatrix} 10 \\ 20 \\ 300 \end{bmatrix} = \begin{bmatrix} 10 \\ 20 \\ 450 \end{bmatrix}$$

Similarly,

$$\sigma_1^{\,0} = \overset{0}{r}_{13} W_3^{\,0} = \begin{bmatrix} 1 & 0 & 0 \\ 0 & 1 & 0 \\ -15 & 20 & 1 \end{bmatrix} \begin{bmatrix} 10 \\ 20 \\ 300 \end{bmatrix} = \begin{bmatrix} 10 \\ 20 \\ 550 \end{bmatrix}$$

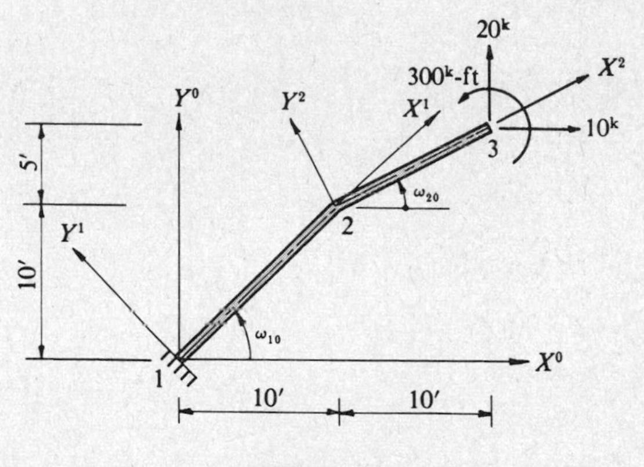

Fig. P-2.1

Alternately,

$$\sigma_1^{\,0} = \overset{0}{r}_{12} \sigma_2^{\,0} = \begin{bmatrix} 1 & 0 & 0 \\ 0 & 1 & 0 \\ -10 & 10 & 1 \end{bmatrix} \begin{bmatrix} 10 \\ 20 \\ 450 \end{bmatrix} = \begin{bmatrix} 10 \\ 20 \\ 550 \end{bmatrix} \qquad \text{Check.}$$

Note: $\sigma_1^{\,0} = \overset{0}{r}_{12} \sigma_2^{\,0} = \overset{0}{r}_{12} \overset{0}{r}_{23} W_3^{\,0} = \overset{0}{r}_{13} W_3^{\,0}$ from which $\overset{0}{r}_{13} = \overset{0}{r}_{12} \overset{0}{r}_{23}$

2.2. Using the results of the preceding problem, determine the stress vectors σ_3^2, σ_2^2, σ_2^1, σ_1^1 in the cantilever bar of Fig. P-2.1.

$$\omega_{20} = \tan^{-1}(5/10) = 26.6° \qquad \omega_{10} = \tan^{-1}(10/10) = 45° \qquad \omega_{12} = \omega_{10} - \omega_{20} = 18.4°$$

$$\sigma_3^{\,2} = \omega^{20} \sigma_3^{\,0} = \begin{bmatrix} 0.894 & 0.447 & 0 \\ -0.447 & 0.894 & 0 \\ 0 & 0 & 1 \end{bmatrix} \begin{bmatrix} 10 \\ 20 \\ 300 \end{bmatrix} = \begin{bmatrix} 17.88 \\ 13.41 \\ 300.00 \end{bmatrix}$$

Note: $\sigma_3^0 = W_3^0$.

$$\sigma_2^{\,2} = \omega^{20} \sigma_2^{\,0} = \begin{bmatrix} 0.894 & 0.447 & 0 \\ -0.447 & 0.894 & 0 \\ 0 & 0 & 1 \end{bmatrix} \begin{bmatrix} 10 \\ 20 \\ 450 \end{bmatrix} = \begin{bmatrix} 17.88 \\ 13.41 \\ 450.00 \end{bmatrix}$$

$$\sigma_2^{\,1} = \omega^{10} \sigma_2^{\,0} = \begin{bmatrix} 0.707 & 0.707 & 0 \\ -0.707 & 0.707 & 0 \\ 0 & 0 & 1 \end{bmatrix} \begin{bmatrix} 10 \\ 20 \\ 450 \end{bmatrix} = \begin{bmatrix} 21.21 \\ 7.07 \\ 450.00 \end{bmatrix}$$

Alternately,

$$\sigma_2^{\,1} = \omega^{12} \sigma_2^{\,2} = \begin{bmatrix} 0.949 & 0.316 & 0 \\ -0.316 & 0.949 & 0 \\ 0 & 0 & 1 \end{bmatrix} \begin{bmatrix} 17.88 \\ 13.41 \\ 450.00 \end{bmatrix} = \begin{bmatrix} 21.21 \\ 7.07 \\ 450.00 \end{bmatrix}$$

$$\sigma_1^{\,1} = \omega^{10} \sigma_1^{\,0} = \begin{bmatrix} 0.707 & 0.707 & 0 \\ -0.707 & 0.707 & 0 \\ 0 & 0 & 1 \end{bmatrix} \begin{bmatrix} 10 \\ 20 \\ 550 \end{bmatrix} = \begin{bmatrix} 21.21 \\ 7.07 \\ 550.00 \end{bmatrix}$$

Note: $\sigma_2^{\,1} = \omega^{12} \sigma_2^{\,2} = \omega^{12} \omega^{20} \sigma_2^{\,0} = \omega^{10} \sigma_2^{\,0}$ from which $\omega^{10} = \omega^{12} \omega^{20}$

2.3. Using the general transport matrices (*2.12*), compute the stress vectors $\sigma_4{}^4$, $\sigma_3{}^3$, $\sigma_2{}^2$ and $\sigma_1{}^1$ in the semicircular cantilever bar of Fig. P-2.3.

$$\omega_{40} = 0°, \qquad \omega_{30} = 60°, \qquad \omega_{20} = 120°, \qquad \omega_{10} = 180°$$

The general transport matrix relation gives

$$\begin{bmatrix} \sigma_4{}^4 \\ \sigma_3{}^3 \\ \sigma_2{}^2 \\ \sigma_1{}^1 \end{bmatrix} = \begin{bmatrix} \overset{44}{t}_{44} & 0 & 0 & 0 \\ \overset{34}{t}_{34} & \overset{33}{t}_{33} & 0 & 0 \\ \overset{24}{t}_{24} & \overset{23}{t}_{23} & \overset{22}{t}_{22} & 0 \\ \overset{14}{t}_{14} & \overset{13}{t}_{13} & \overset{12}{t}_{12} & \overset{11}{t}_{11} \end{bmatrix} \begin{bmatrix} W_4{}^4 \\ 0 \\ 0 \\ 0 \end{bmatrix}$$

which reduces to

$$\sigma_4{}^4 = \overset{44}{t}_{44} W_4{}^4, \qquad \sigma_3{}^3 = \overset{34}{t}_{34} W_4{}^4, \qquad \sigma_2{}^2 = \overset{24}{t}_{24} W_4{}^4, \qquad \sigma_1{}^1 = \overset{14}{t}_{14} W_4{}^4$$

where

$$\overset{44}{t}_{44} = \overset{40}{\omega}\,\overset{0}{r}_{44}\,\overset{04}{\omega} = I \qquad \overset{34}{t}_{34} = \overset{30}{\omega}\,\overset{0}{r}_{34}\,\overset{04}{\omega}$$

$$\overset{24}{t}_{24} = \overset{20}{\omega}\,\overset{0}{r}_{24}\,\overset{04}{\omega} \qquad \overset{14}{t}_{14} = \overset{10}{\omega}\,\overset{0}{r}_{14}\,\overset{04}{\omega}$$

The following values (in ft) apply in the *r*-matrices:

$$\overset{0}{x}_{44} = 0 \qquad \overset{0}{y}_{44} = 0 \qquad \overset{0}{x}_{34} = 17.32 \qquad \overset{0}{y}_{34} = 10$$

$$\overset{0}{x}_{24} = 17.32 \qquad \overset{0}{y}_{24} = 30 \qquad \overset{0}{x}_{14} = 0 \qquad \overset{0}{y}_{14} = 40$$

Fig. P-2.3

Substitution of proper values gives

$$\overset{34}{t}_{34} = \begin{bmatrix} 0.5 & 0.866 & 0 \\ -0.866 & 0.5 & 0 \\ 0 & 0 & 1 \end{bmatrix} \begin{bmatrix} 1 & 0 & 0 \\ 0 & 1 & 0 \\ -10 & 17.32 & 1 \end{bmatrix} = \begin{bmatrix} 0.5 & 0.866 & 0 \\ -0.866 & 0.5 & 0 \\ -10 & 17.32 & 1 \end{bmatrix}$$

$$\overset{24}{t}_{24} = \begin{bmatrix} -0.5 & 0.866 & 0 \\ -0.866 & -0.5 & 0 \\ 0 & 0 & 1 \end{bmatrix} \begin{bmatrix} 1 & 0 & 0 \\ 0 & 1 & 0 \\ -30 & 17.32 & 1 \end{bmatrix} = \begin{bmatrix} -0.5 & 0.866 & 0 \\ -0.866 & -0.5 & 0 \\ -30 & 17.32 & 1 \end{bmatrix}$$

$$\overset{14}{t}_{14} = \begin{bmatrix} -1 & 0 & 0 \\ 0 & -1 & 0 \\ 0 & 0 & 1 \end{bmatrix} \begin{bmatrix} 1 & 0 & 0 \\ 0 & 1 & 0 \\ -40 & 0 & 1 \end{bmatrix} = \begin{bmatrix} -1 & 0 & 0 \\ 0 & -1 & 0 \\ -40 & 0 & 1 \end{bmatrix}$$

Postmultiplying these matrices by $W_4{}^4 = \{15, -25, +100\}$ gives

$$\sigma_4{}^4 = \begin{bmatrix} 15 \\ -25 \\ 100 \end{bmatrix} \qquad \sigma_3{}^3 = \begin{bmatrix} -\ 14.15 \\ -\ 25.49 \\ -483.00 \end{bmatrix} \qquad \sigma_2{}^2 = \begin{bmatrix} -\ 29.15 \\ -\ 0.49 \\ -783.00 \end{bmatrix} \qquad \sigma_1{}^1 = \begin{bmatrix} -\ 15.0 \\ +\ 25.0 \\ -500.0 \end{bmatrix}$$

INTERMEDIATE LOADS

2.4. Using the general transport equation, determine the stress vectors at 1, 2, 3, 4 and 5 in the simple parabolic arch of Fig. P-2.4. Apply the general transport matrix (*2.15*).

Equation of the parabola:

$$y = \frac{4h}{l^2}(x)(l - x)$$

or
$$y = \frac{4(20)}{80^2}(x)(80 - x) = \frac{x(80 - x)}{80}$$

Slope $y' = (80 - 2x)/80 = (40 - x)/40$.

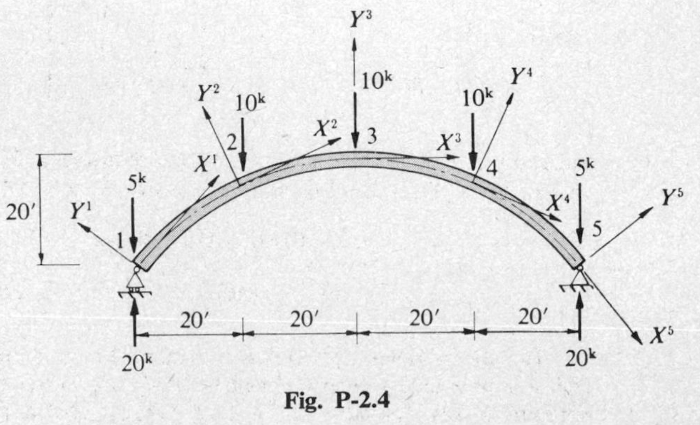

Fig. P-2.4

x ft	y ft	y'	ω degrees
0	0	1.0	45.0
20	15	0.5	26.6
40	20	0.0	0.0
60	15	−0.5	−26.6
80	0	−1.0	−45.0

$$\begin{bmatrix} \sigma_5^5 \\ \sigma_4^4 \\ \sigma_3^3 \\ \sigma_2^2 \\ \sigma_1^1 \end{bmatrix} = \begin{bmatrix} \overset{50}{t}_{55} & 0 & 0 & 0 & 0 \\ \overset{40}{t}_{45} & \overset{40}{t}_{44} & 0 & 0 & 0 \\ \overset{30}{t}_{35} & \overset{30}{t}_{34} & \overset{30}{t}_{33} & 0 & 0 \\ \overset{20}{t}_{25} & \overset{20}{t}_{24} & \overset{20}{t}_{23} & \overset{20}{t}_{22} & 0 \\ \overset{10}{t}_{15} & \overset{10}{t}_{14} & \overset{10}{t}_{13} & \overset{10}{t}_{12} & \overset{10}{t}_{11} \end{bmatrix} \begin{bmatrix} W_5^0 \\ W_4^0 \\ W_3^0 \\ W_2^0 \\ W_1^0 \end{bmatrix}$$

All t-matrices are 3×3 and are as follows:

$$\overset{50}{t}_{55} = \overset{50}{\omega}\overset{0}{r}_{55} \qquad \overset{40}{t}_{45} = \overset{40}{\omega}\overset{0}{r}_{45} \qquad \overset{40}{t}_{44} = \overset{40}{\omega}\overset{0}{r}_{44} \qquad \overset{30}{t}_{35} = \overset{30}{\omega}\overset{0}{r}_{35} \qquad \overset{30}{t}_{34} = \overset{30}{\omega}\overset{0}{r}_{34}$$

$$\overset{30}{t}_{33} = \overset{30}{\omega}\overset{0}{r}_{33} \qquad \overset{20}{t}_{25} = \overset{20}{\omega}\overset{0}{r}_{25} \qquad \overset{20}{t}_{24} = \overset{20}{\omega}\overset{0}{r}_{24} \qquad \overset{20}{t}_{23} = \overset{20}{\omega}\overset{0}{r}_{23} \qquad \overset{20}{t}_{22} = \overset{20}{\omega}\overset{0}{r}_{22}$$

$$\overset{10}{t}_{15} = \overset{10}{\omega}\overset{0}{r}_{15} \qquad \overset{10}{t}_{14} = \overset{10}{\omega}\overset{0}{r}_{14} \qquad \overset{10}{t}_{13} = \overset{10}{\omega}\overset{0}{r}_{13} \qquad \overset{10}{t}_{12} = \overset{10}{\omega}\overset{0}{r}_{12} \qquad \overset{10}{t}_{11} = \overset{10}{\omega}\overset{0}{r}_{11}$$

$$\omega^{50} = \begin{bmatrix} 0.707 & -0.707 & 0 \\ 0.707 & 0.707 & 0 \\ 0 & 0 & 1 \end{bmatrix} \qquad \omega^{40} = \begin{bmatrix} 0.894 & -0.447 & 0 \\ 0.447 & 0.894 & 0 \\ 0 & 0 & 1 \end{bmatrix}$$

$$\omega^{30} = I, \qquad \omega^{10} = \omega^{50)T} \quad \text{and} \quad \omega^{20} = \omega^{40)T}$$

Also, $\overset{0}{r}_{55} = \overset{0}{r}_{44} = \overset{0}{r}_{33} = \overset{0}{r}_{22} = \overset{0}{r}_{11} = I$ and

$$\overset{0}{r}_{45} = \begin{bmatrix} 1 & 0 & 0 \\ 0 & 1 & 0 \\ 15 & 20 & 1 \end{bmatrix} \qquad \overset{0}{r}_{35} = \begin{bmatrix} 1 & 0 & 0 \\ 0 & 1 & 0 \\ 20 & 40 & 1 \end{bmatrix} \qquad \overset{0}{r}_{34} = \begin{bmatrix} 1 & 0 & 0 \\ 0 & 1 & 0 \\ 5 & 20 & 1 \end{bmatrix}$$

$$\overset{0}{r}_{25} = \begin{bmatrix} 1 & 0 & 0 \\ 0 & 1 & 0 \\ 15 & 60 & 1 \end{bmatrix} \qquad \overset{0}{r}_{24} = \begin{bmatrix} 1 & 0 & 0 \\ 0 & 1 & 0 \\ 0 & 40 & 1 \end{bmatrix} \qquad \overset{0}{r}_{23} = \begin{bmatrix} 1 & 0 & 0 \\ 0 & 1 & 0 \\ -5 & 20 & 1 \end{bmatrix}$$

$$\overset{0}{r}_{15} = \begin{bmatrix} 1 & 0 & 0 \\ 0 & 1 & 0 \\ 0 & 80 & 1 \end{bmatrix} \qquad \overset{0}{r}_{14} = \begin{bmatrix} 1 & 0 & 0 \\ 0 & 1 & 0 \\ -15 & 60 & 1 \end{bmatrix} \qquad \overset{0}{r}_{13} = \begin{bmatrix} 1 & 0 & 0 \\ 0 & 1 & 0 \\ -20 & 40 & 1 \end{bmatrix} \qquad \overset{0}{r}_{12} = \begin{bmatrix} 1 & 0 & 0 \\ 0 & 1 & 0 \\ -15 & 20 & 1 \end{bmatrix}$$

Substituting these in the expressions for t-matrices and using $W_5^0 = W_1^0 = \{0, 15, 0\}$ and $W_2^0 = W_3^0 = W_4^0 = \{0, -10, 0\}$, the following values of σ_5^5, σ_4^4, σ_3^3, σ_2^2 and σ_1^1 are obtained:

$$\sigma_5^5 = \{-10.61, +10.61, 0\} \qquad \sigma_4^4 = \{-2.24, 4.47, 300\}$$

$$\sigma_3^3 = \{0, -5, 400\} \qquad \sigma_2^2 = \{6.71, -13.41, 300\} \qquad \sigma_1^1 = \{0, 0, 0\}$$

It may be noted that this is a symmetrical structure loaded symmetrically. Therefore symmetrical values of N_x^i, M_z^i and antisymmetrical values of N_y^i are expected on symmetrically located sections. For example, σ_2^2 will compare in this manner with σ_4^4 if σ_4^4 were computed at the right of the load at 4 excluding the effect of W_4^0.

2.5. Derive the joint load parabolic formula given in Table 2-1.

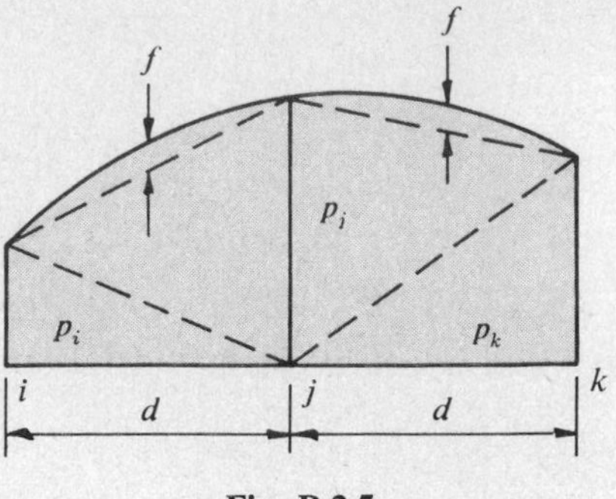

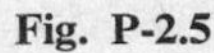
Fig. P-2.5

The joint load P_j is the sum of the static reactions of loads on segments ij and jk at j. From Fig. P-2.5,

$$P_j = p_i d/6 + 2p_j d/3 + p_k d/6 + (2)2fd/(3)(2)$$
$$= d(p_i + 4p_j + p_k + 4f)/6$$

The value of f can be computed from the geometry of the parabola describing the load variation which can be taken as $p = ax^2 + bx + c$. The constants a, b and c can be computed from known values p_i, p_j and p_k at $x = 0$, $x = d$ and $x = 2d$ for origin chosen at i. Thus $f = (-p_i + 2p_j - p_k)/8$. Substituting in the expression for P_j, $P_j = d(p_i + 10p_j + p_k)/12$.

2.6. For the simple beam shown in Fig. P-2.6*a*, determine the shears and bending moments at sections spaced two feet apart. Use the method of successive summation (Newmark's Method) in terms of the joint loads. Compare these results with those computed by the conventional approach.

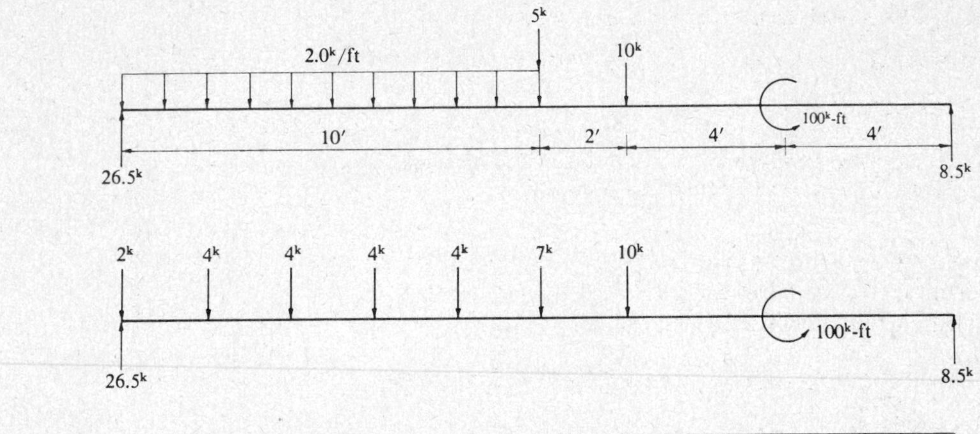

(c)

V		−24.5	−20.5	−16.5	−12.5	−8.5	−1.5	8.5	8.5	8.5	8.5
V · d		−49	−41	−33	−25	−17	−3	17	17	17	17
M	0	49	90	123	148	165	168	151	134 / 34	17	0

Fig. P-2.6a, b, c

The given system of loads (Fig. *a*) is replaced by the equivalent system (Fig. *b*), and the computations performed by means of (*2.18*).

The comparison of the values computed by this method with the exact values is shown in Fig. *d* and *e*.

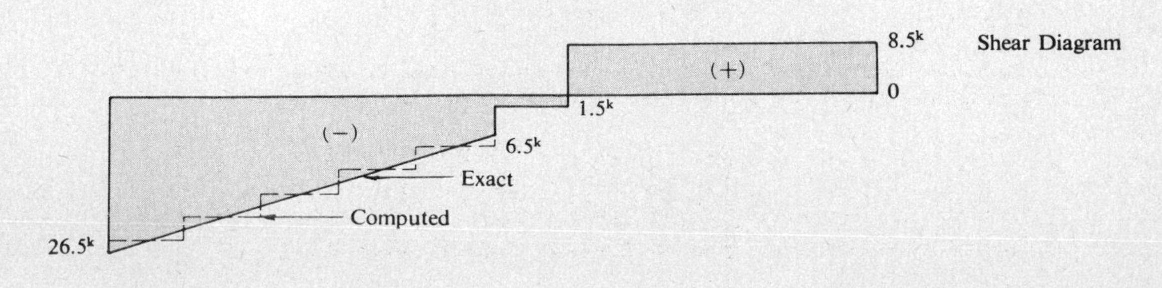

Fig. P-2.6d

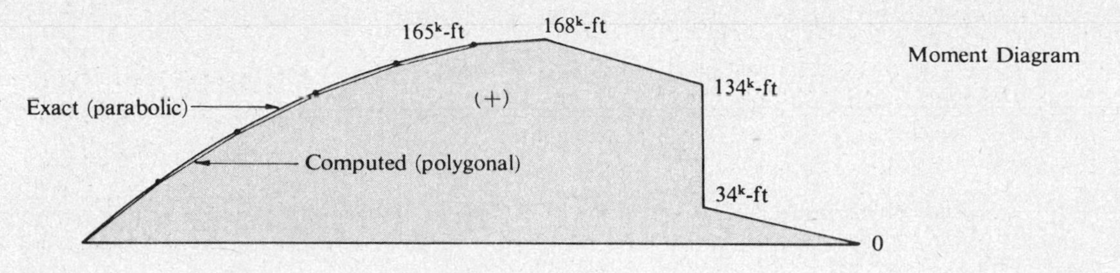

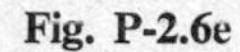
Fig. P-2.6e

2.7. Using the virtual displacements method (*1.6*), derive the relation between the joint load P_j and the bending moments at stations i, j, k in the simple beam of Fig. P-2.7*a*.

The virtual work of Fig. *b* for $\bar{\delta}_j = +1$ is

$$(-M_i + M_j)(1/d) + (M_j - M_k)(1/d) - P_j(1) = 0$$

from which $P_j = (-M_i + 2M_j - M_k)/d$.

This also means that the load P_j is equal to the angle change of the bending moment diagram at j.

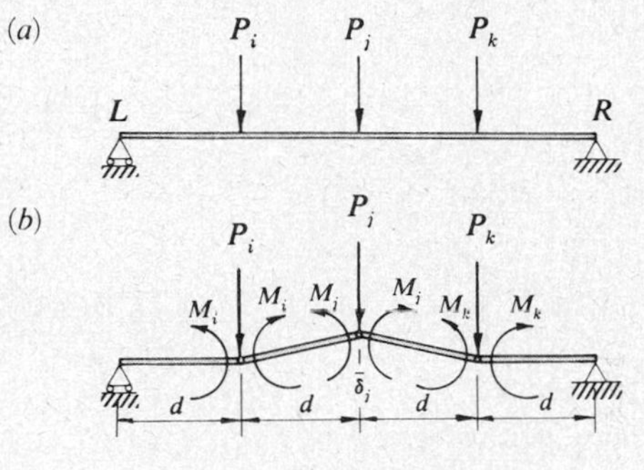

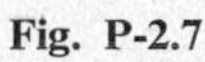
Fig. P-2.7

2.8. Using the virtual displacements method (*1.6*), derive the coefficients of $\beta^{)-1}$ in (*2.21*) for the simple beam of Fig. P-2.8*a*.

The virtual work of the mechanism of Fig. *b* for $\bar{\delta}_1 = +1$ is

$$-P_1(1) - P_2(3/4) - P_3(1/2) - P_4(1/4) + M_1(1/d + 1/4d) = 0$$

and that of Fig. *c* for $\bar{\delta}_2 = +1$ is

$$-P_1(1/2) - P_2(1) - P_3(2/3) - P_4(1/3) + M_2(1/2d + 1/3d) = 0$$

The virtual work computed for similar mechanisms for $\bar{\delta}_3 = +1$, $\bar{\delta}_4 = +1$ yield the expressions for M_3 and M_4 respectively. The rearrangement of these four equations leads to

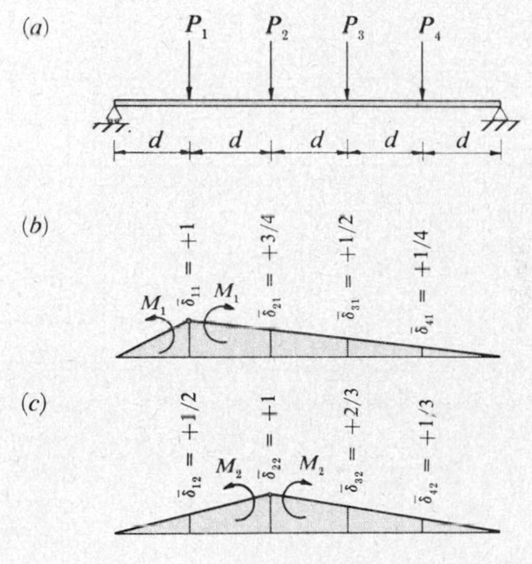

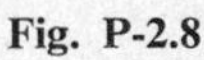
Fig. P-2.8

$$\begin{bmatrix} M_1 \\ M_2 \\ M_3 \\ M_4 \end{bmatrix} = \frac{d}{5} \begin{bmatrix} 4 & 3 & 2 & 1 \\ 3 & 6 & 4 & 2 \\ 2 & 4 & 6 & 3 \\ 1 & 2 & 3 & 4 \end{bmatrix} \begin{bmatrix} P_1 \\ P_2 \\ P_3 \\ P_4 \end{bmatrix} = \beta^{)-1}P$$

It may be checked that the coefficients of $\beta^{)-1}$ above are indeed the influence values for the bending moments at the respective stations. The general form of matrix $\beta^{)-1}$ for a beam with m segments is

$$\beta^{)-1} = \frac{d}{m} \begin{bmatrix} m-1 & m-2 & m-3 & m-4 & \cdots & 1 \\ m-2 & 2(m-2) & 2(m-3) & 2(m-4) & \cdots & 2 \\ m-3 & 2(m-3) & 3(m-3) & 3(m-4) & \cdots & 3 \\ m-4 & 2(m-4) & 3(m-4) & 4(m-4) & \cdots & 4 \\ \cdots & \cdots & \cdots & \cdots & \cdots & \cdots \\ 1 & 2 & 3 & 4 & \cdots & m-1 \end{bmatrix}$$

Supplementary Problems

2.9. Using the linear transport matrices, compute the reactions at E and A of the three-hinge frame shown in Fig. P-2.9. (Hint: Start with the unknown stress vector at E, transport it to points C and A. Then enforce condition of zero moments at the hinges.)

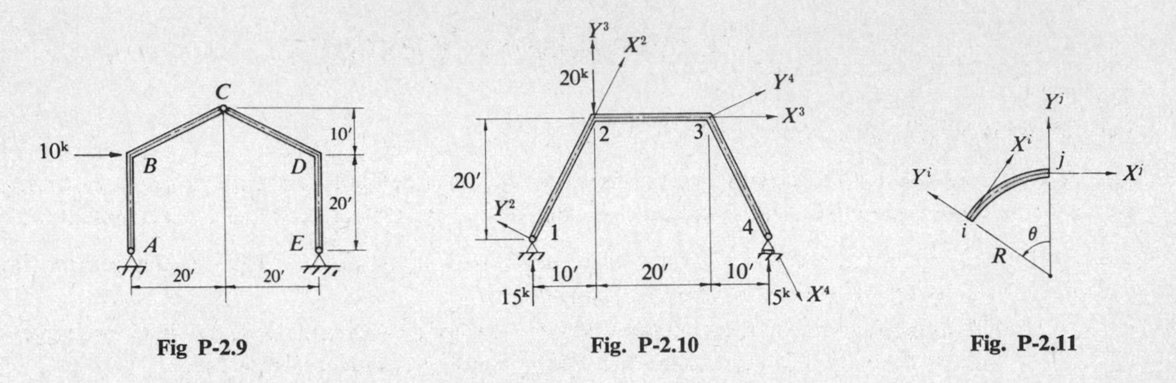

Fig P-2.9

Fig. P-2.10

Fig. P-2.11

2.10. Compute the stress vectors σ_4^4, σ_3^3, σ_2^2, σ_1^1 for the simple frame shown in Fig. P-2.10. Also compute σ_2^3 in the member $\overline{23}$.

2.11. Develop the transport matrix t_{ij}^{ij} relating the stress vectors σ_i^i and σ_j^j of the circular arc ij of Fig. P-2.11, for (*a*) $\theta = 30°$, (*b*) $\theta = 45°$ and (*c*) $\theta = 60°$.

2.12. Using Newmark's Method compute the maximum bending moment in a simply supported beam loaded by a triangular load, shown in Fig. P-2.12. Use 2-ft-long segments.

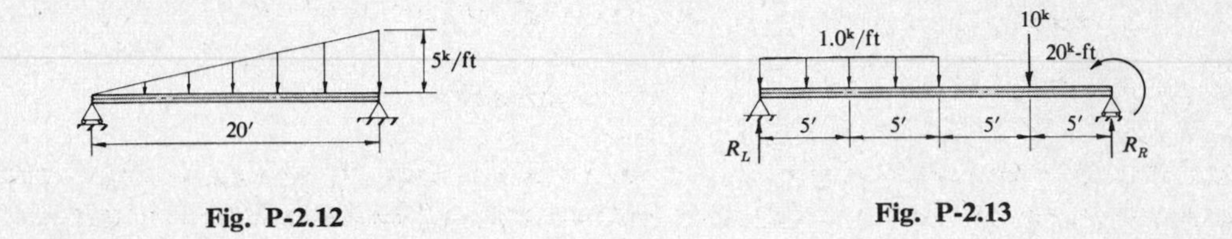

Fig. P-2.12

Fig. P-2.13

2.13. For the simple beam shown in Fig. P-2.13, use the virtual displacement method to compute (*a*) reactions R_L and R_R, (*b*) bending moments M_i, M_j and M_k.

Chapter 3

Deformation Vector

3.1 ELEMENTAL DEFORMATIONS

A bar acted upon by external causes suffers deformations defined by the *linear and angular displacements* of its cross section. For their calculation the following properties of the bar are assumed:

(1) *Cross-sectional dimensions* are *small* compared to the total length of the bar so that the shearing deformations may be neglected.

(2) *Radius of curvature* of the undeformed bar axis is *large* so that the stress-deformation relationships developed for a straight bar are applicable without modification.

The *basic unit* of deformation analysis is the *elemental flexibility* defined as the deformation of bar element ds produced by a unit stress. Since this stress is a force or a moment and the deformations are linear or angular, two elemental flexibilities are recognized:

(1) *Force-Linear Elemental Flexibility* (Fig. 3-1*a*)

$$\lambda^s_{sx} = dx^s/EA_s \qquad (3.1a)$$

(2) *Moment-Angular Elemental Flexibility* (Fig. 3-1*b*)

$$\lambda^s_{sz} = dx^s/EI_s \qquad (3.1b)$$

where $dx^s = ds =$ elemental length, $E =$ modulus of elasticity, $A_s =$ area of cross section at s, $I_s =$ moment of inertia of the cross section about the axis of flexure at s. The superscript s identifies the system.

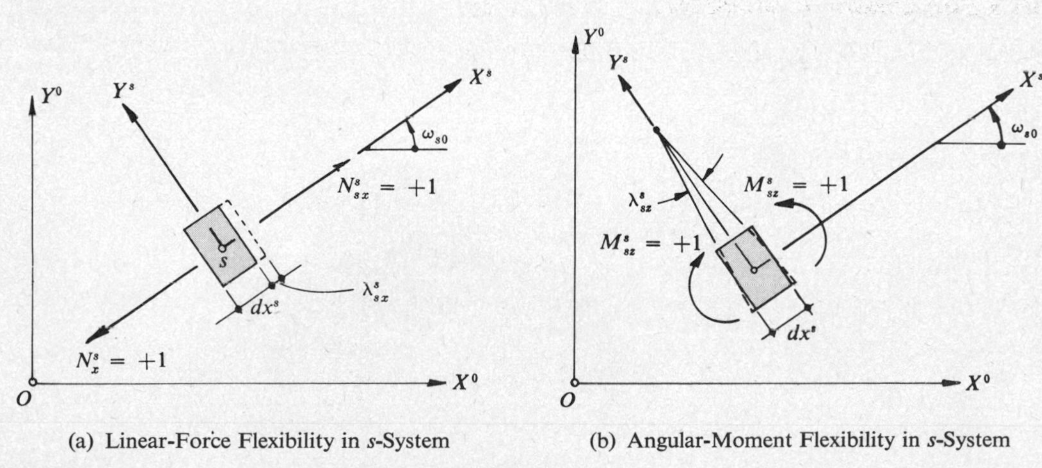

(a) Linear-Force Flexibility in s-System　　(b) Angular-Moment Flexibility in s-System

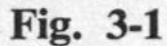

Fig. 3-1

In terms of (*3.1a, b*) the elemental deformation equals the elemental flexibility multiplied by the respective stress.

In full matrix form,

$$\begin{bmatrix} d\delta^s_{sx} \\ d\delta^s_{sy} \\ d\theta^s_{sz} \end{bmatrix} = \begin{bmatrix} \lambda^s_{sx} & 0 & 0 \\ 0 & 0 & 0 \\ 0 & 0 & \lambda^s_{sz} \end{bmatrix} \begin{bmatrix} N^s_{sx} \\ N^s_{sy} \\ M^s_{sz} \end{bmatrix}$$

or symbolically

$$d\Delta_s{}^s = \lambda_s{}^s \sigma_s{}^s \tag{3.2}$$

where $d\Delta_s{}^s$ = elemental deformation vector matrix, [3 × 1], $\lambda_s{}^s$ = elemental flexibility matrix, [3 × 3], and $\sigma_s{}^s$ = stress vector matrix, [3 × 1]. All three matrices are related to the section s and s-system.

3.2 ANGULAR TRANSPORT

The angular transport relationships developed in statics of planar bars are applicable here. Thus the elemental deformation vector at s in 0-system is

$$d\Delta_s{}^0 = \omega^{0s}\, d\Delta_s{}^s = \lambda_s{}^0 \sigma_s{}^0 \tag{3.3}$$

where ω^{0s}, ω^{s0} = angular transport matrices.

In full matrix form (*3.3*) is

$$\begin{bmatrix} d\delta^0_{sx} \\ d\delta^0_{sy} \\ d\theta^0_{sz} \end{bmatrix} = \begin{bmatrix} \cos\omega_{s0} & -\sin\omega_{s0} & 0 \\ \sin\omega_{s0} & \cos\omega_{s0} & 0 \\ 0 & 0 & 1 \end{bmatrix} \begin{bmatrix} \lambda^s_{sx} & 0 & 0 \\ 0 & 0 & 0 \\ 0 & 0 & \lambda^s_{sz} \end{bmatrix} \begin{bmatrix} \cos\omega_{s0} & \sin\omega_{s0} & 0 \\ -\sin\omega_{s0} & \cos\omega_{s0} & 0 \\ 0 & 0 & 1 \end{bmatrix} \begin{bmatrix} N^0_{sx} \\ N^0_{sy} \\ M^0_{sz} \end{bmatrix}$$

$$= \begin{bmatrix} \lambda^0_{sxx} & \lambda^0_{sxy} & 0 \\ \lambda^0_{syx} & \lambda^0_{syy} & 0 \\ 0 & 0 & \lambda^0_{szz} \end{bmatrix} \begin{bmatrix} N^0_{sx} \\ N^0_{sy} \\ M^0_{sz} \end{bmatrix}$$

where

$$\omega^{0s} \lambda_s{}^s \omega^{s0} = \lambda_s{}^0 \tag{3.4}$$

is the *elemental flexibility matrix* at s in 0-system.

Since

$$\omega^{s0)T} = \omega^{0s}$$

the relationship (*3.4*) is a typical *congruent transformation* which preserves the symmetry of the elemental flexibility matrix.

3.3 LINEAR TRANSPORT

The elemental deformations given by (*3.2*) produce linear and angular displacements at m shown in Fig. 3-2*a*, *b* below. Since the entire bar is assumed to be rigid with the exception of ds, the resulting displacements at m become

$$d\Delta_m{}^s = p^s_{ms}\, d\Delta_s{}^s \quad \text{or} \quad d\Delta_m{}^0 = p^0_{ms}\, d\Delta_s{}^0 \tag{3.5}$$

where

$$p^s_{ms} = r^{s)T}_{sm} \qquad \text{and} \qquad p^0_{ms} = r^{0)T}_{sm}$$

are the transposes of the linear transport matrices r^s_{sm} and r^0_{sm} respectively.

The elemental displacement at m in terms of $W_m{}^0$ is

$$d\Delta_m{}^0 = p^0_{ms} \lambda_s{}^0 r^0_{sm} W_m{}^0 \tag{3.6a}$$

Similarly, the elemental displacement at k is

$$d\Delta_k{}^0 = p^0_{ks} \lambda_s{}^0 r^0_{sm} W_m{}^0 \tag{3.6b}$$

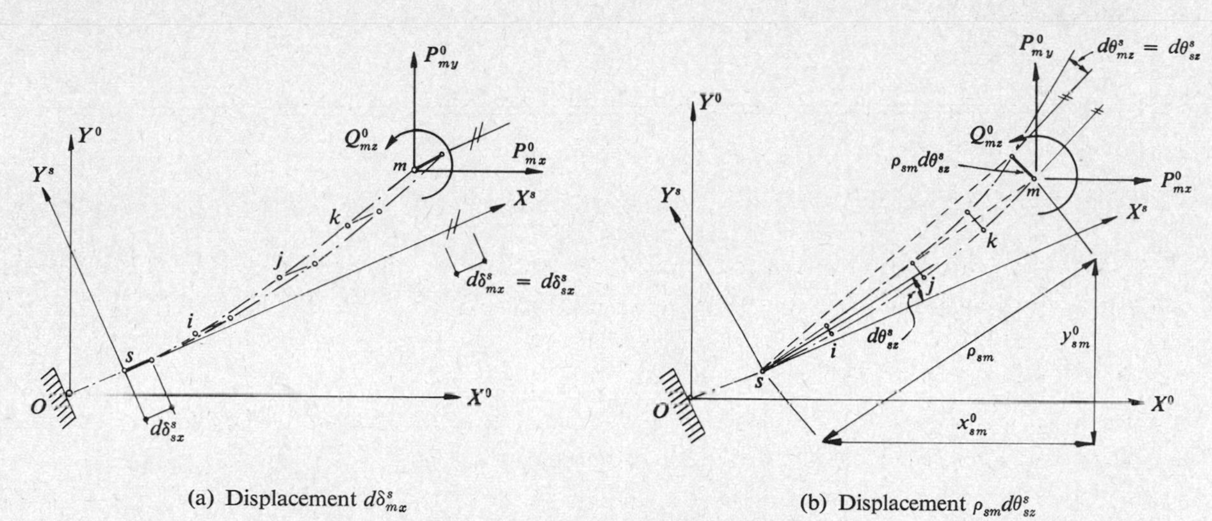

(a) Displacement $d\delta^s_{mz}$ (b) Displacement $\rho_{sm} d\theta^s_{sz}$

Fig. 3-2. Elemental Displacements

3.4 GENERAL TRANSPORT

The elemental deformation at s in s-direction introduces at i in i-direction a displacement

$$d\Delta_i{}^i = p^i_{is}\omega^{is}\, d\Delta_s{}^s = p^i_{is}\omega^{is}\lambda_s{}^s\sigma_s{}^s$$

or

$$d\Delta_i{}^i = \omega^{is}p^s_{is}\, d\Delta_s{}^s = \omega^{is}p^s_{is}\lambda_s{}^s\sigma_s{}^s$$

where

$$p^i_{is}\omega^{is} = \omega^{is}p^s_{is} = s^{is}_{is} \tag{3.7}$$

is the *transpose of the general transport matrix* t^{si}_{si}.

The notion of the *general transport chain* follows automatically as

$$s^{js}_{js} = \omega^{ji}p^i_{ji}\omega^{is}p^s_{is} = p^j_{ji}\omega^{ji}p^i_{is}\omega^{is} = s^{ji}_{ji}s^{is}_{is} \tag{3.8}$$

3.5 INTERMEDIATE ELEMENTAL DEFORMATIONS

If additional elemental deformations enter the transport, they must be inserted in the transport chain. Physically, this means that additional elements of the bar are allowed to become elastic.

With $\Delta_i{}^0, \Delta_j{}^0, \Delta_k{}^0, \Delta_m{}^0$ introduced as the resultant displacement vectors at the respective stations due to $d\Delta_i{}^0, d\Delta_j{}^0, d\Delta_k{}^0, d\Delta_m{}^0$, the displacement vector for the entire bar becomes

$$\begin{bmatrix} \Delta_m{}^0 \\ \Delta_k{}^0 \\ \Delta_j{}^0 \\ \Delta_i{}^0 \end{bmatrix} = \begin{bmatrix} I & p^0_{mk} & p^0_{mj} & p^0_{mi} \\ 0 & I & p^0_{kj} & p^0_{ki} \\ 0 & 0 & I & p^0_{ji} \\ 0 & 0 & 0 & I \end{bmatrix} \begin{bmatrix} d\Delta_m{}^0 \\ d\Delta_k{}^0 \\ d\Delta_j{}^0 \\ d\Delta_i{}^0 \end{bmatrix} \tag{3.9}$$

If the displacement vectors are measured at each station in the respective member system and the elemental deformation vectors are given in 0-system, then

$$\begin{bmatrix} \Delta_m{}^m \\ \Delta_k{}^k \\ \Delta_j{}^j \\ \Delta_i{}^i \end{bmatrix} = \begin{bmatrix} \omega^{m0} & 0 & 0 & 0 \\ 0 & \omega^{k0} & 0 & 0 \\ 0 & 0 & \omega^{j0} & 0 \\ 0 & 0 & 0 & \omega^{i0} \end{bmatrix} \begin{bmatrix} I & p^0_{mk} & p^0_{mj} & p^0_{mi} \\ 0 & I & p^0_{kj} & p^0_{ki} \\ 0 & 0 & I & p^0_{ji} \\ 0 & 0 & 0 & I \end{bmatrix} \begin{bmatrix} d\Delta_m{}^0 \\ d\Delta_k{}^0 \\ d\Delta_j{}^0 \\ d\Delta_i{}^0 \end{bmatrix}$$

Finally, if the displacement vectors and the elemental deformation vectors are measured and given in prescribed systems, then

$$\begin{bmatrix} \Delta_m{}^d \\ \Delta_k{}^c \\ \Delta_j{}^b \\ \Delta_i{}^a \end{bmatrix} = \begin{bmatrix} \omega^{d0} & 0 & 0 & 0 \\ 0 & \omega^{c0} & 0 & 0 \\ 0 & 0 & \omega^{b0} & 0 \\ 0 & 0 & 0 & \omega^{a0} \end{bmatrix} \begin{bmatrix} I & p^0_{mk} & p^0_{mj} & p^0_{mi} \\ 0 & I & p^0_{kj} & p^0_{ki} \\ 0 & 0 & I & p^0_{ji} \\ 0 & 0 & 0 & I \end{bmatrix} \begin{bmatrix} \omega^{0m} & 0 & 0 & 0 \\ 0 & \omega^{0k} & 0 & 0 \\ 0 & 0 & \omega^{0j} & 0 \\ 0 & 0 & 0 & \omega^{0i} \end{bmatrix} \begin{bmatrix} d\Delta_m{}^m \\ d\Delta_k{}^k \\ d\Delta_j{}^j \\ d\Delta_i{}^i \end{bmatrix}$$

which again is a general transport equation shown below.

$$\begin{bmatrix} \Delta_m{}^d \\ \Delta_k{}^c \\ \Delta_j{}^b \\ \Delta_i{}^a \end{bmatrix} = \begin{bmatrix} s^{dm}_{mm} & s^{dk}_{mk} & s^{dj}_{mj} & s^{di}_{mi} \\ 0 & s^{ck}_{kk} & s^{cj}_{kj} & s^{ci}_{ki} \\ 0 & 0 & s^{bj}_{jj} & s^{bi}_{ji} \\ 0 & 0 & 0 & s^{ai}_{ii} \end{bmatrix} \begin{bmatrix} d\Delta_m{}^m \\ d\Delta_k{}^k \\ d\Delta_j{}^j \\ d\Delta_i{}^i \end{bmatrix} \tag{3.10}$$

Thus the *static effect* is related to the *static cause* by means of the *general transport matrix* (*2.15*) and the *deformation effect* is related to the *deformation cause* by means of the *transpose of the same matrix*.

3.6 DEFORMATION EQUATIONS

If all elements of the bar LR (Fig. 2-7) are allowed to deform, the relationships between the end displacements and the integral sum of all elemental deformations are

$$\Delta_R{}^0 = \int_L^R p^0_{Rs}\lambda_s{}^0\sigma_s{}^0 + p^0_{RL}\Delta_L{}^0 \qquad \text{or} \qquad \Delta_L{}^0 = -\int_L^R p^0_{Ls}\lambda_s{}^0\sigma_s{}^0 + p^0_{LR}\Delta_R{}^0 \tag{3.11}$$

where s is an arbitrarily selected cross section in LR and $\Delta_L{}^0$, $\Delta_R{}^0$ are positive displacement vectors at L, R respectively.

3.7 EQUIVALENT DEFORMATIONS

As the magnitude and direction of the elemental deformations vary over a given segment of the structure, it becomes again necessary (to avoid integral expressions) to replace such distributed vectors by an equivalent system of single vectors called *joint deformations*. For this purpose the deformation diagram, the intensity of which is $\lambda_s{}^0\sigma_s{}^0$, is divided into a certain number of strips of equal or unequal length and each strip is treated as a simple beam loaded by this diagram. Since $\lambda_s{}^0$ includes the variation of cross section, this procedure applies to members of constant or variable dimensions. The reactions of these simple beams are then applied as the equivalent deformation vectors (joint deformations) on the axis of the given structure. With this transformation completed, (*3.9*) or (*3.10*) can be applied in *discrete model form*.

For deformation curves defined by analytical functions this again can be done by integration or by various approximations. For irregular deformation curves, only approximate equivalents are available. Two most common approximations given in Table 2-1 are also applicable here.

The *joint deformation expressions* due to flexure only, rearranged in matrix form give the following *joint deformation matrix*:

$$\underbrace{\begin{bmatrix} \gamma_i \\ \gamma_j \\ \gamma_k \end{bmatrix}}_{\gamma} = \underbrace{\begin{bmatrix} c_i & c_{ij} & 0 \\ c_{ji} & c_j & c_{jk} \\ 0 & c_{kj} & c_k \end{bmatrix}}_{\alpha} \underbrace{\begin{bmatrix} 1/EI_i & 0 & 0 \\ 0 & 1/EI_j & 0 \\ 0 & 0 & 1/EI_k \end{bmatrix}}_{1/EI} \underbrace{\begin{bmatrix} M_i \\ M_j \\ M_k \end{bmatrix}}_{M}$$

where I_i, I_j, I_k are the cross-sectional moments of inertia at i, j, k respectively.

This matrix equation can be written for any number of joints and expressed symbolically as

$$\gamma = \alpha(1/EI)M \tag{3.12}$$

3.8 NEWMARK'S METHOD, PART II

For straight beams acted upon by transverse loads (Fig. 2-8), the linear transport equation (*3.9*) reduces to

$$\theta_j = \theta_k - \gamma_j \qquad \delta_j = \delta_k + \theta_k d \tag{3.13}$$

where γ_j is the joint deformation defined by (*3.12*) in terms of formulas of Table 2-1.

For the beam of Fig. 2-8, $EI = 33{,}333^{\text{k}}\text{-ft}^2$ is given and is assumed to be constant for the entire length. The joint deformations in terms of the bending moments inserted in the trapezoidal formulas are recorded in the top line of Fig. 3-3.

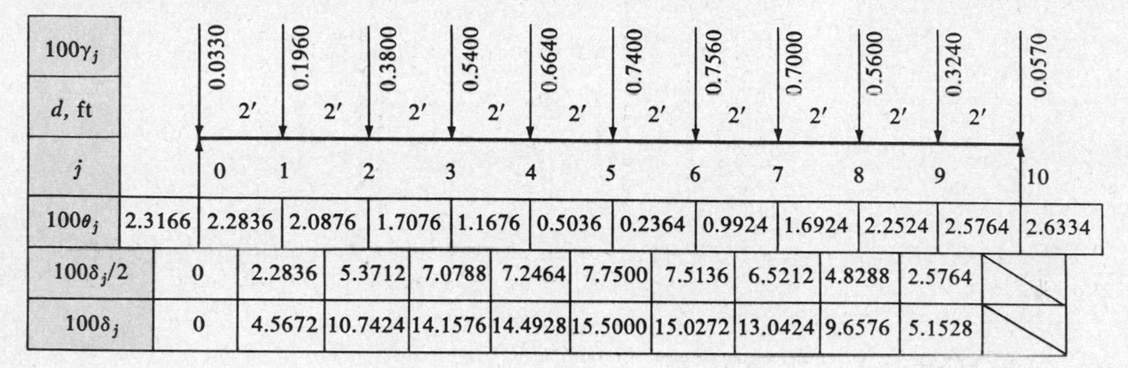

j		0		1		2		3		4		5		6		7		8		9		10	
$100\gamma_j$		0.0330		0.1960		0.3800		0.5400		0.6640		0.7400		0.7560		0.7000		0.5600		0.3240		0.0570	
d, ft			2′		2′		2′		2′		2′		2′		2′		2′		2′		2′		
$100\theta_j$	2.3166		2.2836		2.0876		1.7076		1.1676		0.5036		0.2364		0.9924		1.6924		2.2524		2.5764		2.6334
$100\delta_j/2$		0		2.2836		5.3712		7.0788		7.2464		7.7500		7.5136		6.5212		4.8288		2.5764			
$100\delta_j$		0		4.5672		10.7424		14.1576		14.4928		15.5000		15.0272		13.0424		9.6576		5.1528			

Fig. 3-3. Deformations in Simple Beam

With the joint deformations known, equations (*3.13*) can be used for the successive calculation of slopes and deflections of the elastic curve at the selected stations as shown in Fig. 3-3. The starting value is either

$$\theta_{10} = (0.9)\,\gamma_9 + (0.8)\,\gamma_8 + \cdots + (0.2)\,\gamma_2 + (0.1)\,\gamma_1$$

or

$$\theta_0 = (0.1)\,\gamma_9 + (0.2)\,\gamma_8 + \cdots + (0.8)\,\gamma_2 + (0.9)\,\gamma_1$$

This procedure known as Newmark's Method, Part II, is analogical to Part I (Section 2.10) and offers the same numerical controls.

3.9 DEFLECTION MATRIX

For a straight bar acted upon by a system of transverse loads (Fig. 2-9), the *angle changes* of the *string polygon* inscribed to the elastic curve (Fig. 3-4) are given by

$$\gamma_j = (-\delta_i + 2\delta_j - \delta_k)/d \tag{3.14}$$

where δ_i, δ_j, δ_k are the deflections at i, j, k and d is the spacing of these deflections.

For the entire bar of Fig. 3-4,

$$\underbrace{\frac{1}{d}\begin{bmatrix} 2 & -1 & 0 \\ -1 & 2 & -1 \\ 0 & -1 & 2 \end{bmatrix}}_{\beta} \underbrace{\begin{bmatrix} \delta_i \\ \delta_j \\ \delta_k \end{bmatrix}}_{\delta} = \underbrace{\begin{bmatrix} \gamma_i \\ \gamma_j \\ \gamma_k \end{bmatrix}}_{\gamma}$$

and symbolically

$$\beta\delta = \gamma \tag{3.15}$$

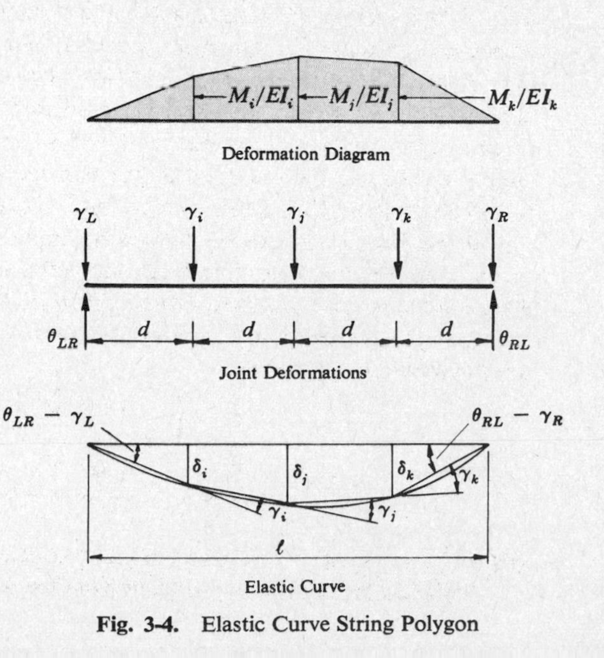

Fig. 3-4. Elastic Curve String Polygon

Combining (*3.12*), (*3.15*) and (*2.21*),

$$\beta\delta = \alpha(1/EI)M = \alpha(1/EI)\,\beta^{)-1}\alpha p$$

from which

$$\delta = \underbrace{\beta^{-1}\alpha}_{m}(1/EI)\,\underbrace{\beta^{)-1}\alpha}_{m} p = m(1/EI)\,mp \tag{3.16}$$

In a completely general case

$$\delta = \beta^{-1)T}\alpha(1/EI)\,\beta^{-1}\alpha p \tag{3.17}$$

where $\beta^{-1)T}$ is the transpose of β^{-1}. In this case $\beta^{-1)T} = \beta^{-1}$.

Solved Problems

LINEAR AND ANGULAR TRANSPORT

3.1. Using the virtual forces principle (*1.8*), derive the transport equations (*3.6a, b*).

Let $\bar{W}_k{}^0$ be any force system applied at k which induces $\bar{\sigma}_s{}^s$ virtual stresses at s (Fig. 3-2). Then from (*1.8*),

$$\bar{W}_k^{0)T}\, d\Delta_k{}^0 = \bar{\sigma}_s^{s)T}\, d\Delta_s{}^s$$

But

$$\bar{\sigma}_s{}^s = \omega^{s0}\,r^0_{sk}\bar{W}_k{}^0 \qquad \text{and} \qquad d\Delta_s{}^s = \lambda_s{}^s\omega^{s0}\,r^0_{sm}W_m{}^0$$

Hence

$$\bar{W}_k^{0)T}\, d\Delta_k{}^0 = \bar{W}_k^{0)T}\,r_{sk}^{0)T}\,\omega^{s0)T}\lambda_s{}^s\omega^{s0}\,r^0_{sm}W_m{}^0 = \bar{W}_k^{0)T}\,p^0_{ks}\lambda_s{}^0 r^0_{sm}W_m{}^0$$

Since this relation is true for any and every value of $\bar{W}_k{}^0$, $d\Delta_k{}^0 = p^0_{ks}\lambda_s{}^0 r^0_{sm}W_m{}^0$ which is (*3.6b*).

For the special case where the point k is chosen coincidental with the point m, the above equation reduces to (*3.6a*).

3.2. Using Engesser's theorem (*1.10*), derive the transport equations (*3.9, 10*).

The strain energy U stored in a *linearly* elastic system $= \Sigma_i U_i = \frac{1}{2}\Sigma_i\, \sigma_i^{i)T}\lambda_i{}^i\sigma_i{}^i$ where U_i is the energy stored in a typical ith segment of the system. From Engesser's theorem,

$$\Delta_j{}^b = \partial U/\partial P_j{}^b = \sum_i \sigma_i^{i)T\,P_j^b=1}\lambda_i{}^i\sigma_i{}^i$$

where $\sigma_i^{i\,P_j^b=1}$ is the stress induced at i due to $P_j{}^b = 1$.

Now $\sigma_i{}^i = \sum_{\substack{k\\ k\neq j}} t^{in}_{ik}\sigma_k{}^n + t^{ib}_{ij}\sigma_j{}^b$ where n's and b are any desired directions and $\sigma_i^{i)P_j^b=1} = t^{ib}_{ij}\sigma_j^{b)P_j^b=1}$. Substituting,

$$\Delta_j{}^b = \sum_i \sigma_j^{b)T\,P_j^b=1}\,t_{ij}^{ib)T}\lambda_i{}^i\sigma_i{}^i$$

However,

$$t_{ij}^{ib)T} = s^{bi}_{ji} \qquad \text{and} \qquad \lambda_i{}^i\sigma_i{}^i = d\Delta_i{}^i \qquad \text{and} \qquad \sigma_j^{b)T\,P_j^b=1} = [1, 0, 0] \text{ in } b\text{-direction}$$

Hence $\Delta_j{}^b = \Sigma_i\, s^{bi}_{ji}\, d\Delta_i{}^i$ which is (*3.10*) in a slightly different form.

Equation (*3-9*) is only a special case of (*3.10*) where b and i directions are the same as o-direction. Thus

$$\Delta_j{}^0 = \sum_i s^{00}_{ji}\, d\Delta_i{}^0$$

But $s^{00}_{ji} = p^0_{ji}\omega^{00} = p^0_{ji}$ since $\omega^{00} = I$. Hence $\Delta_j{}^0 = \Sigma_i\, p^0_{ji}\, d\Delta_i{}^0$ which is equation (*3.9*).

3.3. Using the transport equations compute the end displacements of the cantilever bar of Fig. P-2.1. $EI = 1 \times 10^6$ k-ft² and $EA = 1 \times 10^6$ k are constant properties for the entire bar.

From equation (3.9) and Fig. P-2.1,

$$\Delta_3{}^0 = \sum_{i=1}^{3} p_{3i}^0 \, d\Delta_i{}^0$$

$$= p_{31}^0 \, d\Delta_1{}^0 + p_{32}^0 \, d\Delta_2{}^0 + p_{33}^0 \, d\Delta_3{}^0$$

$$p_{31}^0 = \begin{bmatrix} 1 & 0 & -15 \\ 0 & 1 & 20 \\ 0 & 0 & 1 \end{bmatrix}$$

$$p_{32}^0 = \begin{bmatrix} 1 & 0 & -5 \\ 0 & 1 & 10 \\ 0 & 0 & 1 \end{bmatrix}$$

$$p_{33}^0 = I$$

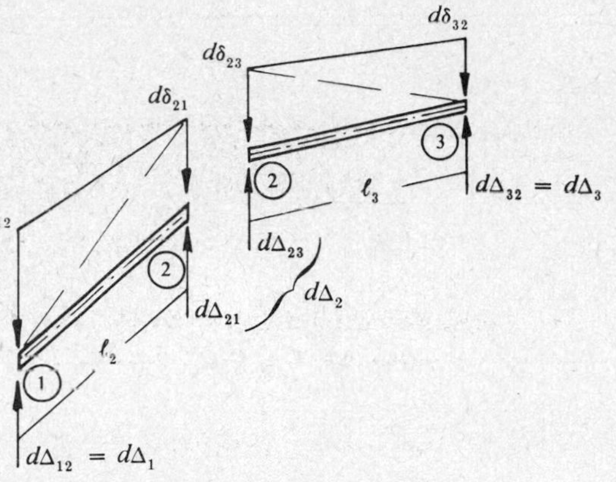

Fig. P-3.3

$$d\Delta_1{}^0 = d\Delta_{12}^0 = \frac{l_2}{6}(2\, d\delta_{12}^0 + d\delta_{21}^0)$$

$$d\Delta_2{}^0 = d\Delta_{21}^0 + d\Delta_{23}^0 = \frac{l_2}{6}(2\, d\delta_{21}^0 + d\delta_{12}^0) + \frac{l_3}{6}(2\, d\delta_{23}^0 + d\delta_{32}^0)$$

and

$$d\Delta_3{}^0 = d\Delta_{32}^0 = \frac{l_3}{6}(2\, d\delta_{32}^0 + d\delta_{23}^0)$$

where $l_2 - l_{12} - 14.14$ ft and $l_3 - l_{23} - 11.18$ ft.

$$d\delta_{12}^0 = \lambda_1{}^0 \sigma_1{}^0 = \omega^{01} \lambda_1{}^1 \omega^{10} \sigma_1{}^0, \qquad d\delta_{21}^0 = \lambda_2{}^0 \sigma_2{}^0 = \omega^{01} \lambda_2{}^1 \omega^{10} \sigma_2{}^0$$

$$d\delta_{23}^0 = \lambda_2{}^0 \sigma_2{}^0 = \omega^{02} \lambda_2{}^2 \omega^{20} \sigma_2{}^0, \qquad d\delta_{32}^0 = \lambda_3{}^0 \sigma_3{}^0 = \omega^{02} \lambda_3{}^2 \omega^{20} \sigma_3{}^0$$

Using the values of $\sigma_1{}^0$, $\sigma_2{}^0$, $\sigma_3{}^0$, ω^{10}, ω^{20} from Problem 2.1 and using

$$\lambda_1{}^1 = \lambda_2{}^1 = \lambda_2{}^2 = \lambda_3{}^2 = \begin{bmatrix} 1/EA & 0 & 0 \\ 0 & 0 & 0 \\ 0 & 0 & 1/EI \end{bmatrix} = \begin{bmatrix} 10^{-6} & 0 & 0 \\ 0 & 0 & 0 \\ 0 & 0 & 10^{-6} \end{bmatrix}$$

the elemental deformations become

$$d\delta_{12}^0 = 10^{-6}\{15, 15, 550\}, \qquad d\delta_{21}^0 = 10^{-6}\{15, 15, 450\}$$

$$d\delta_{23}^0 = 10^{-6}\{16, 8, 450\}, \qquad d\delta_{32}^0 = 10^{-6}\{16, 8, 300\}$$

and the joint deformations become

$$d\Delta_1{}^0 = 10^{-6}\{106.05, 106.05, 3652.90\}, \qquad d\Delta_2{}^0 = 10^{-6}\{195.49, 150.77, 5653.17\}$$

and

$$d\Delta_3{}^0 = 10^{-6}\{89.44, 44.72, 1956.50\}$$

On substitution of these values the total end deformation at 3 becomes

$$\Delta_3{}^0 = 10^{-3}\{-82.67, 129.89, 11.26\}$$

3.4. Compute the displacements of the semicircular cantilever bar of Fig. P-2.3 at 2, 3 and 4. $EI = 10^6$ k-ft² and $EA = 10^6$ k are constant for the entire bar. Take advantage of the equal spacing of the stations and show its effect on the formation of the transport chain.

The deformation transport matrix relating any two consecutive stations, say i and j, on a circular bar can be computed using its geometry shown in Fig. P-3.4a below.

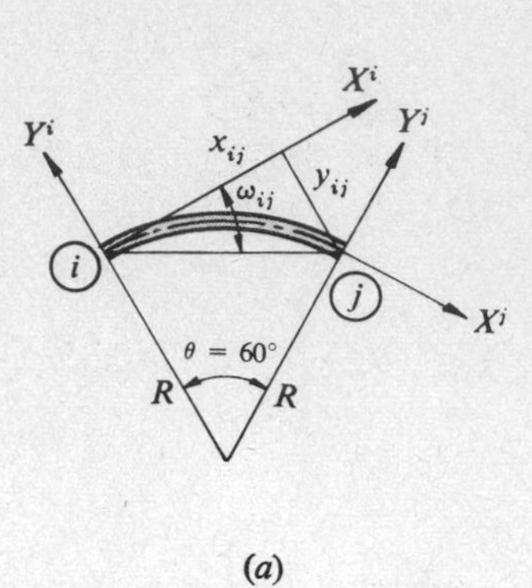

(a)

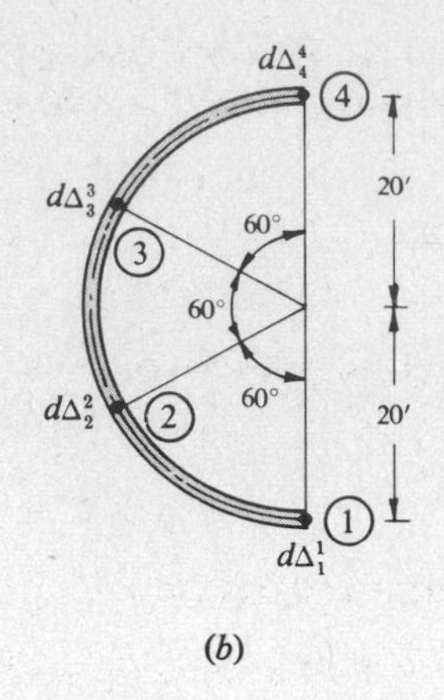

(b)

Fig. P-3.4

For $\omega_{ji} = -\theta/2 = -30°$ and $R = 20.00$ ft,

$$y_{ij}^i = -10.00 \text{ ft}, \qquad x_{ij}^i = 17.32 \text{ ft}$$

$$\Delta_j^j = s_{ji}^{ji}\, d\Delta_i^i$$

where $s_{ji}^{ji} = \omega^{ji} p_{ji}^i$,

$$\omega^{ji} = \begin{bmatrix} 0.5 & -0.866 & 0 \\ 0.866 & 0.5 & 0 \\ 0 & 0 & 1 \end{bmatrix} \quad \text{and} \quad p_{ji}^i = \begin{bmatrix} 1 & 0 & 10.00 \\ 0 & 1 & 17.32 \\ 0 & 0 & 1 \end{bmatrix}$$

$$\therefore \quad s_{ji}^{ji} = \begin{bmatrix} 0.5 & -0.866 & -10.00 \\ 0.866 & 0.5 & 17.32 \\ 0 & 0 & 1 \end{bmatrix}$$

For the given bar, stations 1, 2, 3 and 4 are equally spaced and advantage can be taken of this fact in transporting the effect of deformations from one station to the next by using the same transport matrix. This is shown by the following manipulation.

First let $s_{43}^{43} = s_{32}^{32} = s_{21}^{21} = s_{ij}^{ij} = [s]$

From equation (*3.10*),

$$\begin{bmatrix} \Delta_4^4 \\ \Delta_3^3 \\ \Delta_2^2 \\ \Delta_1^1 \end{bmatrix} = \begin{bmatrix} s_{44}^{44} & s_{43}^{43} & s_{42}^{42} & s_{41}^{41} \\ 0 & s_{33}^{33} & s_{32}^{32} & s_{31}^{31} \\ 0 & 0 & s_{22}^{22} & s_{21}^{21} \\ 0 & 0 & 0 & s_{11}^{11} \end{bmatrix} \begin{bmatrix} d\Delta_4^4 \\ d\Delta_3^3 \\ d\Delta_2^2 \\ d\Delta_1^1 \end{bmatrix} \quad \text{and} \quad s_{44}^{44} = s_{33}^{33} = s_{22}^{22} = s_{11}^{11} = I$$

Also $\quad s_{42}^{42} = s_{43}^{43} s_{32}^{32} = [s]^2, \quad s_{31}^{31} = s_{32}^{32} s_{21}^{21} = [s]^2 \quad$ and $\quad s_{41}^{41} = s_{43}^{43} s_{32}^{32} s_{21}^{21} = [s]^3$

Therefore

$$\Delta_1^1 = d\Delta_1^1$$
$$\Delta_2^2 = d\Delta_2^2 + [s]\, d\Delta_1^1 = d\Delta_2^2 + [s]\, \Delta_1^1$$
$$\Delta_3^3 = d\Delta_3^3 + [s]\, d\Delta_2^2 + [s]^2\, d\Delta_1^1 = d\Delta_3^3 + [s]\, \Delta_2^2$$
$$\Delta_4^4 = d\Delta_4^4 + [s]\, d\Delta_3^3 + [s]^2\, d\Delta_2^2 + [s]^3\, d\Delta_1^1 = d\Delta_4^4 + [s]\, \Delta_3^3$$

Now $d\Delta_1^1 = \lambda_1^1 \sigma_1^1$, $d\Delta_2^2 = \lambda_2^2 \sigma_2^2$, $d\Delta_3^3 = \lambda_3^3 \sigma_3^3$ and $d\Delta_4^4 = \lambda_4^4 \sigma_4^4$

where

$$\lambda = \begin{bmatrix} l/EA & 0 & 0 \\ 0 & 0 & 0 \\ 0 & 0 & l/EI \end{bmatrix} \quad \begin{matrix} \text{and} \quad l = \dfrac{\pi(20)}{6} = 10.472 \text{ ft for stations 1 and 4} \\ \text{and} \quad l = \dfrac{\pi(20)}{3} = 20.944 \text{ ft for stations 2 and 3.} \end{matrix}$$

Using these values and the given values of EI and EA and the values of stress vectors $\sigma_1^1, \sigma_2^2, \sigma_3^3, \sigma_4^4$ computed in Problem 2.3, the following deformation vectors are obtained:

$$\Delta_1^1 = 10^{-3}\begin{bmatrix} -0.157 \\ 0 \\ -5.236 \end{bmatrix}, \quad \Delta_2^2 = 10^{-3}\begin{bmatrix} 51.67 \\ -90.82 \\ -21.64 \end{bmatrix}, \quad \Delta_3^3 = 10^{-3}\begin{bmatrix} 320.54 \\ -375.92 \\ -31.75 \end{bmatrix}, \quad \Delta_4^4 = 10^{-3}\begin{bmatrix} 803.49 \\ -460.56 \\ -30.70 \end{bmatrix}$$

These deformations in o-system are

$$\Delta_1^0 = \omega^{01}\Delta_1^1, \quad \Delta_2^0 = \omega^{02}\Delta_2^2, \quad \Delta_3^0 = \omega^{03}\Delta_3^3 \quad \text{and} \quad \Delta_4^0 = \omega^{04}\Delta_4^4$$

NEWMARK'S METHOD

3.5. Show the relationship of the transport equations and Newmark's Method.

The transport equation (*3.9*) can be reduced to simpler equations for a straight bar the longitudinal axis of which can be taken as X^0. Then from (*3.9*) referring to all quantities in o-system,

$$\Delta_i = d\Delta_i$$

$$\Delta_j = d\Delta_j + p_{ji}\, d\Delta_i = d\Delta_j + p_{ji}\Delta_i$$

$$\Delta_k = d\Delta_k + p_{kj}\, d\Delta_j + p_{ki}\, d\Delta_i = d\Delta_k + p_{kj}(d\Delta_j + p_{ji}\, d\Delta_i) = d\Delta_k + p_{kj}\Delta_j \text{ since } p_{ki} = p_{kj}\, p_{ji}$$

In general,

$$\Delta_n = d\Delta_n + \sum_{m=1}^{n} p_{nm}\, d\Delta_m = d\Delta_n + p_{n,n-1}\left(d\Delta_{n-1} + \sum_{m=1}^{n-1} p_{n-1,m}\, d\Delta_m\right) = d\Delta_n + p_{n,n-1}\Delta_{n-1}$$

This shows that the deformation at any point can be related to that at the preceding point by a simple relation and thus deformations can be transported from point to point successively.

Referring again to any two consecutive points j and k and noting that $y_{ji} = 0$, we have

$$\begin{bmatrix} \Delta_{kx} \\ \Delta_{ky} \\ \Delta_{kz} \end{bmatrix} = \begin{bmatrix} d\delta_{kx} \\ d\delta_{ky} \\ d\theta_{kz} \end{bmatrix} + \begin{bmatrix} 1 & 0 & 0 \\ 0 & 1 & x_{jk} \\ 0 & 0 & 1 \end{bmatrix}\begin{bmatrix} \Delta_{jx} \\ \Delta_{jy} \\ \theta_{jz} \end{bmatrix}$$

If only transverse deformations are significant and needed, this reduces to

$$\begin{bmatrix} \Delta_{ky} \\ \theta_{kz} \end{bmatrix} = \begin{bmatrix} d\delta_{ky} \\ d\theta_{kz} \end{bmatrix} + \begin{bmatrix} 1 & x_{jk} \\ 0 & 1 \end{bmatrix}\begin{bmatrix} \Delta_{jy} \\ \theta_{jz} \end{bmatrix}$$

which in scalar from becomes

$$\Delta_{ky} = d\delta_{ky} + \Delta_{jy} + x_{jk}\theta_{jz}$$

$$\theta_{kz} = d\theta_{kz} + \theta_{jz}$$

Neglecting the shear deformation $d\delta_{ky}$ and denoting $x_{jk} = d$ and $d\theta_{kz} = \gamma_k$ gives

$$\Delta_k = \Delta_j + \theta_j d$$

$$\theta_k = \theta_j + \gamma_k$$

The physical interpretation of these equations used in Newmark's Method is clear from Fig. P-3.5.

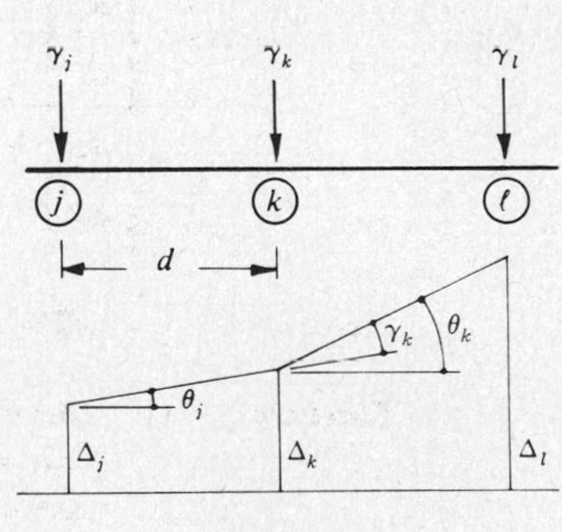

Fig. P-3.5

3.6. Observe the similarity of the stress and deformation transport equations. Representing the elemental deformations and the displacements by the respective vectors, show the analogy between the statics of loads and stresses and the kinematics of deformation and displacement vectors.

Observe equations (*2.15*) and (*3.10*) and consider one typical term taken out of each relating, say, points i and k. Using completely general prescribed reference systems, say a-system at i and b-system at k, the load-stress relation is $\sigma_k{}^a = t_{ik}^{ab} W_k{}^b$ and the displacement-deformation relation is $\Delta_k{}^b = s_{ki}^{ba}\, d\Delta_i{}^a$. These relations can be written slightly differently as $d\sigma_i{}^a = t_{ik}^{ab}\, d\sigma_k{}^b$ and $d\Delta_k{}^b = s_{ki}^{ba}\, d\Delta_i{}^a$ where $d\sigma_i{}^a$ represents only that part of total $\sigma_i{}^a$ which is induced due to $d\sigma_k{}^b$ (the stress or load that is being transported from k to i) and similarly $d\Delta_k{}^b$ represents only that part of the total displacement $\Delta_k{}^b$ which is induced as a result of the deformation $d\Delta_i{}^a$. However, from the latter relation, $d\Delta_i{}^a = s_{ki}^{ba)-1}\, d\Delta_k{}^b = t_{ik}^{ab}\, d\Delta_k{}^b$ which is similar in form to the stress relation.

Physically this means that the deformation vectors can be treated as analogous load vectors and the resulting "stress" vectors computed from them will be the real displacement vectors. This, in fact, is the so-called conjugate analogy. It should be pointed out that care should be exercised in employing proper boundary conditions in solving problems using this analogy.

3.7. Explain Newmark's Method, Part II, in terms of the analogy developed in the preceding problem.

In view of the analogy described in the preceding problem, equations (*3.13*) for Newmark's Method, Part II, can immediately be recognized as analogous to equations (*2.18*), Newmark's Method, Part I, wherein the slope θ is analogous to the shear force V and the deflection Δ is analogous to the bending moment M.

Newmark's Method, Part II, therefore suggests that if joint deformations γ's are treated as analogous joint loads (called elastic loads or conjugate loads), the shears and moments computed therefrom using the same technique as for real loads, are equal respectively to the slopes and deflections of the real beam.

3.8. Using Newmark's Method, Part II, compute the slopes and deflections of the simple beam of Fig. P-2.6. The cross section of the beam is rectangular with width b = constant and the height h varies linearly from h_0 at the ends to $2h_0$ at the midspan.

Let

$$h_j/h_0 = \alpha_j, \qquad M_j/EI_j = (M_j/EI_0)(I_0/I_j) = M_j/\alpha_j^3 EI_0$$

and

$$\gamma_j = \frac{2}{6EI_0}\left(\frac{M_i}{\alpha_i^3} + \frac{4M_j}{\alpha_j^3} + \frac{M_k}{\alpha_k^3}\right)$$

h_0 $2h_0$ h_0

α_j	1.0	1.2	1.4	1.6	1.8	2.0	1.8	1.6	1.4	1.2	1.0
$1/\alpha_j^3$	1.0	0.579	0.364	0.244	0.171	0.125	0.171	0.244	0.364	0.579	1.0
M_j	0	49	90	123	148	165	168	151	134 34	17	0
M_j/α_j^3	0	28.356	32.799	30.029	25.376	20.625	28.805	36.865	48.834 12.391	9.834	0
$EI_0\gamma_j$	↓ 9.452 ↑ 257.227	↓ 48.741	↓ 63.193	↓ 59.431	↓ 50.720	↓ 45.561	↓ 57.570	↓ 75.033	↓ 56.384	↓ 17.247	↓ 3.279 ↑ 229.384

$EI_0\theta_j$	−247.77	−199.03	−135.84	−76.41	−25.69	19.87	77.44	152.47	208.86	226.11

$EI_0\Delta_j/2$	0	−247.77	−446.81	−582.65	−659.06	−684.75	−664.88	−587.44	−434.96	−226.11	0
$EI_0\Delta_j$	0	−495.6	−893.6	−1165.3	−1318.1	−1369.5	−1329.8	−1174.9	−869.9	−452.2	0

3.9. Show the modification of Newmark's Method for the deformation analysis of a compound beam of Fig. P-3.9*a* below.

The beam shown is a statically determinate beam. The reactions and moment values at selected stations can be computed using equations of statics or by using Newmark's Method, Part I. No modifications are necessary for these statical calculations.

For deformation analysis, the joint deformations γ's can be computed using the calculated moment values as for any other beam. However, since the hinge assures only a continuity of deflections and not the continuity of slope at its location, there exists at that station a finite angle change which must be shown as an additional joint deformation at that point. The magnitude of this angular deformation at the hinge, ϕ_H (Fig. P-3.9*b*), can be computed from the statics of the (conjugate) beam loaded by joint deformations γ's. The deformation analysis can then be completed using Newmark's Method in the usual manner.

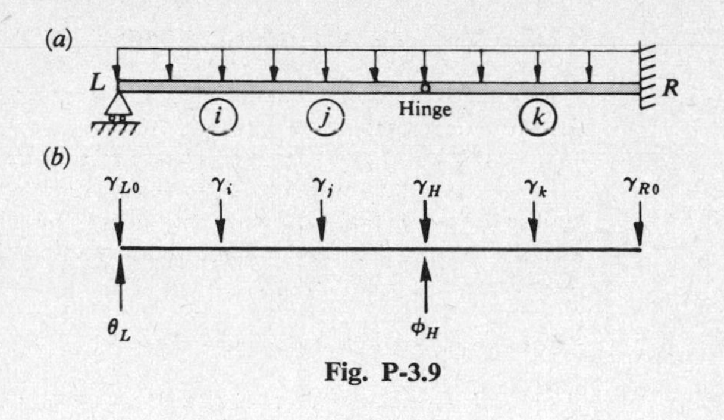

Fig. P-3.9

Supplementary Problems

3.10. Rewrite equations (*3.9*) and (*3.10*) to compute deformations Δ's induced as a result of bending only, by deleting the axial and shear deformation terms from $d\Delta$'s and corresponding columns from the deformation transport matrices.

3.11. Use the principle of virtual forces to compute Δ^0_{Bx} for the frame shown in Fig. P-2.9.

3.12. Use the principle of virtual forces to compute Δ^0_{4x} for the frame shown in Fig. P-2.10. Consider bending deformations only.

3.13. Using Newmark's Method compute the displacements at 2 ft intervals on the beam shown in Fig. P-2.12.

3.14. Compute the displacements at stations 1, 2, 3 and 4 of the beam shown in Fig. P-3.14. (See also Problem 3.9.) The beam has a constant cross section.

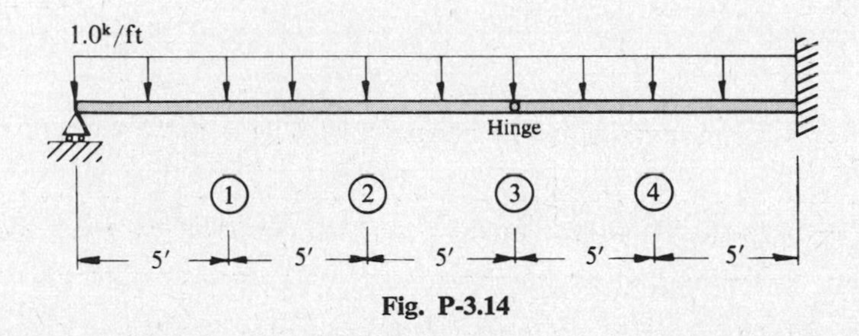

Fig. P-3.14

Chapter 4

Transport Matrix

4.1 CONCEPT

Stress and deformation equations developed in the preceding chapters can be assembled into *two matrix equations*:

$$\hat{H}_L{}^L = \hat{T}_{LR}^{LR}\hat{H}_R{}^R \qquad \text{and} \qquad \hat{H}_R{}^R = \hat{T}_{RL}^{RL}\hat{H}_L{}^L \tag{4.1}$$

where

$$\hat{H}_L{}^L = \{1, N_{Lx}^L, N_{Ly}^L, M_{Lz}^L, \delta_{Lx}^L, \delta_{Ly}^L, \theta_{Lz}^L\}, \qquad \hat{H}_R{}^R = \{1, N_{Rx}^R, N_{Ry}^R, M_{Rz}^R, \delta_{Rx}^R, \delta_{Ry}^R, \theta_{Rz}^R\}$$

are the *state vectors* of the left and right end of the curved planar bar LR respectively. The linear dependence of these vectors is given by the *state vector transport matrices*

$$\hat{T}_{LR}^{LR} = \begin{bmatrix} 1 & 0 & 0 \\ a_L{}^L & t_{LR}^{LR} & 0 \\ b_L{}^L & d_{LR}^{LR} & s_{LR}^{LR} \end{bmatrix} \qquad \hat{T}_{RL}^{RL} = \begin{bmatrix} 1 & 0 & 0 \\ a_R{}^R & t_{RL}^{RL} & 0 \\ b_R{}^R & d_{RL}^{RL} & s_{RL}^{RL} \end{bmatrix} \tag{4.2}$$

the submatrices of which are

$a_L{}^L$, $a_R{}^R$ = Stress load effect matrices, $[3 \times 1]$
$b_L{}^L$, $b_R{}^R$ = Deformation load effect matrices, $[3 \times 1]$
t_{LR}^{LR}, t_{RL}^{RL} = Stress vector general transport matrices, $[3 \times 3]$
s_{LR}^{LR}, s_{RL}^{RL} = Deformation vector general transport matrices, $[3 \times 3]$
d_{LR}^{LR}, d_{RL}^{RL} = Deviation matrices, $[3 \times 3]$.

For a complete development of $\hat{T}_{LR}^{LR}$ and $\hat{T}_{RL}^{RL}$ refer to Problem 4.1 and Fig. 4-1.

The state vector transport matrices give a clear, systematic and complete record of stress and deformation properties of the curved bar; they are *specific* for the given bar and load, and *independent* of the end conditions.

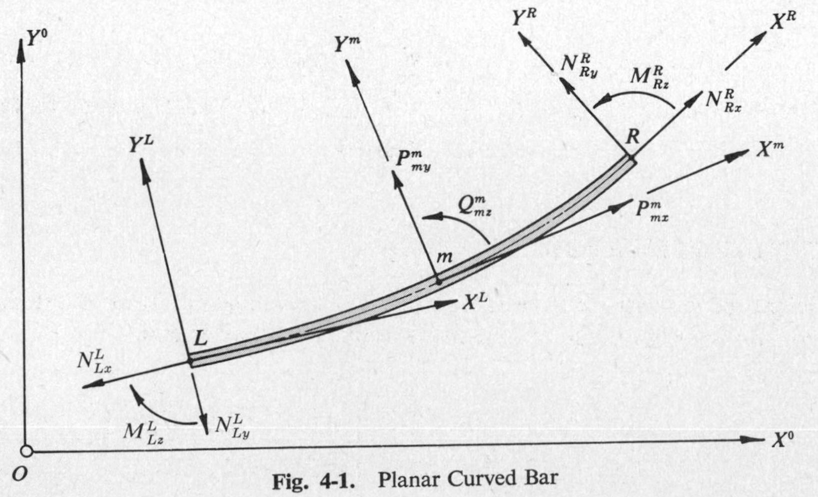

Fig. 4-1. Planar Curved Bar

4.2 LOAD EFFECT COEFFICIENTS

The coefficients of submatrices a and b have a *physical meaning* and can be interpreted as *functions of a loaded cantilever bar.*

From Fig. 4-2*a*,

$$a_L{}^L = \{a_{Lx}^L, a_{Ly}^L, a_{Lz}^L\} \qquad \text{and} \qquad b_L{}^L = \{b_{Lx}^L, b_{Ly}^L, b_{Lz}^L\}$$

are the end stresses and deviations of a cantilever beam LR at the fixed end L;

$$a_L{}^L = \sum_L^R t_{Lm}^{Lm} W_m{}^m \qquad\qquad b_L{}^L = -\sum_L^R s_{Ls}^{Ls}\, d\Delta_s{}^s \tag{4.3}$$

where $W_m{}^m$ is the load vector at m and $d\Delta_0{}^s$ is the elemental deformation vector at s.

Similarly from Fig. 4-2*b*,

$$a_R{}^R = \{a_{Rx}^R, a_{Ry}^R, a_{Rz}^R\} \qquad \text{and} \qquad b_R{}^R = \{b_{Rx}^R, b_{Ry}^R, b_{Rz}^R\}$$

are the end stresses and deformations of a cantilever beam LR at the fixed end R;

$$a_R{}^R = -\sum_L^R t_{Rm}^{Rm} W_m{}^m \qquad\qquad b_R{}^R = \sum_L^R s_{Rs}^{Rs}\, d\Delta_s{}^s \tag{4.4}$$

For particular cases refer to Problems 4.2 and 4.3.

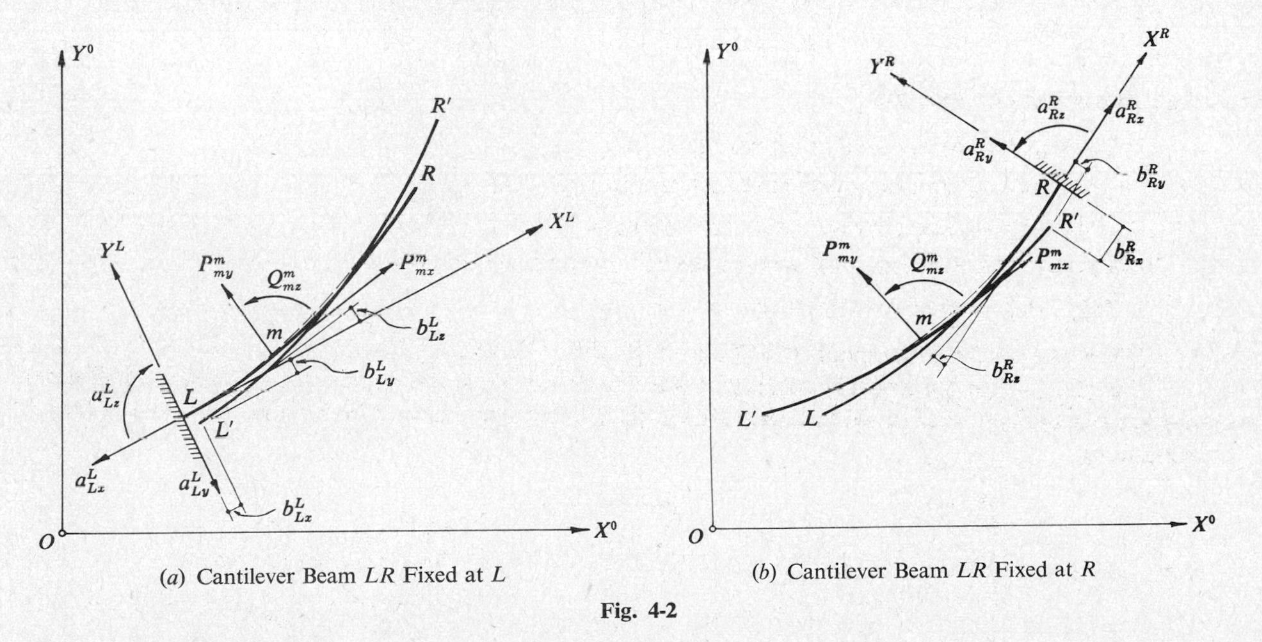

(*a*) Cantilever Beam LR Fixed at L (*b*) Cantilever Beam LR Fixed at R

Fig. 4-2

4.3 DEVIATION COEFFICIENTS

The coefficients of submatrix d have again a physical meaning and can be interpreted as the *deviations of the respective cantilever beam* due to unit stress applied at the free end.

From Fig. 4-3,

$$d_{LR}^{LR} = -\sum_L^R s_{Ls}^{Ls} \lambda_s{}^s t_{sR}^{sR} = \begin{bmatrix} d_{LRxx}^{LR} & d_{LRxy}^{LR} & d_{LRxz}^{LR} \\ d_{LRyx}^{LR} & d_{LRyy}^{LR} & d_{LRyz}^{LR} \\ d_{LRzx}^{LR} & d_{LRzy}^{LR} & d_{LRzz}^{LR} \end{bmatrix} \tag{4.5}$$

and similarly

$$d^{RL}_{RL} = \sum_{L}^{R} s^{Rs}_{Rs} \lambda_s {}^s t^{sL}_{sL} = \begin{bmatrix} d^{RL}_{RLxx} & d^{RL}_{RLxy} & d^{RL}_{RLxz} \\ d^{RL}_{RLyx} & d^{RL}_{RLyy} & d^{RL}_{RLyz} \\ d^{RL}_{RLzx} & d^{RL}_{RLzy} & d^{RL}_{RLzz} \end{bmatrix} \tag{4.6}$$

For particular solutions refer again to Problems 4.2 and 4.3.

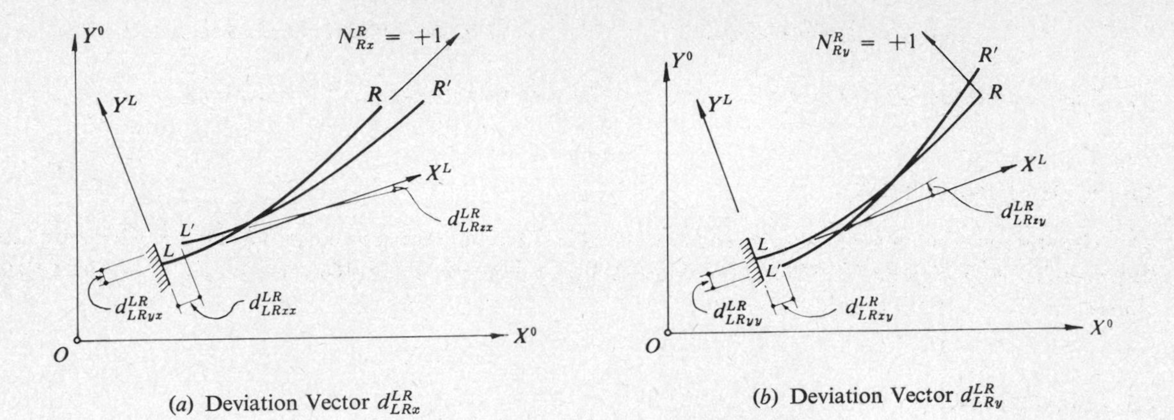

(a) Deviation Vector d^{LR}_{LRx} (b) Deviation Vector d^{LR}_{LRy}

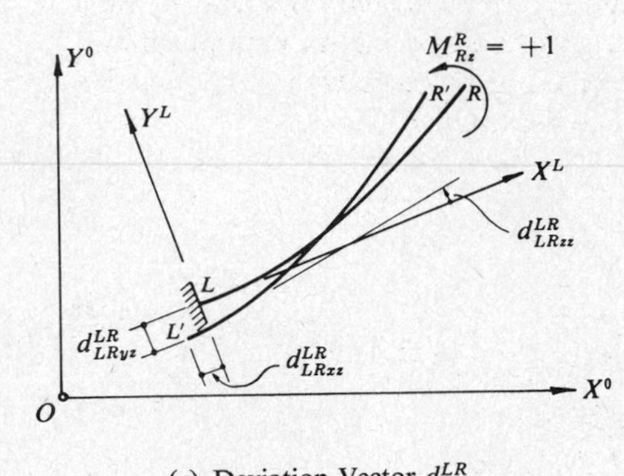

(c) Deviation Vector d^{LR}_{LRz}

Fig. 4-3. Deviation Vectors

4.4 GENERAL PROPERTIES OF TRANSPORT MATRIX

The transport matrices and their submatrices possess the following characteristics:

(a) *Inverse Relationships*

$$\hat{T}^{LR}_{LR} \cdot \hat{T}^{RL}_{RL} = I \qquad t^{LR}_{LR} \cdot t^{RL}_{RL} = I \qquad s^{LR}_{LR} \cdot s^{RL}_{RL} = I \tag{4.7}$$

(b) *Shift Relationships*

$$\begin{bmatrix} a_L{}^L \\ b_L{}^L \end{bmatrix} = - \begin{bmatrix} t^{LR}_{LR} & 0 \\ d^{LR}_{LR} & s^{LR}_{LR} \end{bmatrix} \begin{bmatrix} a_R{}^R \\ b_R{}^R \end{bmatrix} \qquad \begin{bmatrix} a_R{}^R \\ b_R{}^R \end{bmatrix} = - \begin{bmatrix} t^{RL}_{RL} & 0 \\ d^{RL}_{RL} & s^{RL}_{RL} \end{bmatrix} \begin{bmatrix} a_L{}^L \\ b_L{}^L \end{bmatrix} \tag{4.8}$$

$$d^{LR}_{LR} = -s^{LR}_{LR} d^{RL}_{RL} t^{LR}_{LR} \qquad d^{RL}_{RL} = -s^{RL}_{RL} d^{LR}_{LR} t^{RL}_{RL} \tag{4.9}$$

4.5 SIGN CONVENTION

The stress vectors are governed by the sign convention of the flexibility method, whereas the signs of displacements are those of analytic geometry (Figs. 4-4 and 4-5).

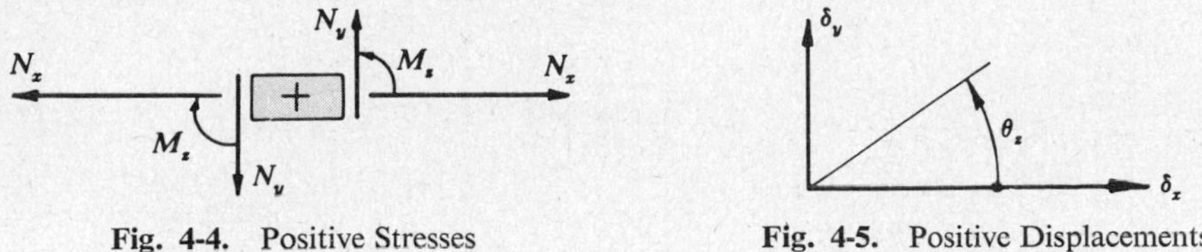

Fig. 4-4. Positive Stresses **Fig. 4-5.** Positive Displacements

The load vector $W_m{}^m$ is positive if acting in the direction of axes X^m, Y^m, Z^m.

4.6 END CONDITIONS

The state vector must satisfy the end conditions of the member, the most common of which are those shown in Table 4-1, page 36. The spring constants introduced in this table are: $K_{\Delta x}$, $K_{\Delta y}$ = linear spring constants, K_ϕ = angular spring constant.

4.7 TRANSPORT CHAIN

Once the transport equations are available for a single segment, their extension to the analysis of multisegment structures is accomplished by matrix multiplication.

Let the bent frame il be given by its geometry (s_j, s_k, s_l and A_j, A_k, A_l, I_j, I_k, I_l) and the modulus of elasticity E and be loaded as shown in Fig. 4-6.

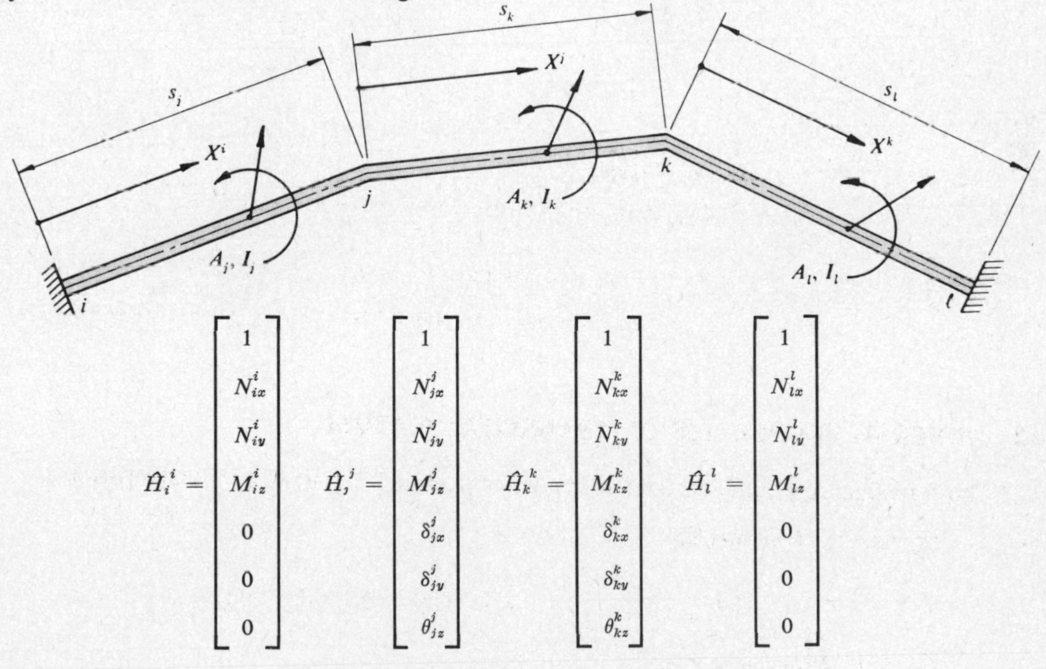

$$\hat{H}_i{}^i = \begin{bmatrix} 1 \\ N_{ix}^i \\ N_{iy}^i \\ M_{iz}^i \\ 0 \\ 0 \\ 0 \end{bmatrix} \quad \hat{H}_j{}^j = \begin{bmatrix} 1 \\ N_{jx}^j \\ N_{jy}^j \\ M_{jz}^j \\ \delta_{jx}^j \\ \delta_{jy}^j \\ \theta_{jz}^j \end{bmatrix} \quad \hat{H}_k{}^k = \begin{bmatrix} 1 \\ N_{kx}^k \\ N_{ky}^k \\ M_{kz}^k \\ \delta_{kx}^k \\ \delta_{ky}^k \\ \theta_{kz}^k \end{bmatrix} \quad \hat{H}_l{}^l = \begin{bmatrix} 1 \\ N_{lx}^l \\ N_{ly}^l \\ M_{lz}^l \\ 0 \\ 0 \\ 0 \end{bmatrix}$$

Fig. 4-6. State Vectors of Bent Frame

Beginning at i,

$$\hat{H}_i{}^i = \hat{T}_{ij}^{ij}\hat{H}_j{}^j \qquad \hat{H}_j{}^j = \hat{T}_{jk}^{jk}\hat{H}_k{}^k \qquad \hat{H}_k{}^k = \hat{T}_{kl}^{kl}\hat{H}_l{}^l \tag{4.10}$$

where $\hat{H}_i{}^i$, $\hat{H}_j{}^j$, $\hat{H}_k{}^k$, $\hat{H}_l{}^l$ are the state vectors at the respective sections and $\hat{T}_{ij}^{ij}$, $\hat{T}_{jk}^{jk}$, $\hat{T}_{kl}^{kl}$ are the transport matrices of the respective segments.

Table 4-1. End Conditions

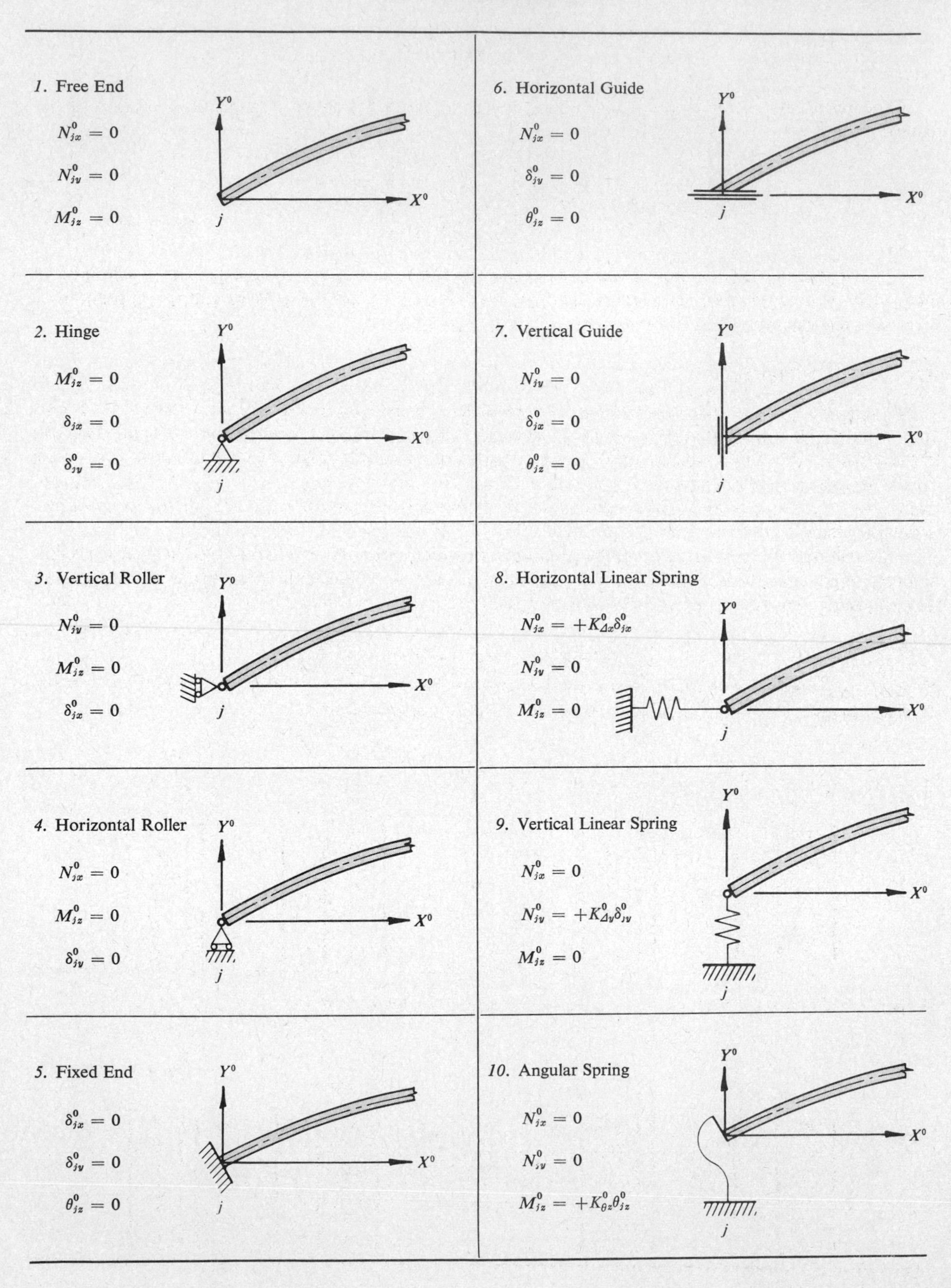

Combining these three separate equations by successive substitution,

$$\hat{H}_i^{\,i} = \underbrace{\hat{T}_{ij}^{ij}\hat{T}_{jk}^{jk}\hat{T}_{kl}^{kl}}_{\hat{T}_{il}^{il}}\hat{H}_l^{\,l} \tag{4.11}$$

The result of the chain product is a new transport matrix $\hat{T}_{il}^{il}$ connecting the state vectors of the exterior ends:

$$\hat{T}_{il}^{il} = \begin{bmatrix} 1 & 0 & 0 \\ a_{il}^{il} & t_{il}^{il} & 0 \\ b_{il}^{il} & d_{il}^{il} & s_{il}^{il} \end{bmatrix} \tag{4.12}$$

This matrix is *characteristic* for the given frame and *independent* of the end conditions. It is designated as the *transport chain* (since it transports all effects to one section) and it may be extended as a generalization of (I-6.8) to any system of planar bars with linear topology.

4.8 APPLICATIONS

The application of the transport matrix is extended in this volume to the analysis of planar beams and frames of all kinds. Similarly as before (Chapter I-6) the transport method makes no distinction between the statically determinate and statically indeterminate systems. In one transport chain, there are always *twelve boundary values* involved (N_{Lx}, N_{Ly}, M_{Lz}, δ_{Lx}, δ_{Ly}, θ_{Lz} and N_{Rx}, N_{Ry}, M_{Rz}, δ_{Rx}, δ_{Ry}, θ_{Rz}) of which *six* are always *known*, and *six* are *unknown*. Thus six equations are necessary for the solution of a given problem.

The transport matrix provides these equations, of which *three* and *only three* must be solved simultaneously. Four typical cases are symbolically outlined in Table 4-2. This table shows again that in all cases, regardless of the type of support or end conditions, the transport matrix remains the same.

Table 4-2. Single Span Frames

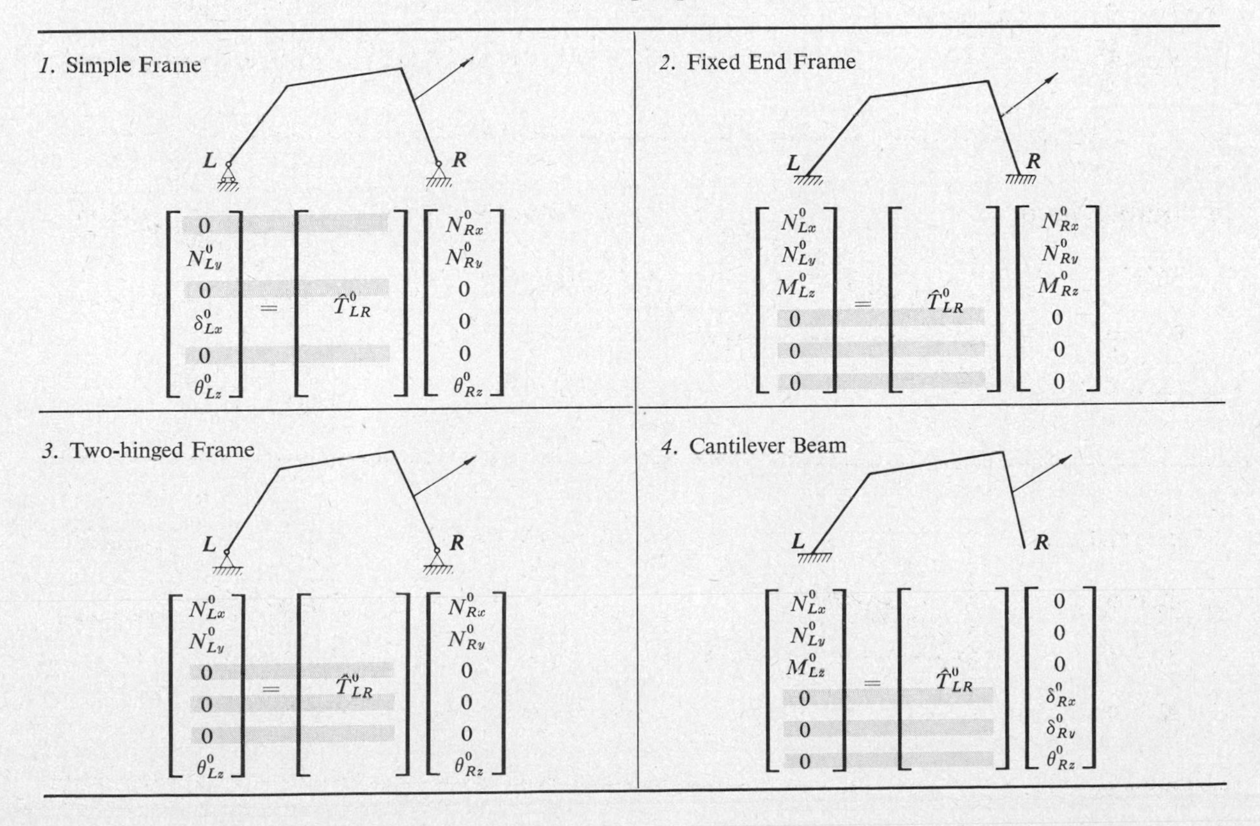

Solved Problems

DERIVATIONS

4.1. Derive the transport matrices $\hat{T}_{LR}^{LR}$ and $\hat{T}_{RL}^{RL}$ for the planar curved bar of Fig. 4-1.

From the static equilibrium of the bar LR in Fig. 4-1,

$$\sigma_L{}^L = t_{LR}^{LR}\sigma_R{}^R + \underbrace{t_{Lm}^{Lm}W_m{}^m}_{a_L{}^L} \qquad \text{and} \qquad \sigma_R{}^R = t_{RL}^{RL}\sigma_L{}^L \underbrace{- t_{Rm}^{Rm}W_m{}^m}_{a_R{}^R} \tag{1}$$

where $a_L{}^L$ and $a_R{}^R$ are the stress load effect matrices [(*4.3*) and (*4.4*)].

If several load vectors are acting on LR,

$$a_L{}^L = \sum_L^R t_{Lm}^{Lm}W_m{}^m \qquad \text{and} \qquad a_R{}^R = -\sum_L^R t_{Rm}^{Rm}W_m{}^m \tag{2}$$

which are the static equations in (*4.3*) and (*4.4*).

With (*1*) and (*2*) known, the second submatrix row of $\hat{T}_{LR}^{LR}$ and $\hat{T}_{RL}^{RL}$ in (*4.2*) is available.

The third submatrix row of (*4.2*) must consist of three parts: the load effect, the end stress effect and the end displacement effect. Thus

$$\Delta_L{}^L = \Delta_L{}^L(W_m{}^m) + \Delta_L{}^L(\sigma_R{}^R) + \Delta_L{}^L(\Delta_R{}^R) \qquad \Delta_R{}^R = \Delta_R{}^R(W_m{}^m) + \Delta_R{}^R(\sigma_L{}^L) + \Delta_R{}^R(\Delta_L{}^L) \tag{3}$$

where, by (*3.11*),

$$\Delta_L{}^L(W_m{}^m) = \underbrace{-\sum_L^R s_{Ls}^{Ls}\lambda_s{}^s t_{sm}^{sm}W_m{}^m}_{b_L{}^L} \qquad \Delta_R{}^R(W_m{}^m) = \underbrace{\sum_L^R s_{Rs}^{Rs}\lambda_s{}^s t_{sm}^{sm}W_m{}^m}_{b_R{}^R} \tag{4}$$

$$\Delta_L{}^L(\sigma_R{}^R) = \underbrace{-\sum_L^R s_{Ls}^{Ls}\lambda_s{}^s t_{sR}^{sR}\sigma_R{}^R}_{d_{LR}^{LR}\sigma_R{}^R} \qquad \Delta_R{}^R(\sigma_L{}^L) = \underbrace{\sum_L^R s_{Rs}^{Rs}\lambda_s{}^s t_{sL}^{sL}\sigma_L{}^L}_{d_{RL}^{RL}\sigma_L{}^L} \tag{5}$$

$$\Delta_L{}^L(\Delta_R{}^R) = s_{LR}^{LR}\Delta_R{}^R \qquad \Delta_R{}^R(\Delta_L{}^L) = s_{RL}^{RL}\Delta_L{}^L \tag{6}$$

The assembly of (*1*) and (*4, 5, 6*) gives the transport equations (*4.1*).

$$\underbrace{\begin{bmatrix} 1 \\ \sigma_L{}^L \\ \Delta_L{}^L \end{bmatrix}}_{H_L{}^L} = \underbrace{\begin{bmatrix} 1 & 0 & 0 \\ a_L{}^L & t_{LR}^{LR} & 0 \\ b_L{}^L & d_{LR}^{LR} & s_{LR}^{LR} \end{bmatrix}}_{\hat{T}_{LR}^{LR}} \underbrace{\begin{bmatrix} 1 \\ \sigma_R{}^R \\ \Delta_R{}^R \end{bmatrix}}_{H_R{}^R} \qquad \underbrace{\begin{bmatrix} 1 \\ \sigma_R{}^R \\ \Delta_R{}^R \end{bmatrix}}_{H_R{}^R} = \underbrace{\begin{bmatrix} 1 & 0 & 0 \\ a_R{}^R & t_{RL}^{RL} & 0 \\ b_R{}^R & d_{RL}^{RL} & s_{RL}^{RL} \end{bmatrix}}_{\hat{T}_{RL}^{RL}} \underbrace{\begin{bmatrix} 1 \\ \sigma_L{}^L \\ \Delta_L{}^L \end{bmatrix}}_{H_L{}^L} \tag{7}$$

4.2. Construct matrices $\hat{T}_{LR}$ and $\hat{T}_{RL}$ for the straight bar LR of constant cross section, shown in Fig. P-4.2.

The derivation of the component matrices of $\hat{T}_{LR}$ is given in Table P-4.2L and is self-explanatory. A similar derivation for the components of $\hat{T}_{RL}$ is given in Table P-4.2R.

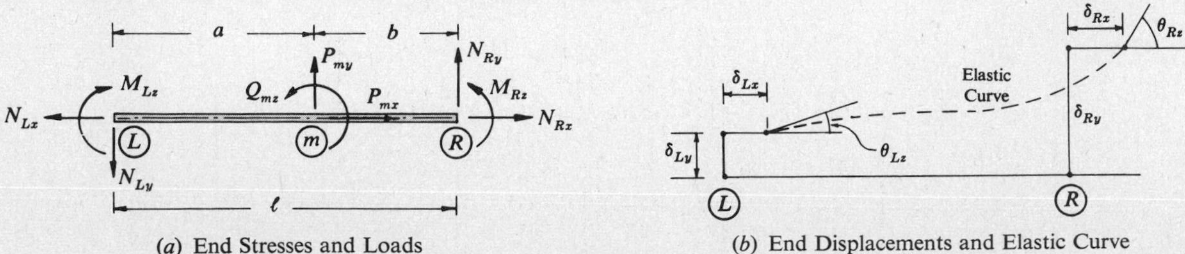

(*a*) End Stresses and Loads (*b*) End Displacements and Elastic Curve

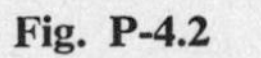

Fig. P-4.2

Table P-4.2L. Components of $\hat{T}_{LR}$

(a) Left End Load Effects

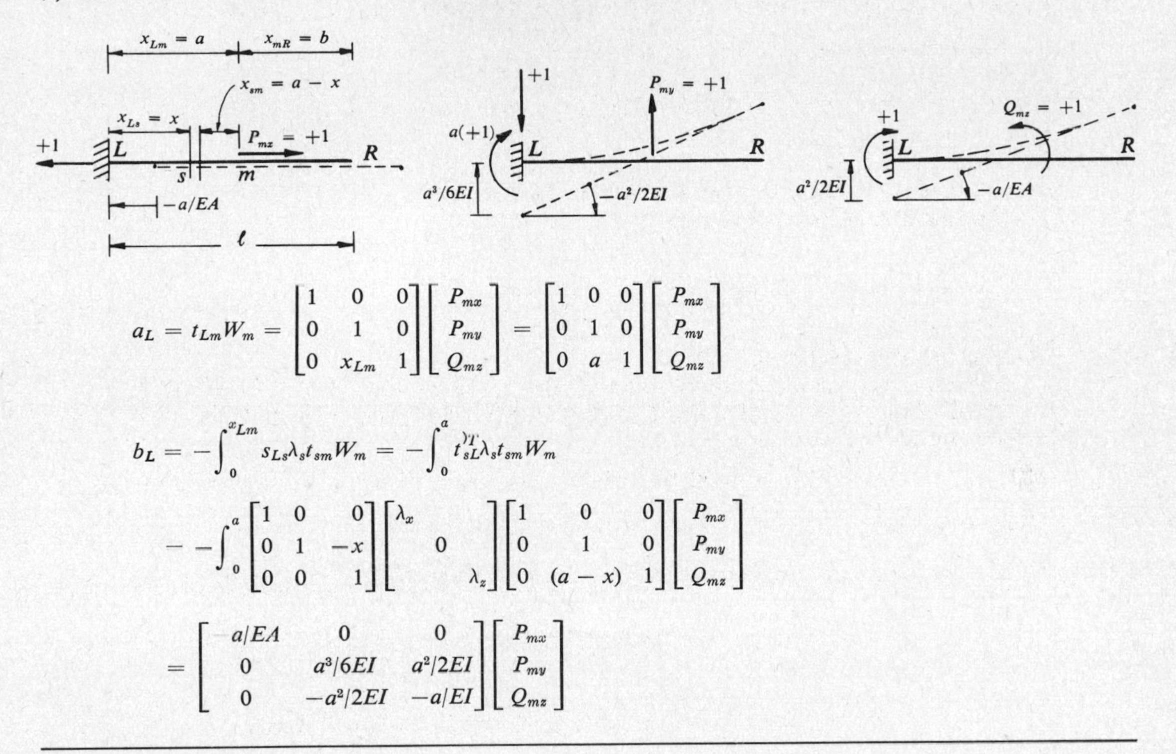

$$a_L = t_{Lm}W_m = \begin{bmatrix} 1 & 0 & 0 \\ 0 & 1 & 0 \\ 0 & x_{Lm} & 1 \end{bmatrix}\begin{bmatrix} P_{mx} \\ P_{my} \\ Q_{mz} \end{bmatrix} = \begin{bmatrix} 1 & 0 & 0 \\ 0 & 1 & 0 \\ 0 & a & 1 \end{bmatrix}\begin{bmatrix} P_{mx} \\ P_{my} \\ Q_{mz} \end{bmatrix}$$

$$b_L = -\int_0^{x_{Lm}} s_{Ls}\lambda_s t_{sm} W_m = -\int_0^a t_{sL}^T \lambda_s t_{sm} W_m$$

$$= -\int_0^a \begin{bmatrix} 1 & 0 & 0 \\ 0 & 1 & -x \\ 0 & 0 & 1 \end{bmatrix}\begin{bmatrix} \lambda_x & & \\ & 0 & \\ & & \lambda_z \end{bmatrix}\begin{bmatrix} 1 & 0 & 0 \\ 0 & 1 & 0 \\ 0 & (a-x) & 1 \end{bmatrix}\begin{bmatrix} P_{mx} \\ P_{my} \\ Q_{mz} \end{bmatrix}$$

$$= \begin{bmatrix} -a/EA & 0 & 0 \\ 0 & a^3/6EI & a^2/2EI \\ 0 & -a^2/2EI & -a/EI \end{bmatrix}\begin{bmatrix} P_{mx} \\ P_{my} \\ Q_{mz} \end{bmatrix}$$

(b) Left End Stress Effects

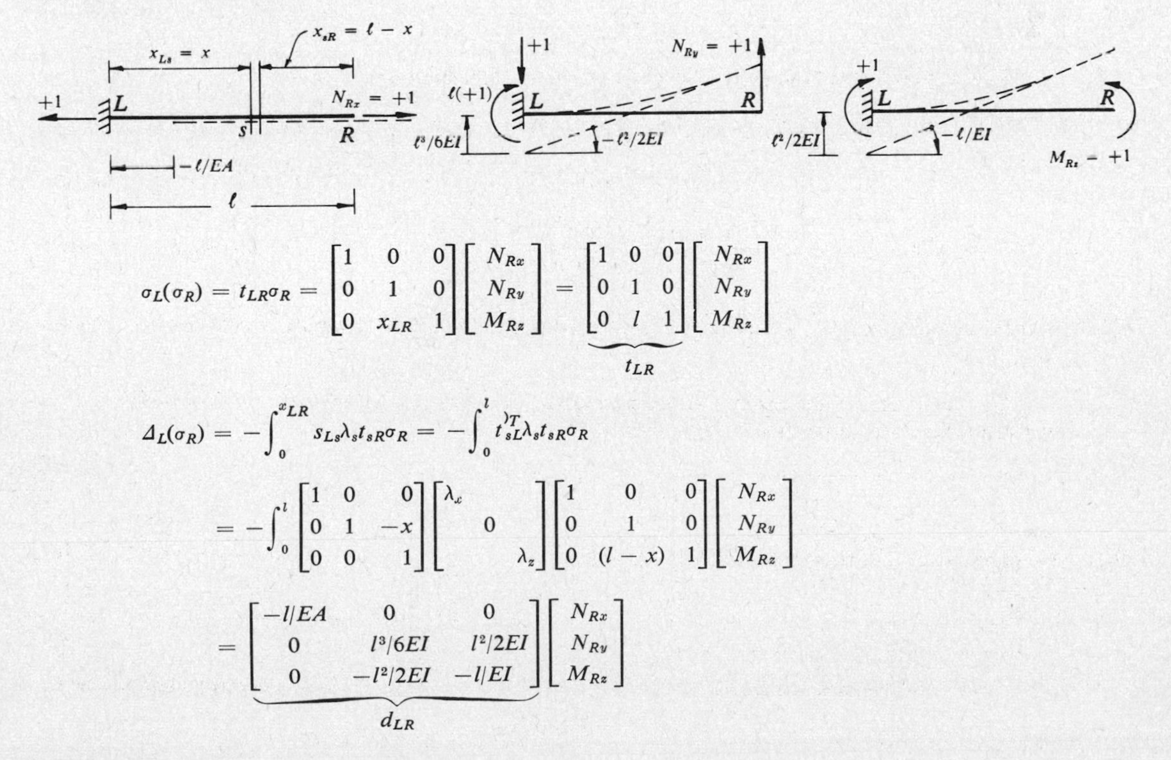

$$\sigma_L(\sigma_R) = t_{LR}\sigma_R = \begin{bmatrix} 1 & 0 & 0 \\ 0 & 1 & 0 \\ 0 & x_{LR} & 1 \end{bmatrix}\begin{bmatrix} N_{Rx} \\ N_{Ry} \\ M_{Rz} \end{bmatrix} = \underbrace{\begin{bmatrix} 1 & 0 & 0 \\ 0 & 1 & 0 \\ 0 & l & 1 \end{bmatrix}}_{t_{LR}}\begin{bmatrix} N_{Rx} \\ N_{Ry} \\ M_{Rz} \end{bmatrix}$$

$$\Delta_L(\sigma_R) = -\int_0^{x_{LR}} s_{Ls}\lambda_s t_{sR}\sigma_R = -\int_0^l t_{sL}^T \lambda_s t_{sR}\sigma_R$$

$$= -\int_0^l \begin{bmatrix} 1 & 0 & 0 \\ 0 & 1 & -x \\ 0 & 0 & 1 \end{bmatrix}\begin{bmatrix} \lambda_x & & \\ & 0 & \\ & & \lambda_z \end{bmatrix}\begin{bmatrix} 1 & 0 & 0 \\ 0 & 1 & 0 \\ 0 & (l-x) & 1 \end{bmatrix}\begin{bmatrix} N_{Rx} \\ N_{Ry} \\ M_{Rz} \end{bmatrix}$$

$$= \underbrace{\begin{bmatrix} -l/EA & 0 & 0 \\ 0 & l^3/6EI & l^2/2EI \\ 0 & -l^2/2EI & -l/EI \end{bmatrix}}_{d_{LR}}\begin{bmatrix} N_{Rx} \\ N_{Ry} \\ M_{Rz} \end{bmatrix}$$

(c) Left End Displacement Effects

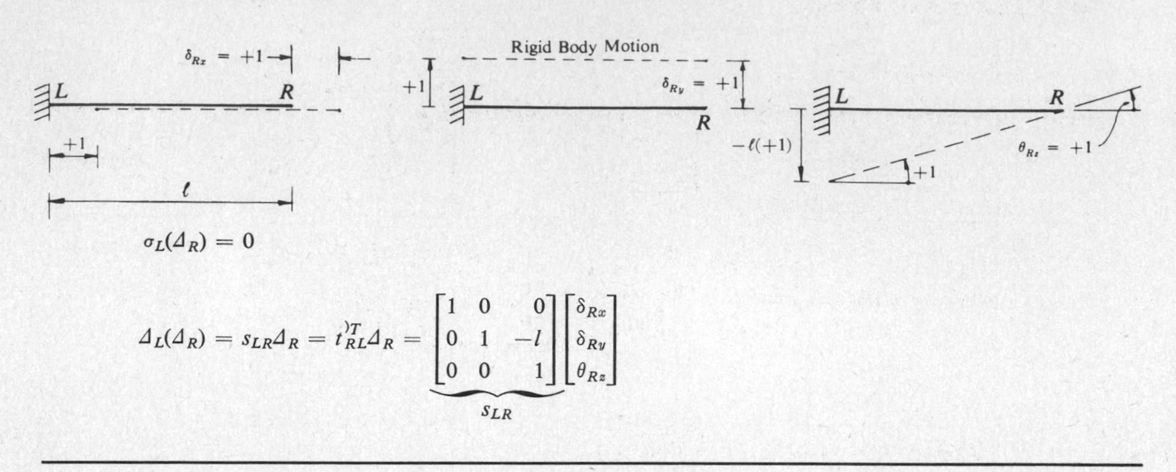

$$\sigma_L(\Delta_R) = 0$$

$$\Delta_L(\Delta_R) = s_{LR}\Delta_R = t_{RL}^{)T}\Delta_R = \underbrace{\begin{bmatrix} 1 & 0 & 0 \\ 0 & 1 & -l \\ 0 & 0 & 1 \end{bmatrix}}_{s_{LR}} \begin{bmatrix} \delta_{Rx} \\ \delta_{Ry} \\ \theta_{Rz} \end{bmatrix}$$

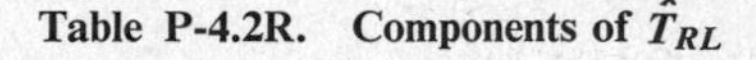

Table P-4.2R. Components of $\hat{T}_{RL}$

(a) Right End Load Effects

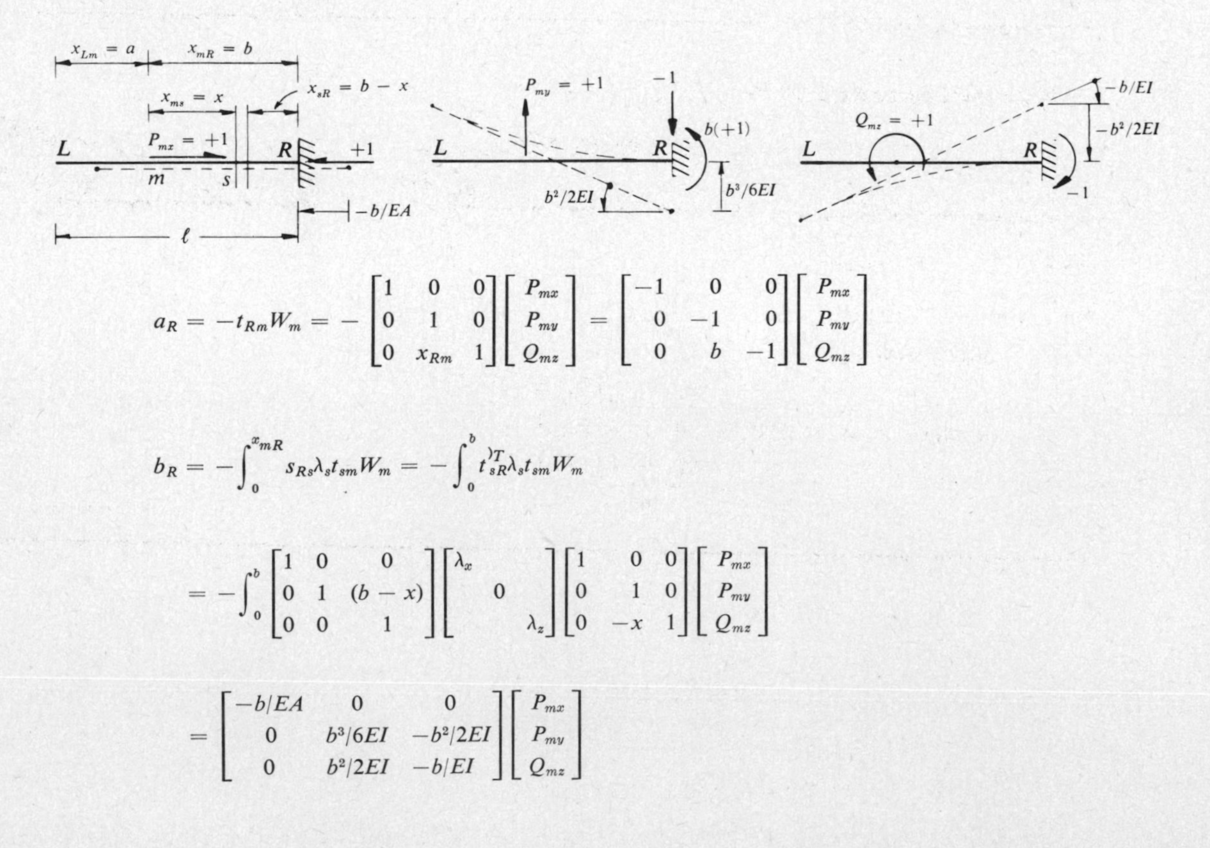

$$a_R = -t_{Rm}W_m = -\begin{bmatrix} 1 & 0 & 0 \\ 0 & 1 & 0 \\ 0 & x_{Rm} & 1 \end{bmatrix} \begin{bmatrix} P_{mx} \\ P_{my} \\ Q_{mz} \end{bmatrix} = \begin{bmatrix} -1 & 0 & 0 \\ 0 & -1 & 0 \\ 0 & b & -1 \end{bmatrix} \begin{bmatrix} P_{mx} \\ P_{my} \\ Q_{mz} \end{bmatrix}$$

$$b_R = -\int_0^{x_{mR}} s_{Rs}\lambda_s t_{sm} W_m = -\int_0^b t_{sR}^{)T}\lambda_s t_{sm} W_m$$

$$= -\int_0^b \begin{bmatrix} 1 & 0 & 0 \\ 0 & 1 & (b-x) \\ 0 & 0 & 1 \end{bmatrix} \begin{bmatrix} \lambda_x & & \\ & 0 & \\ & & \lambda_z \end{bmatrix} \begin{bmatrix} 1 & 0 & 0 \\ 0 & 1 & 0 \\ 0 & -x & 1 \end{bmatrix} \begin{bmatrix} P_{mx} \\ P_{my} \\ Q_{mz} \end{bmatrix}$$

$$= \begin{bmatrix} -b/EA & 0 & 0 \\ 0 & b^3/6EI & -b^2/2EI \\ 0 & b^2/2EI & -b/EI \end{bmatrix} \begin{bmatrix} P_{mx} \\ P_{my} \\ Q_{mz} \end{bmatrix}$$

(*b*) Right End Stress Effects

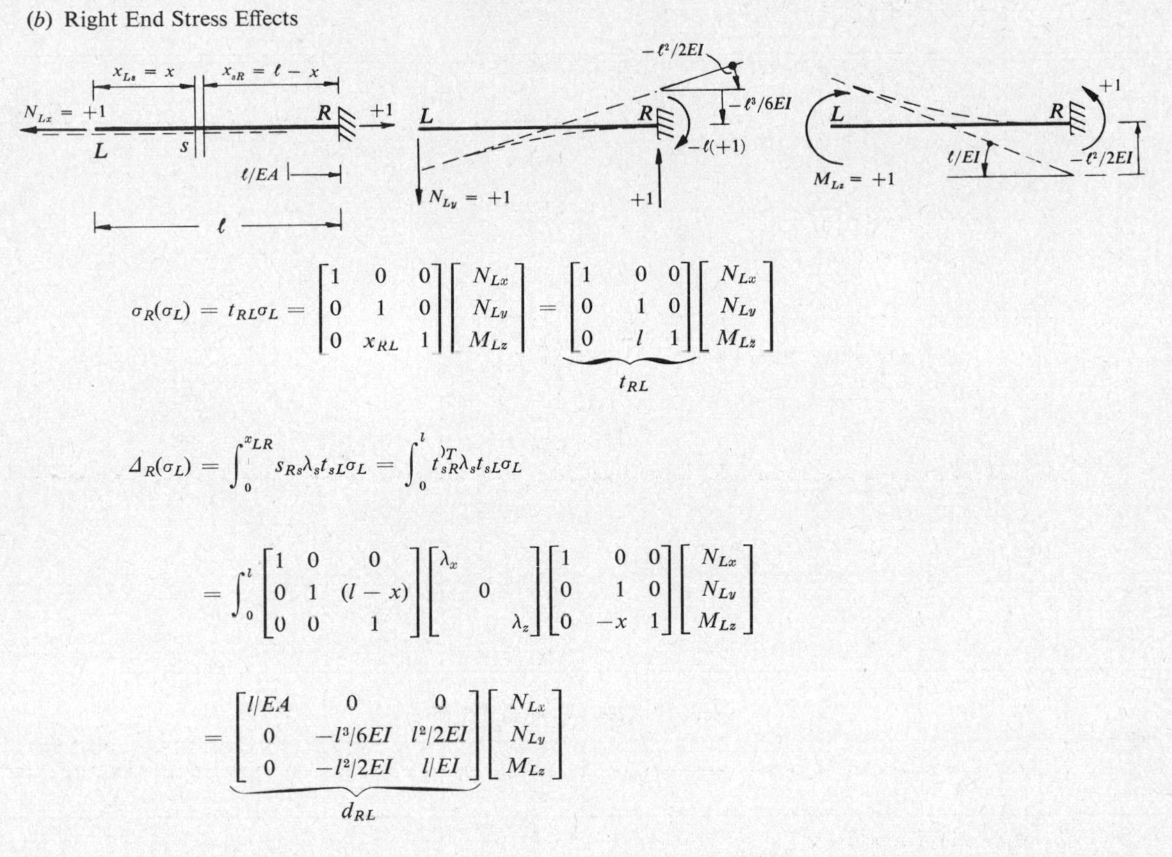

$$\sigma_R(\sigma_L) = t_{RL}\sigma_L = \begin{bmatrix} 1 & 0 & 0 \\ 0 & 1 & 0 \\ 0 & x_{RL} & 1 \end{bmatrix} \begin{bmatrix} N_{Lx} \\ N_{Ly} \\ M_{Lz} \end{bmatrix} = \underbrace{\begin{bmatrix} 1 & 0 & 0 \\ 0 & 1 & 0 \\ 0 & l & 1 \end{bmatrix}}_{t_{RL}} \begin{bmatrix} N_{Lx} \\ N_{Ly} \\ M_{Lz} \end{bmatrix}$$

$$\Delta_R(\sigma_L) = \int_0^{x_{LR}} s_{Rs}\lambda_s t_{sL}\sigma_L = \int_0^l t_{sR}^{)T}\lambda_s t_{sL}\sigma_L$$

$$= \int_0^l \begin{bmatrix} 1 & 0 & 0 \\ 0 & 1 & (l-x) \\ 0 & 0 & 1 \end{bmatrix} \begin{bmatrix} \lambda_x & & \\ & 0 & \\ & & \lambda_z \end{bmatrix} \begin{bmatrix} 1 & 0 & 0 \\ 0 & 1 & 0 \\ 0 & -x & 1 \end{bmatrix} \begin{bmatrix} N_{Lx} \\ N_{Ly} \\ M_{Lz} \end{bmatrix}$$

$$= \underbrace{\begin{bmatrix} l/EA & 0 & 0 \\ 0 & -l^3/6EI & l^2/2EI \\ 0 & -l^2/2EI & l/EI \end{bmatrix}}_{d_{RL}} \begin{bmatrix} N_{Lx} \\ N_{Ly} \\ M_{Lz} \end{bmatrix}$$

(*c*) Right End Displacement Effects

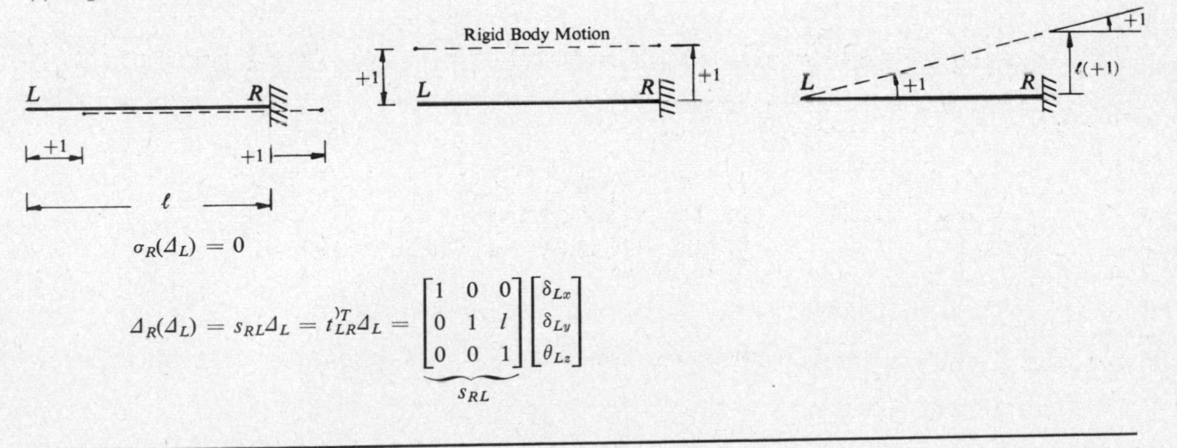

$$\sigma_R(\Delta_L) = 0$$

$$\Delta_R(\Delta_L) = s_{RL}\Delta_L = t_{LR}^{)T}\Delta_L = \underbrace{\begin{bmatrix} 1 & 0 & 0 \\ 0 & 1 & l \\ 0 & 0 & 1 \end{bmatrix}}_{s_{RL}} \begin{bmatrix} \delta_{Lx} \\ \delta_{Ly} \\ \theta_{Lz} \end{bmatrix}$$

4.3. Derive the matrices d_{LR}^0 and d_{RL}^0 for the symmetrical parabolic bar of Fig. P-4.3. Assume $\lambda_{sx} \simeq 0$ and $EI_s = EI_c \sec \omega_s$.

Tables P-4.3a and P-4.3b show the required derivations and the physical interpretations of each element of the matrices d_{LR}^0 and d_{RL}^0. In the integration of the terms involved, $y = (4h/l^2)\,x(l-x)$ and $\lambda_z = ds/EI_s = dx/EI_c$ are used.

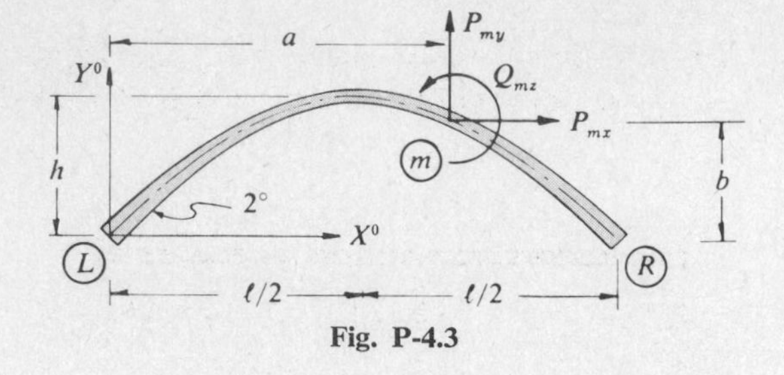

Fig. P-4.3

Table P-4.3a. Components of d_{LR}^0 — Parabolic Bar

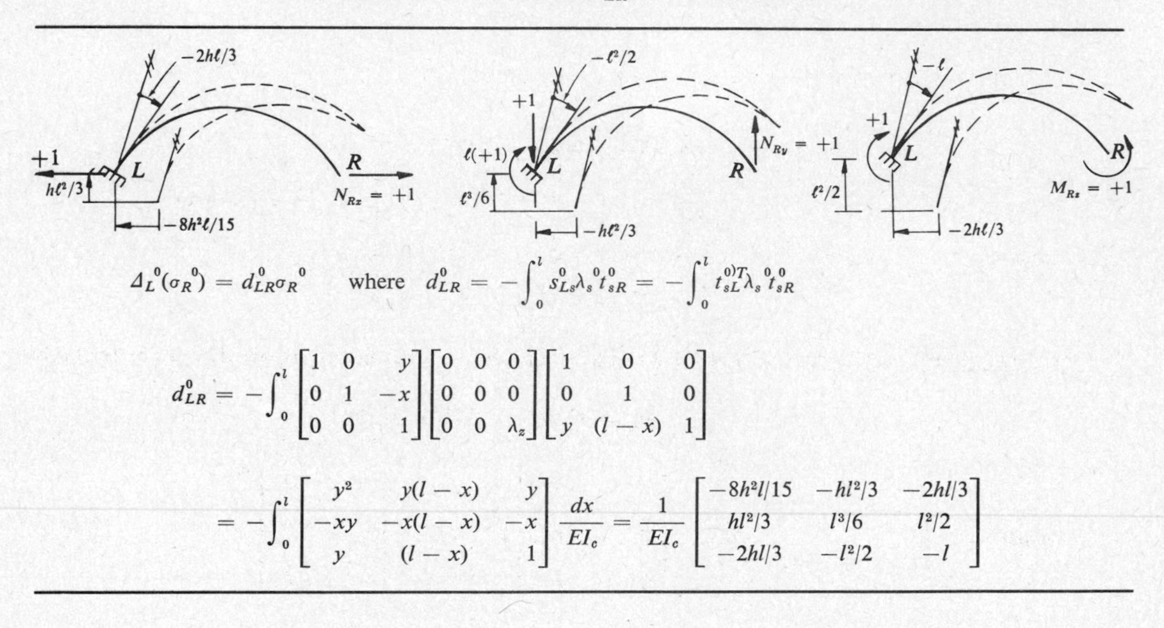

$$\Delta_L^0(\sigma_R^0) = d_{LR}^0 \sigma_R^0 \quad \text{where} \quad d_{LR}^0 = -\int_0^l s_{Ls}^0 \lambda_s^0 t_{sR}^0 = -\int_0^l t_{sL}^{0)T} \lambda_s^0 t_{sR}^0$$

$$d_{LR}^0 = -\int_0^l \begin{bmatrix} 1 & 0 & y \\ 0 & 1 & -x \\ 0 & 0 & 1 \end{bmatrix} \begin{bmatrix} 0 & 0 & 0 \\ 0 & 0 & 0 \\ 0 & 0 & \lambda_z \end{bmatrix} \begin{bmatrix} 1 & 0 & 0 \\ 0 & 1 & 0 \\ y & (l-x) & 1 \end{bmatrix}$$

$$= -\int_0^l \begin{bmatrix} y^2 & y(l-x) & y \\ -xy & -x(l-x) & -x \\ y & (l-x) & 1 \end{bmatrix} \frac{dx}{EI_c} = \frac{1}{EI_c} \begin{bmatrix} -8h^2l/15 & -hl^2/3 & -2hl/3 \\ hl^2/3 & l^3/6 & l^2/2 \\ -2hl/3 & -l^2/2 & -l \end{bmatrix}$$

Table P-4.3b. Components of d_{RL}^0 — Parabolic Bar

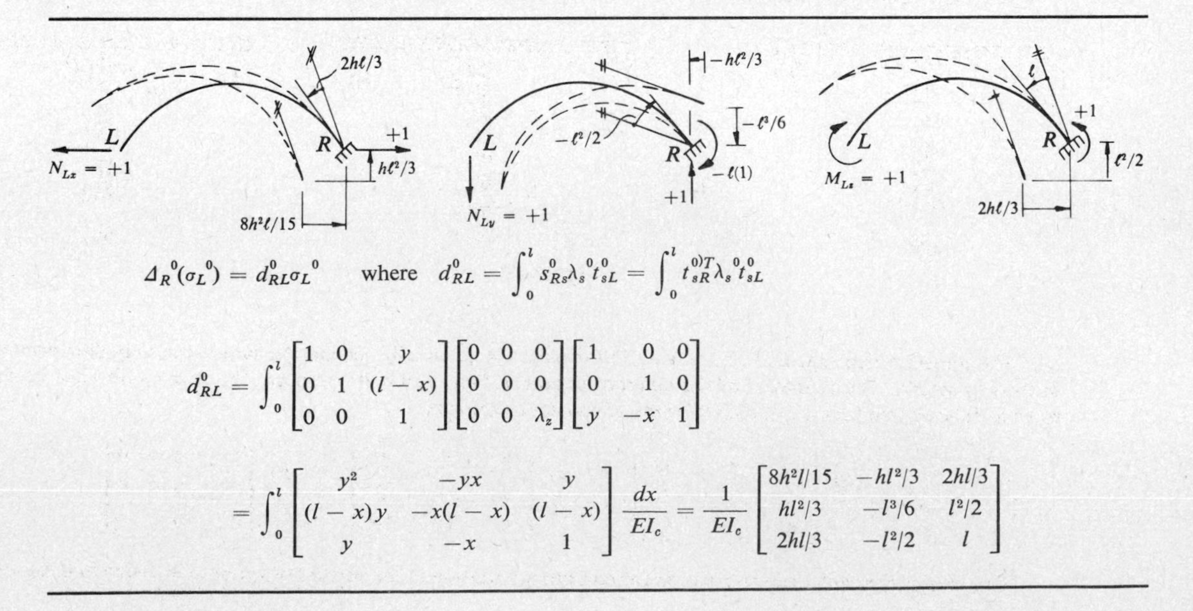

$$\Delta_R^0(\sigma_L^0) = d_{RL}^0 \sigma_L^0 \quad \text{where} \quad d_{RL}^0 = \int_0^l s_{Rs}^0 \lambda_s^0 t_{sL}^0 = \int_0^l t_{sR}^{0)T} \lambda_s^0 t_{sL}^0$$

$$d_{RL}^0 = \int_0^l \begin{bmatrix} 1 & 0 & y \\ 0 & 1 & (l-x) \\ 0 & 0 & 1 \end{bmatrix} \begin{bmatrix} 0 & 0 & 0 \\ 0 & 0 & 0 \\ 0 & 0 & \lambda_z \end{bmatrix} \begin{bmatrix} 1 & 0 & 0 \\ 0 & 1 & 0 \\ y & -x & 1 \end{bmatrix}$$

$$= \int_0^l \begin{bmatrix} y^2 & -yx & y \\ (l-x)y & -x(l-x) & (l-x) \\ y & -x & 1 \end{bmatrix} \frac{dx}{EI_c} = \frac{1}{EI_c} \begin{bmatrix} 8h^2l/15 & -hl^2/3 & 2hl/3 \\ hl^2/3 & -l^3/6 & l^2/2 \\ 2hl/3 & -l^2/2 & l \end{bmatrix}$$

4.4. Derive the joint matrices J^0_{ijk} and J^0_{kji} to include the effects of linearly elastic spring constraints at the joint j in the transport chain (Fig. P-4.4a).

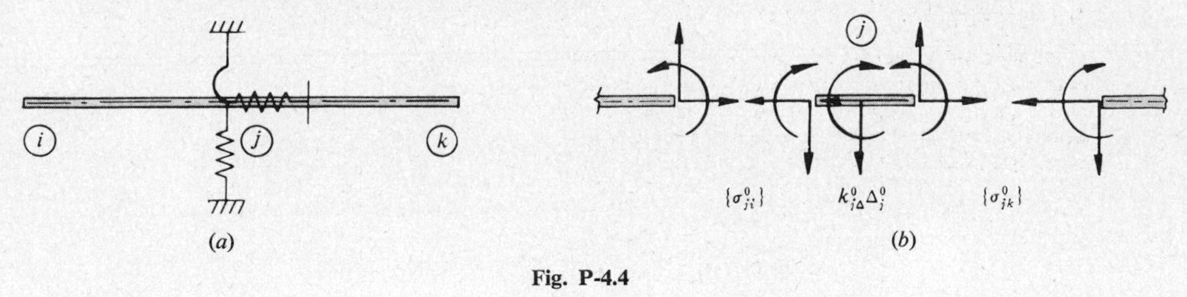

Fig. P-4.4

From Fig. P-4.4b, for $\Delta_j^0 = \{\delta^0_{jx}, \delta^0_{jy}, \theta^0_{jz}\}$,

$$\sigma^0_{ji} = \sigma^0_{jk} - k^0_{j\Delta}\Delta^0_j, \qquad \sigma^0_{jk} = \sigma^0_{ji} + k^0_{j\Delta}\Delta^0_j$$

where
$$k^0_{j\Delta} = \begin{bmatrix} k^0_{j\Delta x} & 0 & 0 \\ 0 & k^0_{j\Delta y} & 0 \\ 0 & 0 & k^0_{j\theta z} \end{bmatrix}$$

Since $\Delta^0_{ji} = \Delta^0_{jk} = \Delta_j^0$, the following relations between the state vectors $\hat{H}^0_{ji}$ and $\hat{H}^0_{jk}$ can be established:

$$\hat{H}^0_{ji} = J^0_{ijk}\hat{H}^0_{jk}, \qquad \hat{H}^0_{jk} = J^0_{kji}\hat{H}^0_{ji}$$

where
$$J^0_{ijk} = \begin{bmatrix} 1 & 0 & 0 \\ 0 & I & -k^0_{j\Delta} \\ 0 & 0 & I \end{bmatrix}, \qquad J^0_{kji} = \begin{bmatrix} 1 & 0 & 0 \\ 0 & I & k^0_{j\Delta} \\ 0 & 0 & I \end{bmatrix}$$

and I is a unit matrix, [3 × 3].

4.5. Derive the joint matrices J^0_{ijk} and J^0_{kji} to include the effect of column supports at j, shown in Fig. P-4.5, in the transport chain.

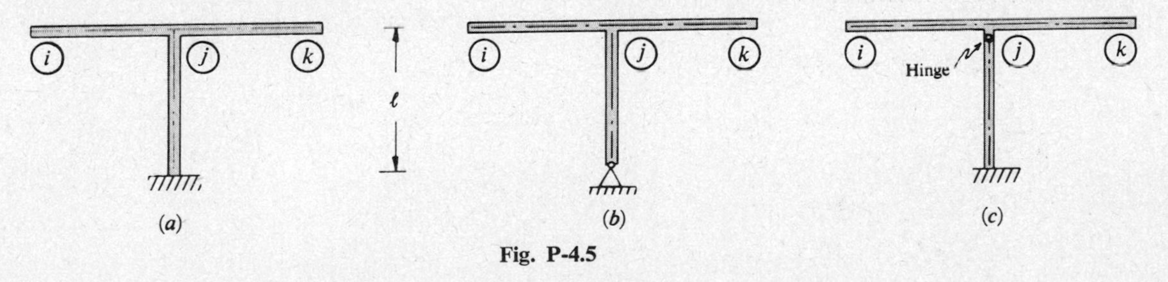

Fig. P-4.5

The joint matrices J^0_{ijk} and J^0_{kji} derived in Problem 4.4 essentially remain the same—the only difference being in the $k^0_{j\Delta}$ matrix. The stiffnesses of the columns shown in Figs. a, b and c respectively, at the joint j can be shown to be as follows (see Chapter 10) for columns of constant sections:

$$k^0_{j\Delta} = \frac{EI}{l^3}\begin{bmatrix} 12 & 0 & 6l \\ 0 & (A/I)l^2 & 0 \\ 6l & 0 & 4l^2 \end{bmatrix}, \quad \frac{EI}{l^3}\begin{bmatrix} 3 & 0 & 3l \\ 0 & (A/I)l^2 & 0 \\ 3l & 0 & 3l^2 \end{bmatrix}, \quad \frac{EI}{l^3}\begin{bmatrix} 3 & 0 & 0 \\ 0 & (A/I)l^2 & 0 \\ 0 & 0 & 0 \end{bmatrix}$$

The necessary angular transformation for column orientation in the vertical direction is included in these values.

TRANSPORT CHAIN

4.6. Using the transport matrix method, solve the frame shown in Fig. P-11.1. Use $EA = 2EI$ for all bars.

This frame is represented by Case *2* in Table 4-2. The state vectors at 1 and 4 are related by the equation

$$\hat{H}_1{}^0 = \hat{T}^0_{14}\hat{H}_4{}^0 \qquad (1)$$

where $\hat{T}^0_{14}$ is the transport chain $\hat{T}^0_{12}\hat{T}^0_{23}\hat{T}^0_{34}$ and the state vectors at the intermediate joints are related by

$$\hat{H}_1{}^0 = \hat{T}^0_{12}\hat{H}_2{}^0, \qquad \hat{H}_2{}^0 = \hat{T}^0_{23}\hat{H}_3{}^0, \qquad \hat{H}_3{}^0 = \hat{T}^0_{34}\hat{H}_4{}^0 \qquad (2, 3, 4)$$

The given loads can be assumed to be applied just to the right of the respective joints at which they are applied. All state vectors and related matrices are measured in the *o*-system.

The following values are established to construct the state vector transport matrices:

$$a^0_{12} = b^0_{12} = 0, \qquad a^0_{23} = \{0, -10, 0\}, \qquad b^0_{23} = 0, \qquad a^0_{34} = \{20, 0, 0\}, \qquad b^0_{34} = 0$$

$$t^0_{12} = \begin{bmatrix} 1 & 0 & 0 \\ 0 & 1 & 0 \\ -24 & 18 & 1 \end{bmatrix}, \qquad t^0_{23} = \begin{bmatrix} 1 & 0 & 0 \\ 0 & 1 & 0 \\ 0 & 40 & 1 \end{bmatrix}, \qquad t^0_{34} = \begin{bmatrix} 1 & 0 & 0 \\ 0 & 1 & 0 \\ 24 & 18 & 1 \end{bmatrix}$$

$$s^0_{12} = \begin{bmatrix} 1 & 0 & 24 \\ 0 & 1 & -18 \\ 0 & 0 & 1 \end{bmatrix}, \qquad s^0_{23} = \begin{bmatrix} 1 & 0 & 0 \\ 0 & 1 & -40 \\ 0 & 0 & 1 \end{bmatrix}, \qquad s^0_{34} = \begin{bmatrix} 1 & 0 & -24 \\ 0 & 1 & -18 \\ 0 & 0 & 1 \end{bmatrix}$$

$$d^0_{12} = -\sum_1^2 s^0_{1s}\lambda_s{}^0 t^0_{s2} = -\sum_1^2 s^0_{1s}\omega^{0s}\lambda_s{}^s\omega^{s0} t^0_{s2} = \frac{1}{EI}\begin{bmatrix} 2{,}874.6 & -2{,}167.2 & -360 \\ -2{,}167.2 & 1{,}610.4 & 270 \\ 360 & -270 & -30 \end{bmatrix}$$

Similarly,

$$d^0_{23} = \frac{40}{6EI}\begin{bmatrix} 3 & 0 & 0 \\ 0 & 1{,}600 & 120 \\ 0 & -120 & -6 \end{bmatrix} \qquad \text{and} \qquad d^0_{34} = \frac{1}{EI}\begin{bmatrix} 2{,}874.6 & 2{,}167.2 & 360 \\ 2{,}167.2 & 1{,}610.4 & 270 \\ -360 & -270 & -30 \end{bmatrix}$$

Substitution of these values provides $\hat{T}^0_{12}$, $\hat{T}^0_{23}$, $\hat{T}^0_{34}$ and $\hat{T}^0_{14}$. The solution is obtained by using the boundary conditions contained in (*1*). Thus from

$$\begin{bmatrix} 1 \\ \sigma_1{}^0 \\ 0 \end{bmatrix} = \begin{bmatrix} 1 & 0 & 0 \\ a^0_{14} & t^0_{14} & 0 \\ b^0_{14} & d^0_{14} & s^0_{14} \end{bmatrix}\begin{bmatrix} 1 \\ \sigma_4{}^0 \\ 0 \end{bmatrix}$$

$0 = b^0_{14} + d^0_{14}\sigma_4{}^0$ and $\sigma_4 = -(d^0_{14})^{-1}b^0_{14}$ which gives $\hat{H}_4{}^0$. Successive substitutions in (*4*), (*3*) and (*2*) then yield $\hat{H}_3{}^0$, $\hat{H}_2{}^0$ and $\hat{H}_1{}^0$. The vectors thus obtained are

$$\hat{H}_1{}^0 = \{1, 6.29, -4.48, -121.1, 0, 0, 0\}$$

$$\hat{H}_2{}^0 = \{1, 6.29, -4.48, 110.6, 15{,}786/EI, -11{,}835/EI, -157/EI\}$$

$$\hat{H}_3{}^0 = \{1, 6.29, 5.52, -110.0, 15{,}660/EI, 11{,}508/EI, -146/EI\}$$

$$\hat{H}_4{}^0 = \{1, -13.71, 5.52, 119.8, 0, 0, 0\}$$

The slight difference in the anti-symmetry of the values is due to the inclusion of axial deformations.

4.7. Analyze the two-span continuous arch on elastic supports shown in Fig. P-8.14 by the transport matrix method. Use $EI_c = 432 \times 10^3$ k-ft², $k^0_{\Delta x} = k^0_{\Delta y} = 200$ k/ft and $k^0_{\theta z} = 20{,}000$ k-ft/rad. Consider only flexural deformation in the arches.

Proceeding from left to right, the transport relations yield

$$\hat{H}^0_{iL} = \hat{T}^0_{iL,kR}\hat{H}^0_{kR} \tag{1}$$

where L refers to the left side of the joint i and R refers to the right side of the joint k.

$$\hat{T}^0_{iL,kR} = J^0_{Lij}\hat{T}^0_{ij}J^0_{ijk}\hat{T}^0_{jk}J^0_{jkR}$$

where J^0_{Lij}, J^0_{ijk} and J^0_{jkR} are the joint matrices discussed in Problem 4.4, respectively, for joints i, j and k. In this case

$$J^0_{Lij} = J^0_{ijk} = J^0_{jkR} = \begin{bmatrix} 1 & 0 & 0 \\ 0 & I & -k_\Delta{}^0 \\ 0 & 0 & I \end{bmatrix} \quad \text{where} \quad k_\Delta{}^0 = \begin{bmatrix} 200 & 0 & 0 \\ 0 & 200 & 0 \\ 0 & 0 & 20{,}000 \end{bmatrix}$$

To construct $\hat{T}^0_{ij}$ and $\hat{T}^0_{jk}$ the following values are needed:

$$a^0_{ij} = b^0_{ij} = 0, \qquad a^0_{jk} = \{0, -20, -400\}$$

$$b^0_{jk} = -\int s^0_{Ls}\lambda_s{}^0 t^0_{sm}W_m{}^0 = \frac{1}{EI_c}\{29{,}583, -46{,}667, 5{,}000\}$$

$$t^0_{ij} = t^0_{jk} = \begin{bmatrix} 1 & 0 & 0 \\ 0 & 1 & 0 \\ 0 & 40 & 1 \end{bmatrix} \quad \text{and} \quad s^0_{ij} = s^0_{jk} = \begin{bmatrix} 1 & 0 & 0 \\ 0 & 1 & -40 \\ 0 & 0 & 1 \end{bmatrix}$$

Using the results of Problem 4.3,

$$d^0_{ij} = d^0_{jk} = \frac{1}{3EI_c}\begin{bmatrix} -6{,}400 & -16{,}000 & -800 \\ 16{,}000 & 32{,}000 & 2{,}400 \\ -800 & -2{,}400 & -120 \end{bmatrix}$$

Substituting these values, the transport chain is evaluated. The solution is then obtained from (*1*) on application of the boundary conditions. Thus from

$$\begin{bmatrix} 1 \\ 0 \\ \Delta^0_{iL} \end{bmatrix} = \begin{bmatrix} 1 & 0 & 0 \\ T^0_{21} & T^0_{22} & T^0_{23} \\ T^0_{31} & T^0_{32} & T^0_{33} \end{bmatrix}\begin{bmatrix} 1 \\ 0 \\ \Delta^0_{kR} \end{bmatrix}$$

in which T^0_{21} ,..., T^0_{33} are appropriate submatrices of $T^0_{iL,kR}$, $0 = T^0_{21} + T^0_{23}\Delta^0_{kR}$ and $\Delta^0_{kR} = -T^{0)-1}_{23}T^0_{21}$. $\hat{H}^0_{kR}$ can now be constructed and other state vectors are obtained as follows:

$$\hat{H}^0_{kj} = J^0_{jkR}\hat{H}^0_{kR}, \qquad \hat{H}^0_{jk} = T^0_{jk}\hat{H}^0_{kj}, \qquad \hat{H}^0_{ji} = J^0_{ijk}\hat{H}^0_{jk} \qquad \text{and} \qquad \hat{H}^0_{ij} = T^0_{ij}\hat{H}^0_{ji}$$

Thus

$$\hat{H}^0_{ij} = \{1, -0.801, -0.396, -11.88, -0.00401, -0.00198, -0.000594\}$$

$$\hat{H}^0_{ji} = \{1, -0.801, -0.396, 3.96, -0.0104, -0.0479, -0.00146\}$$

$$\hat{H}^0_{jk} = \{1, -2.88, -9.97, -25.16, -0.0104, -0.0479, -0.00146\}$$

$$\hat{H}^0_{kj} = \{1, -2.88, 10.03, -26.43, 0.0144, -0.0502, 0.00132\}$$

4.8. Using the results of Problem 4.5, analyze the frame shown in Fig. P-7.7 by the transport matrix method. EI = constant for all bars. Neglect axial deformations.

The transport chain is established for member 0123:

$$\hat{H}_0{}^0 = \hat{T}^0_{03}\hat{H}_3{}^0 \tag{1}$$

where $\hat{T}^0_{03} = \hat{T}^0_{01}J^0_{012}\hat{T}^0_{12}J^0_{123}\hat{T}^0_{23}$.

The transport matrices $\hat{T}^0_{01}$, $\hat{T}^0_{12}$ and $\hat{T}^0_{23}$ are constructed using the following values, all values being computed in the o-system:

$$a^0_{01} = \{0, 0, 100\} \qquad b^0_{01} = \frac{1}{EI}\{0, 7{,}200, -1{,}200\}$$

$$a^0_{12} = \{0, -30, -450\} \qquad b^0_{12} = \frac{1{,}125}{EI}\{0, -30, 4\}$$

$$a^0_{23} = 0 = b_{23}$$

Also

$$t^0_{01} = \begin{bmatrix} 1 & 0 & 0 \\ 0 & 1 & 0 \\ 0 & 24 & 1 \end{bmatrix}, \qquad t^0_{12} = \begin{bmatrix} 1 & 0 & 0 \\ 0 & 1 & 0 \\ 0 & 30 & 1 \end{bmatrix}, \qquad t^0_{23} = \begin{bmatrix} 1 & 0 & 0 \\ 0 & 1 & 0 \\ 0 & 10 & 1 \end{bmatrix}$$

$$s^0_{01} = \begin{bmatrix} 1 & 0 & 0 \\ 0 & 1 & -24 \\ 0 & 0 & 1 \end{bmatrix}, \qquad s^0_{12} = \begin{bmatrix} 1 & 0 & 0 \\ 0 & 1 & -30 \\ 0 & 0 & 1 \end{bmatrix}, \qquad s^0_{23} = \begin{bmatrix} 1 & 0 & 0 \\ 0 & 1 & -10 \\ 0 & 0 & 1 \end{bmatrix}$$

$$d^0_{01} = \frac{1}{EI}\begin{bmatrix} 0 & 0 & 0 \\ 0 & 2{,}304 & 288 \\ 0 & -288 & -24 \end{bmatrix}, \qquad d^0_{12} = \frac{1}{EI}\begin{bmatrix} 0 & 0 & 0 \\ 0 & 4{,}500 & 450 \\ 0 & -450 & -30 \end{bmatrix}, \qquad d^0_{23} = \frac{1}{6EI}\begin{bmatrix} 0 & 0 & 0 \\ 0 & 1000 & 300 \\ 0 & -300 & -60 \end{bmatrix}$$

The joint matrices J^0_{012} and J^0_{123} are computed using the results of Problem 4.5:

$$J^0_{012} = \begin{bmatrix} 1 & 0 & 0 \\ 0 & I & -k^0_{1\Delta} \\ 0 & 0 & I \end{bmatrix} \qquad \text{where } k^0_{1\Delta} = \frac{EI}{12^3}\begin{bmatrix} 12 & 0 & 72 \\ 0 & \infty & 0 \\ 72 & 0 & 576 \end{bmatrix} + \frac{EI}{15^3}\begin{bmatrix} 12 & 0 & -90 \\ 0 & \infty & 0 \\ -90 & 0 & 900 \end{bmatrix}$$

and

$$J^0_{123} = \begin{bmatrix} 1 & 0 & 0 \\ 0 & I & -k^{\Delta}_{20} \\ 0 & 0 & I \end{bmatrix} \qquad \text{where } k^0_{2\Delta} = \frac{EI}{12^3}\begin{bmatrix} 3 & 0 & 36 \\ 0 & \infty & 0 \\ 36 & 0 & 432 \end{bmatrix}$$

The transport chain and the matrix $\hat{T}_{03}$ can now be computed. The solution is obtained by using the boundary conditions appearing in (1):

$$\begin{bmatrix} 1 \\ \hline N^0_{0x} \\ N^0_{0y} \\ \hline 0 \\ 0 \\ 0 \\ \hline \theta^0_{0z} \end{bmatrix} = \begin{bmatrix} 1 & 0 & 0 \\ \hline A_{21} & A_{22} & A_{23} \\ \hline A_{31} & A_{32} & A_{33} \\ \hline A_{41} & A_{42} & A_{43} \end{bmatrix} \begin{bmatrix} 1 \\ \hline 0 \\ -5 \\ 0 \\ \hline \delta^0_{3x} \\ \delta^0_{3y} \\ \theta^0_{3z} \end{bmatrix}$$

Thus

$$0 = A_{31} + A_{32}\sigma_3{}^0 + A_{33}\Delta_3{}^0 \qquad \text{where } \sigma_3{}^0 = \{0, -5, 0\} \qquad \text{and} \qquad \Delta_3{}^0 = -A_{33}^{-1}(A_{31} + A_{32}\sigma_3{}^0)$$

On substituting $\Delta_3{}^0$ back, $\hat{H}_3{}^0$ is reconstructed and other state vectors are then obtained using the following relations:

$$\hat{H}^0_{23} = \hat{T}^0_{23}\hat{H}_3{}^0, \quad \hat{H}^0_{21} = J^0_{123}\hat{H}^0_{23}, \quad \hat{H}^0_{12} = \hat{T}^0_{12}\hat{H}^0_{21}, \quad \hat{H}^0_{10} = J^0_{012}\hat{H}^0_{12} \quad \text{and} \quad \hat{H}_0{}^0 = \hat{T}^0_{01}\hat{H}^0_{10}$$

Computed thus the state vectors are

$$\hat{H}_0{}^0 = \{1, 5.66, -4.12, 0, 0, 0, -96/EI\}$$

$$\hat{H}^0_{10} = \{1, 5.66, -4.12, -1.06, 0, 0, -108/EI\}$$

$$\hat{H}^0_{12} = \{1, -1.75, -14.84, -66.1, 0, 0, -108/EI\}$$

$$\hat{H}^0_{21} = \{1, -1.75, 15.16, -71.0, 0, 0, 84/EI\}$$

$$\hat{H}^0_{23} = \{1, 0, -5.0, -50.0, 0, 0, 84/EI\}$$

$$\hat{H}^0_{32} = \{1, 0, -5.0, 0, 0, -822/EI, -166/EI\}$$

Supplementary Problems

4.9. Derive the expressions for $a_L{}^0$, $a_R{}^0$, $b_L{}^0$ and $b_R{}^0$ for the symmetrical parabolic bar of Fig. P-4.3. Then specialize these values for a uniformly distributed downward load of intensity w/ft. Assume $\lambda_{sx} = 0$ and $EI_s = EI_c \sec \omega_s$.

4.10. Using the state vector transport matrices $\hat{T}^0_{LO}$, $\hat{T}^0_{OR}$, $\hat{T}^0_{RO}$ and $\hat{T}^0_{OL}$ for the inclined members LO and OR, construct the state vector transport matrices $\hat{T}^0_{LR}$ and $\hat{T}^0_{RL}$ for the bent bar shown in Fig. P-4.10.

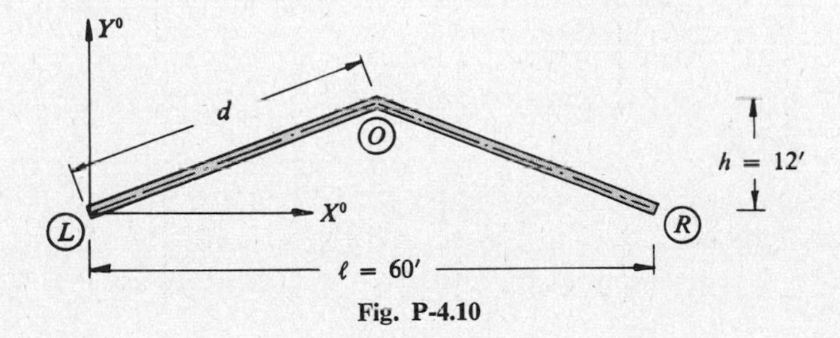

Fig. P-4.10

4.11. Using the results of Problem 4.4 and the transport matrix method, analyze the 5-span continuous beam on elastic supports shown in Fig. P-7.9*a*. Use EI = constant and $k^0_{\Delta y} = EI/1{,}600$ k/ft.

4.12. Using the results of Problem 4.5 and the transport matrix method, solve the frame shown in Fig. P-7.22. Use EI = constant and $(A/I) = 2.0\ \text{ft}^{-2}$ for all bars.

4.13. Analyze the frame shown in Fig. P-9.23 by the transport matrix method. EI = constant and $(A/I) = 2.0\ \text{ft}^{-2}$ for all bars.

4.14. Using the results of Problems 4.10 and 4.5 and the transport matrix method, analyze the 2-span gable frame shown in Fig. P-9.24. Assume EI to be constant and $(A/I) = 2.0\ \text{ft}^{-2}$ for all bars.

Chapter 5

Flexibility Matrix

5.1 FLEXIBILITY METHOD

The flexibility method, frequently called the *force method*, is the oldest and most direct method for analyzing *statically indeterminate structures.* A structure is said to be statically indeterminate if the total number of reactions and stresses exceeds the number of available and independent conditions of static equilibrium. The superfluous forces and moments (which are not necessary for static equilibrium) are called *redundants*, and their number defines the *degree of static indeterminacy* of the structure.

For the analysis of such structures the *conditions of static equilibrium* must be supplemented by the *conditions of deformation* (compatibility or consistent deformation), the number of which must equal the number of redundants.

In order to meet the requirements of statics and deformation, the given structure is resolved into *two component systems*:

(*a*) *Basic System*, obtained from the initial system by removing the redundants (release of redundants), but retaining other causes, such as the applied loads, change in volume, etc.

(*b*) *Complementary System*, obtained from the initial system by retaining the redundants and removing loads, change in volume, etc.

The *selection* of these component systems is arbitrary provided that each one independently is in a state of equilibrium and is also geometrically stable.

5.2 FLEXIBILITY MATRICES

The *stresses* in each system must be a linear combination of the respective static causes (loads and redundants). In matrix form,

$$\sigma_{s0} = q_{s1}W_1 + q_{s2}W_2 + \cdots + q_{sm}W_m \tag{5.1}$$

and

$$\sigma_{sX} = q_{si}X_i + q_{sj}X_j + \cdots + q_{sn}X_n \tag{5.2}$$

where σ_{s0} = stress vector at s in basic system, $[3 \times 1]$,
σ_{sX} = stress vector at s in complementary system, $[3 \times 1]$,
$W_1, W_2, \ldots, W_m$ = load vectors, $[3 \times 1]$,
$X_i, X_j, \ldots, X_n$ = redundant vectors, $[3 \times 1]$,
$q_{s1}, q_{s2}, \ldots, q_{sm}$ = load transfer coefficient matrices, $[3 \times 3]$,
$q_{si}, q_{sj}, \ldots, q_{sn}$ = redundant transfer coefficient matrices, $[3 \times 3]$.

Similarly, the *displacements* at the sections of release must be also a linear combination of the same causes. In matrix form,

$$\begin{aligned}
\Delta_{i0} &= f_{i1}W_1 + f_{i2}W_2 + \cdots + f_{im}W_m \\
\Delta_{j0} &= f_{j1}W_1 + f_{j2}W_2 + \cdots + f_{jm}W_m \\
&\cdots\cdots\cdots\cdots\cdots \\
\Delta_{n0} &= f_{n1}W_1 + f_{n2}W_2 + \cdots + f_{nm}W_m
\end{aligned} \tag{5.3}$$

and

$$
\begin{aligned}
\Delta_{iX} &= f_{ii}X_i + f_{ij}X_j + \cdots + f_{in}X_n \\
\Delta_{jX} &= f_{ji}X_i + f_{jj}X_j + \cdots + f_{jn}X_n \\
&\cdots\cdots\cdots\cdots\cdots\cdots \\
\Delta_{nX} &= f_{ni}X_i + f_{nj}X_j + \cdots + f_{nn}X_n
\end{aligned} \tag{5.4}
$$

where $\Delta_{i0}, \Delta_{j0}, \ldots, \Delta_{n0}$ = displacement vector in basic system at $i, j, \ldots, n$ respectively, $[3 \times 1]$,
$\Delta_{iX}, \Delta_{jX}, \ldots, \Delta_{nX}$ = displacement vector in complementary system at $i, j, \ldots, n$ respectively, $[3 \times 1]$.

The new symbol f_{ab} represents a $[3 \times 3]$ matrix of *flexibility coefficients* defining the displacement vector at a due to unit cause vector at b, where $a = i, j, \ldots, n$ and $b = 1, 2, \ldots, m$ or $= i, j, \ldots, n$.

Equations (*5.3, 4*) in symbolic form are

$$\Delta_0 = lW \qquad \text{and} \qquad \Delta_X = fX \tag{5.5}$$

where l and f are the *unit load and unit redundant flexibility matrices* of the basic and complementary systems, respectively.

5.3 CONDITIONS OF COMPATIBILITY

The *superposition of displacement vectors* Δ_0 and Δ_X must satisfy the conditions of *compatibility*, namely, the algebraic sum of displacements at $i, j, \ldots, n$ must either equal zero or equal the prescribed displacement. Thus

$$\Delta_0 + \Delta_X = \Delta$$

and in terms of (*5.5*),

$$lW + fX = \Delta \tag{5.6}$$

Since there are n redundants and n compatibility conditions,

$$X = -f^{-1}[lW - \Delta] \tag{5.7}$$

Equation (*5.6*) is called the *governing equation* (matrix) of the flexibility analysis.

Two simple examples illustrate the construction of (*5.6*). In the first case, the vertical reactions at i, j, k (Fig. 5-1*a*) are selected as redundants. Thus the simple beams of Fig. 5-1*b* and Fig. 5-1*c* become the component systems. The superposition of their deflections yields the governing matrix equation (*5.6*) given for this case in Fig. 5-1*d*. The coefficients of f and l are deflections due to unit force.

In the second case, the bending moments over supports i, j, k of the same beam (Fig. 5-2*a*) are selected as redundants. The component systems are obtained by placing mechanical hinges at intermediate supports (Fig. 5-2*b*, *c*), which leads to a decomposition of the initial system into a series of simple beams. The superposition of their end angular deviations yields again the governing matrix equation (*5.6*) given for this case in Fig. 5-2*d*. The coefficients of f and l are end angular deviations due to unit moments and unit loads.

Obviously the redundants must have specific and different values in each case, but the *final stress state* must be *the same in both cases*.

5.4 CONSTRUCTION OF SYSTEM FLEXIBILITY MATRIX

Evidently the key to the solution is the construction of matrices f and l, the coefficients of which are the displacements at sections of release produced by unit redundants and unit loads respectively. This can be accomplished by means of deformation geometry, virtual work or strain energy.

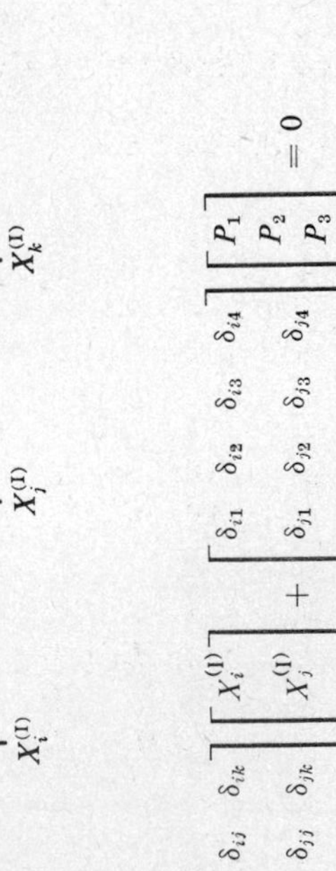

(d)

$$\underbrace{\begin{bmatrix}\delta_{ii}&\delta_{ij}&\delta_{ik}\\ \delta_{ji}&\delta_{jj}&\delta_{jk}\\ \delta_{ki}&\delta_{kj}&\delta_{kk}\end{bmatrix}}_{f^{(I)}}\underbrace{\begin{bmatrix}X_i^{(I)}\\ X_j^{(I)}\\ X_k^{(I)}\end{bmatrix}}_{X^{(I)}}+\underbrace{\begin{bmatrix}\delta_{i1}&\delta_{i2}&\delta_{i3}&\delta_{i4}\\ \delta_{j1}&\delta_{j2}&\delta_{j3}&\delta_{j4}\\ \delta_{k1}&\delta_{k2}&\delta_{k3}&\delta_{k4}\end{bmatrix}}_{l^{(I)}}\underbrace{\begin{bmatrix}P_1\\ P_2\\ P_3\\ P_4\end{bmatrix}}_{P}=0$$

Fig. 5-1. Four Span Continuous Beam, Redundant Forces

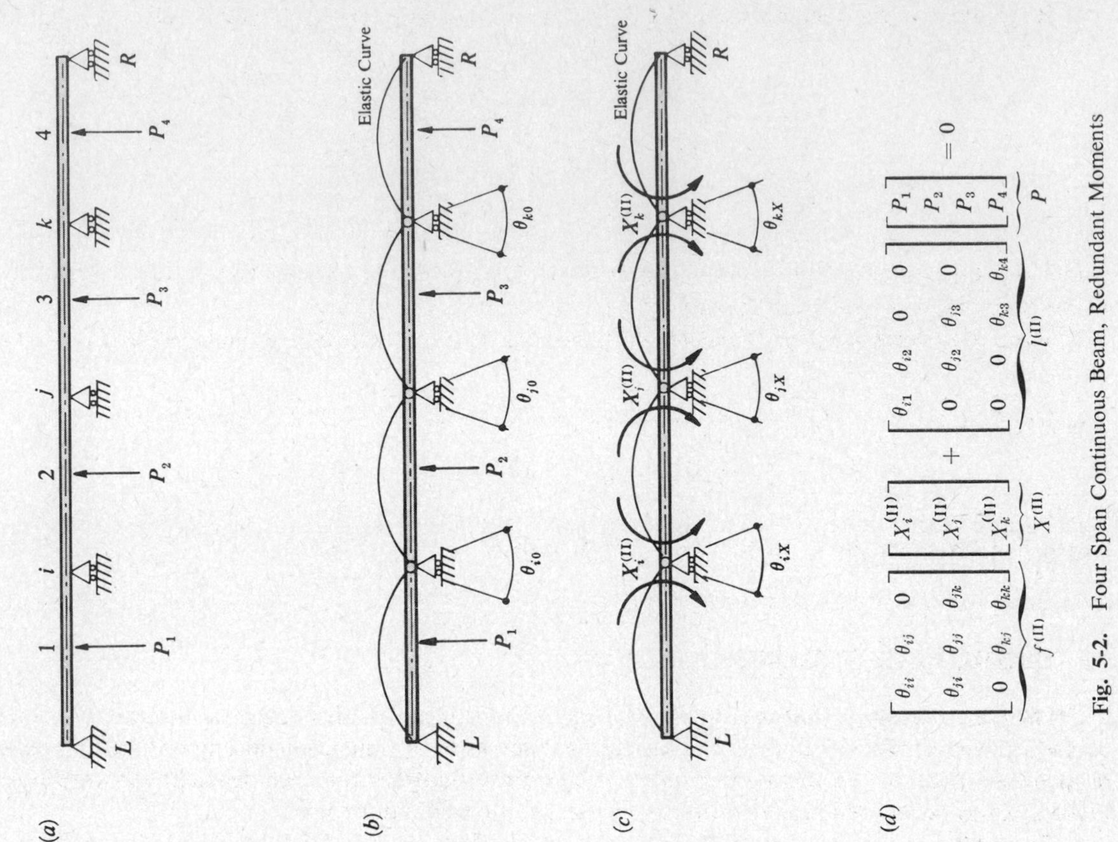

(d)

$$\underbrace{\begin{bmatrix}\theta_{ii}&\theta_{ij}&0\\ \theta_{ji}&\theta_{jj}&\theta_{jk}\\ 0&\theta_{kj}&\theta_{kk}\end{bmatrix}}_{f^{(II)}}\underbrace{\begin{bmatrix}X_i^{(II)}\\ X_j^{(II)}\\ X_k^{(II)}\end{bmatrix}}_{X^{(II)}}+\underbrace{\begin{bmatrix}\theta_{i1}&\theta_{i2}&0&0\\ 0&\theta_{j2}&\theta_{j3}&0\\ 0&0&\theta_{k3}&\theta_{k4}\end{bmatrix}}_{l^{(II)}}\underbrace{\begin{bmatrix}P_1\\ P_2\\ P_3\\ P_4\end{bmatrix}}_{P}=0$$

Fig. 5-2. Four Span Continuous Beam, Redundant Moments

Regardless of the method used, the analytical expressions for the *flexibility submatrix* reduce to

$$f_{aa} = \sum \int q_{sa}^{)T} \lambda_s q_{sa} \tag{5.8}$$

or

$$f_{ab} = \sum \int q_{sa}^{)T} \lambda_s q_{sb} \tag{5.9}$$

where the subscripts a, b have the same general meaning as before; the intergrals are taken for every member of the structure and summed ($\sum$).

The *unit redundant and unit load flexibility matrices* (*5.5*) in terms of (*5.8*) and (*5.9*) become respectively

$$f = \sum \int \{q_{si}\,, q_{sj}\,, \ldots, q_{sn}\}[\lambda_s][q_{si}\,, q_{sj}\,, \ldots, q_{sn}] = \sum \int q_X^{)T} \lambda_s q_X \tag{5.10}$$

$$l = \sum \int \{q_{si}\,, q_{sj}\,, \ldots, q_{sn}\}[\lambda_s][q_{s1}\,, q_{s2}\,, \ldots, q_{sm}] = \sum \int q_X^{)T} \lambda_s q_0 \tag{5.11}$$

where q matrices are those introduced in (*5.1*) and (*5.2*).

5.5 SEGMENTAL FLEXIBILITY MATRIX

The construction of matrices f and l by means of (*5.10*) and (*5.11*) is always possible but not particularly convenient. For large complex structures it serves to advantage to decompose the component systems into a series of segments, compute the flexibility matrices for each segment separately and then reassemble these segmental matrices into a system matrix equation (*5.6*).

The *coefficients of the segmental matrices* are derived by means of (*5.10*) and (*5.11*) from the segmental basic structures of which the most typical ones are the cantilever beam and the simple beam.

(a) Segmental Flexibilities, Cantilever Beam

For the cantilever beam of Fig. 5-3 the *unit stress flexibility matrix* is

$$f = \int_0^s q_X^{)T} \lambda_s q_X = \begin{bmatrix} D_{RR} & 0 & 0 \\ 0 & C_{RR} & B_{RR} \\ 0 & B_{RR} & A_{RR} \end{bmatrix} \tag{5.12}$$

where
$$q_X = \begin{bmatrix} 1 & 0 & 0 \\ 0 & 1 & 0 \\ 0 & s-x & 1 \end{bmatrix}$$

and
$$\lambda_s = \begin{bmatrix} dx/EA & 0 & 0 \\ 0 & 0 & 0 \\ 0 & 0 & dx/EI \end{bmatrix}$$

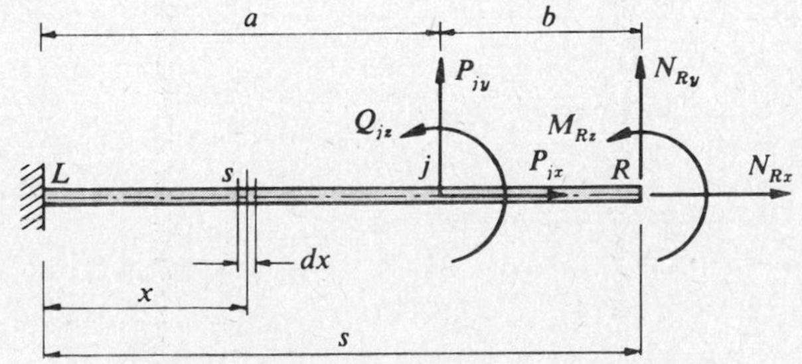

Fig. 5-3. Segmental Basic Structure, Cantilever Beam

Similarly, the *unit load flexibility matrix* is

$$l = \int_0^s q_X^{)T} \lambda_s q_0 = \begin{bmatrix} D_{RP} & 0 & 0 \\ 0 & C_{RP} & B_{RQ} \\ 0 & B_{RP} & A_{RQ} \end{bmatrix} \tag{5.13}$$

Table 5-1. Segmental Flexibilities, Cantilever Beam

Unit Cause	Cross Section	
	Variable	Constant
x, dx, L, R, $N_{Rx} = +1$, D_{RR}, s	$D_{RR} = \int_0^s \frac{dx}{EA}$	$\frac{s}{EA}$
x, dx, $N_{Ry} = +1$, B_{RR}, C_{RR}, L, R, s	$C_{RR} = \int_0^s \frac{(s-x)^2\,dx}{EI}$ $B_{RR} = \int_0^s \frac{(s-x)\,dx}{EI}$	$\frac{s^3}{3EI}$ $\frac{s^2}{2EI}$
x, dx, A_{RR}, B_{RR}, L, R, $M_{Rz} = +1$, s	$A_{RR} = \int_0^s \frac{dx}{EI}$	$\frac{s}{EI}$
a, b, x, dx, $P_{jx} = +1$, L, R, D_{RP}, s	$D_{RP} = \int_0^a \frac{dx}{EA}$	$\frac{a}{EA}$
a, b, x, $P_{jy} = +1$, B_{RP}, dx, C_{RP}, L, R, s	$C_{RP} = \int_0^a \frac{(a-x)(s-x)\,dx}{EI}$ $B_{RP} = \int_0^a \frac{(a-x)\,dx}{EI}$	$\frac{a^2(3s-a)}{6EI}$ $\frac{a^2}{2EI}$
a, b, x, A_{RQ}, dx, $Q_{jz} = +1$, B_{RQ}, L, R, s	$B_{RQ} = \int_0^a \frac{(s-x)\,dx}{EI}$ $A_{RQ} = \int_0^a \frac{dx}{EI}$	$\frac{a(2s-a)}{2EI}$ $\frac{a}{EI}$

Table 5-2. Segmental Flexibilities, Simple Beam

Unit Cause	Cross Section: Variable	Cross Section: Constant
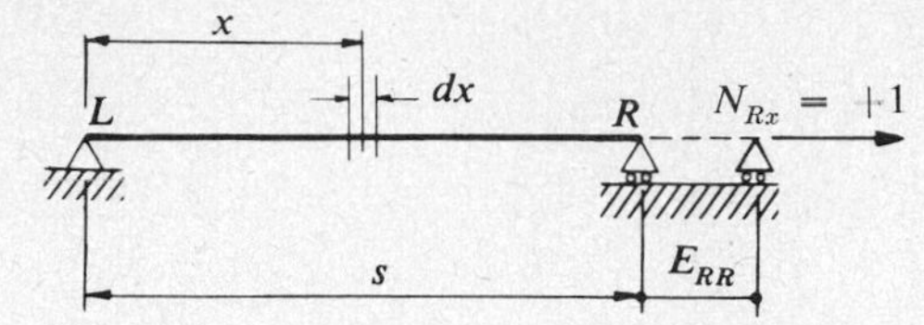 x, dx, L, R, $N_{Rx} = +1$, s, E_{RR}	$E_{RR} = \int_0^s \frac{dx}{EA}$	$\frac{s}{EA}$
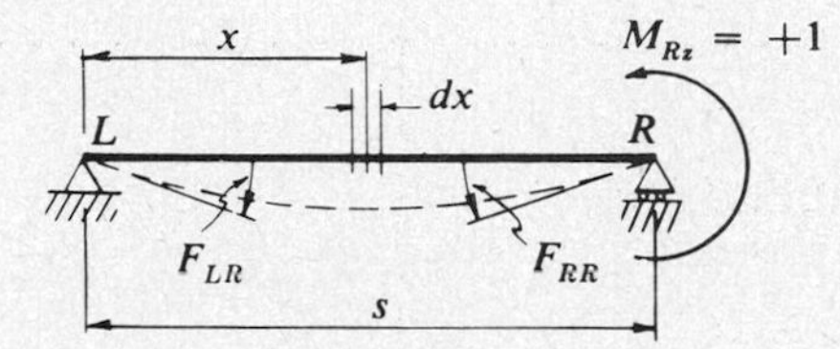 x, dx, $M_{Rz} = +1$, L, R, F_{LR}, F_{RR}, s	$F_{RR} = \int_0^s \frac{x^2\,dx}{s^2EI}$ $F_{LR} = \int_0^s \frac{(s-x)x\,dx}{s^2EI}$	$\frac{s}{3EI}$ $\frac{s}{6EI}$
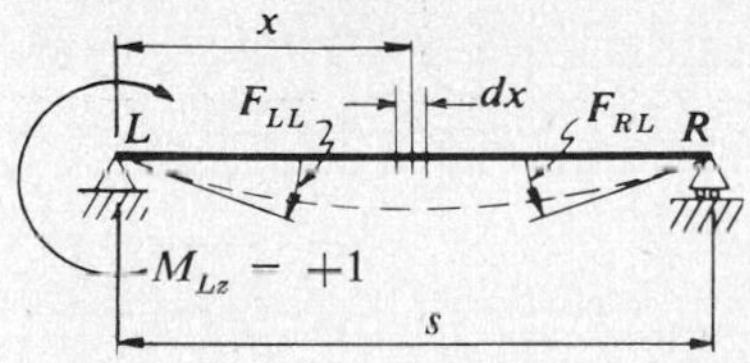 x, F_{LL}, dx, F_{RL}, L, R, $M_{Lz} = +1$, s	$F_{RL} = \int_0^s \frac{x(s-x)\,dx}{s^2EI}$ $F_{LL} = \int_0^s \frac{(s-x)^2\,dx}{s^2EI}$	$\frac{s}{6EI}$ $\frac{s}{3EI}$
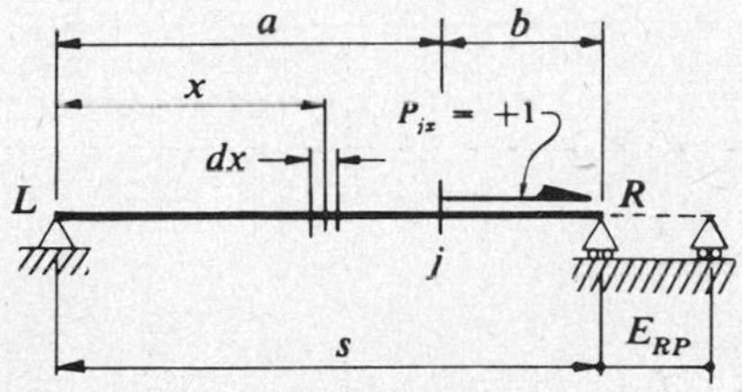 a, b, x, $P_{jx} = +1$, dx, L, R, j, s, E_{RP}	$E_{RP} = \int_0^a \frac{(s-x)\,dx}{EA}$	$\frac{a}{EA}$
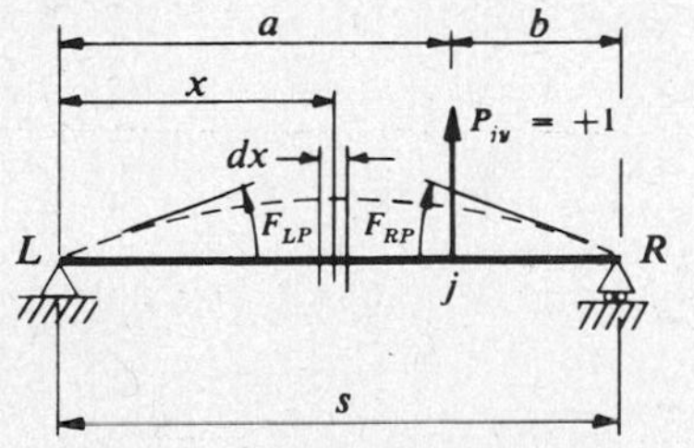 a, b, x, $P_{jy} = +1$, dx, F_{LP}, F_{RP}, L, R, j, s	$F_{RP} = -b\int_0^a \frac{x^2\,dx}{s^2EI} - a\int_a^s \frac{x(s-x)\,dx}{s^2EI}$ $F_{LP} = -b\int_0^a \frac{x(s-x)\,dx}{s^2EI} - a\int_a^s \frac{(s-x)^2\,dx}{s^2EI}$	$-\frac{ab(s+a)}{6sEI}$ $-\frac{ab(s+b)}{6sEI}$
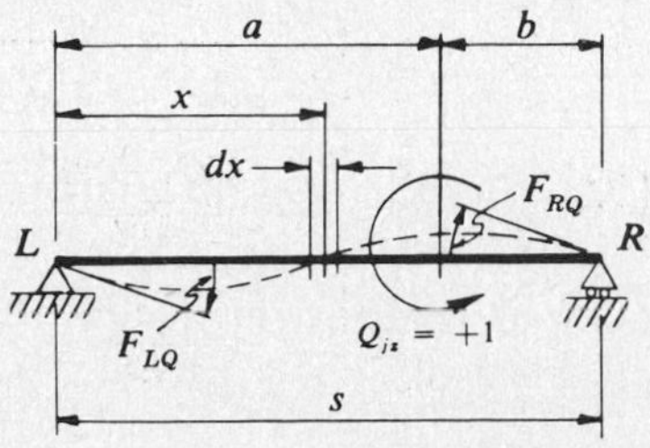 a, b, x, dx, F_{RQ}, L, R, F_{LQ}, $Q_{jz} = +1$, s	$F_{RQ} = \int_0^a \frac{x^2\,dx}{s^2EI} - \int_a^s \frac{x(s-x)\,dx}{s^2EI}$ $F_{LQ} = \int_0^a \frac{x(s-x)\,dx}{s^2EI} - \int_a^s \frac{(s-x)^2\,dx}{s^2EI}$	$-\frac{s^2-3a^2}{6sEI}$ $+\frac{s^2-3b^2}{6sEI}$

where $$q_0(x = 0 \to a) = \begin{bmatrix} 1 & 0 & 0 \\ 0 & 1 & 0 \\ 0 & a - x & 1 \end{bmatrix} \quad \text{and} \quad q_0(x = a \to s) = \begin{bmatrix} 0 & 0 & 0 \\ 0 & 0 & 0 \\ 0 & 0 & 0 \end{bmatrix}$$

The analytical expressions for the coefficients of (*5.12*) and (*5.13*) are given in Table 5-1.

(b) Segmental Flexibilties, Simple Beam

For the simple beam of Fig. 5-4, the *unit stress flexibility matrix* is

$$f = \int_0^s q_X^{)T} \lambda_s q_X = \begin{bmatrix} E_{RR} & 0 & 0 \\ 0 & F_{RR} & F_{RL} \\ 0 & F_{LR} & F_{LL} \end{bmatrix} \tag{5.14}$$

where $$q_X = \begin{bmatrix} 1 & 0 & 0 \\ 0 & -1/s & 1/s \\ 0 & x/s & (s-x)/s \end{bmatrix}$$

and $$\lambda_s = \begin{bmatrix} dx/EA & 0 & 0 \\ 0 & 0 & 0 \\ 0 & 0 & dx/EI \end{bmatrix}$$

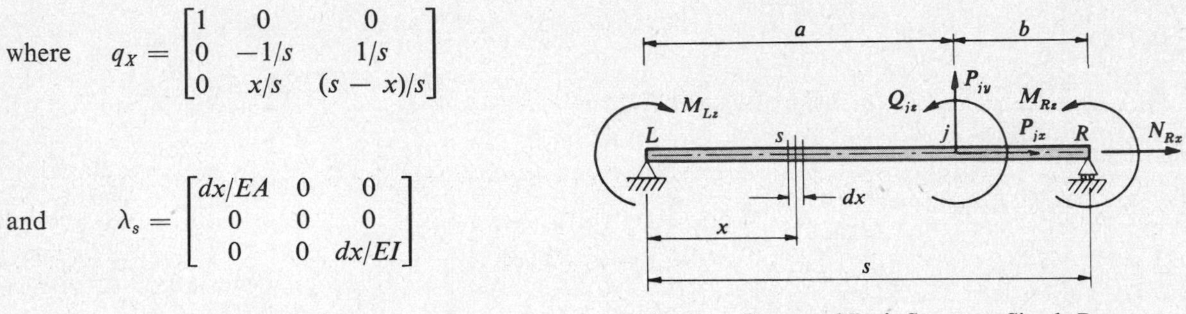

Fig. 5-4. Segmental Basic Structure, Simple Beam

Similarly, the *unit load flexibility matrix* is

$$l = \int_0^s q_X^{)T} \lambda_s q_0 = \begin{bmatrix} E_{RP} & 0 & 0 \\ 0 & F_{RP} & F_{RQ} \\ 0 & F_{LP} & F_{RQ} \end{bmatrix} \tag{5.15}$$

where $$q_0(x = 0 \to a) = \begin{bmatrix} 1 & 0 & 0 \\ 0 & b/s & 1/s \\ 0 & -bx/s & x/s \end{bmatrix} \quad \text{and} \quad q_0(x = a \to s) = \begin{bmatrix} 1 & 0 & 0 \\ 0 & -a/s & -1/s \\ 0 & -a(s-x)/s & -(s-x)/s \end{bmatrix}$$

The analytical expressions for the coefficients of (*5.14*) and (*5.15*) are given in Table 5-2. The displacement is positive if occurring in the direction of positive cause.

5.6 GENERAL TRANSPORT

The segmental flexibility matrix f given by (*5.12*) is the segmental equivalent of the elemental flexibility matrix given in (*3.2*) and can be used in the same context.

To demonstrate this affinity, consider the cantilever beam *om* given by its geometry (s_i, s_j, s_k, s_m and A_i, A_j, A_k, A_m, I_i, I_j, I_k, I_m), the modulus of elasticity E, and loaded as shown in Fig. 5-5*a*, page 55.

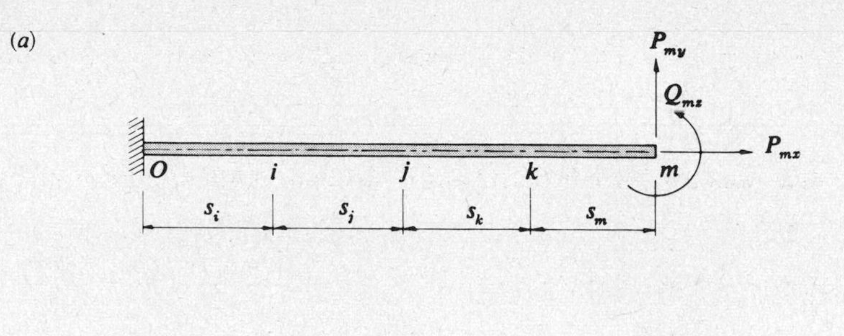

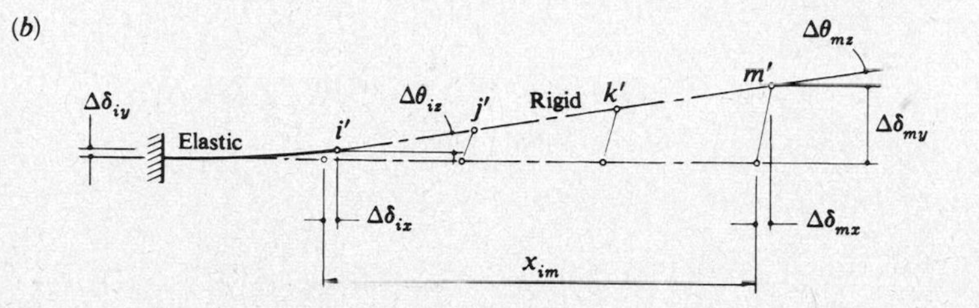

Fig. 5-5. Cantilever Beam, Load at m

Since the entire bar is assumed to be rigid with the exception of segment oi, the resulting displacements at m (Fig. 5-5b) become

$$\Delta\Delta_m{}^0 = p^0_{mi} f^0_{(ii)} \sigma_i{}^0 \tag{5.16}$$

where
$$p^0_{mi} = r^{0)T}_{im}, \qquad f^0_{(ii)} = \begin{bmatrix} s_i/EA_i & 0 & 0 \\ 0 & s_i^3/3EI_i & s_i^2/2EI_i \\ 0 & s_i^2/2EI_i & s_i/EI_i \end{bmatrix}, \qquad \sigma_i{}^0 = r^0_{im} W_m{}^0$$

The segmental displacements at m in terms of W_m are

$$\Delta\Delta_m{}^0 = p^0_{mi} f^0_{(ii)} r^0_{im} W_m{}^0 \tag{5.17a}$$

Similarly, the segmental displacements at k are

$$\Delta\Delta_k{}^0 = p^0_{ki} f^0_{(ii)} r^0_{im} W_m{}^0 \tag{5.17b}$$

If additional segments are allowed to become elastic, and loads are applied at all joints (Fig. 5-6a), the superposition of segmental displacements yields the final displacement vector (Fig. 5-6b) which is

$$\begin{bmatrix} \Delta_m{}^0 \\ \Delta_k{}^0 \\ \Delta_j{}^0 \\ \Delta_i{}^0 \end{bmatrix} = \begin{bmatrix} I & p^0_{mk} & p^0_{mj} & p^0_{mi} \\ 0 & I & p^0_{kj} & p^0_{ki} \\ 0 & 0 & I & p^0_{ji} \\ 0 & 0 & 0 & I \end{bmatrix} \begin{bmatrix} f^0_{(mm)} & 0 & 0 & 0 \\ 0 & f^0_{(kk)} & 0 & 0 \\ 0 & 0 & f^0_{(jj)} & 0 \\ 0 & 0 & 0 & f^0_{(ii)} \end{bmatrix} \begin{bmatrix} I & 0 & 0 & 0 \\ r^0_{km} & I & 0 & 0 \\ r^0_{jm} & r^0_{jk} & I & 0 \\ r^0_{im} & r^0_{ik} & r^0_{ij} & I \end{bmatrix} \begin{bmatrix} W_m{}^0 \\ W_k{}^0 \\ W_j{}^0 \\ W_i^0 \end{bmatrix}$$

or symbolically

$$\Delta^0 = p^0 f^0 r^0 W^0 = r^{0)T} f^0 r^0 W^0 = \Phi^0 W^0 \tag{5.18}$$

where according to (*3.5*) $p^0 = r^{0)T}$ and Φ^0 is the *system flexibility matrix* in which r^0 is a particular form of the transfer matrix q^0.

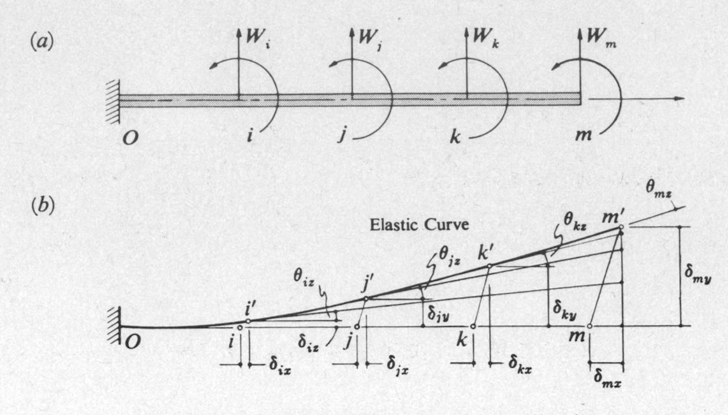

Fig. 5-6. Cantilever Beam, Loads at All Joints

The generalization of (*5.18*) corresponding to Fig. 5-7 is

$$\Delta^0 = s^{0s} f^s t^{s0} W^0 = t^{s0)T} f^s t^{s0} W^0 = \Phi^0 W^0 \tag{5.19}$$

where f^s is the *segmental flexibility matrix chain* consisting of all segmental matrices forming a submatrix diagonal, each one in its own system.

$$f^s = \begin{bmatrix} f^m_{(mm)} & & & \\ & f^k_{(kk)} & & \\ & & f^j_{(jj)} & \\ & & & f^i_{(ii)} \end{bmatrix} \tag{5.20}$$

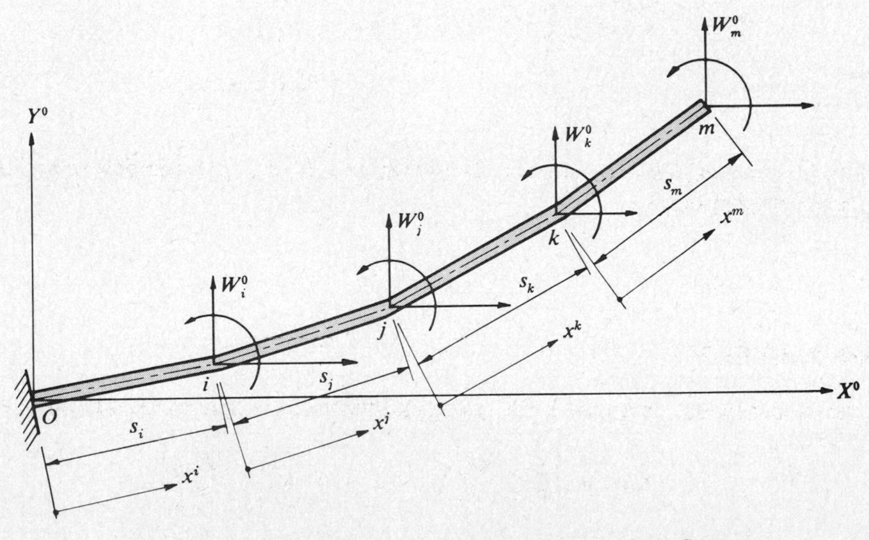

Fig. 5-7. Bent Cantilever Bar, Loads at All Joints in *O*-System

5.7 GENERAL TRANSFER

The segmental flexibility matrix f given by (*5.14*) is the segmental equivalent of the elemental flexibility matrix $\lambda = 1/EI$ in (*3.16*) and can be used in the same context.

To demonstrate this second affinity consider the simple beam om given by its geometry (s_i, s_j, s_k, s_m and A_i, A_j, A_k, A_m, I_i, I_j, I_k, I_m), the modulus of elasticity E and loaded as shown in Fig. 5-8*a*.

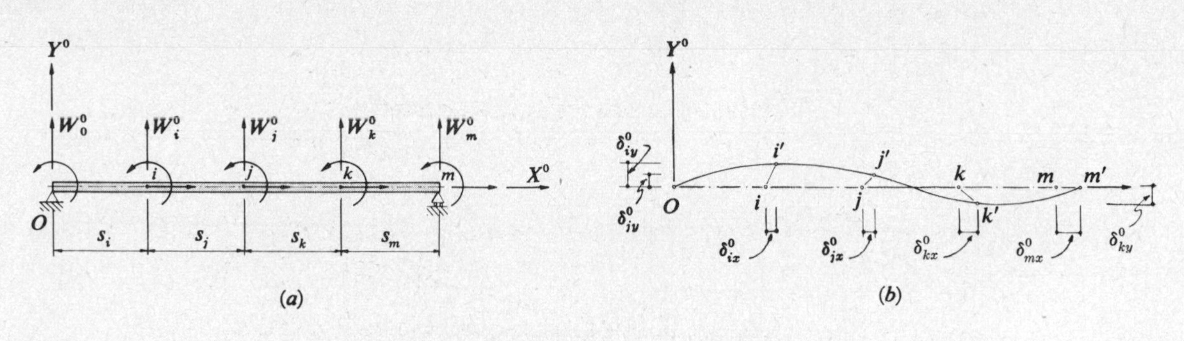

Fig. 5-8. Simple Beam, Loads at All Joints

If all segments are allowed to become elastic, the *final displacement vector* (Fig. 5-8*b*) is

$$\Delta^0 = q^{0)T} f^0 q^0 W^0 = \Phi^0 W^0 \tag{5.21}$$

where

$$q^0 W^0 = \begin{bmatrix} q^0_{(km)m} & q^0_{(km)k} & q^0_{(km)j} & q^0_{(km)i} & q^0_{(km)0} \\ q^0_{(jk)m} & q^0_{(jk)k} & q^0_{(jk)j} & q^0_{(jk)i} & q^0_{(jk)0} \\ q^0_{(ij)m} & q^0_{(ij)k} & q^0_{(ij)j} & q^0_{(ij)i} & q^0_{(ij)0} \\ q^0_{(0i)m} & q^0_{(0i)k} & q^0_{(0i)j} & q^0_{(0i)i} & q^0_{(0i)0} \end{bmatrix}_{(12\times 15)} \begin{bmatrix} W_m^0 \\ W_k^0 \\ W_j^0 \\ W_i^0 \\ W_0^0 \end{bmatrix}_{(15\times 1)} \tag{5.22}$$

$$f^0 = \begin{bmatrix} f^0_{(km)} & & & \\ & f^0_{(jk)} & & \\ & & f^0_{(ij)} & \\ & & & f^0_{(0i)} \end{bmatrix}_{(12\times 12)} \tag{5.23}$$

and Φ^0 is again the *system flexibility matrix*. The extension of (*5.21*) to the deformati on analysis of bent bars is presented in Chapter 9.

5.8 STRING POLYGON

If only transverse loads are applied, the segmental flexibility matrices (*5.14*) and (*5.15*) reduce to

$$f_{(RL)} = \begin{bmatrix} F_{RR} & F_{RL} \\ F_{LR} & F_{LL} \end{bmatrix} \qquad l_{(RL)} = \begin{bmatrix} F_{RP} & F_{RQ} \\ F_{LP} & F_{LQ} \end{bmatrix}$$

and the end angular deviations of the segment LR (Fig. 5-9) become

$$\begin{aligned} \gamma_{RL} &= F_{RR} M_R + F_{RL} M_L + \underbrace{\sum (F_{RP} P + F_{RQ} Q)}_{\tau_{RL}} \\ \gamma_{LR} &= F_{LR} M_R + F_{LL} M_L + \underbrace{\sum (F_{LP} P + F_{LQ} Q)}_{\tau_{LR}} \end{aligned} \tag{5.24}$$

where τ_{RL}, τ_{LR} are the *end angular deviations due to loads* acting in the segment.

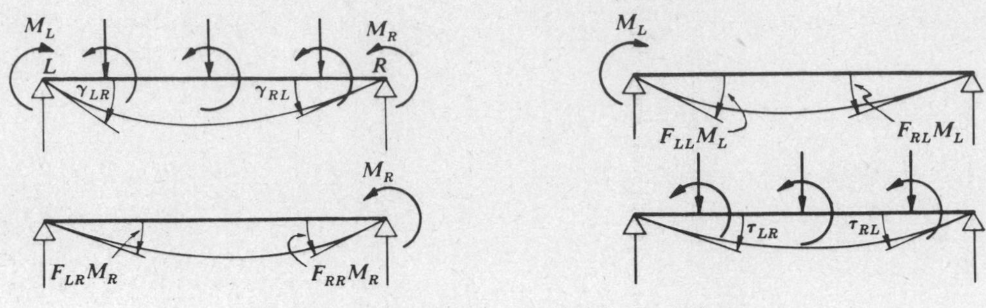

Fig. 5-9. Simple Beam, End Angular Deviations

In terms of (*5.24*), the *angle change of the string polygon* 0, i', j', k', m inscribed to the elastic curve of the simple beam *om* of Fig. 5-10*a*, *b* is given as

$$\gamma_j = \gamma_{ji} + \gamma_{jk} = \frac{\delta_j - \delta_i}{s_i} - \frac{\delta_k - \delta_j}{s_j} = F_{ji}M_i + F_jM_j + F_{jk}M_k + \tau_j \tag{5.25}$$

where $F_j = F_{jj(\text{Left})} + F_{jj(\text{Right})}$,

$\tau_j = \tau_{ji} + \tau_{jk}$,

M_i, M_j, M_k = bending moments at i, j, k respectively,

$\delta_i, \delta_j, \delta_k$ = vertical deflections at i, j, k respectively,

s_i, s_j = segmental lengths.

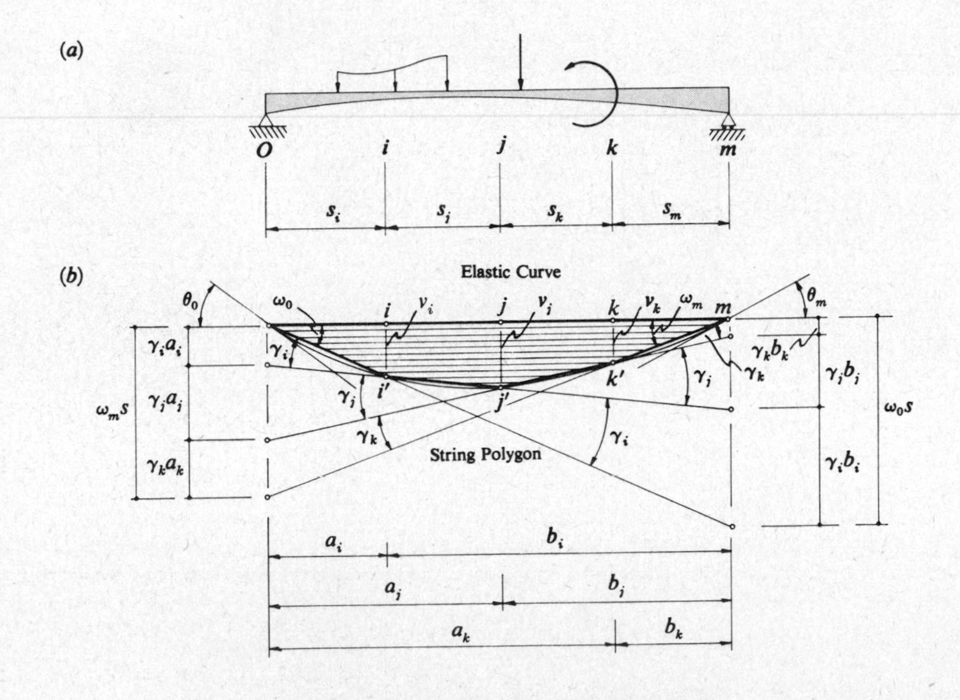

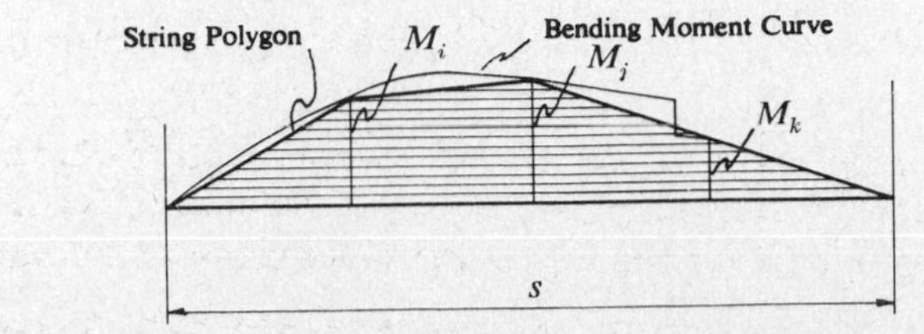

Fig. 5-10. Simple Beam, String Polygon

Using (*5.25*) recurrently, the angle change vector becomes

$$\begin{bmatrix} \gamma_i \\ \gamma_j \\ \gamma_k \end{bmatrix} = \begin{bmatrix} \frac{1}{s_i}+\frac{1}{s_j} & -\frac{1}{s_j} & \\ -\frac{1}{s_j} & \frac{1}{s_j}+\frac{1}{s_k} & -\frac{1}{s_k} \\ & -\frac{1}{s_k} & \frac{1}{s_k}+\frac{1}{s_m} \end{bmatrix} \begin{bmatrix} \delta_i \\ \delta_j \\ \delta_k \end{bmatrix}$$

$$= \begin{bmatrix} F_i & F_{ij} & \\ F_{ji} & F_j & F_{jk} \\ & F_{kj} & F_k \end{bmatrix} \begin{bmatrix} M_i \\ M_j \\ M_k \end{bmatrix} + \begin{bmatrix} \tau_i \\ \tau_j \\ \tau_k \end{bmatrix}$$

or symbolically

$$\gamma = \beta^{)T}\delta = fM + \tau \tag{5.26}$$

which is the generalization of (*3.15*).

From (*5.26*) the *deflection vector* is

$$\delta = \beta^{T)-1} fM + \beta^{T)-1}\tau = m^{)T} fM + m^{)T}\tau \tag{5.27}$$

where

$$\beta^{T)-1} = \begin{bmatrix} m_{ii} & m_{ij} & m_{ik} \\ m_{ji} & m_{jj} & m_{jk} \\ m_{ki} & m_{kj} & m_{kk} \end{bmatrix}^T = m^{)T} \tag{5.28}$$

The coefficients of (*5.28*) are the influence values given in Fig. 5-11.

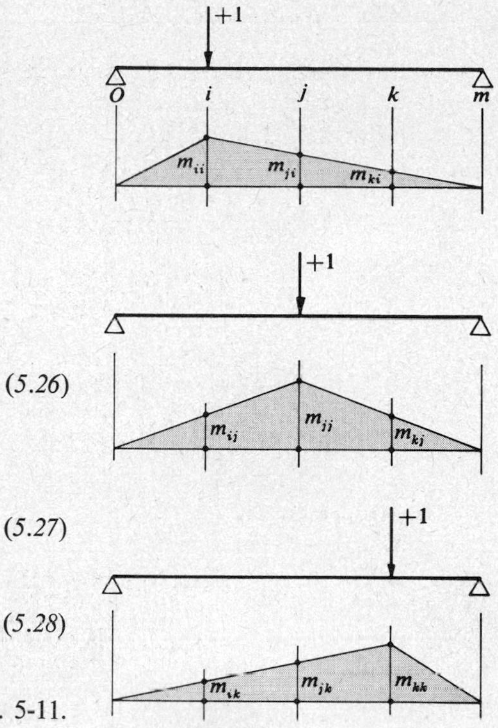

Fig. 5-11. Coefficients of m

5.9 ELASTO-KINEMATICS

The *relationships* of the *string polygon* and the *elastic curve* of Fig. 5-10 are given by the following equations:

(I) String Polygon

(*a*) *End Slopes*

$$\omega_0 = (\gamma_i b_i + \gamma_j b_j + \gamma_k b_k)/s; \qquad \omega_m = (\gamma_i a_i + \gamma_j a_j + \gamma_k a_k)/s; \\ \omega_0 + \omega_m = \gamma_i + \gamma_j + \gamma_k \tag{5.29}$$

(*b*) *String Slopes*

$$\omega_{0i} = \omega_0; \qquad \omega_{ij} = \omega_0 - \gamma_i; \qquad \omega_{jk} = \omega_0 - \gamma_i - \gamma_j; \\ \omega_{km} = \omega_0 - \gamma_i - \gamma_j - \gamma_k \tag{5.30}$$

(*c*) *Coordinates of Vertices*

$$v_i = \omega_0 a_i; \qquad v_j = \omega_0 a_j + \gamma_j(a_j - a_i); \\ v_k = \omega_0 a_k + \gamma_i(a_k - a_i) + \gamma_j(a_k - a_j) \tag{5.31}$$

(II) Elastic Curve

(*a*) *Slopes*

$$\begin{aligned} \theta_0 &= \omega_{0i} + \gamma_{0i} & \theta_i &= \omega_{0i} - \gamma_{i0} = \omega_{ij} + \gamma_{ij} \\ & & \theta_j &= \omega_{ij} - \gamma_{ji} = \omega_{jk} + \gamma_{jk} \\ \theta_m &= \omega_{km} - \gamma_{mk} & \theta_k &= \omega_{jk} - \gamma_{kj} = \omega_{km} + \gamma_{km} \end{aligned} \tag{5.32}$$

(*b*) *Deflections*

$$\delta_i = v_i \qquad \delta_j = v_j \qquad \delta_k = v_k \tag{5.33}$$

5.10 ELASTO-STATICS

The formal similarity of (*5.29, 30, 31*) with the equations for reactions, shears and bending moments of the same beam leads to the concept of the *elasto-static analogy*. This analogy is represented by the *conjugate beam* of Fig. 5-12, the *loads* of which are the *angle changes*. The shear of the conjugate beam equals the slope of the strings and its bending moment diagram is the string polygon of the real beam. Thus the conjugate beam serves as a *transform of convenience* allowing the calculation of deformation relationships (kinematic relationships) by means of equations of static equilibrium. Obviously the matrix formulation of the same is

$$\delta = q^{)T}\gamma \tag{5.34}$$

which is exactly (*5.27*).

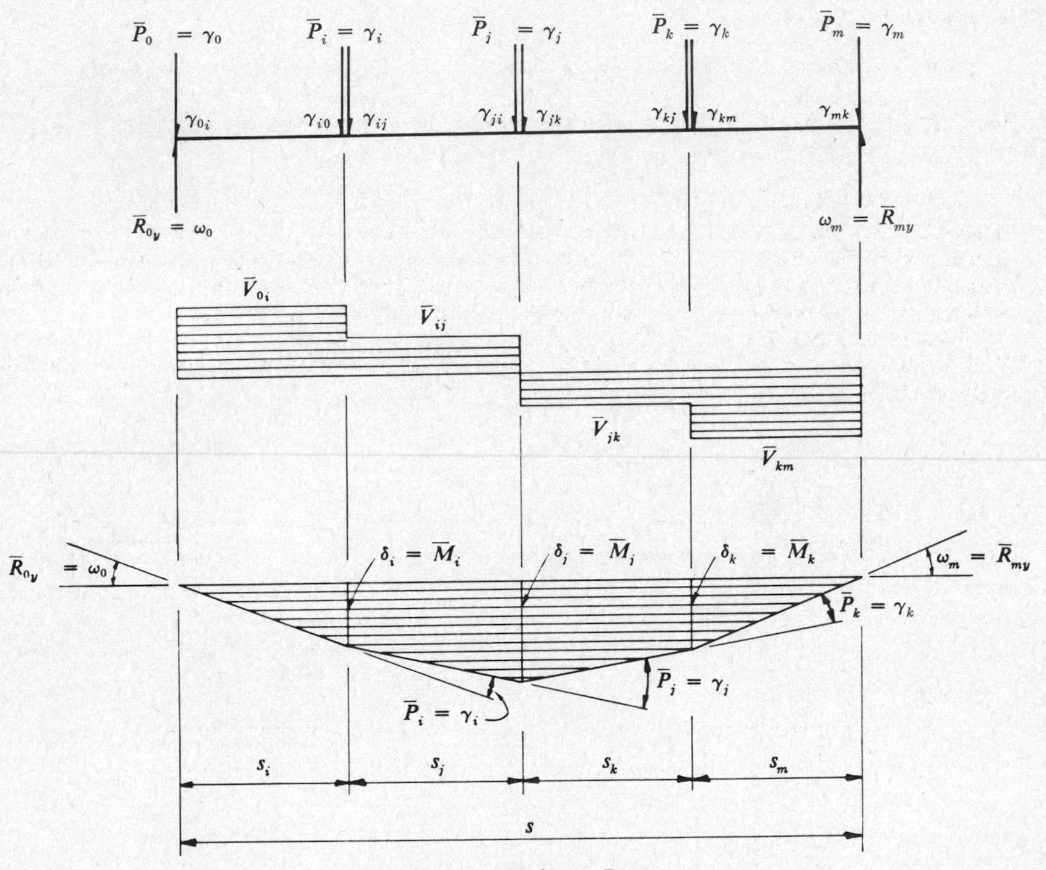

Fig. 5-12. Conjugate Beam

5.11 SECONDARY EFFECTS

The change in volume due to temperature change or moisture content change and the initial imperfections of bars due to errors in fabrication can be included in the flexibility analysis by simply adding to the redundant effect vector and the load effect vector, the *secondary effect vector*.

Solved Problems

SYSTEM FLEXIBILITY MATRIX

5.1. Using relationships (*5.1*), (*5.2*), (*5.3*) and (*5.4*) construct symbolically the system flexibility matrix (*5.7*) for the frame of Fig. P-5.1*a*. Consider only flexural deformations.

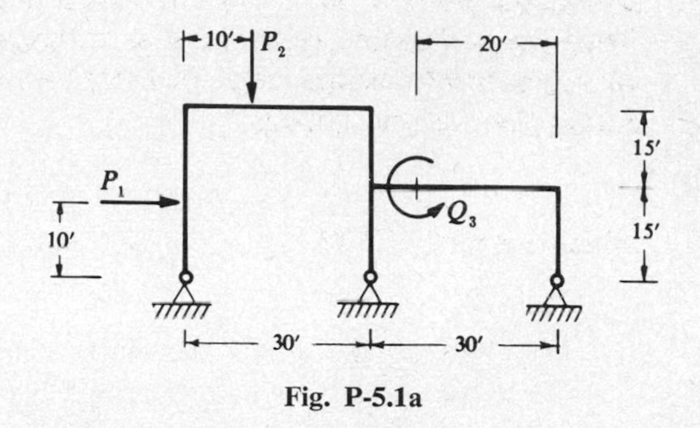

Fig. P-5.1a

Equations (*5.1, 2*) can symbolically be written as

$$\sigma_{s0} = q_{s0}W \quad \text{and} \quad \sigma_{sX} = q_{sX}X$$

Using the virtual forces principle, the deformation vectors can be shown to be

$$\Delta_{j0} = \sum q_{sX}^T \lambda_s q_{s0} W \quad \text{and} \quad \Delta_{jX} = \sum q_{sX}^T \lambda_s q_{sX} X$$

which leads to the definitions (*5.11, 10*) of the unit load and unit redundant flexibility matrices

$$l = \sum q_{sX}^T \lambda_s q_{s0} \quad \text{and} \quad f = \sum q_{sX}^T \lambda_s q_{sX}$$

If bending deformations only are considered, the stress influence coefficients q's reduce to the moment influence coefficients and the flexibility matrix λ_s is replaced by the elemental flexural flexibility value ds/EI. The given frame (Fig. P-5.1*a*) is statically indeterminate to the third degree. Figures (*b*) and (*c*) respectively show the basic system with applied loads and the complementary system with the three redundants chosen.

Figures (*d*), (*e*) and (*f*) show the moment influence values q_{s1}, q_{s2} and q_{s3} induced in the frame due to $P_1 = +1$, $P_2 = +1$ and $Q_3 = +1$ respectively. Similarly, Figures (*g*), (*h*) and (*i*) show the moment influence values q_{si}, q_{sj} and q_{sk} induced by unit redundants X_i, X_j and X_k.

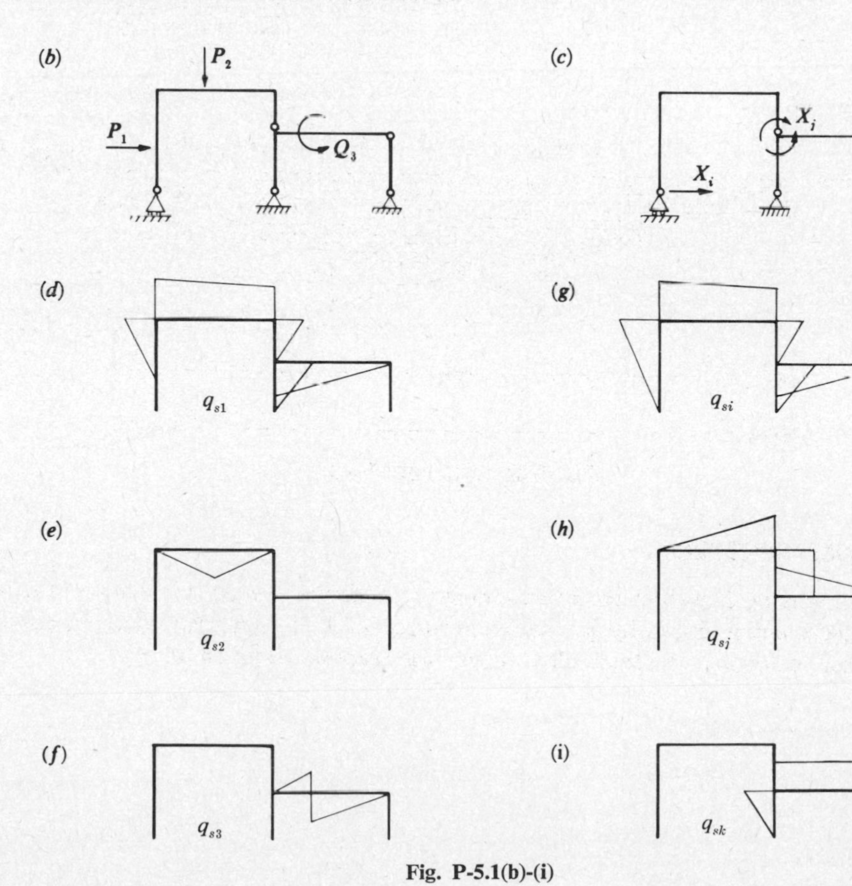

Fig. P-5.1(b)-(i)

The flexibility matrices l and f can now be written as

$$l = \sum \int \begin{bmatrix} q_{si} \\ q_{sj} \\ q_{sk} \end{bmatrix} [\lambda_s][q_{s1}\ q_{s2}\ q_{s3}], \qquad f = \sum \int \begin{bmatrix} q_{si} \\ q_{sj} \\ q_{sk} \end{bmatrix} [\lambda_s][q_{si}\ q_{sj}\ q_{sk}]$$

The system flexibility matrix equation, $lW + fX = 0$, therefore becomes

$$\sum \int \lambda_s \begin{bmatrix} q_{si}q_{s1} & q_{si}q_{s2} & q_{si}q_{s3} \\ q_{sj}q_{s1} & q_{sj}q_{s2} & q_{sj}q_{s3} \\ q_{sk}q_{s1} & q_{sk}q_{s2} & q_{sk}q_{s3} \end{bmatrix} \begin{bmatrix} P_1 \\ P_2 \\ Q_3 \end{bmatrix} + \sum \int \lambda_s \begin{bmatrix} q_{si}q_{si} & q_{si}q_{sj} & q_{si}q_{sk} \\ q_{sj}q_{si} & q_{sj}q_{sj} & q_{sj}q_{sk} \\ q_{sk}q_{si} & q_{sk}q_{sj} & q_{sk}q_{sk} \end{bmatrix} \begin{bmatrix} X_i \\ X_j \\ X_k \end{bmatrix} = 0.$$

5.2. Using the procedure developed in Problem 5.1, construct symbolically the system flexibility matrix (*5.7*) for the frame of Fig. P-5.2*a*. Take advantage of the frame symmetry and consider only flexural deformations.

The frame shown in Fig. P-5.2*a* is statically indeterminate to the sixth degree. The basic system with the three applied loads is shown in (*b*) while the six redundants chosen are shown in (*c*).

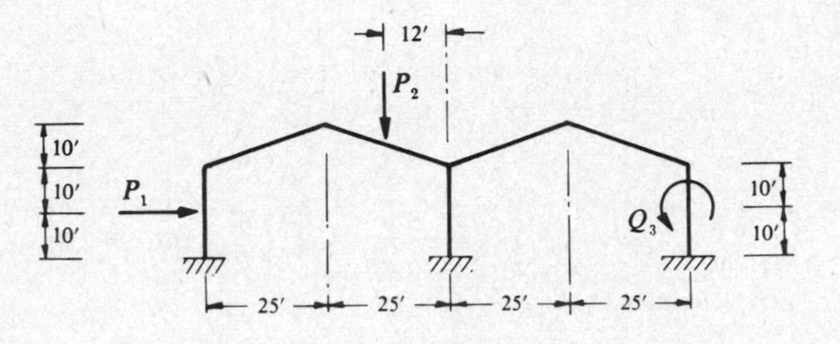

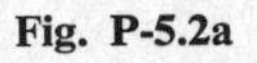
Fig. P-5.2a

(*b*)

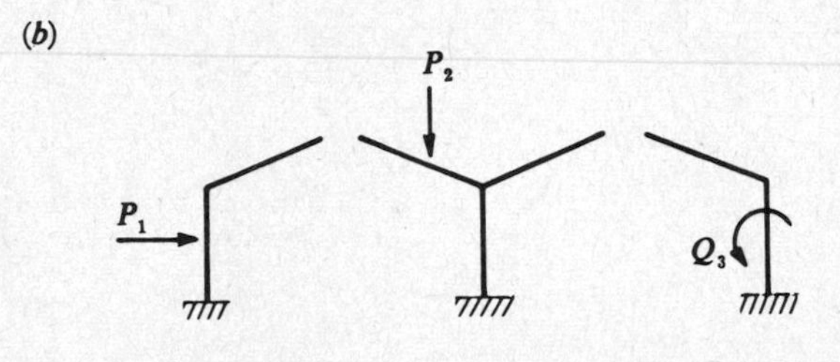

(*c*)

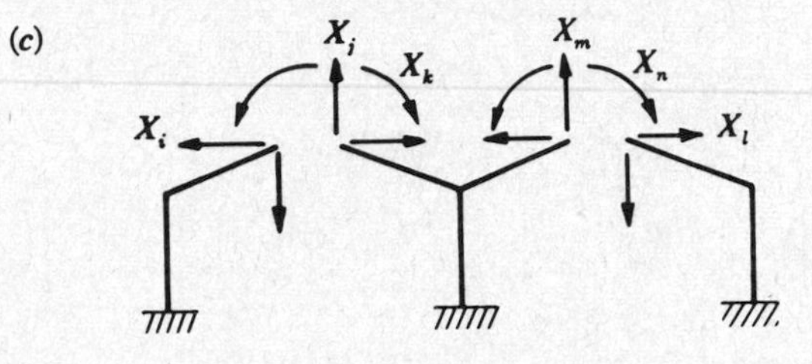

(*d*)

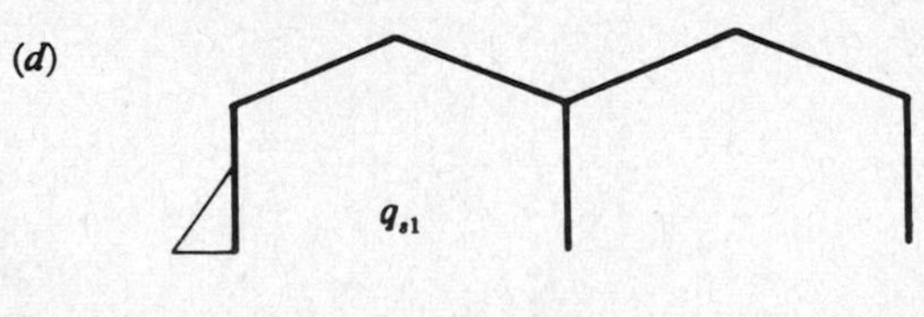

(*g*)

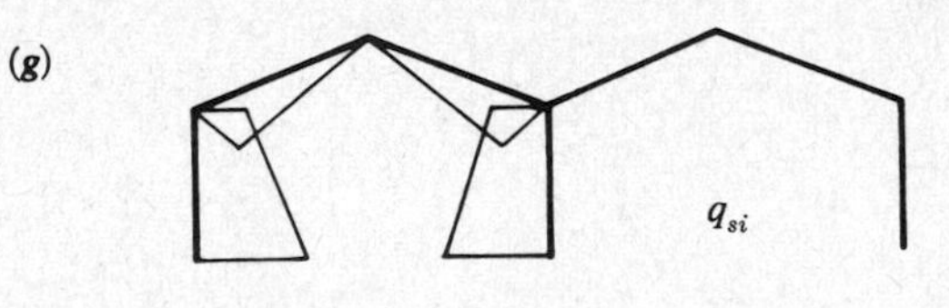

(*e*)

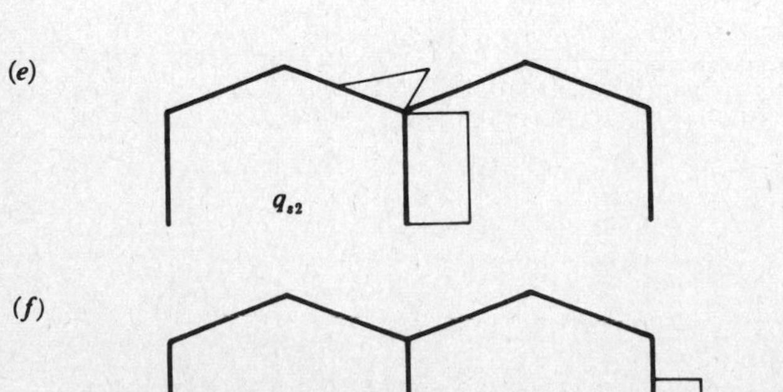

(*h*)

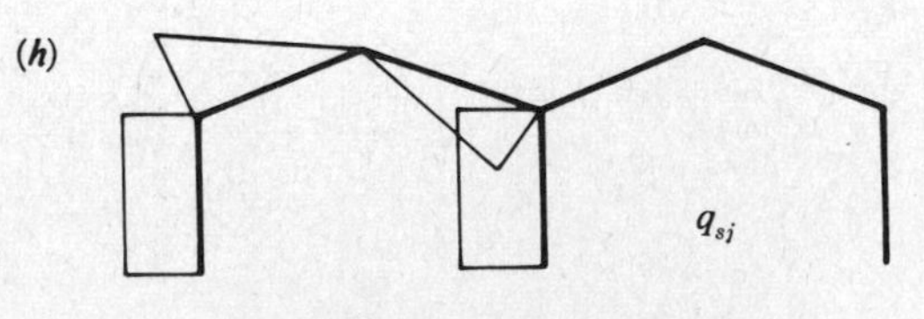

(*f*)

q_{s3}

(*i*)

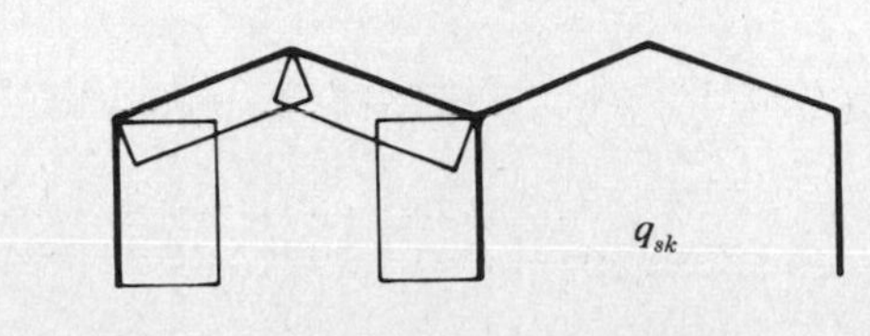

Fig. P-5.2(b)-(i)

As in Problem 5.1, the moment influence values q_{s0}'s due to unit applied loads are shown in (*d*), (*e*) and (*f*). Figures (*g*), (*h*) and (*i*) show the moment influence values due to unit redundants X_i, X_j and X_k. Similar diagrams can be visualized for the other three redundants which are symmetrically situated. The choice of symmetrically located redundants on a symmetrical frame reduces some amount of work since it can readily be concluded that

$$\int q_{si}q_{si}\lambda_s = \int q_{sl}q_{sl}\lambda_s, \qquad \int q_{sj}q_{sj}\lambda_s = \int q_{sm}q_{sm}\lambda_s \qquad \text{and} \qquad \int q_{sk}q_{sk}\lambda_s = \int q_{sn}q_{sn}\lambda_s$$

Further, if each *span* of the frame is symmetrical in itself, considerations of symmetry and antisymmetry of the moment diagrams lead to the conclusion that

$$\int q_{si}q_{sj}\lambda_s = \int q_{sj}q_{si}\lambda_s = 0, \qquad \int q_{sj}q_{sk}\lambda_s = \int q_{sk}q_{sj}\lambda_s = 0$$

Similarly,

$$\int q_{sl}q_{sm}\lambda_s = \int q_{sm}q_{sl}\lambda_s = 0 \qquad \text{and} \qquad \int q_{sm}q_{sn}\lambda_s = \int q_{sn}q_{sm}\lambda_s = 0$$

In general, however, the problem can be set up in a manner very similar to that of Problem 5.1.

$$l = \sum \int q_X{}^T \lambda_s q_0 = \sum \int \begin{bmatrix} q_{si} \\ q_{sj} \\ q_{sk} \\ q_{sl} \\ q_{sm} \\ q_{sn} \end{bmatrix} [\lambda_s][q_{s1} \;\; q_{s2} \;\; q_{s3}]$$

$$f = \sum \int q_X{}^T \lambda_s q_X = \sum \int \begin{bmatrix} q_{si} \\ q_{sj} \\ q_{sk} \\ q_{sl} \\ q_{sm} \\ q_{sn} \end{bmatrix} [\lambda_s][q_{si} \;\; q_{sj} \;\; q_{sk} \;\; q_{sl} \;\; q_{sm} \;\; q_{sn}]$$

And the system flexibility matrix equation becomes

$$\sum \int \lambda_s \begin{bmatrix} q_{si}q_{s1} & q_{si}q_{s2} & q_{si}q_{s3} \\ q_{sj}q_{s1} & q_{sj}q_{s2} & q_{sj}q_{s3} \\ q_{sk}q_{s1} & q_{sk}q_{s2} & q_{sk}q_{s3} \\ q_{sl}q_{s1} & q_{sl}q_{s2} & q_{sl}q_{s3} \\ q_{sm}q_{s1} & q_{sm}q_{s2} & q_{sm}q_{s3} \\ q_{sn}q_{s1} & q_{sn}q_{s2} & q_{sn}q_{s3} \end{bmatrix} \begin{bmatrix} P_1 \\ P_2 \\ Q_3 \end{bmatrix}$$

$$+ \sum \int \lambda_s \begin{bmatrix} q_{si}q_{si} & 0 & q_{si}q_{sk} & q_{si}q_{sl} & q_{si}q_{sm} & q_{si}q_{sn} \\ 0 & q_{sj}q_{sj} & 0 & q_{sj}q_{sl} & q_{sj}q_{sm} & q_{sj}q_{sn} \\ q_{sk}q_{si} & 0 & q_{sk}q_{sk} & q_{sk}q_{sl} & q_{sk}q_{sm} & q_{sk}q_{sn} \\ q_{sl}q_{si} & q_{sl}q_{sj} & q_{sl}q_{sk} & q_{sl}q_{sl} & 0 & q_{sl}q_{sn} \\ q_{sm}q_{si} & q_{sm}q_{sj} & q_{sm}q_{sk} & 0 & q_{sm}q_{sm} & 0 \\ q_{sn}q_{si} & q_{sn}q_{sj} & q_{sn}q_{sk} & q_{sn}q_{sl} & 0 & q_{sn}q_{sn} \end{bmatrix} \begin{bmatrix} X_i \\ X_j \\ X_k \\ X_l \\ X_m \\ X_n \end{bmatrix} = 0$$

SEGMENTAL FLEXIBILITY MATRIX

5.3. Using the virtual forces method derive the analytical expressions for the coefficients of the segmental flexibility matrix given in Table 5-1.

The expressions for the flexibility matrices f and l given in (*5.12*) and (*5.13*) are the direct results of the method of virtual forces.

Using the expressions for q_X, λ_s and q_0 established on pages 51, and 54,

$$f = \int_0^s q_X{}^T \lambda_s q_X = \int_0^s \begin{bmatrix} 1 & 0 & 0 \\ 0 & 1 & s-x \\ 0 & 0 & 1 \end{bmatrix} \begin{bmatrix} \frac{dx}{EA} & 0 & 0 \\ 0 & 0 & 0 \\ 0 & 0 & \frac{dx}{EI} \end{bmatrix} \begin{bmatrix} 1 & 0 & 0 \\ 0 & 1 & 0 \\ 0 & s-x & 1 \end{bmatrix}$$

$$= \int_0^s \begin{bmatrix} \frac{dx}{EA} & 0 & 0 \\ 0 & \frac{(s-x)^2\,dx}{EI} & \frac{(s-x)\,dx}{EI} \\ 0 & \frac{(s-x)\,dx}{EI} & \frac{dx}{EI} \end{bmatrix} = \begin{bmatrix} \frac{s}{EA} & 0 & 0 \\ 0 & \frac{s^3}{3EI} & \frac{s^2}{2EI} \\ 0 & \frac{s^2}{2EI} & \frac{s}{EI} \end{bmatrix}$$

$$l = \int_0^s q_X{}^T \lambda_s q_0 = \int_0^s \begin{bmatrix} 1 & 0 & 0 \\ 0 & 1 & s-x \\ 0 & 0 & 1 \end{bmatrix} \begin{bmatrix} \frac{dx}{EA} & 0 & 0 \\ 0 & 0 & 0 \\ 0 & 0 & \frac{dx}{EI} \end{bmatrix} \begin{bmatrix} 1 & 0 & 0 \\ 0 & 1 & 0 \\ 0 & a-x & 1 \end{bmatrix}$$

$$= \int_0^s \begin{bmatrix} \frac{dx}{EA} & 0 & 0 \\ 0 & \frac{(a-x)(s-x)\,dx}{EI} & \frac{(s-x)\,dx}{EI} \\ 0 & \frac{(a-x)\,dx}{EI} & \frac{dx}{EI} \end{bmatrix} = \begin{bmatrix} \frac{a}{EA} & 0 & 0 \\ 0 & \frac{a^2(3s-a)}{6EI} & \frac{a(2s-a)}{2EI} \\ 0 & \frac{a^2}{2EI} & \frac{a}{EI} \end{bmatrix}$$

The flexibility constants D_{RR}, C_{RR}, B_{RR}, A_{RR} and D_{RP}, C_{RP}, B_{RP}, B_{RQ}, A_{RQ} of Table 5.1 can be extracted from above on comparison with equations (*5.12*) and (*5.13*).

5.4. Using the stress area method derive the analytical expressions for the coefficients of the segmental flexibility matrix given in Table 5-2.

Figure P-5.4(*a*)-(*f*) shows a simply supported beam LR loaded by unit causes for which the flexibility constants are desired, along with the corresponding normal force or bending moment diagrams.

The axial deformations are computed using the Normal Force Area Theorem (*1.2*) while the end angular deformations are computed using the Moment Area Theorem II (*1.5*). Accordingly, referring to the notations of Table 5-2,

$$E_{RR} = \int_0^s \frac{N_x\,dx}{EA} = \int_0^s \frac{(1)\,dx}{EA} = \frac{s}{EA}$$

$$F_{RR} = \frac{t_{LR}}{s} = \frac{1}{s}\int_0^s \frac{M_x x\,dx}{EI} = \frac{1}{s}\int_0^s \frac{(x/s)x\,dx}{EI} = \frac{s}{3EI}$$

$$F_{LR} = \frac{t_{RL}}{s} = \frac{1}{s}\int_0^s \frac{M_x(s-x)\,dx}{EI} = \frac{1}{s}\int_0^s \frac{(x/s)(s-x)\,dx}{EI} = \frac{s}{6EI}$$

$$F_{RL} = \frac{t_{RL}}{s} = \frac{1}{s}\int_0^s \frac{M_x x\,dx}{EI} = \frac{1}{s}\int_0^s \frac{((s-x)/s)x\,dx}{EI} = \frac{s}{6EI}$$

$$F_{LL} = \frac{t_{RL}}{s} = \frac{1}{s}\int_0^s \frac{M_x(s-x)\,dx}{EI} = \frac{1}{s}\int_0^s \frac{((s-x)/s)(s-x)\,dx}{EI} = \frac{s}{3EI}$$

$$E_{RP} = \int_0^s \frac{N_x\,dx}{EA} = \int_0^a \frac{(1)\,dx}{EA} = \frac{a}{EA}$$

$$F_{RP} = \frac{t_{LR}}{s} = \frac{1}{s}\int_0^s \frac{M_x x\,dx}{EI} = \frac{1}{s}\int_0^a \frac{(-bx/s)x\,dx}{EI} + \frac{1}{s}\int_a^s \frac{(-a(s-x)/s)x\,dx}{EI} = -\frac{ab(s+a)}{6sEI}$$

$$F_{LP} = \frac{t_{RL}}{s} = \frac{1}{s}\int_0^s \frac{M_x(s-x)\,dx}{EI} = \frac{1}{s}\int_0^s \frac{(-bx/s)(s-x)\,dx}{EI} + \frac{1}{s}\int_a^s \frac{(-a(s-x)/s)(s-x)\,dx}{EI} = -\frac{ab(s+b)}{6sEI}$$

$$F_{RQ} = \frac{t_{LR}}{s} = \frac{1}{s}\int_0^s \frac{M_x x\,dx}{EI} = \frac{1}{s}\int_0^s \frac{(x/s)x\,dx}{EI} + \frac{1}{s}\int_a^s \frac{(-(s-x)/s)x\,dx}{EI} = -\frac{s^2-3a^2}{6sEI}$$

$$F_{LQ} = \frac{t_{RL}}{s} = \frac{1}{s}\int_0^s \frac{M_x(s-x)\,dx}{EI} = \frac{1}{s}\int_0^a \frac{(x/s)(s-x)\,dx}{EI} + \frac{1}{s}\int_a^s \frac{(-(s-x)/s)(s-x)\,dx}{EI} = \frac{s^2-3b^2}{6sEI}$$

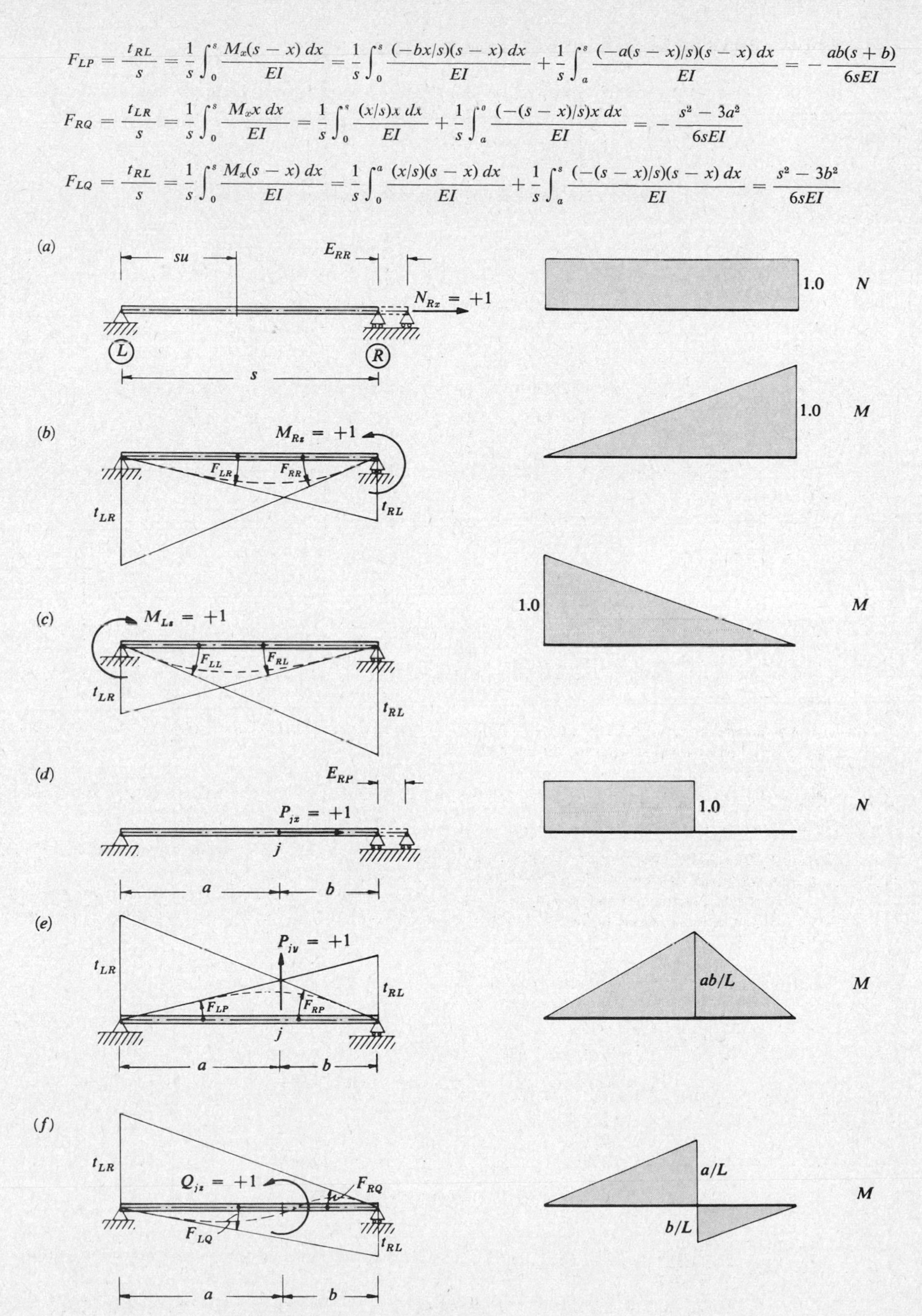

Fig. P-5.4

GENERAL TRANSPORT, SEGMENTAL FLEXIBILITY

5.5. Compute the displacement vector (*5.18*) for the straight cantilever beam of Fig. P-5.5*a*. Assume $EA = 1{,}280{,}640$ k and $EI = 1{,}814{,}900$ k-ft² (W 36X150 steel section).

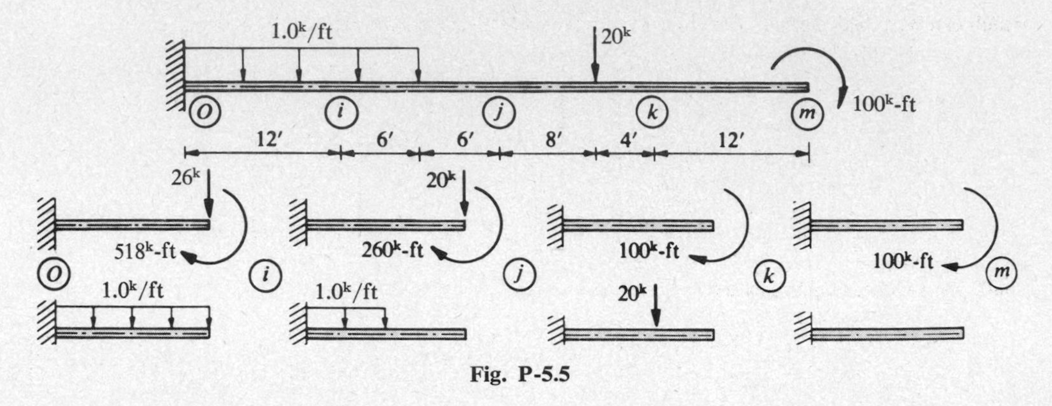

Fig. P-5.5

The development of (*5.18*) shown is for the case in which all external loads are applied at the joints. For a more general case of loading, an extension of (*5.18*) can be used.

A typical term from (*5.18*) basically is

$$\Delta_m^{\,0} = \sum_i \overset{0}{p}_{mi} \Delta\Delta_i^{\,0}$$

where

$$\Delta\Delta_i^{\,0} = \overset{0}{f}_{(ii)} \sigma_i^{\,0} = \overset{0}{f}_{(ii)} \sum_k \overset{0}{r}_{ik} W_k^{\,0}$$

and $\sigma_i^{\,0}$ is the stress vector at the free end of the segment *oi*. For a general type of loading, however, the displacement vector at *i* is the sum of the effects of end loads at *i* and any other loads acting on the segment. Thus

$$\Delta\Delta_i^{\,0} = \overset{0}{f}_{(ii)} \sigma_i^{\,0} + \overset{0}{l}_{i0} W_0^{\,0}$$

where l_{i0}^0 is the unit load flexibility matrix for segment *oi* and $W_0^{\,0}$ represents the loads acting on the segment. Figures P-5.5*a*, *b*, and *c* respectively show the given beam, segments *oi*, *ij*, *jk* and *km* with end forces and the same segments with applied loads acting on them.

Further, for beams loaded with transverse loads only, axial forces and deformations are zero.

The unit stress flexibility matrix reduces to

$$\begin{bmatrix} s^3/3EI & s^2/2EI \\ s^2/2EI & s/EI \end{bmatrix} = \frac{1}{EI}\begin{bmatrix} 576 & 72 \\ 72 & 12 \end{bmatrix}$$

which is the same for all segments in this case.

Postmultiplying this by the end stresses

$$\sigma_i = \begin{bmatrix} -26 \\ -518 \end{bmatrix}, \quad \sigma_j = \begin{bmatrix} -20 \\ -260 \end{bmatrix}, \quad \sigma_k = \begin{bmatrix} 0 \\ -100 \end{bmatrix}, \quad \sigma_m = \begin{bmatrix} 0 \\ -100 \end{bmatrix}$$

gives the deformations at *i*, *j*, *k* and *m* due to the end stresses:

$$\frac{1}{EI}\begin{bmatrix} -52{,}272 \\ -8{,}080 \end{bmatrix}, \quad \frac{1}{EI}\begin{bmatrix} -30{,}240 \\ -4{,}560 \end{bmatrix}, \quad \frac{1}{EI}\begin{bmatrix} -7{,}200 \\ -1{,}200 \end{bmatrix} \quad \text{and} \quad \frac{1}{EI}\begin{bmatrix} -7{,}200 \\ -1{,}200 \end{bmatrix}$$

The end deformations due to loads acting on the segment can be computed using the values developed in Table 5-1, integrating over proper range in case of distributed loads. These additional deformations at the ends *i*, *j*, *k* and *m* are

$$\frac{1}{EI}\begin{bmatrix} -2{,}592 \\ -288 \end{bmatrix}, \quad \frac{1}{EI}\begin{bmatrix} -378 \\ -36 \end{bmatrix}, \quad \frac{1}{EI}\begin{bmatrix} -5{,}973.3 \\ -640 \end{bmatrix} \quad \text{and} \quad \frac{1}{EI}\begin{bmatrix} 0 \\ 0 \end{bmatrix}$$

The total end deformations on the segments therefore become

$$\frac{1}{EI}\begin{bmatrix}-54{,}864\\-8{,}368\end{bmatrix},\quad \frac{1}{EI}\begin{bmatrix}-30{,}618\\-4{,}596\end{bmatrix},\quad \frac{1}{EI}\begin{bmatrix}-13{,}173.3\\-1{,}840\end{bmatrix}\quad\text{and}\quad \frac{1}{EI}\begin{bmatrix}-7{,}200\\-1{,}200\end{bmatrix}$$

which can be substituted in (*5.18*) to compute the total displacement vectors at all joints.

$$\begin{bmatrix}\Delta_m^{\,0}\\ \Delta_k^{\,0}\\ \Delta_j^{\,0}\\ \Delta_i^{\,0}\end{bmatrix}=\begin{bmatrix}I & \overset{0}{p}_{mk} & \overset{0}{p}_{mj} & \overset{0}{p}_{mi}\\ 0 & I & \overset{0}{p}_{kj} & \overset{0}{p}_{ki}\\ 0 & 0 & I & \overset{0}{p}_{ji}\\ 0 & 0 & 0 & I\end{bmatrix}\begin{bmatrix}\Delta\Delta_m^{\,0}\\ \Delta\Delta_k^{\,0}\\ \Delta\Delta_j^{\,0}\\ \Delta\Delta_i^{\,0}\end{bmatrix}$$

where the reduced p matrices are

$$\overset{0}{p}_{ji}=\begin{bmatrix}1 & x_{ij}\\0 & 1\end{bmatrix}=\begin{bmatrix}1 & 12\\0 & 1\end{bmatrix}=\overset{0}{p}_{kj}=\overset{0}{p}_{mk},\quad \overset{0}{p}_{ki}=\overset{0}{p}_{mj}=\begin{bmatrix}1 & 24\\0 & 1\end{bmatrix}\quad\text{and}\quad \overset{0}{p}_{mi}=\begin{bmatrix}1 & 36\\0 & 1\end{bmatrix}$$

The final displacement vectors computed thus are

$$\Delta_i^{\,0}=\begin{bmatrix}\delta_{iy}^0\\ \theta_{iz}^0\end{bmatrix}=\frac{1}{EI}\begin{bmatrix}-54{,}864\\-8{,}368\end{bmatrix}=10^{-4}\begin{bmatrix}-302.3\\-46.1\end{bmatrix}$$

$$\Delta_j^{\,0}=\frac{1}{EI}\begin{bmatrix}-185{,}898\\-12{,}964\end{bmatrix}=10^{-4}\begin{bmatrix}1{,}024.3\\-71.4\end{bmatrix},\qquad \Delta_k^{\,0}=\frac{1}{EI}\begin{bmatrix}354{,}639\\14{,}804\end{bmatrix}=10^{-4}\begin{bmatrix}-1{,}954.0\\-81.6\end{bmatrix}$$

and

$$\Delta_m^{\,0}=\frac{1}{EI}\begin{bmatrix}-539{,}487\\-16{,}004\end{bmatrix}=10^{-4}\begin{bmatrix}-2{,}972.5\\-88.2\end{bmatrix}$$

5.6. Compute the displacement vector (*5.19*) for the bent cantilever beam of Fig. P-5.6. Assume $EA = 255{,}490$ k and $EI = 58{,}322$ k-ft^2 (W 14X30 steel section).

Equation (*5.19*) expanded out for the given problems is

$$\Delta^0=\begin{bmatrix}\Delta_k^{\,0}\\ \Delta_j^{\,0}\\ \Delta_i^{\,0}\end{bmatrix}=\begin{bmatrix}\overset{0k}{s}_{kk} & \overset{0j}{s}_{kj} & \overset{0i}{s}_{ki}\\ 0 & \overset{0j}{s}_{jj} & \overset{0i}{s}_{ji}\\ 0 & 0 & \overset{0i}{s}_{ii}\end{bmatrix}\begin{bmatrix}f^k_{(kk)} & 0 & 0\\ 0 & f^i_{(jj)} & 0\\ 0 & 0 & f^i_{(ii)}\end{bmatrix}\begin{bmatrix}\overset{k0}{t}_{kk} & 0 & 0\\ \overset{j0}{t}_{jk} & \overset{j0}{t}_{jj} & 0\\ \overset{i0}{t}_{ik} & \overset{i0}{t}_{ij} & \overset{i0}{t}_{ii}\end{bmatrix}\begin{bmatrix}W_k^{\,0}\\ 0\\ 0\end{bmatrix}$$

The segmental flexibility matrix

$$f^k_{(kk)}=\begin{bmatrix}s/EA & 0 & 0\\ 0 & s^3/3EI & s^2/2EI\\ 0 & s^2/2EI & S/EI\end{bmatrix}=f^j_{(jj)}$$

where $s = 13.0$ ft and EA and EI are given values. The segmental flexibility matrix $f^i_{(ii)}$ is the same matrix with $s = 12.0$ ft. The stress transport matrices are

$$\overset{k0}{t}_{kk}=\overset{k0}{\omega}\,\overset{0}{r}_{kk}=\overset{k0}{\omega}$$

$$\overset{j0}{t}_{jj}=\overset{j0}{\omega}\,\overset{0}{r}_{jj}=\overset{j0}{\omega}$$

and similarly,

$$\overset{i0}{t}_{ii}=\overset{i0}{\omega},\qquad \overset{j0}{t}_{jk}=\overset{j0}{\omega}\,\overset{0}{r}_{jk}$$

$$\overset{i0}{t}_{ik}=\overset{i0}{\omega}\,\overset{0}{r}_{ik}\quad\text{and}\quad \overset{i0}{t}_{ij}=\overset{i0}{\omega}\,\overset{0}{r}_{ij}$$

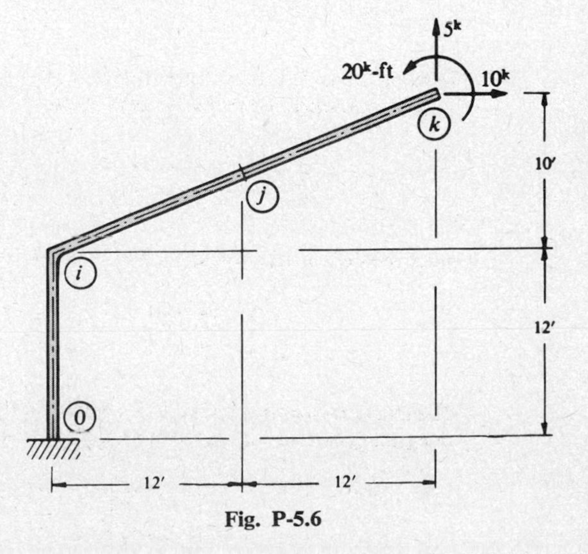

Fig. P-5.6

where

$$\omega^{k0} = \omega^{j0} = \begin{bmatrix} \cos\omega_{k0} & \sin\omega_{k0} & 0 \\ -\sin\omega_{k0} & \cos\omega_{k0} & 0 \\ 0 & 0 & 1 \end{bmatrix} = \begin{bmatrix} 0.923 & 0.385 & 0 \\ -0.385 & 0.923 & 0 \\ 0 & 0 & 1 \end{bmatrix}, \qquad \omega^{i0} = \begin{bmatrix} 0 & 1 & 0 \\ -1 & 0 & 0 \\ 0 & 0 & 1 \end{bmatrix}$$

and

$$r^0_{jk} = r^0_{ij} = \begin{bmatrix} 1 & 0 & 0 \\ 0 & 1 & 0 \\ -5 & 12 & 1 \end{bmatrix}, \qquad r^0_{ik} = \begin{bmatrix} 1 & 0 & 0 \\ 0 & 1 & 0 \\ -10 & 24 & 1 \end{bmatrix}$$

It may be noted that once the matrix t^{s0} is established, s^{0s} is also known since $s^{0s} = t^{s0)T}$.

The load vector $= \{W_k{}^0, 0, 0\}$ where $W_k{}^0 = \{10, 5, 20\}$.

Upon substitution of these values in (*5.19*),

$$\Delta_k{}^0 = 10^{-3}\{17.32, 80.06, 9.25\}, \qquad \Delta_j{}^0 = 10^{-3}\{50.05, 0.06, 3.68\}$$

and

$$\Delta_i{}^0 = 10^{-3}\{49.38, 0.23, -4.12\}$$

GENERAL TRANSFER, SEGMENTAL FLEXIBILITY

5.7. Compute the displacement vector (*5.21*) for the straight simple beam of Fig. P-5.7*a*.

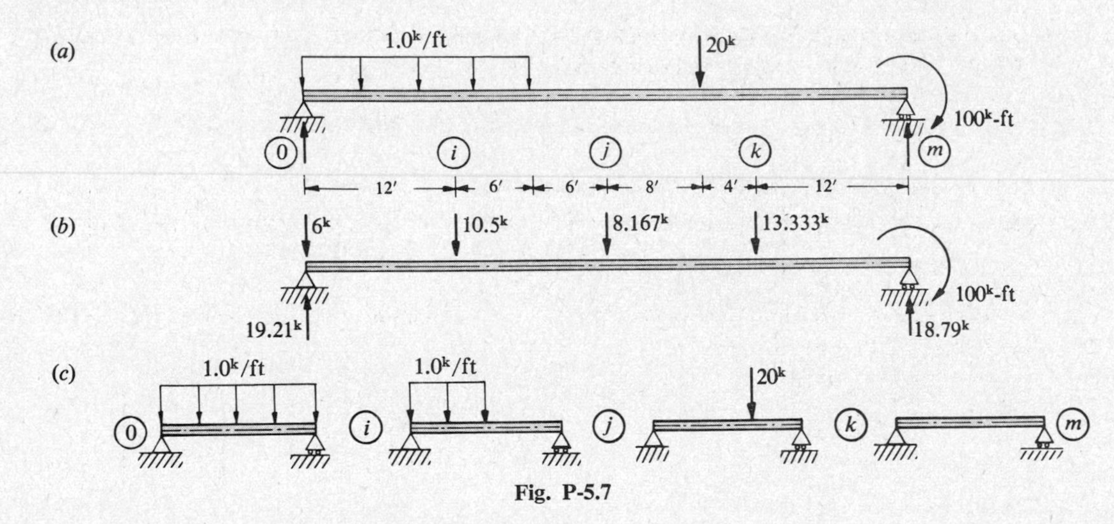

Fig. P-5.7

The development of equation (*5.21*) shown is for the case in which the external loads are all applied at the joints. For cases where loads are of general type, (*5.21*) can be expanded to

$$\Delta^0 = q^{0)T}[f^0 q^0 W^0 + \tau^0]$$

where W^0 represents joint loads statically equivalent to the given loads and τ^0 represents the additional segmental end deformations induced by the loads acting between the joints. This term is comparable to the segmental end deformations $f^0 q^0 W^0$, produced by the segmental end forces.

Figures P-5.7*a*, *b*, *c* show the given beam, statically equivalent joint loads and the segments *oi*, *ij*, *jk* and *km* with the corresponding loads acting between joints.

$$W^0 = \{W_0{}^0, W_i{}^0, W_j{}^0, W_k{}^0, W_m{}^0\}$$

where

$$W_0{}^0 = \begin{bmatrix} 0 \\ 13.21 \\ 0 \end{bmatrix}, \quad W_i{}^0 = \begin{bmatrix} 0 \\ -10.5 \\ 0 \end{bmatrix}, \quad W_j{}^0 = \begin{bmatrix} 0 \\ -8.167 \\ 0 \end{bmatrix}, \quad W_k{}^0 = \begin{bmatrix} 0 \\ -13.333 \\ 0 \end{bmatrix}, \quad W_m{}^0 = \begin{bmatrix} 0 \\ 18.79 \\ -100 \end{bmatrix}$$

The q_0 matrix of (*5.22*) is the matrix of influence coefficients constructed by applying $P_x = +1$, $P_y = +1$ and $Q_z = +1$ at each joint successively.

$$\overset{0}{q} = \begin{bmatrix} 0 & 0 & 0 & 1 & 0 & 0 & 1 & 0 & 0 & 1 & 0 & 0 & 1 & 0 & 0 \\ 0 & 0 & -0.75 & 0 & -9 & 0.25 & 0 & -6 & 0.25 & 0 & -3 & 0.25 & 0 & 0 & 0.25 \\ 0 & 0 & -1 & 0 & 0 & 0 & 0 & 0 & 0 & 0 & 0 & 0 & 0 & 0 & 0 \\ 0 & 0 & 0 & 0 & 0 & 0 & 1 & 0 & 0 & 1 & 0 & 0 & 1 & 0 & 0 \\ 0 & 0 & -0.5 & 0 & -6 & -0.5 & 0 & -12 & 0.5 & 0 & -6 & 0.5 & 0 & 0 & 0.5 \\ 0 & 0 & -0.75 & 0 & -9 & -0.75 & 0 & -6 & 0.25 & 0 & -3 & 0.25 & 0 & 0 & 0.25 \\ 0 & 0 & 0 & 0 & 0 & 0 & 0 & 0 & 0 & 1 & 0 & 0 & 1 & 0 & 0 \\ 0 & 0 & -0.25 & 0 & -3 & -0.25 & 0 & -6 & -0.25 & 0 & -9 & 0.75 & 0 & 0 & 0.75 \\ 0 & 0 & -0.5 & 0 & -6 & -0.5 & 0 & -12 & -0.5 & 0 & -6 & 0.5 & 0 & 0 & 0.5 \\ 0 & 0 & 0 & 0 & 0 & 0 & 0 & 0 & 0 & 0 & 0 & 0 & 1 & 0 & 0 \\ 0 & 0 & 0 & 0 & 0 & 0 & 0 & 0 & 0 & 0 & 0 & 0 & 0 & 0 & 1 \\ 0 & 0 & -0.25 & 0 & -3 & -0.25 & 0 & -6 & -0.25 & 0 & -9 & -0.25 & 0 & 0 & 0.75 \end{bmatrix}$$

The system flexibility chain f^0 is as shown in (*5.23*) where each submatrix is the segmental unit stress flexibility matrix (*5.14*),

$$\overset{0}{f}_{(0i)} = \overset{0}{f}_{(ij)} = \overset{0}{f}_{(jk)} = \overset{0}{f}_{(km)} = \begin{bmatrix} s/EA & 0 & 0 \\ 0 & s/3EI & s/6EI \\ 0 & s/6EI & s/3EI \end{bmatrix} = \frac{1}{EI}\begin{bmatrix} 12EI/EA & 0 & 0 \\ 0 & 4 & 2 \\ 0 & 2 & 4 \end{bmatrix}$$

The τ vector is constructed by computing the segmental end deformations using the load flexibility coefficients of Table 5-2 and using integration in case of distributed loads. Thus

$$\overset{0}{\tau} = \{\overset{0}{\tau}_{(0i)},\ \overset{0}{\tau}_{(ij)},\ \overset{0}{\tau}_{(jk)},\ \overset{0}{\tau}_{(km)}\}$$

where $\overset{0}{\tau}_{(0i)} = \dfrac{1}{EI}\begin{bmatrix} 0 \\ 72 \\ 72 \end{bmatrix}$, $\quad \overset{0}{\tau}_{(ij)} = \dfrac{1}{EI}\begin{bmatrix} 0 \\ 31.5 \\ 40.5 \end{bmatrix}$, $\quad \overset{0}{\tau}_{(jk)} = \dfrac{1}{EI}\begin{bmatrix} 0 \\ 177.78 \\ 142.22 \end{bmatrix}$, $\quad \overset{0}{\tau}_{(km)} = \begin{bmatrix} 0 \\ 0 \\ 0 \end{bmatrix}$

Having established all necessary values, the displacement vector $\Delta^0 = \{\Delta_0{}^0, \Delta_i{}^0, \Delta_j{}^0, \Delta_k{}^0, \Delta_m{}^0\}$ is easily computed. The following values are thus obtained:

$$\Delta_0{}^0 = \frac{1}{EI}\begin{bmatrix} 0 \\ 0 \\ -3{,}187 \end{bmatrix}, \quad \Delta_i{}^0 = \frac{1}{EI}\begin{bmatrix} 0 \\ -33{,}572 \\ -2{,}092 \end{bmatrix}, \quad \Delta_j{}^0 = \frac{1}{EI}\begin{bmatrix} 0 \\ -45{,}994 \\ 77 \end{bmatrix}$$

$$\Delta_k{}^0 = \frac{1}{EI}\begin{bmatrix} 0 \\ -31{,}180 \\ 2{,}296 \end{bmatrix}, \quad \Delta_m{}^0 = \frac{1}{EI}\begin{bmatrix} 0 \\ 0 \\ 2{,}449 \end{bmatrix}$$

5.8. Compute the displacement vector Δ_2 (displacements of the intermediate hinge) in the three-hinged frame of Fig. P-5.8*a* below. Consider only flexural deformations and assume EI to be constant for the entire frame.

Since for the frame shown the loads given are of general type, the general form of (*5.21*) discussed in Problem 5.7 will be used:

$$\Delta^0 = q^{0)T}[f^0 q^0 W^0 + \tau^0]$$

where W^0 are statically equivalent joint loads for the given loads and τ^0 are segmental end deformations due to loads acting between the joints. Figures P-5.8*a*, *b*, and *c* show the given frame, equivalent joint loads and segmental end deformations of segment 12. From Fig. P-5.8*b*, the joint load vector

$$W^0 = \{W_0{}^0, W_1{}^0, W_2{}^0, W_3{}^0, W_4{}^0\}$$

where $W_0^0 = \begin{bmatrix} 2.25 \\ 16.75 \\ 0 \end{bmatrix}$, $W_1^0 = \begin{bmatrix} 5 \\ -12 \\ 0 \end{bmatrix}$, $W_2^0 = \begin{bmatrix} 0 \\ -12 \\ 0 \end{bmatrix}$, $W_3^0 = \begin{bmatrix} 0 \\ 0 \\ 0 \end{bmatrix}$ and $W_4^0 = \begin{bmatrix} -7.25 \\ 7.25 \\ 0 \end{bmatrix}$

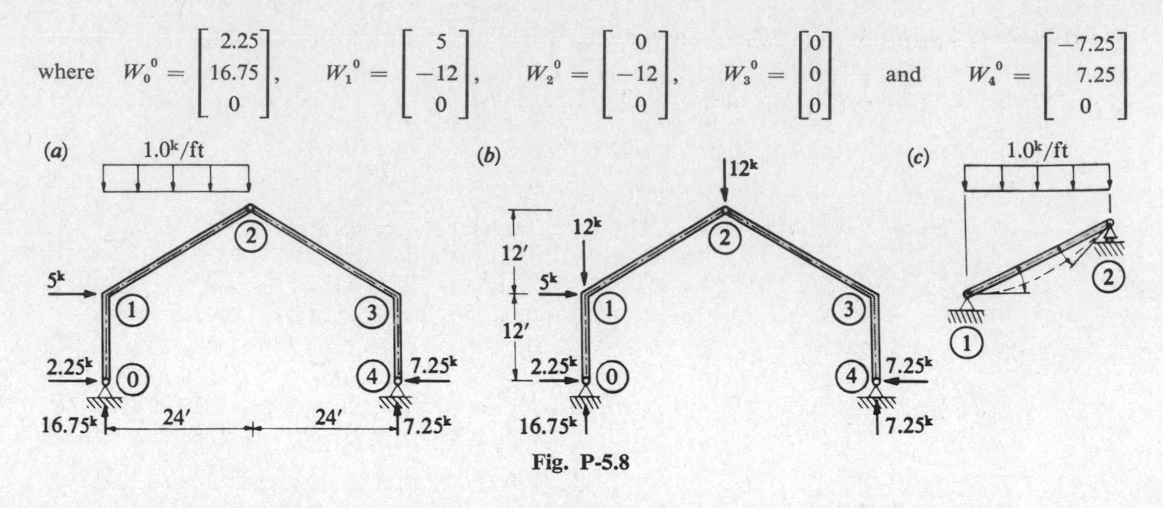

Fig. P-5.8

Since only flexural deformations are considered, the system flexibility chain f^0 becomes

$$f^0 = \begin{bmatrix} f^0_{(01)} & 0 & 0 & 0 \\ 0 & f^0_{(12)} & 0 & 0 \\ 0 & 0 & f^0_{(23)} & 0 \\ 0 & 0 & 0 & f^0_{(34)} \end{bmatrix}_{(8\times 8)}$$

where

$$f^0_{(01)} = f^0_{(34)} = \frac{1}{EI}\begin{bmatrix} \frac{12}{3} & \frac{12}{6} \\ \frac{12}{6} & \frac{12}{3} \end{bmatrix} \quad \text{and} \quad f^0_{(12)} = f^0_{(23)} = \frac{1}{EI}\begin{bmatrix} \frac{26.832}{3} & \frac{26.832}{6} \\ \frac{26.832}{6} & \frac{26.832}{3} \end{bmatrix}$$

The matrix q^0 becomes the segmental end moment influence coefficient matrix (8×15) and is constructed by applying unit values of P_x, P_y and Q_z at each joint and computing the end moments of the segments:

$$q^0 = \begin{bmatrix} 0 & 0 & -0.75 & 9 & 0 & 0.25 & 6 & 6 & 0.25 & 3 & 0 & -0.25 & 0 & 0 & -0.25 \\ 0 & 0 & -1 & 0 & 0 & 0 & 0 & 0 & 0 & 0 & 0 & 0 & 0 & 0 & 0 \\ 0 & 0 & 0 & 0 & 0 & 0 & 0 & 0 & 1 & 0 & 0 & 0 & 0 & 0 & 0 \\ 0 & 0 & -0.75 & 9 & 0 & -0.75 & 6 & 6 & 0.25 & 3 & 0 & -0.25 & 0 & 0 & -0.25 \\ 0 & 0 & 0.25 & -3 & 0 & 0.25 & -6 & 6 & 0.25 & -9 & 0 & 0.75 & 0 & 0 & 0.75 \\ 0 & 0 & 0 & 0 & 0 & 0 & 0 & 0 & 0 & 0 & 0 & 0 & 0 & 0 & 0 \\ 0 & 0 & 0 & 0 & 0 & 0 & 0 & 0 & 0 & 0 & 0 & 0 & 0 & 0 & 0 \\ 0 & 0 & 0.25 & -3 & 0 & 0.25 & -6 & 6 & 0.25 & -9 & 0 & -0.25 & 0 & 0 & 0.75 \end{bmatrix}$$

The τ vector is also a reduced vector as follows and the end slopes of the segments are computed using the load flexibility matrix coefficient from Table 5-2 and integrating in case of the distributed load:

$$\tau^0 = \{\tau^0_{(01)}, \tau^0_{(12)}, \tau^0_{(23)}, \tau^0_{(34)}\}_{(8\times 1)}$$

where $\tau^0_{(01)} = \tau^0_{(23)} = \tau^0_{(34)} = \begin{bmatrix} 0 \\ 0 \end{bmatrix}$ and $\tau^0_{(12)} = \frac{1}{EI}\begin{bmatrix} 643.968 \\ 643.968 \end{bmatrix}$

The values established for W^0, f^0, q^0 and τ^0 can now be substituted in the equation for joint deformations Δ^0. The required deformation vector Δ_2^0 then extracted from

$$\Delta^0 = \{\Delta_0^0, \Delta_1^0. \Delta_2^0, \Delta_3^0, \Delta_4^0\}$$

is

$$\Delta_2^0 = \begin{bmatrix} \Delta^0_{2x} \\ \Delta^0_{2y} \\ \theta^0_{2z} \end{bmatrix} = \frac{1}{EI}\begin{bmatrix} 8524 \\ -4990 \\ 315 \end{bmatrix}$$

STRING POLYGON FLEXIBILITY MATRIX

5.9. Using the string polygon matrix (*5.27*), determine δ_{iy}, δ_{jy}, δ_{ky} in the straight simple beam of Problem 5.7.

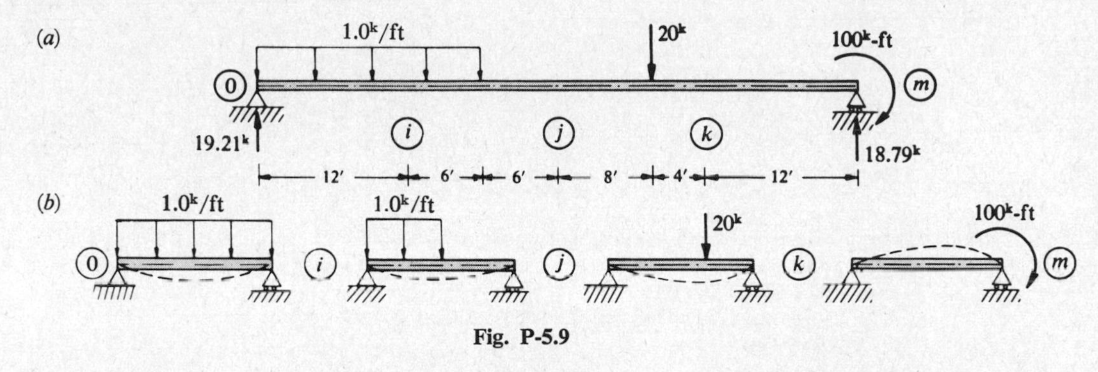

Fig. P-5.9

The points *i, j, k* chosen divide the given beam into four equal segments. The simple span equivalents of these segments are shown in Fig. P-5.9*b*, from which their end slopes (τ values) are calculated using Table 5-2 or any other standard tables. The 100 k-ft end moment at *m* is considered an applied load on segment *km*.

$$\tau_{0i} = \tau_{i0} = \frac{\omega l^3}{24\,EI} = \frac{1(12)^3}{24\,EI} = \frac{72}{EI}$$

$$\tau_{ij} = \frac{9\omega l^3}{384\,EI} = \frac{9(1)(12)^3}{384\,EI} = \frac{40.5}{EI}, \qquad \tau_{ji} = \frac{7\omega l^3}{384\,EI} = \frac{31.5}{EI}$$

$$\tau_{jk} = \frac{Pab(l+b)}{6lEI} = \frac{20(8)(4)(16)}{6(12)\,EI} = \frac{142.22}{EI}, \qquad \tau_{kj} = \frac{Pab(l+a)}{6lEI} = \frac{177.78}{EI}$$

$$\tau_{km} = \frac{ML}{6EI} = \frac{-100(12)}{6EI} = \frac{-200}{EI}, \qquad \tau_{mk} = \frac{ML}{3EI} = \frac{-400}{EI}$$

The elements of τ matrix therefore become

$$\tau_i = \tau_{i0} + \tau_{ij} = 112.5/EI, \qquad \tau_j = \tau_{ji} + \tau_{jk} = 173.72/EI, \qquad \tau_k = \tau_{kj} + \tau_{km} = -22.22/EI$$

The flexibility matrix
$$f = \frac{1}{EI}\begin{bmatrix} 8 & 2 & 0 \\ 2 & 8 & 2 \\ 0 & 2 & 8 \end{bmatrix}$$

where the elements on the main diagonal represent the sum of the near end angular flexibilities at each of points *i, j* and *k* of the simply supported beam segments of 12 ft span each. The off diagonal elements are the far end angular flexibilities of the same segments.

The vector $M = \{158.5, 191.0, 125.5\}$ where the moments M_i, M_j and M_k are computed by simple statics from Fig. P-5.9*a*.

The matrix $m = \begin{bmatrix} 9 & 6 & 3 \\ 6 & 12 & 6 \\ 3 & 6 & 9 \end{bmatrix}$ is computed using (*5.28*) and Fig. 5-11. Then by (*5.27*) the deflection vector δ becomes

$$\begin{bmatrix} \delta_{iy} \\ \delta_{jy} \\ \delta_{ky} \end{bmatrix} = \frac{1}{EI}\begin{bmatrix} 9 & 6 & 3 \\ 6 & 12 & 6 \\ 3 & 6 & 9 \end{bmatrix}\begin{bmatrix} 8 & 2 & 0 \\ 2 & 8 & 2 \\ 0 & 2 & 8 \end{bmatrix}\begin{bmatrix} 158.5 \\ 191.0 \\ 125.5 \end{bmatrix} + \frac{1}{EI}\begin{bmatrix} 9 & 6 & 3 \\ 6 & 12 & 6 \\ 3 & 6 & 3 \end{bmatrix}\begin{bmatrix} 112.50 \\ 173.72 \\ -22.22 \end{bmatrix}$$

$$= \frac{1}{EI}\begin{bmatrix} 33{,}572 \\ 45{,}994 \\ 31{,}180 \end{bmatrix} = 10^{-3}\begin{bmatrix} 146.1 \\ 200.2 \\ 135.7 \end{bmatrix} \quad \text{for } EI = 229{,}784 \text{ k-ft}^2$$

5.10. Using the string polygon matrix (*5.27*), determine δ_{iy}, δ_{jy}, δ_{ky}, δ_{my} in the straight cantilever beam of Problem 5.5.

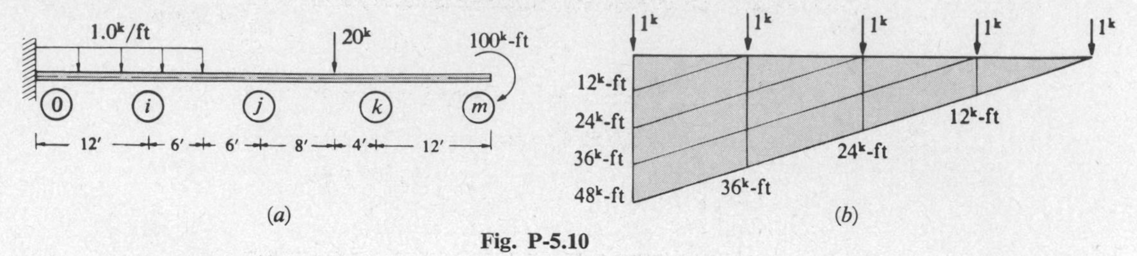

Fig. P-5.10

The geometry of the beam and the loading shown in Fig. P-5.10*a* are the same as those of Fig. P-5.9*a*, except for the support conditions. Previously calculated τ values can therefore be used and the end moment of 100 k-ft is again considered as an applied load.

All five stations are involved in this case and the flexibility matrix becomes

$$f = \frac{1}{EI}\begin{bmatrix} 4 & 2 & 0 & 0 & 0 \\ 2 & 8 & 2 & 0 & 0 \\ 0 & 2 & 8 & 2 & 0 \\ 0 & 0 & 2 & 8 & 2 \\ 0 & 0 & 0 & 2 & 4 \end{bmatrix}$$

The moment vector can be verified to be $M = \{-902, -518, -260, -100, 0\}$.

The τ vector is $1/EI\{72.0, 112.5, 173.72, -22.22, -400.0\}$.

The m matrix of moment influence coefficients is obtained from Fig. P-5.10*b* which shows the moments induced by a unit load applied at each station. Then

$$m^T = \begin{bmatrix} 0 & 0 & 0 & 0 & 0 \\ -12 & 0 & 0 & 0 & 0 \\ -24 & -12 & 0 & 0 & 0 \\ -36 & -24 & -12 & 0 & 0 \\ -48 & -36 & -24 & -12 & 0 \end{bmatrix}$$

Substitution in the string polygon matrix equation (*5.27*) gives the following deflection vector:

$$\delta = \begin{bmatrix} \delta_{oy} \\ \delta_{iy} \\ \delta_{jy} \\ \delta_{ky} \\ \delta_{my} \end{bmatrix} = \frac{1}{EI}\begin{bmatrix} 0 \\ 54{,}864 \\ 185{,}994 \\ 354{,}831 \\ 539{,}775 \end{bmatrix} = 10^{-4}\begin{bmatrix} 0 \\ 302 \\ 1{,}025 \\ 1{,}915 \\ 2{,}974 \end{bmatrix} \qquad \text{for } EI = 1{,}814{,}900 \text{ k-ft}^2$$

CONJUGATE BEAM

5.11. Using the elasto-static analogy (*5.8*), verify results of Problem 5.9.

Figures P-5.11*a*, *b*, and *c* respectively show the given beam, the bending moment diagram and the conjugate beam loaded by the joint elastic loads. The joint elastic loads γ's are calculated using (*5.25*) and the values computed in Problem 5.9. These joint elastic loads can also be verified to be the statical equivalents of the M/EI diagram acting as distributed conjugate load on segments *oi*, *ij*, *jk* and *km*. (See also Problems 3.6, 7.)

Accordingly

$$\gamma_o = [4(0.0) + 2(158.5) + 72.0]/EI = 389.0/EI$$
$$\gamma_i = [2(0.0) + 8(158.5) + 2(191.0) + 112.5]/EI = 1762.5/EI$$
$$\gamma_j = [2(158.5) + 8(191.0) + 2(125.5) + 173.72]/EI = 2269.72/EI$$
$$\gamma_k = [2(191.0) + 8(125.5) + 2(0.0) - 22.22]/EI = 1363.78/EI$$
$$\gamma_m = [2(125.5) + 4(0.0) - 400.0]/EI = -149.00/EI$$

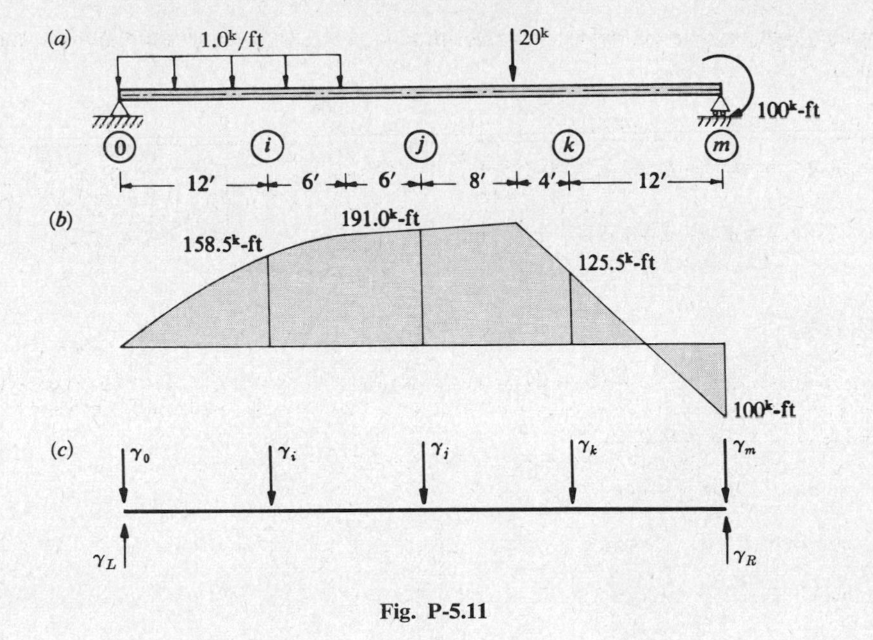

Fig. P-5.11

Simple statical calculations give the moments on the conjugate beam which represent deflections on the given beam. Thus

$$\delta_{iy} = 33{,}572/EI = 0.146 \text{ ft}$$

$$\delta_{jy} = 45{,}994/EI = 0.200 \text{ ft}$$

$$\delta_{ky} = 31{,}180/EI = 0.136 \text{ ft}$$

5.12. Using the elasto-static analogy (*5.8*), verify results of Problem 5.10.

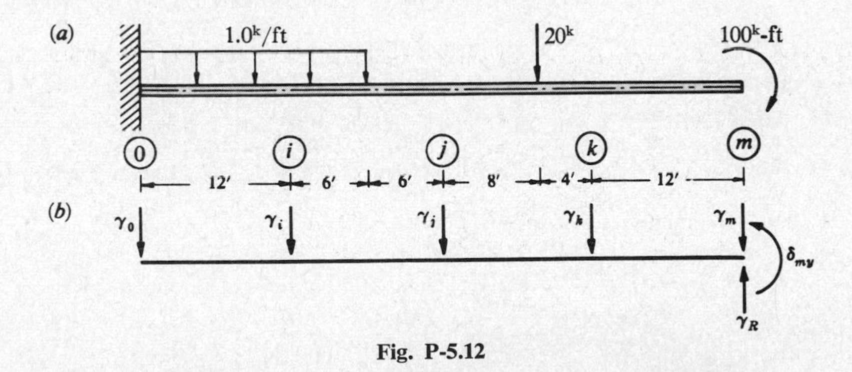

Fig. P-5.12

Figures P-5.12*a* and *b* respectively show the given beam with its loads and the corresponding conjugate beam with the joint elastic loads. The end conditions on the conjugate beam are chosen to be consistent with the end constraints of the real beam. The elastic loads are computed using (*5.25*) and the values computed in Problem 5-10.

Accordingly

$$\gamma_0 = [4(-902) + 2(-518) + 72.0]/EI = -4572.0/EI$$

$$\gamma_i = [2(-902) + 8(-518) + 2(-260) + 112.5]/EI = -6{,}355.5/EI$$

$$\gamma_j = [2(-518) + 8(-260) + 2(-100) + 173.72]/EI = -3{,}142.28/EI$$

$$\gamma_k = [2(-260) + 8(-100) + 2(0) - 22.22]/EI = -1{,}342.22/EI$$

$$\gamma_m = [2(-100) + 4(0) - 400]/EI = -600/EI$$

The deflection values are calculated by simply computing the bending moments on the conjugate beam. These values are

$$\delta = \begin{bmatrix} \delta_{oy} \\ \delta_{iy} \\ \delta_{jy} \\ \delta_{ky} \\ \delta_{my} \end{bmatrix} = \frac{1}{EI} \begin{bmatrix} 0 \\ 54{,}864 \\ 185{,}994 \\ 354{,}831 \\ 539{,}775 \end{bmatrix} = 10^{-4} \begin{bmatrix} 0 \\ 302 \\ 1{,}025 \\ 1{,}915 \\ 2{,}974 \end{bmatrix}$$

Supplementary Problems

5.13. Compute the values of the redundants of Problem 5.1 for $P_1 = 5$ k, $P_2 = 20$ k and $Q_3 = 50$ k-ft. Assume EI to be constant.

5.14. Compute the values of the redundants of Problem 5.2 for $P_1 = 5$ k, $P_2 = 20$ k and $Q_3 = 50$ k-ft. Assume EI to be constant.

5.15. Using the arrangement shown in Fig. 5-2, compute the support moments of the four span continuous beam shown in Fig. P-5.15. Consider only flexural deformations and assume EI to be constant.

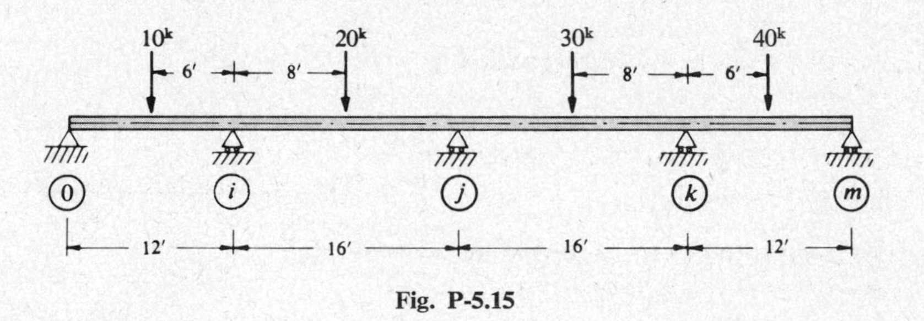

Fig. P-5.15

5.16. Compute the displacement vector (*5.18*) for the straight cantilever bar of Fig. P-5.16. The beam is a W 27×94 steel section and $E = 29{,}000$ k/in².

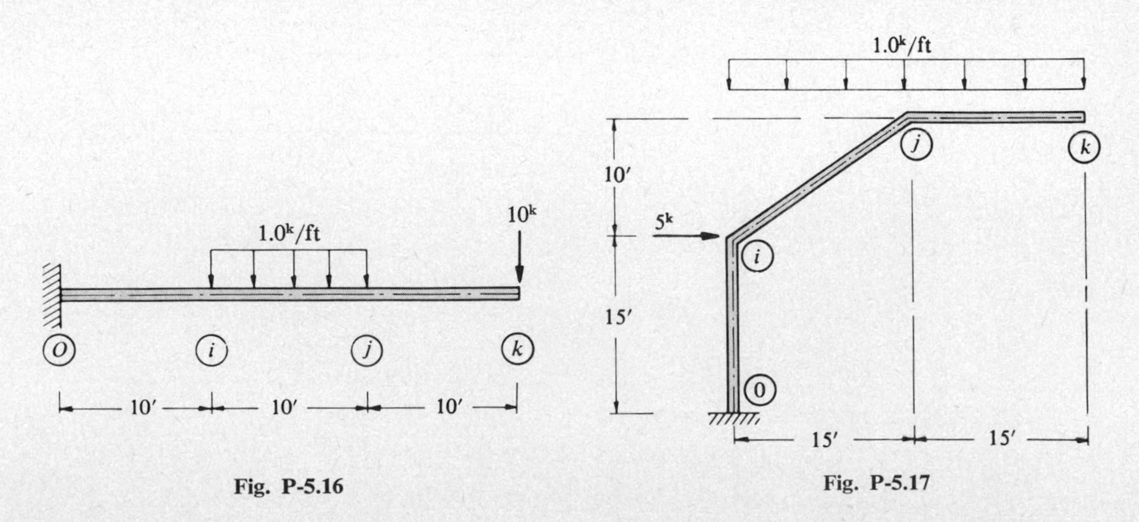

Fig. P-5.16

Fig. P-5.17

5.17. Compute the displacements Δ_k^0 of the bent cantilever of Fig. P-5.17. Assume EA and EI for segment oi to be twice as large as for segments ij and jk.

5.18. Compute the displacement vector (*5.21*) for the straight simple beam of Fig. P-5.18. Assume EA = 648,730 k and EI = 422,200 k-ft².

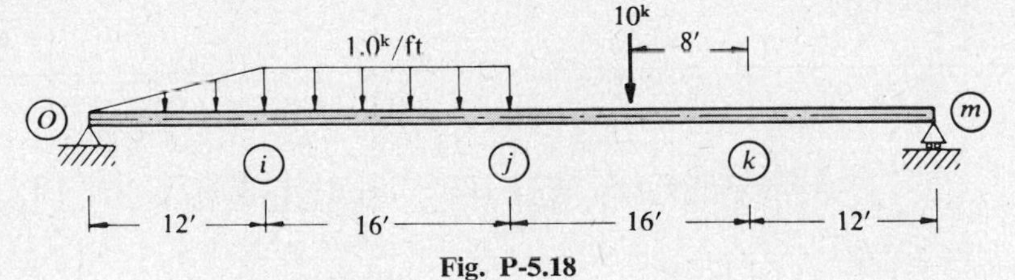

Fig. P-5.18

5.19. Compute the displacement vector (*5.21*) for the straight beam of Fig. P-5.19. Consider only flexural deformations. The beam has a constant cross section.

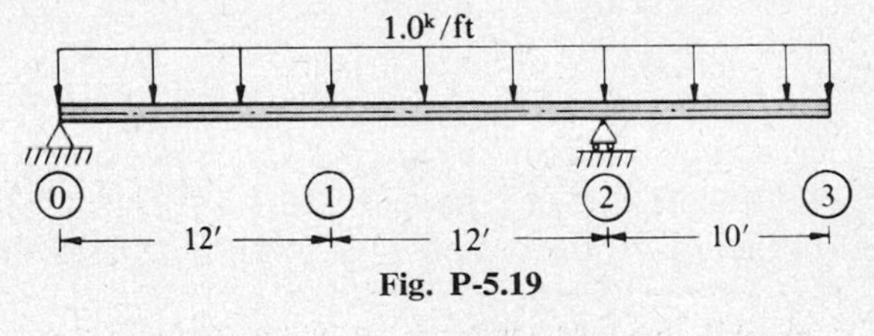

Fig. P-5.19

5.20. Using (*5.21*) for flexural deformation only, compute the displacement Δ_4^0 for the frame shown in Fig. P-2.10. Assume the frame to have a constant cross section.

5.21. Considering flexural deformations only, compute the displacement vector (*5.21*) for the three hinged frame shown in Fig. P-5.21. EI is constant.

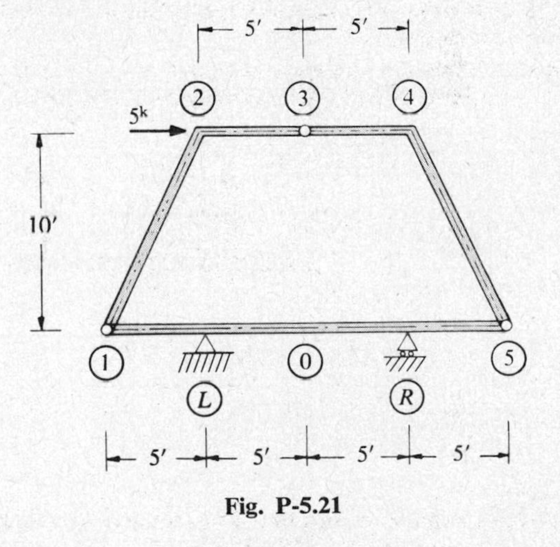

Fig. P-5.21

5.22. Solve Problem 5.16 for deflections by the string polygon matrix equation (*5.27*).

5.23. Solve Problem 5.18 for deflections by the string polygon matrix equation (*5.27*).

5.24. Using the elasto-static analogy (Sec. 5.10), verify the results of Problem 5.18.

5.25. Use the elasto-static analogy (Sec. 5.10) to solve for the deflections of the compound beam of Problem 3.16.

5.26. Verify the results of Problem 5.19 by the elasto-static analogy.

Chapter 6

Variable Cross Section

6.1 INTEGRAND

If the *cross section* of the bar *varies* along its entire length or along one or more segments of the bar, the *area* of the cross section and its *moment of inertia* become *variables* and add considerably to the difficulty of integration (Tables 5-1 and 5-2). In some instances it is possible to carry out the exact integration. In other cases it is not possible to proceed with the given function, and a substitute function or substitute model must be introduced.

Three classes of methods are available for this evaluation:

(1) Integration methods.

(2) Analogies.

(3) Matrix methods.

The most common applications of these methods are discussed in this chapter.

6.2 ALGEBRAIC INTEGRATION

If the cross section is *rectangular* and its *variation* is *linear* or *parabolic* in one or two directions (depth, width or both), the closed form evaluation of the flexibility integral is possible and practical.

Two typical cases,

(*a*) *linear variation* in Y-direction

(*b*) *parabolic variation* in Y-direction

are considered and their component integrals recorded in the respective table (Tables 6-1 and 6-2). The segmental flexibilities in terms of these component integrals are then given in Tables 6-3 and 6-4. The equivalents used in these tables are

$$A = A_L U \qquad I = I_L U^3 \tag{6.1}$$

$$R_{nk} = \int_0^k \frac{u^n\,du}{U} \qquad Q_{nk} = \int_0^k \frac{u^n\,du}{U^3} \qquad [n = 0, 1, 2,...] \tag{6.2}$$

where s = bar length, u = variable position parameter ($x = su$), k = constant position parameter ($a = sk$), A, I = area and moment of inertia of cross section at su respectively, A_L, I_L = area and moment of inertia of cross section at L respectively, U = parameter of variation.

For the derivation and additional discussion refer to Problems 6.1-6.4.

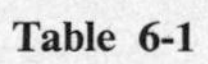

Table 6-1

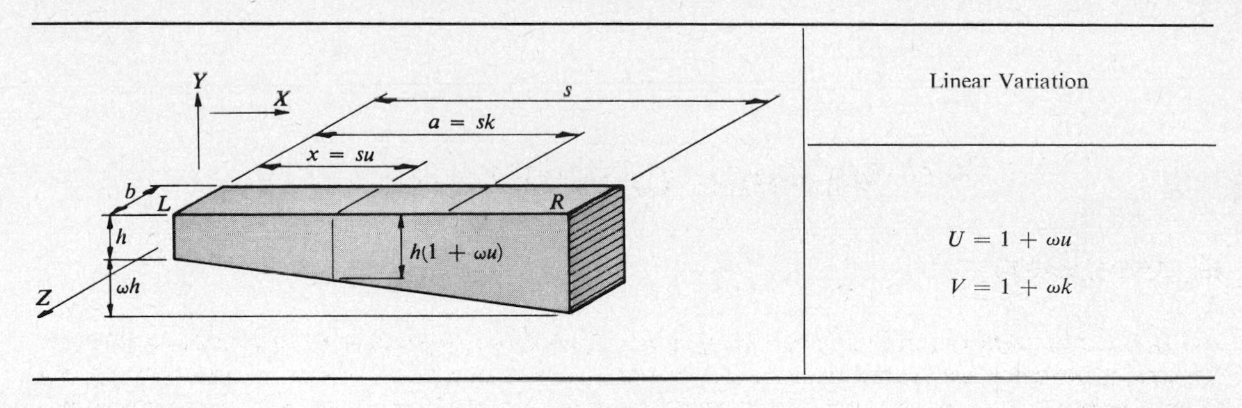

Linear Variation

$$U = 1 + \omega u$$

$$V = 1 + \omega k$$

R-Functions

$$R_{0k} = \int_0^k \frac{du}{U} = \frac{1}{\omega} \ln V$$

$$R_{1k} = \int_0^k \frac{u\,du}{U} = \frac{1}{\omega^2} [\omega k - \ln V]$$

$$R_{2k} = \int_0^k \frac{u^2\,du}{U} = \frac{1}{\omega^3} \left[\frac{\omega k}{2} (\omega k - 2) + \ln V \right]$$

$$R_{3k} = \int_0^k \frac{u^3\,du}{U} = \frac{1}{\omega^4} \left[\frac{\omega k}{6} (6 - 3\omega k + 2\omega^2 k^2) - \ln V \right]$$

$$R_{4k} = \int_0^k \frac{u^4\,du}{U} = \frac{1}{\omega^5} \left[\frac{\omega k}{12} (3\omega^3 k^3 - 4\omega^2 k^2 + 6\omega k - 12) + \ln V \right]$$

$$R_{5k} = \int_0^k \frac{u^5\,du}{U} = \frac{1}{\omega^6} \left[\frac{\omega k}{60} (12\omega^4 k^4 - 15\omega^3 k^3 + 20\omega^2 k^2 - 30\omega k + 60) - \ln V \right]$$

Q-Functions

$$Q_{0k} = \int_0^k \frac{du}{U^3} = \frac{k(2 + \omega k)}{2V^2}$$

$$Q_{1k} = \int_0^k \frac{u\,du}{U^3} = \frac{k^2}{2V^2}$$

$$Q_{2k} = \int_0^k \frac{u^2\,du}{U^3} = \frac{1}{\omega^3} \left[\ln V - \frac{\omega k(2 + 3\omega k)}{2V^2} \right]$$

$$Q_{3k} = \int_0^k \frac{u^3\,du}{U^3} = \frac{1}{\omega^4} \left[\frac{\omega k(6 + 9\omega k + 2\omega^2 k^2)}{2V^2} - 3 \ln V \right]$$

$$Q_{4k} = \int_0^k \frac{u^4\,du}{U^3} = \frac{1}{\omega^5} \left[\frac{\omega k(2 + \omega k)(\omega^2 k^2 - 6\omega k - 6)}{2V^2} + 6 \ln V \right]$$

$$Q_{5k} = \int_0^k \frac{u^5\,du}{U^3} = \frac{1}{\omega^6} \left[\frac{\omega k(60 + 90\omega k + 20\omega^2 k^2 - 5\omega^3 k^3 + 2\omega^4 k^4)}{6V^2} - 10 \ln V \right]$$

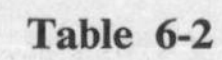
Table 6-2

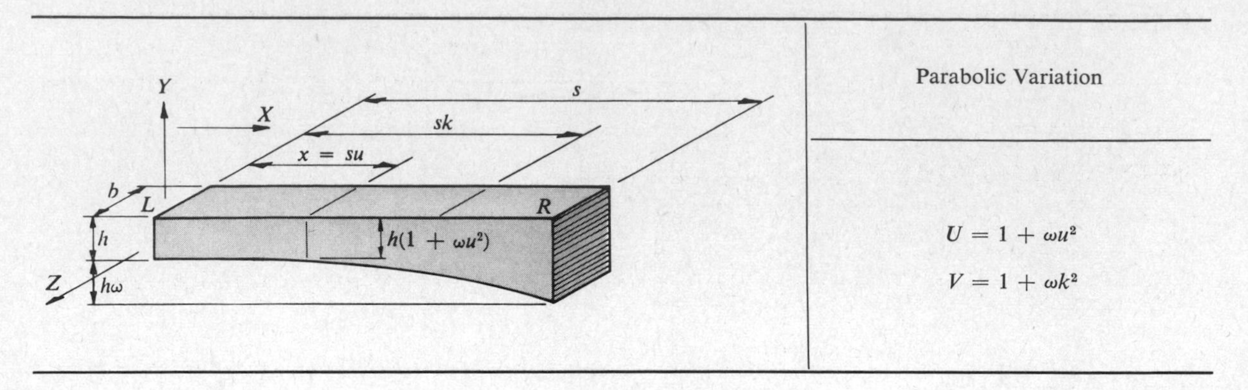

Parabolic Variation

$U = 1 + \omega u^2$

$V = 1 + \omega k^2$

R-Functions

$$R_{0k} = \int_0^k \frac{du}{U} = \frac{\tan^{-1} k\sqrt{\omega}}{\sqrt{\omega}}$$

$$R_{1k} = \int_0^k \frac{u\,du}{U} = \frac{\ln V}{2\omega}$$

$$R_{2k} = \int_0^k \frac{u^2\,du}{U} = \frac{k}{\omega}\left[1 - \frac{\tan^{-1} k\sqrt{\omega}}{k\sqrt{\omega}}\right]$$

$$R_{3k} = \int_0^k \frac{u^3\,du}{U} = \frac{k^2}{2\omega}\left[1 - \frac{\ln V}{\omega k^2}\right]$$

$$R_{4k} = \int_0^k \frac{u^4\,du}{U} = \frac{k}{\omega^2}\left[\frac{\omega k^2 - 3}{3} + \frac{\tan^{-1} k\sqrt{\omega}}{k\sqrt{\omega}}\right]$$

$$R_{5k} = \int_0^k \frac{u^5\,du}{U} = \frac{k^2}{2\omega^2}\left[\frac{\omega k^2 - 2}{2} + \frac{\ln V}{\omega k^2}\right]$$

Q-Functions

$$Q_{0k} = \int_0^k \frac{du}{U^3} = \frac{k}{8}\left[\frac{5 + 3\omega k^2}{V^2} + \frac{3\tan^{-1} k\sqrt{\omega}}{k\sqrt{\omega}}\right]$$

$$Q_{1k} = \int_0^k \frac{u\,du}{U^3} = \frac{k^2(2 + \omega k^2)}{4V^2}$$

$$Q_{2k} = \int_0^k \frac{u^2\,du}{U^3} = \frac{k}{8\omega}\left[\frac{\omega k^2 - 1}{V^2} + \frac{\tan^{-1} k\sqrt{\omega}}{k\sqrt{\omega}}\right]$$

$$Q_{3k} = \int_0^k \frac{u^3\,du}{U^3} = \frac{k^4}{4V^2}$$

$$Q_{4k} = \int_0^k \frac{u^4\,du}{U^3} = \frac{k}{8\omega^2}\left[\frac{3\tan^{-1} k\sqrt{\omega}}{k\sqrt{\omega}} - \frac{3 + 5\omega k^2}{V^2}\right]$$

$$Q_{5k} = \int_0^k \frac{u^5\,du}{U^3} = \frac{1}{\omega^3}\left[\frac{1}{2}\ln V - \frac{\omega k^2(2 + 3\omega k^2)}{4V^2}\right]$$

Table 6-3. Segmental Flexibilities, Cantilever Beam

Unit Cause	Coefficients ($k = 1$)	
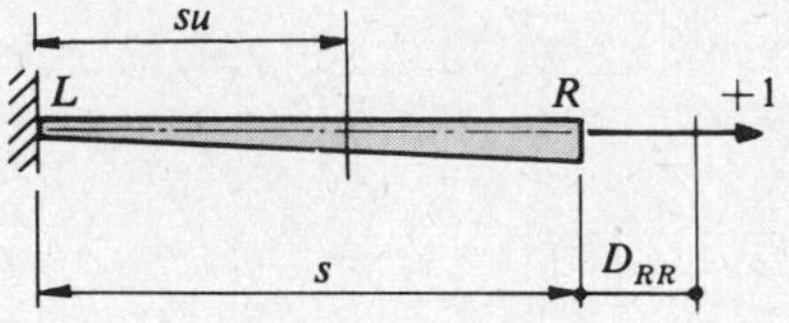 su, L, R, $+1$, s, D_{RR}	$D_{RR} = \dfrac{s}{EA_L} R_0$	
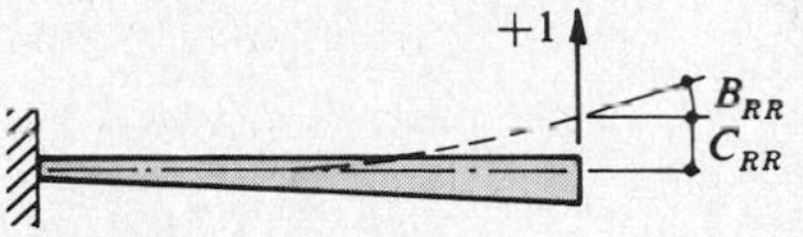 $+1$, B_{RR}, C_{RR}	$C_{RR} = \dfrac{s^3}{EI_L}(Q_0 - 2Q_1 + Q_2)$	$B_{RR} = \dfrac{s^2}{EI_L}(Q_0 - Q_1)$
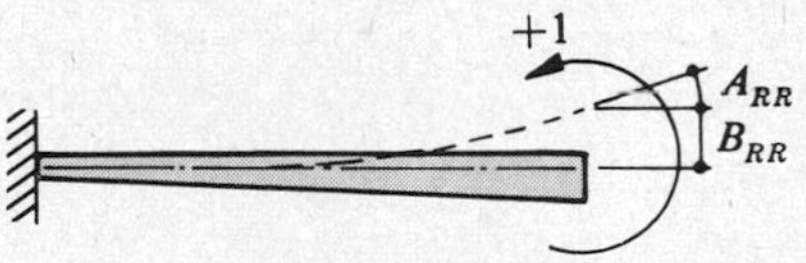 $+1$, A_{RR}, B_{RR}	$B_{RR} = \dfrac{s^2}{EI_L}(Q_0 - Q_1)$	$A_{RR} = \dfrac{s}{EI_L} Q_0$

Note: For unit load flexibilities refer to Problem 6.3.

Table 6-4. Segmental Flexibilities, Simple Beam

Unit Cause	Coefficients ($k = 1$)	
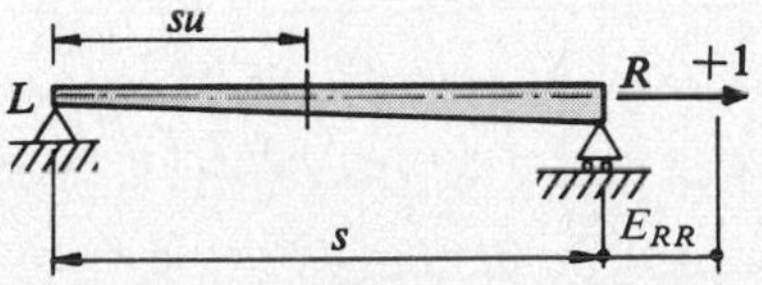 su, L, R, $+1$, s, E_{RR}	$E_{RR} = \dfrac{s}{EA_L} R_0$	
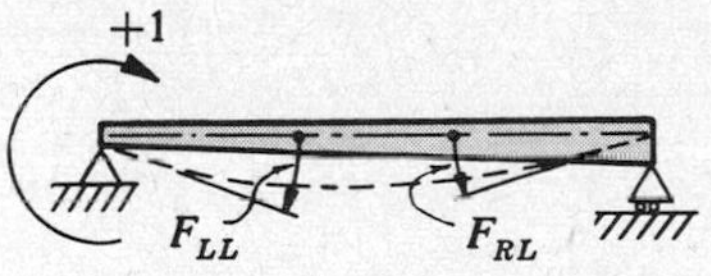 $+1$, F_{LL}, F_{RL}	$F_{LL} = \dfrac{s}{EI_L}(Q_0 - 2Q_1 + Q_2)$	$F_{RL} = \dfrac{s}{EI_L}(Q_1 - Q_2)$
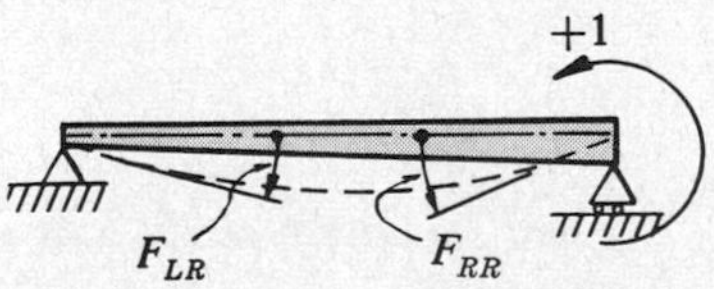 $+1$, F_{LR}, F_{RR}	$F_{LR} = \dfrac{s}{EI_L}(Q_1 - Q_2)$	$F_{RR} = \dfrac{s}{EI_L} Q_2$
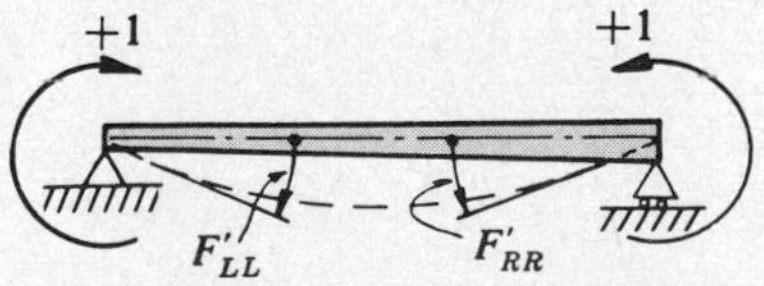 $+1$, $+1$, F'_{LL}, F'_{RR}	$F'_{LL} = \dfrac{s}{EI_L}(Q_0 - Q_1)$	$F'_{RR} = \dfrac{s}{EI_L} Q_1$
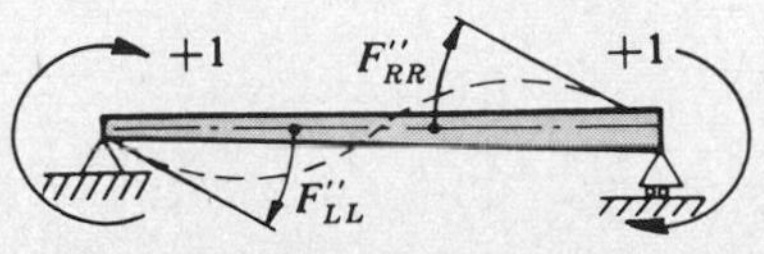 $+1$, F''_{RR}, $+1$, F''_{LL}	$F''_{LL} = \dfrac{s}{EI_L}(Q_0 - 3Q_1 + Q_3)$	$F''_{RR} = \dfrac{s}{EI_L}(Q_0 - 2Q_1)$

Note: For unit load flexibilities refer to Problem 6.4.

6.3 SUBSTITUTE INTEGRATION

In cases of *I-beams, T-beams or box beams* (Fig. 6-1) having *linear* or *curvilinear variation* of cross section in one or two directions (wedged beams), the moment of inertia becomes a polynomial of higher degree and the evaluation of Q_{nk} is not feasible.

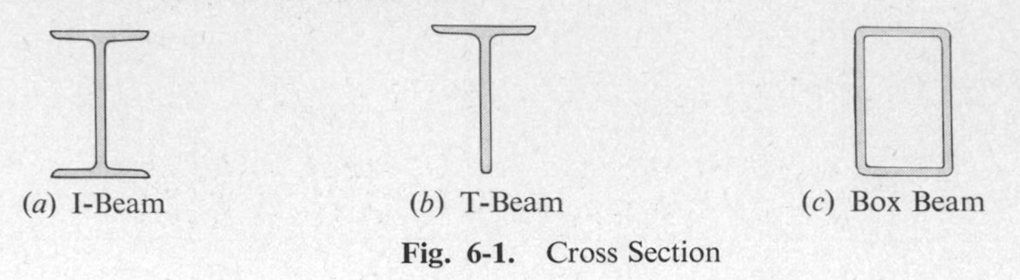

(*a*) I-Beam (*b*) T-Beam (*c*) Box Beam

Fig. 6-1. Cross Section

(*a*) *Linear Variation*

In order to surmount the difficulty, the variation of A and I in this case (Fig. 6-2*a*) can be represented with sufficient accuracy as

$$A_u = A_L(1+\omega u)^\mu = A_L U^\mu \qquad I_u = I_L(1+\omega u)^\rho = I_L U^\rho \tag{6.3}$$

where

$$\omega = h_R/h_L - 1, \quad \mu = (\log A_R - \log A_L)/(\log h_R - \log h_L), \quad \rho = (\log I_R - \log I_L)/(\log h_R - \log h_L)$$

Component integrals R_{nk} and Q_{nk} in terms of U^μ and U^ρ are recorded in Table 6-5. For applications refer to Problems 6.5 and 6.6.

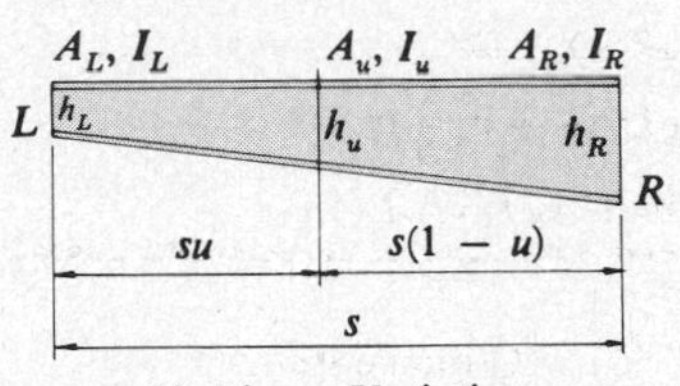

(*a*) Linear Variation

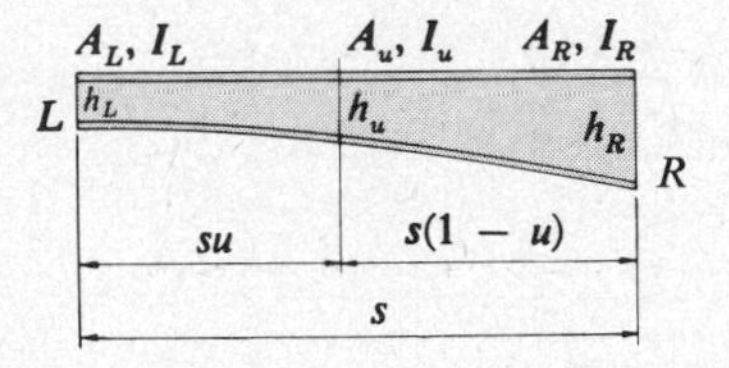

(*b*) Curvilinear Variation

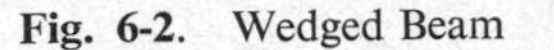

Fig. 6-2. Wedged Beam

Table 6-5. Wedged Beam, Linear Variation

Equivalents	
$a_0 = [(1+k\omega)^{1-\mu} - 1]/(1-\mu)$	$b_0 = [(1+k\omega)^{1-\rho} - 1]/(1-\rho)$
$a_1 = [(1+k\omega)^{2-\mu} - 1]/(2-\mu)$	$b_1 = [(1+k\omega)^{2-\rho} - 1]/(2-\rho)$
$a_n = [(1+k\omega)^{n+1-\mu} - 1]/(n+1-\mu)$	$b_n = [(1+k\omega)^{n+1-\rho} - 1]/(n+1-\rho)$
$[n = 0, 1, 2, \ldots]$	$[n = 0, 1, 2, \ldots]$
R-Functions	*Q*-Functions
$R_{0k} = \int_0^k \frac{du}{U^\mu} = (a_0)/\omega$	$Q_{0k} = \int_0^k \frac{du}{U^\rho} = (b_0)/\omega$
$R_{1k} = \int_0^k \frac{u\,du}{u^\mu} = (a_1 - a_0)/\omega^2$	$Q_{1k} = \int_0^k \frac{u\,du}{U^\rho} = (b_1 - b_0)/\omega^2$
$R_{2k} = \int_0^k \frac{u^2\,du}{U^\mu} = (a_2 - 2a_1 + a_0)/\omega^3$	$Q_{2\rho} = \int_0^k \frac{u^2\,du}{U^\rho} = (b_2 - 2b_1 + b_0)/\omega^3$
$R_{nk} = \int_0^k \frac{u^n\,du}{U^\mu} = \left[a_n - \binom{n}{1}a_{n-1} + \binom{n}{2}a_{n-2} \cdots \pm a_0\right]\Big/\omega^{n+1}$	$Q_{nk} = \int_0^k \frac{u^n\,du}{U^\rho} = \left[b_n - \binom{n}{1}b_{n-1} + \binom{n}{2}b_{n-2} \cdots \pm b_0\right]\Big/\omega^{n+1}$

(b) Curvilinear Variation

If the variation is nonlinear but continuous in one or two directions, new power functions may be introduced (Fig. 6-2*b*):

$$A_u = \frac{A_L}{1 - ru^\mu} = A_L U_\mu \qquad I_u = \frac{I_L}{1 - qu^\rho} = I_L U_\rho \tag{6.4}$$

where

$$r = 1 - A_L/A_R \qquad q = 1 - I_L/I_R$$

$$\mu = \frac{\log[(A_t - A_L)/A_t]}{\log[(A_R - A_L)/A_R]} \qquad \rho = \frac{\log[(I_t - I_L)/I_t]}{\log[(I_R - I_L)/I_R]}$$

in which A_t, I_t are the area and moment of inertia of an intermediate cross section at $u = t$ (commonly 0.5) respectively.

Component integrals R_{nk} and Q_{nk} in terms of U_μ and U_ρ are again recorded in Table 6-6. For additional information and applications, see Problems 6.7 and 6.8.

Table 6-6. Wedged Beam, Curvilinear Variation

Equivalents	
$c_0 = rk^\mu/(\mu + 1)$	$d_0 = qk^\rho/(\rho + 1)$
$c_1 = rk^\mu/(\mu + 2)$	$d_1 = qk^\rho/(\rho + 2)$
$c_n = rk^\mu/(\mu + n + 1)$	$d_n = qk^\rho/(\rho + n + 1)$
$[n = 0, 1, 2, \ldots]$	$[n = 0, 1, 2, \ldots]$
***R*-Functions**	***Q*-Functions**
$R_{0k} = \int_0^k \frac{du}{U_\mu} = k(1 - c_1)$	$Q_{0k} = \int_0^k \frac{du}{U_\rho} = k(1 - d_1)$
$R_{1k} = \int_0^k \frac{u\,du}{U_\mu} = k^2\left(\frac{1}{2} - c_2\right)$	$Q_{1k} = \int_0^k \frac{u\,du}{U_\rho} = k^2\left(\frac{1}{2} - d_2\right)$
$R_{2k} = \int_0^k \frac{u^2\,du}{U_\mu} = k^3\left(\frac{1}{3} - c_3\right)$	$Q_{2k} = \int_0^k \frac{u^2\,du}{U_\rho} = k^3\left(\frac{1}{3} - d_3\right)$
$R_{nk} = \int_0^k \frac{u^n\,du}{U_\mu} = k^{n+1}\left(\frac{1}{n+1} - c_{n+1}\right)$	$Q_{nk} = \int_0^k \frac{u^n\,du}{U_\rho} = k^{n+1}\left(\frac{1}{n+1} - d_{n+1}\right)$

6.4 NUMERICAL INTEGRATION

Whenever the algebraic integration or the substitute integration is not feasible, the numerical value of the flexibility integrals can be found (to any degree of accuracy) by means of any of several *quadrature formulas* which express the integral as a linear combination of a selected set of integrands.

Since the flexibility integrals represent areas enclosed by the respective *integrand function* $\psi(x)$, the following procedure may be applied:

(1) The segment s is divided into an arbitrary number of (equal or unequal) intervals.

(2) The value of integrands is determined numerically for each interval.

(3) The area corresponding to each interval is computed by the chosen quadrature formula.

(4) Finally, the values of elemental areas are summed.

Three most common *composite quadrature formulas* are:

(*a*) *Trapezoidal Rule* ($\Delta x = s/m$)

$$\int_0^s \psi(x)\,dx \cong (\Delta x/2)[\psi_0 + 2\psi_1 + 2\psi_2 + \cdots + 2\psi_{m-2} + 2\psi_{m-1} + \psi_m] \tag{6.5a}$$

(*b*) *Simpson's Rule* ($\Delta x = s/2m$)

$$\int_0^s \psi(x)\,dx \cong (\Delta x/3)[\psi_0 + 4\psi_1 + 2\psi_2 + 4\psi_3 + \cdots + 4\psi_{2m-3} + 2\psi_{2m-2} + 4\psi_{2m-1} + \psi_{2m}] \tag{6.5b}$$

(*c*) *Simpson's Rule* ($\Delta x = s/3m$)

$$\int_0^s \psi(x)\,dx \cong (3\Delta x/8)[\psi_0 + 3\psi_1 + 3\psi_2 + 2\psi_3 + 3\psi_4 + 3\psi_5 + 2\psi_6 + \cdots + 2\psi_{3m-3} + 3\psi_{3m-2} + 3\psi_{3m-1} + \psi_{3m}] \tag{6.5c}$$

The *results* of numerical integration are of course only *approximate*, but offer a sufficient accuracy for engineering purposes. The accuracy depends on the shape of $\psi(x)$ and on the number of intervals (Problems 6.9, 6.10 and 6.11).

6.5 ANALOGIES

Another group of numerical methods available for the calculation of segmental flexibilities is based on the *elasto-static analogy*, generally known as the *conjugate beam method.* Two major forms of this analogy are the *Newmark's Method* (Sec. 3.8) and the *String Polygon Method* (Sec. 5.8) (Problems 6.12 and 6.13).

In Newmark's Method the bar is divided into an arbitrary number of discrete elements (usually of equal length) and all *functions* are assumed to have a *linear* or *parabolic variation.* The string polygon method deals with long elements of unequal length and a *true functional variation* is included.

6.6 MATRIX METHODS

Obviously, the segmental flexibility matrix for a finite segment decomposed into m finite elements must be a system matrix. Consequently, the methods of matrix construction introduced in Chapter 5 must be applicable here. Since only end deformations are required, some modifications are necessary.

(a) General Transport (Equations 5.18 and 5.19)

For the cantilever beam of Fig. 5-6, the *unit stress segmental flexibility matrix* is

$$f^0_{mm} = [I \quad r^{0)T}_{km} \quad r^{0)T}_{jm} \quad r^{0)T}_{im}] \begin{bmatrix} f^0_{(mm)} & & & \\ & f^0_{(kk)} & & \\ & & f^0_{(jj)} & \\ & & & f^0_{(ii)} \end{bmatrix} \begin{bmatrix} I \\ r^0_{km} \\ r^0_{jm} \\ r^0_{im} \end{bmatrix} \tag{6.6}$$

and the *unit load segmental flexibility matrix* of the same beam is

$$l^0_{mW} = [I \quad r^{0)T}_{km} \quad r^{0)T}_{jm} \quad r^{0)T}_{im}] \begin{bmatrix} f^0_{(mm)} & & & \\ & f^0_{(kk)} & & \\ & & f^0_{(jj)} & \\ & & & f^0_{(ii)} \end{bmatrix} \begin{bmatrix} I & 0 & 0 & 0 \\ r^0_{km} & I & 0 & 0 \\ r^0_{jm} & r^0_{jk} & I & 0 \\ r^0_{im} & r^0_{ik} & r^0_{ij} & I \end{bmatrix} \tag{6.7}$$

For the cantilever bar of Fig. 5-7 the formation of (*6.6*) and (*6.7*) is accomplished analogically by means of (*5.19*).

(b) General Transfer (Equation 5.21)

For the simple beam of Fig. 5-8, the *unit stress segmental flexibility matrix* is

$$f^0_{(om)} = [q^{0)T}_{(km)} \quad q^{0)T}_{(jk)} \quad q^{0)T}_{(ij)} \quad q^{0)T}_{(oi)}] \begin{bmatrix} f^0_{(km)} & & & \\ & f^0_{(jk)} & & \\ & & f^0_{(ij)} & \\ & & & f^0_{(oi)} \end{bmatrix} \begin{bmatrix} q^0_{(km)} \\ q^0_{(jk)} \\ q^0_{(ij)} \\ q^0_{(oi)} \end{bmatrix} \tag{6.8}$$

and the *unit load segmental flexibility matrix* is

$$l^0_{(om)W} = [q^{0)T}_{(km)} \quad q^{0)T}_{(jk)} \quad q^{0)T}_{(ij)} \quad q^{0)T}_{(oi)}] \begin{bmatrix} f^0_{(km)} & & & \\ & f^0_{(jk)} & & \\ & & f^0_{(ij)} & \\ & & & f^0_{(io)} \end{bmatrix} \begin{bmatrix} q^0_{(km)m} & q^0_{(km)k} & q^0_{(km)j} & q^0_{(km)i} & q^0_{(km)o} \\ q^0_{(jk)m} & q^0_{(jk)k} & q^0_{(jk)j} & q^0_{(jk)i} & q^0_{(jk)o} \\ q^0_{(ij)m} & q^0_{(ij)k} & q^0_{(ij)j} & q^0_{(ij)i} & q^0_{(ij)o} \\ q^0_{(oi)m} & q^0_{(oi)k} & q^0_{(oi)j} & q^0_{(oi)i} & q^0_{(oi)o} \end{bmatrix} \tag{6.9}$$

The applications are restricted here to straight bars only (Problem *6.15*); the generalization of (*6.8*) and (*6.9*) is introduced in Chapters 8 and 9.

(c) String Polygon (Equation 5.29)

When the segmental flexibilities are required for a straight simple beam of Fig. 5-10 and only flexural deformations are considered, the string polygon matrix (*5.27*) is particularly useful as shown in Problem 6.16.

Solved Problems

ALGEBRAIC INTEGRATION

6.1. Verify the values of A_{RR}, B_{RR}, C_{RR} and D_{RR} given in Table 6-3. Then compute these values for a cantilever bar of a rectangular section the depth of which at the free end R is half that at the fixed end L. The width of the section remains constant.

Applying the expressions established in Table 5-1 and verified in Problem 5.3 to the variable section beam shown in Figure P-6.1 gives

$$A_{RR} = \int_0^s \frac{dx}{EI_x}$$

$$B_{RR} = \int_0^s \frac{(s-x)\,dx}{EI_x}$$

$$C_{RR} = \int_0^s \frac{(s-x)^2\,dx}{EI_x}$$

$$D_{RR} = \int_0^s \frac{dx}{EA_x}$$

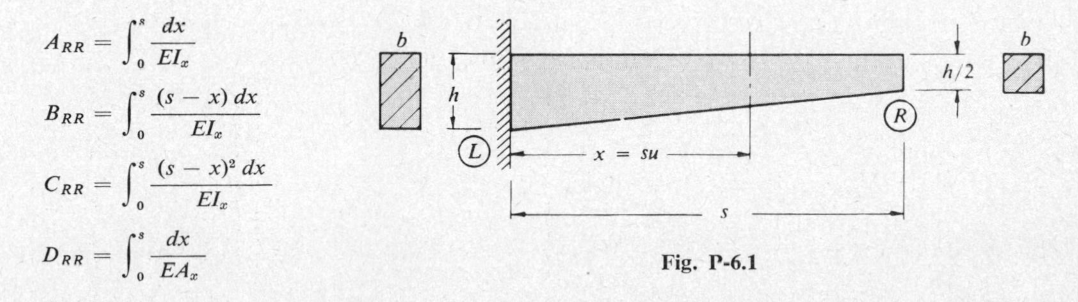

Fig. P-6.1

Using the notations used in Table 6-1, $A_x = bh_x = bh(1 + \omega u) = a_L U$ and $I_x = bh_x^3/12 = bh^3(1 + \omega u)^3/12 = I_L U^3$. Also $dx = d(su) = s\,du$.

$$\therefore \quad A_{RR} = \int_0^s \frac{dx}{EI_x} = \int_0^1 \frac{s\,du}{EI_L U^3} = \frac{s}{EI_L}\int_0^1 \frac{du}{U^3} = \frac{s}{EI_L} Q_0$$

$$B_{RR} = \int_0^s \frac{(s-x)\,dx}{EI_x} = \int_0^1 \frac{(s-su)s\,du}{EI_L U^3} = \frac{s^2}{EI_L}\int_0^1 \frac{(1-u)\,du}{U^3} = \frac{s^2}{EI_L}(Q_0 - Q_1)$$

$$C_{RR} = \int_0^s \frac{(s-x)^2\,dx}{EI_x} = \int_0^1 \frac{(s-su)^2\,s\,du}{EI_L U^3} = \frac{s^3}{EI_L}\left[\int_0^1 \frac{du}{U^3} - 2\int_0^1 \frac{u\,du}{U^3} + \int_0^1 \frac{u^2\,du}{U^3}\right] = \frac{s^3}{EI_L}(Q_0 - 2Q_1 + Q_2)$$

$$D_{RR} = \int_0^s \frac{dx}{EA_x} = \int_0^1 \frac{s\,du}{EA_L U} = \frac{s}{EA_L}\int \frac{du}{U} = \frac{s}{EA_L} R_0$$

For the beam given, $\omega = -0.5$, $k = 1$; therefore $V = 0.5$.

$$\therefore \quad Q_0 = \frac{k(2+\omega k)}{2V^2} = \frac{(1)(2-0.5)}{2(0.5)^2} = 3.0$$

$$Q_1 = \frac{k^2}{2V^2} = \frac{1}{2(0.5)^2} = 2.0$$

$$Q_2 = \frac{1}{\omega^3}\left[\ln V - \frac{\omega k(2+3\omega k)}{2V^2}\right] = \frac{1}{(-0.5)^3}\left[\ln 0.5 - \frac{(-0.5)(1)(2+3(-0.5)(1))}{2(0.5)^2}\right]$$

$$= -8[\ln 0.5 + 0.5] = -8(-0.69315 + 0.5) = 1.545$$

$$R_0 = \frac{1}{\omega}\ln V = \frac{1}{-0.5}\ln(0.5) = 1.3863$$

Substituting these values gives

$$A_{RR} = \frac{3s}{EI_L}, \qquad B_{RR} = \frac{s^2}{EI_L}, \qquad C_{RR} = \frac{0.545s^3}{EI_L} \qquad \text{and} \qquad D_{RR} = \frac{1.3863s}{EA_L}$$

6.2. Verify the expressions of the segmental flexibilities of a simple beam E_{RR}, F_{LL}, F_{RL}, F_{LR} and F_{RR} given in Table 6-4. Then compute these values for a simple beam of constant width and of depth varying parabolically from h at the left end to $2h$ at the right end such that $h_x = h(1+u^2)$ where $u = x/s$.

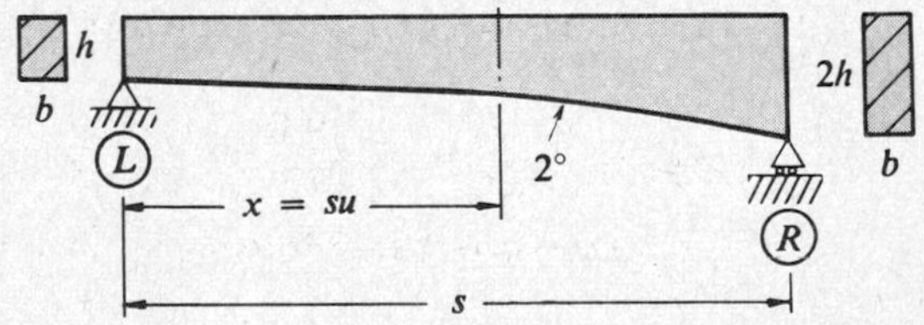

Using the notations of Table 6-2, page 78, for the given beam,

$$A_x = bh_x = bh(1+u^2) = A_L(1+u^2) = A_L U$$

$$I_x = bh_x^3/12 = bh^3(1+u^2)^3/12 = I_L(1+u^2)^3 = I_L U^3$$

Also $dx = d(su) = s\,du$.

Then from Tables 5-2 and 6-2,

Fig. P-6.2

$$E_{RR} = \int_0^s \frac{dx}{EA_x} = \int_0^1 \frac{s\,du}{EA_L U} = \frac{s}{EA_L}\int_0^1 \frac{du}{U} = \frac{s}{EA_L} R_0$$

$$F_{LL} = \int_0^s \frac{(s-x)^2\,dx}{s^2 EI_x} = \int_0^1 \frac{(s-su)^2\,s\,du}{s^2 EI_L U^3} = \frac{s}{EI_L}\int_0^1 \frac{(1-u)^2\,du}{U^3}$$

$$= \frac{s}{EI_L}\left[\int_0^1 \frac{du}{U^3} - 2\int_0^1 \frac{u\,du}{U^3} + \int_0^1 \frac{u^2\,du}{U^3}\right] = \frac{s}{EI_L}[Q_0 - 2Q_1 + Q_2]$$

$$F_{RL} = F_{LR} = \int_0^s \frac{(s-x)x\,dx}{s^2 EI_x} = \int_0^1 \frac{(s-su)(su)(s\,du)}{s^2 EI_L U^3} = \frac{s}{EI_L}\int_0^1 \frac{(u-u^2)\,du}{U^3} = \frac{s}{EI_L}[Q_1 - Q_2]$$

$$F_{RR} = \int_0^s \frac{x^2\,dx}{s^2 EI_x} = \int_0^1 \frac{s^2u^2(s\,du)}{s^2 EI_L U^3} = \frac{s}{EI_L}\int_0^1 \frac{u^2\,du}{U^3} = \frac{s}{EI_L} Q_2$$

From Table 6-2, for $k = 1$, $\omega = 1$ and $V = 2$,

$$R_0 = \frac{\tan^{-1} k\sqrt{\omega}}{\sqrt{\omega}} = \tan^{-1} 1 = 0.7854$$

$$Q_0 = \frac{k}{8}\left[\frac{5 + 3\omega k^2}{V^2} + \frac{3\tan^{-1} k\sqrt{\omega}}{k\sqrt{\omega}}\right] = \frac{1}{8}\left[\frac{5+3}{4} + \frac{3\tan^{-1} 1}{1}\right] = 0.5445$$

$$Q_1 = \frac{k^2(2 + \omega k^2)}{4V^2} = \frac{1(3)}{16} = 0.1875$$

$$Q_2 = \frac{k}{8\omega}\left[\frac{k^2 - 1}{V^2} + \frac{\tan^{-1} k\sqrt{\omega}}{k\sqrt{\omega}}\right] = \frac{1}{8}\left[\frac{1-1}{4} + \frac{\tan^{-1} 1}{1}\right] = 0.0982$$

Substituting these values into the flexibility expressions above,

$$E_{RR} = \frac{0.7854s}{EA_L}, \qquad F_{LL} = \frac{0.2677s}{EI_L}, \qquad F_{RL} = F_{LR} = \frac{0.0893s}{EI_L} \quad \text{and} \quad F_{RR} = \frac{0.0982s}{EI_L}$$

6.3. Develop the expressions for the unit load flexibilities D_{RP}, C_{RP}, B_{RP}, B_{RQ} and A_{RQ} of Table 5-1 for the variable cross section beam of Problem 6.1.

Using the values established in Problem 6.1 and Table 6-1 and noting that $k = k$ and $V = 1 - 0.5k$,

$$D_{RP} = \int_0^a \frac{dx}{EA_x} = \int_0^k \frac{s\,du}{EA_L U} = \frac{s}{EA_L}\int_0^k \frac{du}{U} = \frac{s}{EA_L} R_{0k} = \frac{\ln V}{\omega}\frac{s}{EA_L} = -2\ln(1 - 0.5k)\frac{s}{EA_L}$$

$$C_{RP} = \int_0^a \frac{(a-x)(s-x)\,dx}{EI_x} = \int_0^k \frac{(sk - su)(s - su)s\,du}{EI_L U^3} = \frac{s^3}{EI_L}\int_0^k \frac{(k-u)(1-u)\,du}{U^3}$$

$$= \frac{s^3}{EI_L}[kQ_{0k} - (1+k)Q_{1k} + Q_{2k}]$$

$$= \frac{s^3}{EI_L}[k^2(2 - 0.5k)/2(1 - 0.5k)^2 - (1+k)k^2/2(1 - 0.5k)^2 - 8\{\ln(1 - 0.5k) + 0.5k(2 - 1.5k)/2(1 - 0.5k)^2\}]$$

$$B_{RP} = \int_0^a \frac{(a-x)\,dx}{EI_x} = \int_0^k \frac{(sk - su)s\,du}{EI_L U^3} = \frac{s^2}{EI_L}\int_0^k \frac{(k-u)\,du}{U^3} = \frac{s^2}{EI_L}(kQ_{0k} - Q_{1k})$$

$$= \frac{s^2}{EI_L}[k^2(2 - 0.5k)/2(1 - 0.5k)^2 - k^2/2(1 - 0.5k)^2] = \frac{s^2}{EI_L}[k^2/2(1 - 0.5k)]$$

$$B_{RQ} = \int_0^a \frac{(s-x)\,dx}{EI_x} = \int_0^k \frac{(s - su)s\,du}{EI_L U^3} = \frac{s^2}{EI_L}\int_0^k \frac{(1-u)\,du}{U^3} = \frac{s^2}{EI_L}(Q_{0k} - Q_{1k})$$

$$= \frac{s^2}{EI_L}[k(2 - 0.5k)/2(1 - 0.5k)^2 - k^2/2(1 - 0.5k)^2] = \frac{s^2}{EI_L}[k(2 - 1.5k)/2(1 - 0.5k)^2]$$

$$A_{RQ} = \int_0^a \frac{dx}{EI_x} = \int_0^k \frac{s\,du}{EI_L U^3} = \frac{s}{EI_L}Q_{0k} = \frac{s}{EI_L}[k(2 - 0.5k)/2(1 - 0.5k)^2]$$

It may be verified that for $k = 1$ these values reduce to the segmental flexibility values of Problem 6.1.

6.4. Develop the expressions for the unit load flexibilities E_{RP}, F_{RP}, F_{LP}, F_{RQ} and F_{LQ} of Table 5-2 for the variable section simple beam of Problem 6.2.

Using the values established in Problem 6.2 and Table 6-2,

$$E_{RP} = \int_0^a \frac{dx}{EA_x} = \int_0^k \frac{s\,du}{EA_L U} = \frac{s}{EA_L} R_{0k}$$

$$F_{RP} = -b\int_0^a \frac{x^2\,dx}{s^2 EI_x} - a\int_a^s \frac{x(s-x)\,dx}{s^2 EI_x} = -s(1-k)\int_0^k \frac{s^2u^2(s\,du)}{s^2 EI_L U^3} - sk\int_k^1 \frac{su(s - su)s\,du}{s^2 EI_L U}$$

$$= -\frac{s^2(1-k)}{EI_L}\int_0^k \frac{u^2\,du}{U^3} - \frac{s^2k}{EI_L}\int_k^1 \frac{(u - u^2)\,du}{U^3}$$

$$= -\frac{s^2(1-k)}{EI_L}\int_0^k \frac{u^2\,du}{U^3} - \frac{s^2k}{EI_L}\left[\int_0^1 \frac{(u-u^2)\,du}{U^3} - \int_0^k \frac{(u-u^2)\,du}{U^3}\right]$$

$$= -\frac{s^2}{EI_L}[(1-k)Q_{2k} + k\{Q_1 - Q_2 - (Q_{1k} - Q_{2k})\}] = -\frac{s^2}{EI_L}[k(Q_1 - Q_2 - Q_{1k}) + Q_{2k}]$$

$$F_{LP} = -b\int_0^a \frac{x(s-x)\,dx}{s^2EI_x} - a\int_a^s \frac{(s-x)^2\,dx}{s^2EI_x} = -s(1-k)\int_0^k \frac{su(s-su)s\,du}{s^2EI_LU^3} - sk\int_k^1 \frac{(s-su)^2\,s\,du}{s^2EI_LU^3}$$

$$= -\frac{s^2(1-k)}{EI_L}\int_0^k \frac{(u-u^2)\,du}{U^3} - \frac{s^2k}{EI_L}\int_k^1 \frac{(1-u)^2\,du}{U^3}$$

$$= -\frac{s^2(1-k)}{EI_L}\int_0^k \frac{(u-u^2)\,du}{U^3} - \frac{s^2k}{EI_L}\left[\int_0^1 \frac{(1-u)^2\,du}{U^3} - \int_0^k \frac{(1-u^2)\,du}{U^3}\right]$$

$$= -\frac{s^2}{EI_L}[(1-k)(Q_{1k}-Q_{2k}) + k\{Q_0 - 2Q_1 + Q_2 - (Q_{0k} - 2Q_{1k} + Q_{2k})\}]$$

$$= -\frac{s^2}{EI_L}[k(Q_0 - 2Q_1 + Q_2 - Q_{0k}) + (1+k)Q_{1k} - Q_{2k}]$$

$$F_{RQ} = \int_0^a \frac{x^2\,dx}{s^2EI_x} - \int_a^s \frac{x(s-x)\,dx}{s^2EI_x} = \int_0^k \frac{s^2u^2(s\,du)}{s^2EI_LU^3} - \int_k^1 \frac{su(s-su)s\,du}{s^2EI_LU^3}$$

$$= \frac{s}{EI_L}\int_0^k \frac{u^2\,du}{U^3} - \frac{s}{EI_L}\int_k^1 \frac{(u-u^2)\,du}{U^3} = \frac{s}{EI_L}\int_0^k \frac{u^2\,du}{U^3} - \frac{s}{EI_L}\left[\int_0^1 \frac{(u-u^2)\,du}{U^3} - \int_0^k \frac{(u-u^2)\,du}{U^3}\right]$$

$$= \frac{s}{EI_L}[Q_{2k} - \{(Q_1 - Q_2) - (Q_{1k} - Q_{2k})\}] = \frac{s}{EI_L}[-Q_1 + Q_2 + Q_{1k}]$$

$$F_{LQ} = \int_0^a \frac{x(s-x)\,dx}{s^2EI_x} - \int_a^s \frac{(s-x)^2\,dx}{s^2EI_x} = \int_0^k \frac{su(s-su)s\,du}{s^2EI_LU^3} - \int_k^1 \frac{(s-su)^2\,s\,du}{s^2EI_LU^3}$$

$$= \frac{s}{EI_L}\int_0^k \frac{u(1-u)\,du}{U^3} - \frac{s}{EI_L}\int_k^1 \frac{(1-u)^2\,du}{U^3} = \frac{s}{EI_L}\int_0^k \frac{u(1-u)\,du}{U^3} - \frac{s}{EI_L}\left[\int_0^1 \frac{(1-u)^2\,du}{U^3} - \int_0^k \frac{(1-u)^2\,du}{U^3}\right]$$

$$= \frac{s}{EI_L}[Q_{1k} - Q_{2k} - \{(Q_0 - 2Q_1 + Q_2) - (Q_{0k} - 2Q_{1k} + Q_{2k})\}] = \frac{s}{EI_L}[-Q_0 + 2Q_1 - Q_2 + Q_{0k} - Q_{1k}]$$

SUBSTITUTE INTEGRATION

6.5. For the cantilever box beam shown in Fig. P-6.5 compute the flexibility constants A_{RR}, B_{RR}, C_{RR} and D_{RR} of Tables 5-1 and 6-3. The following properties are given for the beam:

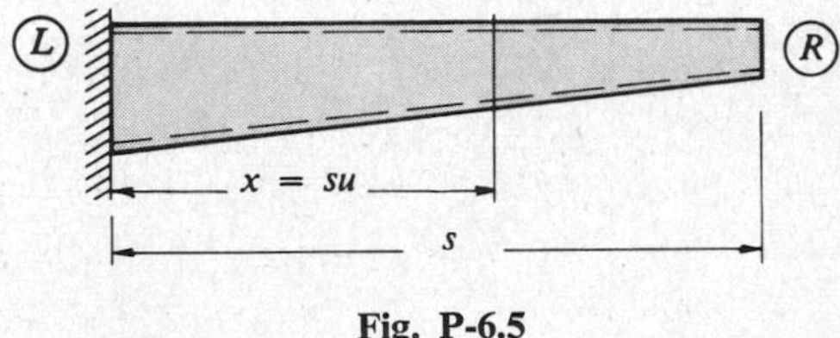

Fig. P-6.5

$h_L = 24$ in $\quad A_L = 27$ in^2 $\quad I_L = 2736$ in^4

$h_R = 12$ in $\quad A_R = 21$ in^2 $\quad I_R = 612$ in^4

From *(6.3)*,

$$\omega = 12/24 - 1 = -0.5$$
$$\mu = (\log 21 - \log 27)/(\log 12 - \log 24) = 0.3626$$
$$\rho = (\log 612 - \log 2736)/(\log 12 - \log 24) = 2.1605$$

From Table 6-5, for $k = 1$,

$$b_0 = [(1+k\omega)^{1-\rho} - 1]/(1-\rho) = [(0.5)^{-1.1605} - 1]/(-1.1605) = -1.0633$$
$$b_1 = [(1+k\omega)^{2-\rho} - 1]/(2-\rho) = [(0.5)^{-0.1605} - 1]/(-0.1605) = -0.7302$$
$$b_2 = [(1+k\omega)^{3-\rho} - 1]/(3-\rho) = [(0.5)^{0.8395} - 1]/0.8395 = -0.5255$$
$$a_0 = [(1+k\omega)^{1-\mu} - 1]/(1-\mu) = [(0.5)^{0.6374} - 1]/0.6374 = -0.5603$$

From Tables 5-1 and 6-3 and equation *(6.3)*

$$A_{RR} = \int_0^s \frac{dx}{EI_x} = \int_0^1 \frac{s\,du}{EI_LU^\rho} = \frac{s}{EI_L}\int_0^1 \frac{du}{U^\rho} = \frac{s}{EI_L}Q_0 = \frac{b_0}{\omega}\frac{s}{EI_L} = 2.1266\frac{s}{EI_L}$$

$$B_{RR} = \int_0^s \frac{(s-x)\,dx}{EI_x} = \int_0^1 \frac{(s-su)s\,du}{EI_LU^\rho} = \frac{s^2}{EI_L}\left[\int_0^1 \frac{du}{U^\rho} - \int_0^1 \frac{u\,du}{U^\rho}\right] = \frac{s^2}{EI_L}[Q_0 - Q_1]$$

$$= \frac{s^2}{EI_L}[b_0/\omega - (b_1 - b_0)/\omega^2] = 0.7942\frac{s^2}{EI_L}$$

$$C_{RR} = \int_0^s \frac{(s-x)^2\,dx}{EI_x} = \int_0^1 \frac{(s-su)^2\,s\,du}{EI_L U^\rho} = \frac{s^3}{EI_L}\left[\int_0^1 \frac{du}{U^\rho} - 2\int_0^1 \frac{u\,du}{U^\rho} + \int_0^1 \frac{u^2\,du}{U^\rho}\right] = \frac{s^3}{EI_L}[Q_0 - 2Q_1 + Q_2]$$

$$= \frac{s^3}{EI_L}[b_0/\omega - 2(b_1 - b_0)/\omega^2 + (b_2 - 2b_1 + b_0)/\omega^3] = 0.4890\,\frac{s^3}{EI_L}$$

$$D_{RR} = \int_0^s \frac{dx}{EA_x} = \int_0^1 \frac{s\,du}{EA_L U^\mu} = \frac{s}{EA_L}\int_0^1 \frac{du}{U^\mu} = \frac{s}{EA_L}R_0 = \frac{a_0}{\omega}\frac{s}{EA_L} = 1.1206\,\frac{s}{EA_L}$$

6.6. Develop the expressions for the unit load flexibilities D_{RP}, C_{RP}, B_{RP}, B_{RQ} and A_{RQ} of Table 5-1 for the tapered box beam of Problem 6.5.

Using the values established in Problem 6.5 and Table 6-5,

$$D_{RP} = \int_0^a \frac{dx}{EA_x} = \int_0^k \frac{s\,du}{EA_L U^\mu} = \frac{s}{EA_L}\int_0^k \frac{du}{U^\mu} = \frac{s}{EA_L}R_{0k}$$

$$C_{RP} = \int_0^a \frac{(a-x)(s-x)\,dx}{EI_x} = \int_0^k \frac{(sk-su)(s-su)s\,du}{EI_L U^\rho} = \frac{s^3}{EI_L}\int_0^k \frac{(k-u)(1-u)\,du}{U^\rho}$$

$$= \frac{s^3}{EI_L}[kQ_{0k} - (1+k)Q_{1k} + Q_{2k}]$$

$$B_{RP} = \int_0^a \frac{(a-x)\,dx}{EI_x} = \int_0^k \frac{(sk-su)s\,du}{EI_L U^\rho} = \frac{s^2}{EI_L}\int_0^k \frac{(k-u)\,du}{U^\rho} = \frac{s^2}{EI_L}[kQ_{0k} - Q_{1k}]$$

$$B_{RQ} = \int_0^a \frac{(s-x)\,dx}{EI_x} = \int_0^k \frac{(s-su)s\,du}{EI_L U^\rho} = \frac{s^2}{EI_L}\int_0^k \frac{(1-u)\,du}{U^\rho} = \frac{s^2}{EI_L}[Q_{0k} - Q_{1k}]$$

$$A_{RQ} = \int_0^a \frac{dx}{EI_x} = \int_0^k \frac{s\,du}{EI_L U^\rho} = \frac{s}{EI_L}\int_0^k \frac{du}{U^\rho} = \frac{s}{EI_L}Q_{0k}$$

It may be verified that these values coincide with the unit stress flexibility values of Problem 6.5 for $k = 1$.

6.7. Compute the flexibility coefficients E_{RR}, F_{RR}, F_{RL}, F_{LR} and F_{LL} of Table 6-4 for the simply supported I-beam of Fig. P-6.7. The width is constant and the depth varies parabolically such that $h_R = 2h_L$. Assume $A_L = 21\text{ in}^2$, $A_R = 27\text{ in}^2$, $I_L = 612\text{ in}^4$, and $I_R = 2736\text{ in}^4$. Also assume $A_t = 22.5\text{ in}^2$ and $I_t = 988\text{ in}^4$ at $u = 0.5$.

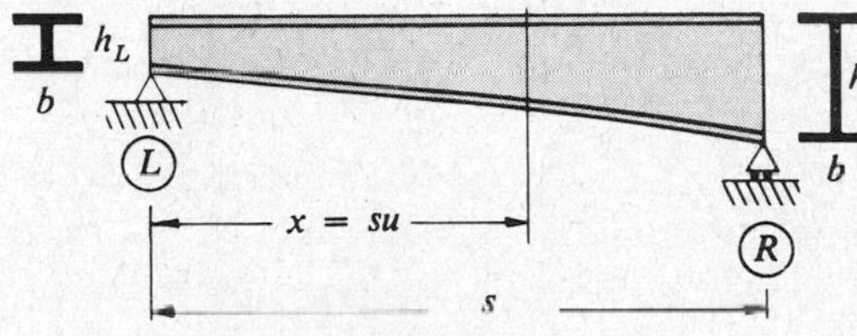

h_L b (L) $x = su$ s (R) h_R b

Fig. P-6.7

For the given beam, using the given values in *(6.4)*,

$$r = 1 - 21/27 = 0.2222, \qquad q = 1 - 612/2736 = 0.7763$$

$$\mu = \frac{\log[(22.5 - 21.0)/22.5]}{\log[(27.0 - 21.0)/27.0]} = 1.8005, \qquad \rho = \frac{\log[(988 - 612)/988]}{\log[(2{,}736 - 612)/2{,}736]} = 3.8161$$

From Table 6-6, for $k = 1$,

$$c_1 = rk^\mu/(\mu + 2) = 0.2222(1)/3.8005 = 0.05847$$
$$d_1 = qk^\rho/(\rho + 2) = 0.7763(1)/5.8161 = 0.13347$$
$$d_2 = qk^\rho/(\rho + 3) = 0.7763(1)/6.8161 = 0.11389$$
$$d_3 = qk^\rho/(\rho + 4) = 0.7763(1)/7.8161 = 0.09932$$

Therefore for $k = 1$,

$$R_0 = k(1 - c_1) = 1.0 - 0.05847 = 0.94153$$
$$Q_0 = k(1 - d_1) = 1.0 - 0.13347 = 0.86653$$
$$Q_1 = k^2(1/2 - d_2) = 0.5 - 0.11389 = 0.38611$$
$$Q_2 = k^3(1/3 - d_3) = 0.33333 - 0.09932 = 0.23401$$

Then from Tables 5-2 and 6-4 and equation (*6.4*),

$$E_{RR} = \int_0^s \frac{dx}{EA_x} = \int_0^1 \frac{s\,du}{EA_L U_\mu} = \frac{s}{EA_L}\int_0^1 \frac{du}{U_\mu} = \frac{s}{EA_L}R_0 = 0.94153\frac{s}{EA_L}$$

$$F_{RR} = \int_0^s \frac{x^2\,dx}{s^2 EI_x} = \int_0^1 \frac{s^2u^2(s\,du)}{s^2EI_LU_\rho} = \frac{s}{EI_L}\int_0^1 \frac{u^2\,du}{U_\rho} = \frac{s}{EI_L}Q_2 = 0.23401\frac{s}{EI_L}$$

$$F_{RL} = F_{LR} = \int_0^s \frac{x(s-x)\,dx}{s^2EI_x} = \int_0^1 \frac{su(s-su)s\,du}{s^2EI_LU_\rho} = \frac{s}{EI_L}\int_0^1 \frac{(u-u^2)\,du}{U_\rho} = \frac{s}{EI_L}(Q_1-Q_2) = 0.15210\frac{s}{EI_L}$$

$$F_{LL} = \int_0^s \frac{(s-x)^2\,dx}{s^2EI_x} = \int_0^1 \frac{(s-su)^2\,s\,du}{s^2EI_LU_\rho} = \frac{s}{EI_L}\int_0^1 \frac{(1-u)^2\,du}{U_\rho} = \frac{s}{EI_L}(Q_0-2Q_1+Q_2) = 0.32832\frac{s}{EI_L}$$

6.8. Establish the unit load flexibilities E_{RP}, F_{RP}, F_{LP}, F_{RQ} and F_{LQ} of Table 5-2 for the variable section I-beam of Problem 6.7.

The similarity of equations (*6.4*) and (*6.1*) and also of the definitions of the component integrals R and Q of Tables 6-2 and 6-6 suggests the identity of the required expressions with those established in Problem 6-4. Hence

$$E_{RP} = \frac{s}{EA_L}R_{0k}$$

$$F_{RP} = -\frac{s^2}{EI_L}[k(Q_1-Q_2-Q_{1k})+Q_{2k}]$$

$$F_{LP} = -\frac{s^2}{EI_L}[k(Q_0-2Q_1+Q_2-Q_{0k})+(1+k)Q_{1k}-Q_{2k}]$$

$$F_{RQ} = \frac{s}{EI_L}[-Q_1+Q_2+Q_{1k}]$$

$$F_{LQ} = \frac{s}{EI_L}[-Q_0+2Q_1-Q_2+Q_{0k}-Q_{1k}]$$

The R and Q values, however, are to be evaluated using Table 6-6.

NUMERICAL INTEGRATION

6.9. Using the composite quadrature formula (*6.5a*), check the results of Problem 6.1 Use $m = 5$.

From Problem 6.1, $A_u = A_LU$ and $I_u = I_LU^3$ where $U = 1 - 0.5u$.

Figure P-6.9 shows the beam divided into five equal segments. The beam properties in terms of U and U^3 at stations 0 through 5 are also shown.

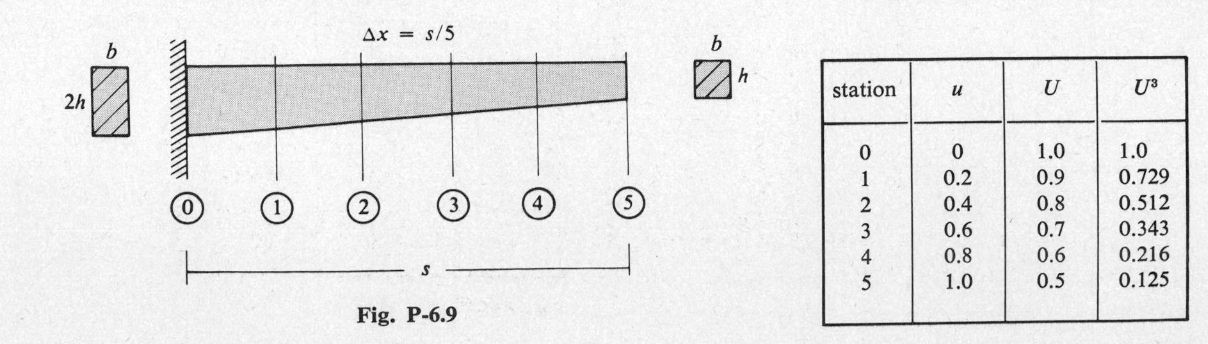

station	u	U	U^3
0	0	1.0	1.0
1	0.2	0.9	0.729
2	0.4	0.8	0.512
3	0.6	0.7	0.343
4	0.8	0.6	0.216
5	1.0	0.5	0.125

Fig. P-6.9

Then applying the Trapezoidal Rule (*6.5a*),

$$A_{RR} = \int_0^s \frac{dx}{EI_x} = \frac{1}{EI_L}\int_0^s \frac{1}{U^3}\,dx$$

$$= \frac{1}{EI_L}\left(\frac{\Delta x}{2}\right)\left[\frac{1}{1} + \frac{2}{0.729} + \frac{2}{0.512} + \frac{2}{0.343} + \frac{2}{0.216} + \frac{1}{0.125}\right] = 3.074\,\frac{s}{EI_L}$$

$$B_{RR} = \int_0^s \frac{(s-x)\,dx}{EI_x} = \frac{s}{EI_L}\int_0^s \frac{(1-u)\,dx}{U^3}$$

$$= \frac{s}{EI_L}\left(\frac{\Delta x}{2}\right)\left[1\frac{1}{1} + 2\frac{0.8}{0.729} + 2\frac{0.6}{0.512} + 2\frac{0.4}{0.343} + 2\frac{0.2}{0.216} + 1\frac{0}{0.125}\right] = 0.97229\,\frac{s^2}{EI_L}$$

$$C_{RR} = \int_0^s \frac{(s-x)^2\,dx}{EI_x} = \frac{s^2}{EI_L}\int_0^s \frac{(1-u)^2\,dx}{U^3}$$

$$= \frac{s^2}{EI_L}\left(\frac{\Delta x}{2}\right)\left[1\frac{1}{1} + 2\frac{(0.8)^2}{0.729} + 2\frac{(0.6)^2}{0.512} + 2\frac{(0.4)^2}{0.343} + 2\frac{(0.2)^2}{0.216} + 1\frac{0^2}{0.125}\right] = 0.54654\,\frac{s^3}{EI_L}$$

$$D_{RR} = \int_0^s \frac{dx}{EA_x} = \frac{1}{EA_L}\int_0^s \frac{1}{U}\,dx$$

$$= \frac{1}{EA_L}\left(\frac{\Delta x}{2}\right)\left[\frac{1}{1} + \frac{2}{0.9} + \frac{2}{0.8} + \frac{2}{0.7} + \frac{2}{0.6} + \frac{1}{0.5}\right] = 1.3913\,\frac{s}{EA_L}$$

These results are within 3% of those of Problem 6.1 with only five segments used on the beam. Better accuracy if desired can be obtained by increasing the number of segments.

6.10. Using the composite quadrature formula (*6.5b*), check the results of Problem 6.2. Use $m = 5$ (10 segments).

From Problem 6.5, $A_u = A_L U$ and $I_u = I_L U^3$ where $U = 1 + u^2$. Figure P-6.10 shows stations 0 through 10, and the corresponding cross section properties in terms of U and U^3.

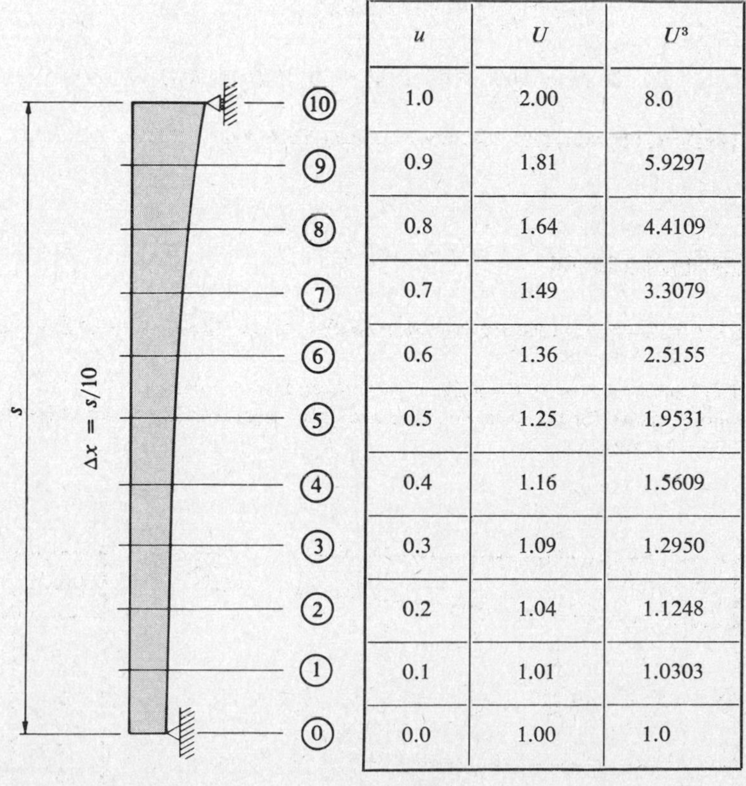

u	U	U^3
1.0	2.00	8.0
0.9	1.81	5.9297
0.8	1.64	4.4109
0.7	1.49	3.3079
0.6	1.36	2.5155
0.5	1.25	1.9531
0.4	1.16	1.5609
0.3	1.09	1.2950
0.2	1.04	1.1248
0.1	1.01	1.0303
0.0	1.00	1.0

Fig. P-6.10

Then applying Simpson's Rule (*6.5b*),

$$E_{RR} = \int_0^s \frac{dx}{EA_x} = \frac{1}{EA_L}\int_0^s \frac{1}{U}\,dx$$

$$= \frac{1}{EA_L}\left(\frac{\Delta x}{3}\right)\left[\frac{1}{1} + \frac{4}{1.01} + \frac{2}{1.04} + \frac{4}{1.09} + \frac{2}{1.16} + \frac{4}{1.25} + \frac{2}{1.36} + \frac{4}{1.49} + \frac{2}{1.64} + \frac{4}{1.81} + \frac{1}{2.0}\right]$$

$$= \frac{0.7854s}{EA_L}$$

$$F_{RR} = \int_0^s \frac{x^2\,dx}{s^2 EI_x} = \frac{1}{EI_L}\int_0^s \frac{u^2\,dx}{U^3}$$

$$= \frac{1}{EI_L}\left(\frac{\Delta x}{3}\right)\left[1\frac{0}{1} + 4\frac{0.1^2}{1.0303} + 2\frac{0.2^2}{1.1248} + 4\frac{0.3^2}{1.2950} + 2\frac{0.4^2}{1.5609} + 4\frac{0.5^2}{1.9531} + 2\frac{0.6^2}{2.5155}\right.$$

$$\left. + 4\frac{0.7^2}{3.3079} + 2\frac{0.8^2}{4.4109} + 4\frac{0.9^2}{5.9297} + 1\frac{1.0^2}{8.0}\right]$$

$$= 0.09818\frac{s}{EI_L}$$

$$F_{LR} = F_{RL} = \int_0^s \frac{x(s-x)\,dx}{s^2 EI_x} = \frac{1}{EI_L}\int_0^s \frac{(u-u^2)\,dx}{U^3}$$

$$= \frac{1}{EI_L}\left(\frac{\Delta x}{3}\right)\left[1\frac{0}{1} + 4\frac{(0.1-0.1^2)}{1.0303} + 2\frac{(0.2-0.2^2)}{1.1248} + 4\frac{(0.3-0.3^2)}{1.2950} + 2\frac{(0.4-0.4^2)}{1.5609} + 4\frac{(0.5-0.5^2)}{1.9531}\right.$$

$$\left. + 2\frac{(0.6-0.6^2)}{2.5155} + 4\frac{(0.7-0.7^2)}{3.3079} + 2\frac{(0.8-0.8^2)}{4.4109} + 4\frac{(0.9-0.9^2)}{5.9297} + 1\frac{(1-1^2)}{8.0}\right]$$

$$= 0.08934\frac{s}{EI_L}$$

$$F_{LL} = \int_0^s \frac{(s-x)^2\,dx}{s^2 EI_x} = \frac{1}{EI_L}\int_0^s \frac{(1-u)^2}{U^3}\,dx$$

$$= \frac{1}{EI_L}\left(\frac{\Delta x}{3}\right)\left[1\frac{1.0^2}{1} + 4\frac{0.9^2}{1.0303} + 2\frac{0.8^2}{1.1248} + 4\frac{0.7^2}{1.2950} + 2\frac{0.6^2}{1.5609} + 4\frac{0.5^2}{1.9531} + 2\frac{0.4^2}{2.5155}\right.$$

$$\left. + 4\frac{0.3^2}{3.3079} + 2\frac{0.2^2}{4.4109} + 4\frac{0.1^2}{5.9297} + 1\frac{0.0}{8.0}\right]$$

$$= 0.2677\frac{s}{EI_L}$$

These values can be verified to be the same as those obtained in Problem 6.2.

6.11. Using the composite quadrature formula (*6.5c*), check the results of Problem 6.5. Use $m = 3$ (9 segments).

Figure P-6.11 shows stations 0 through 9 on the given tapered box beam. From Problem 6.5,

$$U = 1 - 0.5u, \qquad \mu = 0.3626 \qquad \text{and} \qquad \rho = 2.1605$$

The values of U, U^μ at U^ρ at each station are computed and shown at respective stations. Then from Table 5-1 and equations (*6.3*) and (*6.5c*),

$$D_{RR} = \int_0^s \frac{dx}{EA_x} = \frac{1}{EA_L}\int_0^s \frac{dx}{U^\mu}$$

$$= \frac{1}{EA_L}\left(\frac{3\Delta x}{8}\right)\left[\frac{1}{1.0} + \frac{3}{0.97952} + \frac{3}{0.95820} + \frac{2}{0.93602} + \frac{3}{0.91292} + \frac{3}{0.88870}\right.$$

$$\left. + \frac{2}{0.86330} + \frac{3}{0.83647} + \frac{3}{0.80863} + \frac{1}{0.77778}\right]$$

$$= \frac{3}{8}\left(\frac{s}{9}\right)\frac{26.8911}{EA_L} = 1.1205\frac{s}{EA_L}$$

$$C_{RR} = \int_0^s \frac{(s-x)^2\,dx}{EI_x} = \frac{s^2}{EI_L}\int_0^s \frac{(1-u)^2\,dx}{U^\rho}$$

$$= \frac{s^2}{EI_L}\left(\frac{3\Delta x}{8}\right)\left[1\,\frac{1}{1} + 3\,\frac{0.8889^2}{0.88394} + 3\,\frac{0.7778^2}{0.77535} + 2\,\frac{0.6667^2}{0.67436} + 3\,\frac{0.5556^2}{0.58107} + 3\,\frac{0.4444^2}{0.49504}\right.$$

$$\left. + 2\,\frac{0.3333^2}{0.41649} + 3\,\frac{0.2222^2}{0.34507} + 3\,\frac{0.1111^2}{0.28091} + 1\,\frac{0}{0.22368}\right]$$

$$= \frac{3}{8}\left(\frac{s}{9}\right)\frac{11.22564 s^2}{EI_L} = 0.4677\,\frac{s^3}{EI_L}$$

$$B_{RR} = \int_0^s \frac{(s-x)\,dx}{EI_x} = \frac{s}{EI_L}\int_s^s \frac{(1-u)\,dx}{U^\rho}$$

$$= \frac{s}{EI_L}\left(\frac{3\Delta x}{8}\right)\left[1\,\frac{1}{1} + 3\,\frac{0.8889}{0.88394} - 3\,\frac{0.7778}{0.77535} + 2\,\frac{0.6667}{0.67436} + 3\,\frac{0.5556}{0.58107} + 3\,\frac{0.4444}{0.49504}\right.$$

$$\left. + 2\,\frac{0.3333}{0.41649} + 3\,\frac{0.2222}{0.34507} + 3\,\frac{0.1111}{0.28091} + 1\,\frac{0}{0.22368}\right]$$

$$= \frac{3}{8}\left(\frac{s}{9}\right)\frac{19.3841 s}{EI_L} = 0.8035\,\frac{s^2}{EI_L}$$

$$A_{RR} = \int_0^s \frac{dx}{EI_x} = \frac{1}{EI_L}\int_0^s \frac{dx}{U^\rho}$$

$$= \frac{1}{EI_L}\left(\frac{3\Delta x}{8}\right)\left[\frac{1}{1} + \frac{3}{0.88394} + \frac{3}{0.77535} + \frac{2}{0.67436} + \frac{3}{0.58107} + \frac{3}{0.49504}\right.$$

$$\left. + \frac{2}{0.41649} + \frac{3}{0.34507} + \frac{3}{0.28091} + \frac{1}{0.22368}\right]$$

$$= \frac{3}{8}\left(\frac{s}{9}\right)\frac{51.0980}{EI_L} = 2.1291\,\frac{s}{EI_L}$$

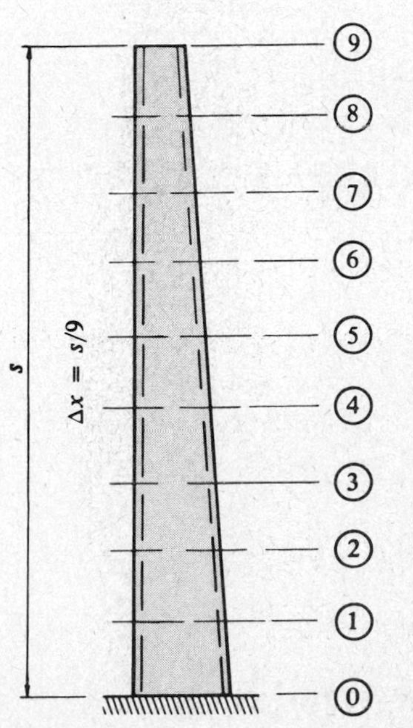

u	U	U^μ	U^ρ
1.0	0.5000	0.77778	0.22368
0.8889	0.5556	0.80863	0.28091
0.7778	0.6111	0.83647	0.34507
0.6667	0.6667	0.86330	0.41649
0.5556	0.7222	0.88870	0.49504
0.4444	0.7778	0.91292	0.58107
0.3333	0.8333	0.93602	0.67436
0.2222	0.8889	0.95820	0.77535
0.1111	0.9445	0.97952	0.88394
0.0	1.0	1.0	1.0

Fig. P-6.11

ANALOGIES

6.12. Compute the angular flexibilities F_{RR}, F_{LL}, F_{RL} and F_{LR} of the simple beam of variable cross section of Problems 6.2 and 6.10 using Newmark's Method (Sec. 3.8). Use $\Delta x = s/10$.

Figure P-6.12*a* shows the given beam with stations 0 through 10. The corresponding relative moment of inertia at each station computed in Problem 6.10 is recorded against the same. The bending moment M_i induced at each station due to $M_R = +1$ and relative M_i/EI_i value for each station are recorded next. The last two steps are repeated for $M_L = +1$.

The conjugate beams with the conjugate loads induced due to $M_R = +1$ and $M_L = +1$ are shown in (*c*) and (*d*) respectively. These conjugate loads are computed by applying the Trapezoidal Formula (Table 2-1) to the M_i/EI_i values computed above.

Thus a typical conjugate load $\gamma_j = \dfrac{\Delta x}{6}\left[\dfrac{M_i}{EI_i} + \dfrac{4M_j}{EI_j} + \dfrac{M_k}{EI_k}\right]$

(*a*) $\Delta x = s/10$, s; ends (R) and (L); stations 0 to 10

(*b*)

Station	I_L/I_i	Due to $M_R = +1$: M_i	Due to $M_R = +1$: $EI_L \dfrac{M_i}{EI_i}$	Due to $M_L = +1$: M_i	Due to $M_L = +1$: $EI_L \dfrac{M_i}{EI_i}$
10	0.1250	1.0	0.12500	0.0	0.0
9	0.1686	0.9	0.15174	0.1	0.01686
8	0.2267	0.8	0.18136	0.2	0.04534
7	0.3023	0.7	0.21161	0.3	0.09069
6	0.3975	0.6	0.23850	0.4	0.15900
5	0.5120	0.5	0.25600	0.5	0.25600
4	0.6407	0.4	0.25268	0.6	0.38442
3	0.7722	0.3	0.23166	0.7	0.54054
2	0.8890	0.2	0.17780	0.8	0.71120
1	0.9706	0.1	0.9706	0.9	0.87354
0	1.0	0.0	0.0	1.0	1.0

All conjugate loads multiplied by $6EI_L/\Delta x$

Station	(*c*) Load	(*c*) Reaction	(*d*) Load	(*d*) Reaction
10	0.40174	5.8628	0.01686	5.4031
9	0.91332		0.11278	
8	1.08879		0.28891	
7	1.26630		0.56710	
6	1.42161		0.98269	
5	1.51518		1.56742	
4	1.49838		2.33422	
3	1.35712		3.25778	
2	1.03992		4.25888	
1	0.56604		5.20536	
0	0.09706	5.3027	2.87354	16.0624

Fig. P-6.12

The end reactions of the conjugate beam computed by simple statics are the desired flexibility values. Thus

$$F_{RR} = \frac{\Delta x}{6EI_L}(5.8628) = 0.09771\frac{s}{EI_L}$$

$$F_{LL} = \frac{\Delta x}{6EI_L}(16.0624) = 0.2677\frac{s}{EI_L}$$

$$F_{RL} = \frac{\Delta x}{6EI_L}(5.4031) = 0.09005\frac{s}{EI_L}$$

$$F_{LR} = \frac{\Delta x}{6EI_L}(5.3027) = 0.08838\frac{s}{EI_L}$$

for $\Delta x = s/10$. It may be noted that theoretically $F_{RL} = F_{LR}$ and an average value from above may be used. Also these values may be compared with those obtained in Problems 6.2 and 6.10.

6.13. Using the string polygon method (Sec. 5.8), compute the end angular flexibilities of the stepped simple beam of Figure P-6.13*a*.

For the constant section segments $0i$, ij and jk, from Table 5-2,

$$F_{00(\text{right})} = \frac{0.3s}{3E(2I)} = F_{ii(\text{left})}, \qquad F_{ii(\text{right})} = \frac{0.3s}{3EI} = F_{jj(\text{left})}, \qquad F_{jj(\text{right})} = \frac{0.4s}{3E(2I)} = F_{kk(\text{left})}$$

$$F_{0i} = F_{i0} = \frac{0.3s}{6E(2I)}, \qquad F_{ij} = F_{jk}\frac{0.3s}{6EI}, \qquad F_{jk} = F_{kj} = \frac{0.4s}{6E(2I)}$$

$$\therefore \quad F_i = F_{ii(\text{left})} + F_{ii(\text{right})} = \frac{0.15s}{EI}, \qquad F_j = F_{jj(\text{left})} + F_{jj(\text{right})} = \frac{0.1667s}{EI}$$

$$F_0 = F_{00(\text{right})} = \frac{0.05s}{EI}, \qquad F_k = F_{kk(\text{left})} = \frac{0.0667s}{EI}$$

Figure (*b*) shows the moment diagram due to a unit end moment $M_k = +1$ applied at k, from which $M_0 = 0$, $M_1 = 0.3$ and $M_j = 0.6$ and $M_k = 1.0$. The elastic loads (conjugate loads) shown in Fig. (*c*) and computed using (*5.25*) are therefore

$$\gamma_0 = F_0M_0 + F_{0i}M_i = 0.0075s/EI$$
$$\gamma_i = F_{i0}M_0 + F_iM_i + F_{ij}M_j = 0.075s/EI$$
$$\gamma_j = F_{jk}M_i + F_jM_j + F_{jk}M_k = 0.1483s/EI$$
$$\gamma_k = F_{kj}M_j + F_kM_k = 0.0867s/EI$$

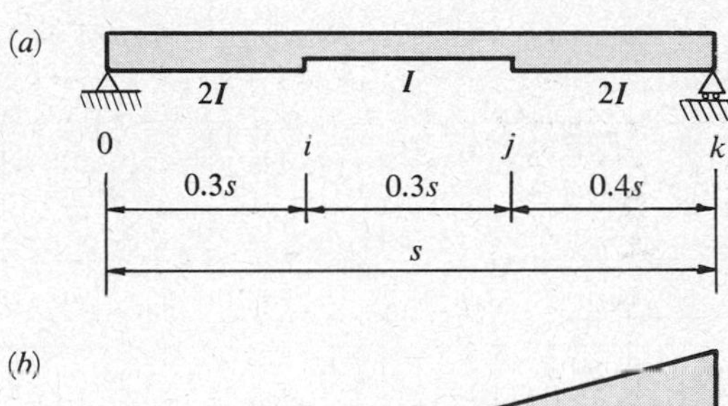

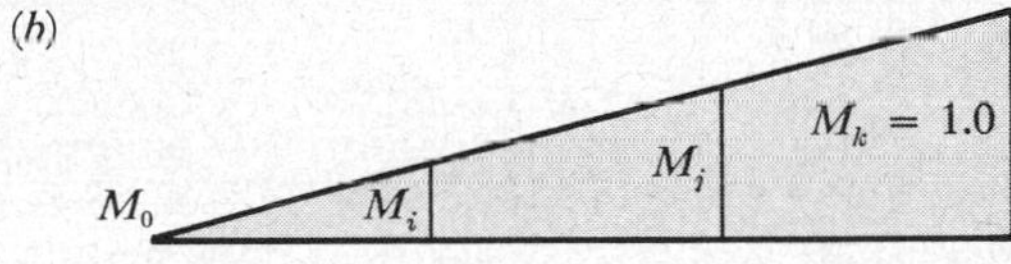

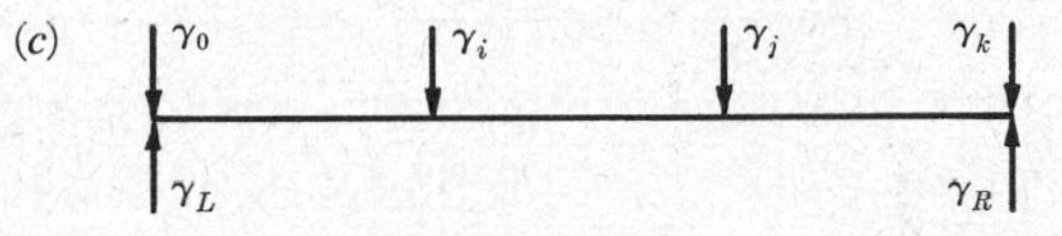

Fig. P-6.13

The end slopes of the given beam which are the beam flexibilities are the end shears (reactions) on the conjugate beam and are simply computed using statics. Thus for the given beam,

$$F_{RR} = 0.1982s/EI \quad \text{and} \quad F_{LR} = 0.1193s/EI$$

The beam flexibilities F_{LL} and F_{RL} are similarly calculated by applying a unit moment $M_0 = +1$ at 0, for which $M_i = 0.7$, $M_j = 0.4$ and $M_k = 0$. The corresponding conjugate loads can be verified to be

$$\gamma_0 = 0.0675s/EI, \qquad \gamma_i = 0.15s/EI, \qquad \gamma_j = 0.1017s/EI, \qquad \gamma_k = 0.0133s/EI$$

and the end reactions on the conjugate beam are

$$\gamma_L = 0.2132s/EI \quad \text{and} \quad \gamma_R = 0.1193s/EI$$

Thus

$$F_{LL} = 0.2132s/EI \quad \text{and} \quad F_{RL} = 0.1193s/EI$$

MATRIX METHODS

6.14. Using (*6.6*), compute the unit stress segmental flexibility matrix of the stepped cantilever bar of Fig. P-6.14. The relative cross-sectional properties of segments $0i$, ij and jk are tabulated below.

Segment	Area	Moment of Inertia
jk	A	I
ij	$1.1429A$	$2.3824I$
$0i$	$1.2857A$	$4.4706I$

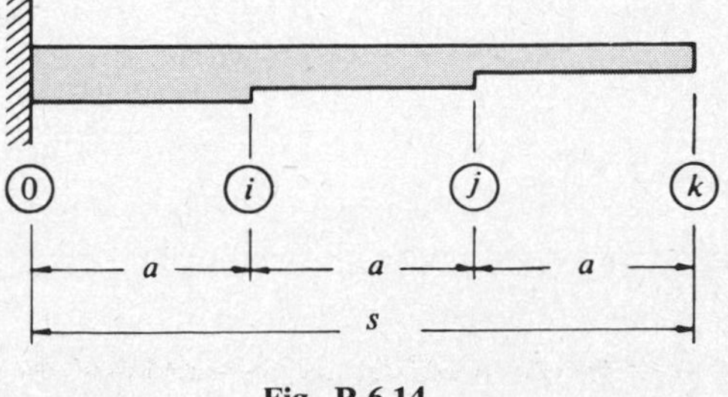

Fig. P-6.14

Equation (*6.6*) for the given beam becomes

$$f^0_{kk} = [I \; r^{0)T}_{jk} \; r^{0)T}_{ik}] \begin{bmatrix} f^0_{(kk)} & 0 & 0 \\ 0 & f^0_{(jj)} & 0 \\ 0 & 0 & f^0_{(ii)} \end{bmatrix} \begin{bmatrix} I \\ r^0_{jk} \\ r^0_{ik} \end{bmatrix} = f^0_{(kk)} + r^{0)T}_{jk} f^0_{(jj)} r^0_{jk} + r^{0)T}_{ik} f^0_{(ii)} r^0_{ik}$$

Now

$$r^0_{jk} = \begin{bmatrix} 1 & 0 & 0 \\ 0 & 1 & 0 \\ 0 & a & 1 \end{bmatrix}, \qquad r^0_{ik} = \begin{bmatrix} 1 & 0 & 0 \\ 0 & 1 & 0 \\ 0 & 2a & 1 \end{bmatrix}$$

from which $r^{0)T}_{jk}$ and $r^{0)T}_{ik}$ can also be obtained.

$$f^0_{(kk)} = \begin{bmatrix} \frac{a}{EA} & 0 & 0 \\ 0 & \frac{a^3}{3EI} & \frac{a^2}{2EI} \\ 0 & \frac{a^2}{2EI} & \frac{a}{EI} \end{bmatrix}$$

and $f^0_{(jj)}$ and $f^0_{(ii)}$ are similar values with proper values of A and I substituted.

The required flexibility matrix upon substitution of these values therefore becomes

$$f^0_{kk} = \begin{bmatrix} 2.6528\frac{a}{EA} & 0 & 0 \\ 0 & 2.7294\frac{a^3}{EI} & 1.6888\frac{a^2}{EI} \\ 0 & 1.6888\frac{a^2}{EI} & 1.6434\frac{a}{EI} \end{bmatrix} = \begin{bmatrix} 0.8843\frac{s}{EA} & 0 & 0 \\ 0 & 0.1011\frac{s^3}{EI} & 0.1876\frac{s^2}{EI} \\ 0 & 0.1876\frac{s^2}{EI} & 0.5478\frac{s}{EI} \end{bmatrix} \quad \text{for } a = \frac{s}{3}$$

6.15. Compute the unit stress segmental flexibility matrix of the stepped simple beam of Fig. P-6.13(*a*) by using equation (*6.8*). Consider flexural deformations only.

Equation (*6.8*) for the given beam considering flexural deformations only reduces to

$$f^0_{(0k)(2\times 2)} = [q^{0)T}_{(jk)} \; q^{0)T}_{(ij)} \; q^{0)T}_{(0i)}]_{(2\times 6)} \begin{bmatrix} f^0_{(jk)} & 0 & 0 \\ 0 & f^0_{(ij)} & 0 \\ 0 & 0 & f^0_{(0i)} \end{bmatrix}_{(6\times 6)} \begin{bmatrix} q^0_{(jk)} \\ q^0_{(ij)} \\ q^0_{(0i)} \end{bmatrix}_{(6\times 2)} = q^{0)T} f^0 q^0$$

where q^0 is the matrix of influence values of end moments on the segments jk, ij and $0i$ due to unit end moments on the given beam. This matrix can be verified to be

$$q^0 = \begin{bmatrix} 1.0 & 0 \\ 0.6 & 0.4 \\ 0.6 & 0.4 \\ 0.3 & 0.7 \\ 0.3 & 0.7 \\ 0 & 1.0 \end{bmatrix}$$

The submatrices $f^0_{(jk)}$, $f^0_{(ij)}$ and $f^0_{(0i)}$ of f^0 are the reduced unit stress flexibility matrices of the respective segments.

$$f^0_{(jk)} = \begin{bmatrix} \frac{0.4s}{3E(2I)} & \frac{0.4s}{6E(2I)} \\ \frac{0.4s}{6E(2I)} & \frac{0.4s}{3E(2I)} \end{bmatrix}, \quad f^0_{(ij)} = \begin{bmatrix} \frac{0.3s}{3EI} & \frac{0.3s}{6EI} \\ \frac{0.3s}{6EI} & \frac{0.3s}{3EI} \end{bmatrix}, \quad f^0_{(0i)} = \begin{bmatrix} \frac{0.3s}{3E(2I)} & \frac{0.3s}{6E(2I)} \\ \frac{0.3s}{3E(2I)} & \frac{0.3s}{3E(2I)} \end{bmatrix}$$

The required flexibility matrix upon substitution of these values therefore becomes

$$f^0_{(0k)} = \begin{bmatrix} 0.1982\frac{s}{EI} & 0.1193\frac{s}{EI} \\ 0.1193\frac{s}{EI} & 0.2132\frac{s}{EI} \end{bmatrix}$$

6.16. Compute the angular flexibilities of the simple beam shown in Fig. P-6.16 by the string polygon matrix approach using the values obtained in Problem 6.2.

A relation between the end slopes (*5.29*) and the string polygon functions discussed in (*5.26*) can be developed as follows: From (*5.29*), for the given beam considered consisting of three segments shown,

$$\begin{bmatrix}\gamma_L\\ \gamma_R\end{bmatrix} = \begin{bmatrix}\omega_0\\ \omega_k\end{bmatrix} = \frac{1}{s}\begin{bmatrix}b_0 & b_i & b_j & b_k\\ a_0 & a_i & a_j & a_k\end{bmatrix}\begin{bmatrix}\gamma_0\\ \gamma_i\\ \gamma_j\\ \gamma_k\end{bmatrix}$$

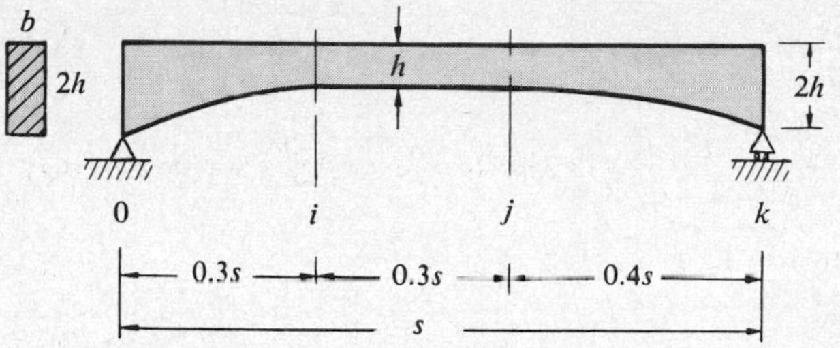

b, 2h, h, 2h, 0, i, j, k, 0.3s, 0.3s, 0.4s, s

Fig. P-6.16

From (*5.26*),

$$\begin{bmatrix}\gamma_0\\ \gamma_i\\ \gamma_j\\ \gamma_k\end{bmatrix} = \begin{bmatrix}F_0 & F_{0i} & 0 & 0\\ F_{i0} & F_i & F_{ij} & 0\\ 0 & F_{ji} & F_j & F_{jk}\\ 0 & 0 & F_{kj} & F_k\end{bmatrix}\begin{bmatrix}M_0\\ M_i\\ M_j\\ M_k\end{bmatrix}$$

However, in terms of end moments M_L and M_R,

$$\begin{bmatrix}M_0\\ M_i\\ M_j\\ M_k\end{bmatrix} = \frac{1}{s}\begin{bmatrix}b_0 & a_0\\ b_i & a_i\\ b_j & a_j\\ b_k & a_k\end{bmatrix}\begin{bmatrix}M_L\\ M_R\end{bmatrix}$$

$$\therefore \quad \begin{bmatrix}\gamma_L\\ \gamma_R\end{bmatrix} = \frac{1}{s^2}\begin{bmatrix}b_0 & b_i & b_j & b_k\\ a_0 & a_i & a_j & a_k\end{bmatrix}\begin{bmatrix}F_0 & F_{0i} & 0 & 0\\ F_{i0} & F_i & F_{ij} & 0\\ 0 & F_{ji} & F_j & F_{jk}\\ 0 & 0 & F_{kj} & F_k\end{bmatrix}\begin{bmatrix}b_0 & a_0\\ b_i & a_i\\ b_j & a_j\\ b_k & a_k\end{bmatrix}\begin{bmatrix}M_L\\ M_R\end{bmatrix} = \begin{bmatrix}F_{LL} & F_{LR}\\ F_{RL} & F_{RR}\end{bmatrix}\begin{bmatrix}M_L\\ M_R\end{bmatrix}$$

The similarity of the flexibility matrix seen above with (*6.8*) is obvious.

For the given problem,

$$a_0 = 0.0s, \quad a_i = 0.3s, \quad a_j = 0.6s, \quad a_k = 1.0s$$

$$b_0 = 1.0s, \quad b_i = 0.7s, \quad b_j = 0.4s, \quad b_k = 0.0s$$

and using values obtained in Problem 6.2, for $I_i = I_j = I_{\min} = I$,

$$F_0 = F_{00(\text{right})} = 0.0982(0.3s)/EI = 0.02946s/EI$$

$$F_i = F_{ii(\text{left})} + F_{ii(\text{right})} = 0.2677(0.3s)/EI + 0.3s/EI = 0.18031s/EI$$

$$F_j = F_{jj(\text{left})} + F_{jj(\text{right})} = 0.3s/3EI + 0.2677(0.4s)/EI = 0.20708s/EI$$

$$F_k = F_{kk(\text{left})} = 0.0982(0.4s)/EI = 0.03928s/EI$$

and

$$F_{0i} = F_{i0} = 0.0893(0.3s)/EI = 0.02679s/EI$$

$$F_{ij} = F_{ji} = 0.3s/6EI = 0.05s/EI$$

$$F_{jk} = F_{kj} = 0.0893(0.4s)/EI = 0.03572s/EI.$$

Substituting the above values, the required flexibility matrix is obtained as follows:

$$\begin{bmatrix}F_{LL} & F_{LR}\\ F_{RL} & F_{RR}\end{bmatrix} = \frac{s}{EI}\begin{bmatrix}0.21645 & 0.13689\\ 0.13689 & 0.19092\end{bmatrix}$$

Supplementary Problems

6.17. Develop algebraic expressions for the unit stress flexibilities A_{RR}, B_{RR}, C_{RR} and D_{RR} of the cantilever bar shown in Fig. P-6.17. The bar is of rectangular section of constant width and the depth varies parabolically such that $h_u = h_R(1 + \omega u'^2)$ where $u' = 1 - u$, and ω is a constant.

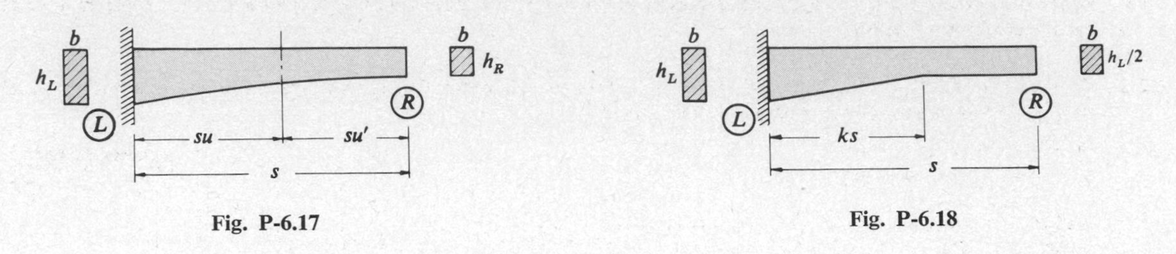

Fig. P-6.17

Fig. P-6.18

6.18. Use algebraic integration (Sec. 6.2) to compute the unit stress flexibilities A_{RR}, B_{RR}, C_{RR} and D_{RR} of the cantilever bar of Fig. P-6.18. Then simplify the results for $k = 0.5$ and $k = 1.0$.

6.19. Compute the unit stress flexibilities E_{RR}, F_{RR}, F_{RL}, F_{LR} and F_{LL} of the simple beam shown in Fig. P-6.19 by algebraic integration. The beam has a rectangular section of constant width. Then simplify the results for $k = 0$ and $k = 0.5$.

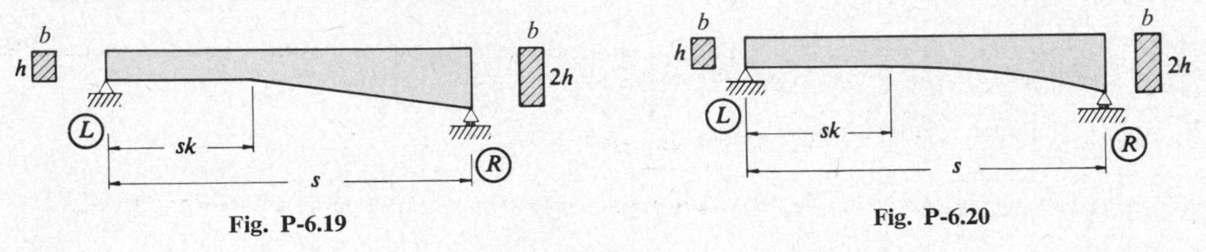

Fig. P-6.19

Fig. P-6.20

6.20. Rework Problem 6.19 if the linearly varying depth of the beam was instead varying parabolically as shown in Fig. P-6.20

6.21. Use substitute integration formulas (Sec. 6.3) to compute the flexibility constants E_{RR}, F_{RR}, F_{RL}, F_{LR} and F_{LL} of the simply supported tapered I-beam shown in Fig. P-6.21. Assume $h_L = 10''$, $h_R = 24''$, $A_L = 20$ in², $A_R = 27$ in², $I_L = 417$ in⁴ and $I_R = 2736$ in⁴.

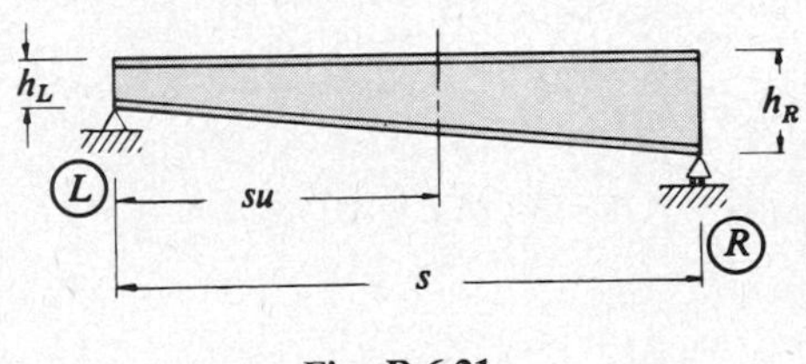

Fig. P-6.21

6.22. Develop expressions for the unit load flexibilities E_{RP}, F_{RP}, F_{LP}, F_{RQ} and F_{LQ} of Table 5-2 for the variable section I-beam of Problem 6.21.

6.23. Check the results of Problem 6.17 by the Trapezoidal Rule (*6.5a*) using $m = 10$, for $\omega = 1$.

6.24. Check the results of Problem 6.19 by Simpson's Rule (*6.5b*) for $k = 0.5$, using $m = 5$.

6.25. Compute using (*6.5b*) the segmental flexibilities E_{RR}, F_{RR}, F_{RL}, F_{LR} and F_{LL} of a simple beam of rectangular section shown in Fig. P-6.25. The beam depth varies parabolically and symmetrically about the midspan section. Use $m = 6$.

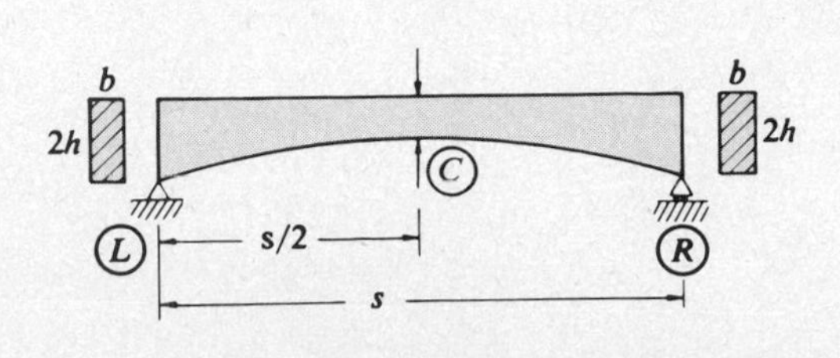

Fig. P-6.25

6.26. Check the results of Problem 6.21 by Simpson's Rule (*6.5c*) using $m = 4$.

6.27. Using Newmark's Method, check the results of Problem 6.18 for $k = 0.5$. Use $\Delta x = s/10$.

6.28. Check the values of end angular flexibilities computed in Problem 6.25 by Newmark's Method using $\Delta x = s/12$.

6.29. Using the results of Problem 6.2 and the string polygon method, verify the values of the end angular flexibilities of the beam of Problem 6.20 for $k = 0.5$.

6.30. Verify the values of the end angular flexibilities of the beam of Problem 6.25 by using the results of Problem 6.2 and the string polygon method.

6.31. Using the flexibilities of the beam of Problem 6.19 for $k = 0$, apply the string polygon method to compute the end angular flexibilities of the beam shown in Fig. P-6.31.

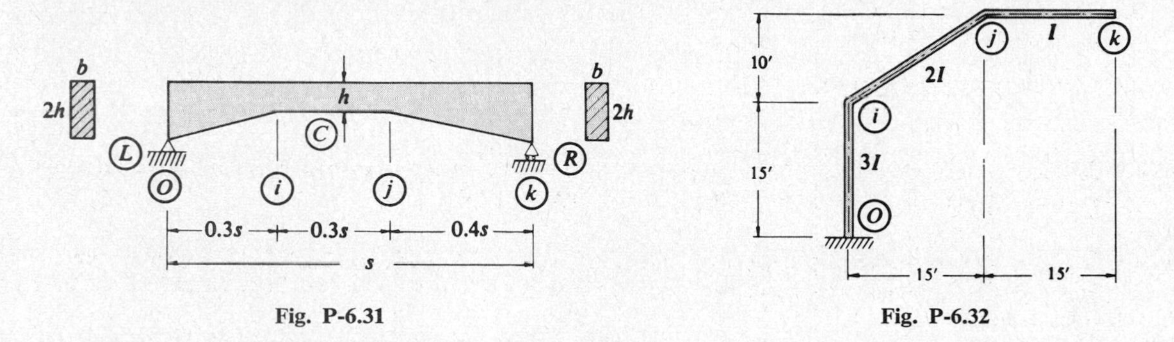

Fig. P-6.31

Fig. P-6.32

6.32. Using the general transport matrix method (Sec. 6.6*a*) and (*5.19*) compute the unit stress flexibility matrix of the bent cantilever bar of Figure P-6.32. Consider flexural deformations only.

6.33. Solve Problem 6.31 using equation (*6.8*) and results of Problem 6.19 for $k = 0$.

6.34. Using (*6.9*) compute the end slopes of the beam of Problem 6.31 due to a unit downward force applied at j.

Chapter 7

Continuous Beam

7.1 SYSTEM

A continuous beam is a slender bar supported at more than two points and acted upon by causes producing primarily bending. According to the number of spans, the beam is designated as two, three,... or *m span beam*. Continuous beams in general are statically indeterminate systems (Fig. 7-1); their degree of statical indeterminacy is defined by the number of *redundants* as

$$n = r - f - 3 > 0 \tag{7.1}$$

where n = number of redundants, r = number of independent reactions, f = number of special conditions. Obviously, if $n = 0$ the beam is *statically determinate* and if $n < 0$ the beam is *geometrically unstable*.

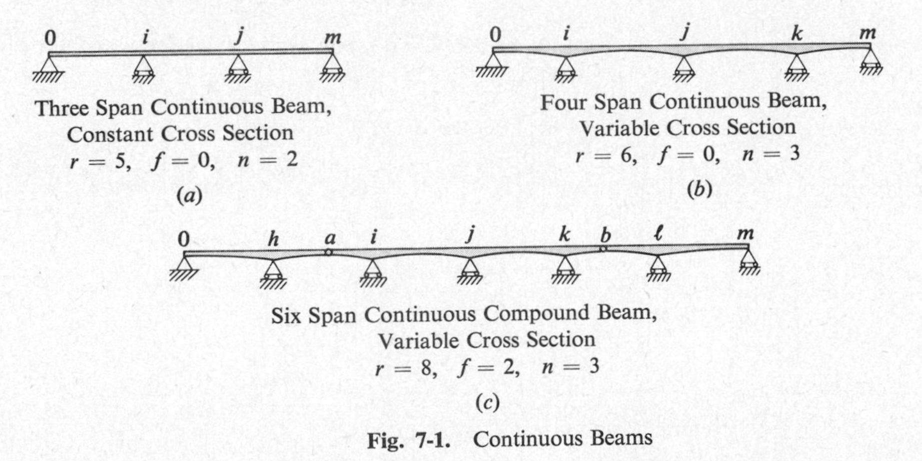

Fig. 7-1. Continuous Beams

7.2 ANALYSIS

Although all *three classes of methods* (Section 1.6) are suitable for the analysis of continuous beams, three forms of the *flexibility method*, known as the *three-, four- and five-moment equations*, offer some definite advantages and are discussed in subsequent sections of this chapter. A detailed derivation of these equations is given in Problems 7.1, 7.2 and 7.3.

7.3 THREE-MOMENT EQUATION

(a) Governing Equation

The *compatibility condition* written for the intermediate support j (any support) in the continuous beam of Fig. 7-2*a* in terms of deformations of the *basic system* (Fig. 7-2*b*) and those of the *complementary system* (Fig. 7-2*c*, *d*, *e*) is

$$F_{ji}X_i + F_jX_j + F_{jk}X_k + \tau_j = 0 \tag{7.2}$$

where X_i, X_j, X_k = redundant moments at i, j, k respectively and F_{ji}, F_j, F_{jk}, τ_j = end angular deviations (flexibilities) defined in (*5.25*).

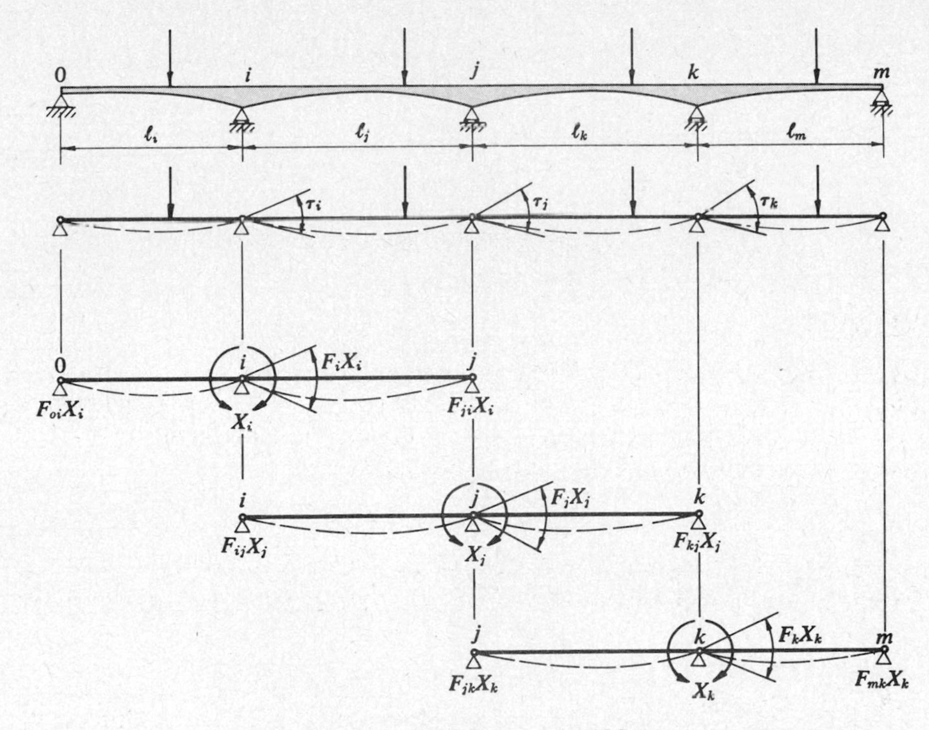

Fig. 7-2. Continuous Beam on Rigid Supports

Equation (*7.2*) is known as the *general three-moment equation*, which can be used as a *recurrent formula* for the construction of the system flexibility matrix given below.

$$\begin{bmatrix} F_i & F_{ij} & 0 \\ F_{ji} & F_j & F_{jk} \\ 0 & F_{kj} & F_k \end{bmatrix} \begin{bmatrix} X_i \\ X_j \\ X_k \end{bmatrix} + \begin{bmatrix} \tau_i \\ \tau_j \\ \tau_k \end{bmatrix} = 0$$

For the complete derivation of (*7.2*) by the virtual forces method and the physical interpretation of the elastic constants, refer to Problem 7.1.

(b) Special Forms

If the *cross section* of the beam is *constant, but different* in *each span*, (*7.2*) becomes

$$\left(\frac{l_j}{I_j}\right) M_i + 2\left(\frac{l_j}{I_j} + \frac{l_k}{I_k}\right) M_j + \left(\frac{l_k}{I_k}\right) M_k + 6E\tau_j = 0 \tag{7.3}$$

where l_j, l_k are the span lengths adjacent to j and I_j, I_k are the moments of inertia corresponding to these spans.

Finally, if the *cross sections* are the *same in all spans* and *supports* are *equally spaced*, (*7.2*) reduces to

$$M_i + 4M_j + M_k + 6EI\tau_j/l = 0 \tag{7.4}$$

(c) Primary and Secondary Effects

Load terms $\tau_j = \tau_{ji} + \tau_{jk}$ represent the sum of end angular deviations of the basic structure due to loads (and/or other effects) at j. Their analytical expressions are given under designation of F_{LP}, F_{RP}, F_{LQ}, F_{RQ} in Table 5-2. Their influence lines are given in Tables 7-1 and 7-2. For other load conditions refer to Table 7-3 or to a more extensive set of tables in the first volume (Problems I-5.37 to I-5.40).

Table 7-1.* Influence Values τ_{ij} and τ_{ji}

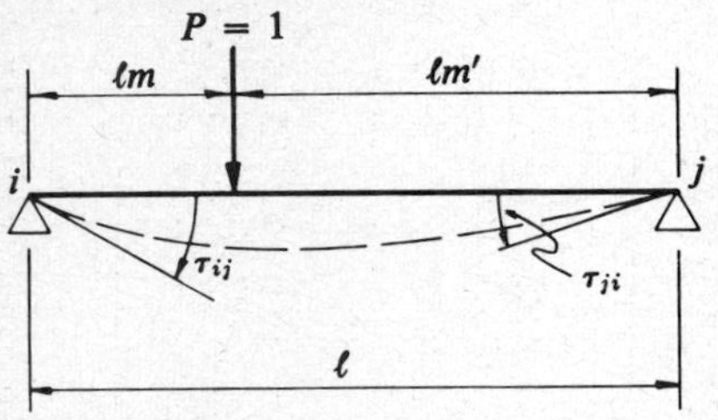

$P = 1$, ℓm, $\ell m'$, i, j, τ_{ij}, τ_{ji}, ℓ

$$\tau_{ij} = \frac{l^2}{EI}\eta \qquad \eta_{max} = \eta_{m=0.4226} = 0.06415$$

$$\tau_{ji} = \frac{l^2}{EI}\eta' \qquad \eta'_{max} = \eta'_{m=0.5774} = 0.06415$$

100 Point Table of Influence Values η and η'

m	0	1	2	3	4	5	6	7	8	9	m
0.0	0.00000	0.00328	0.00647	0.00955	0.01254	0.01544	0.01824	0.02094	0.02355	0.02607	0.0
	0.00000	0.00166	0.00333	0.00499	0.00666	0.00831	0.00996	0.01161	0.01325	0.01488	
0.1	0.02850	0.03084	0.03309	0.03525	0.03732	0.03931	0.04122	0.04304	0.04477	0.04643	0.1
	0.01650	0.01811	0.01971	0.02130	0.02299	0.02444	0.02598	0.02751	0.02903	0.03052	
0.2	0.04800	0.04949	0.05091	0.05224	0.05350	0.05469	0.05580	0.05683	0.05779	0.05868	0.2
	0.03200	0.03346	0.03489	0.03631	0.03770	0.03906	0.04040	0.03172	0.04301	0.04427	
0.3	0.05950	0.06025	0.06093	0.06154	0.06209	0.06256	0.06298	0.06333	0.06361	0.06384	0.3
	0.04550	0.04670	0.04787	0.04901	0.05012	0.05119	0.05222	0.05322	0.05419	0.05511	
0.4	0.06400	0.06410	0.06415	0.06413	0.06406	0.06394	0.06376	0.06352	0.06232	0.06289	0.4
	0.05600	0.05685	0.05765	0.05842	0.05914	0.05981	0.06044	0.06103	0.06157	0.06206	
0.5	0.06250	0.06206	0.06157	0.06103	0.06044	0.05981	0.05914	0.05842	0.05765	0.05685	0.5
	0.06250	0.06289	0.06232	0.06352	0.06376	0.06294	0.06406	0.06413	0.06415	0.06410	
0.6	0.05600	0.05511	0.05419	0.05322	0.05222	0.05119	0.05012	0.04901	0.04787	0.04670	0.6
	0.06400	0.06384	0.06361	0.06333	0.06298	0.06256	0.06208	0.06154	0.06093	0.06025	
0.7	0.04550	0.04427	0.04301	0.04172	0.04040	0.03906	0.03770	0.03631	0.03489	0.03346	0.7
	0.05950	0.05868	0.05779	0.05683	0.05580	0.05469	0.05350	0.05224	0.05091	0.04949	
0.8	0.03200	0.03052	0.02903	0.02751	0.02598	0.02444	0.02288	0.02130	0.01971	0.01811	0.8
	0.04800	0.04643	0.04477	0.04304	0.04122	0.03931	0.03732	0.03525	0.03309	0.03084	
0.9	0.01650	0.01488	0.01325	0.01161	0.00996	0.00831	0.00666	0.00499	0.00333	0.00166	0.9
	0.02850	0.02607	0.02355	0.02094	0.01824	0.01544	0.01254	0.00955	0.00647	0.00328	

*Source: J. J. Tuma, Flexibilities, Vol. I, School of Civil Engineering, Research Publication No. 9, Oklahoma State University, p. 32, 1963.

Table 7-2.* Influence Values τ_{ij} and τ_{ji}

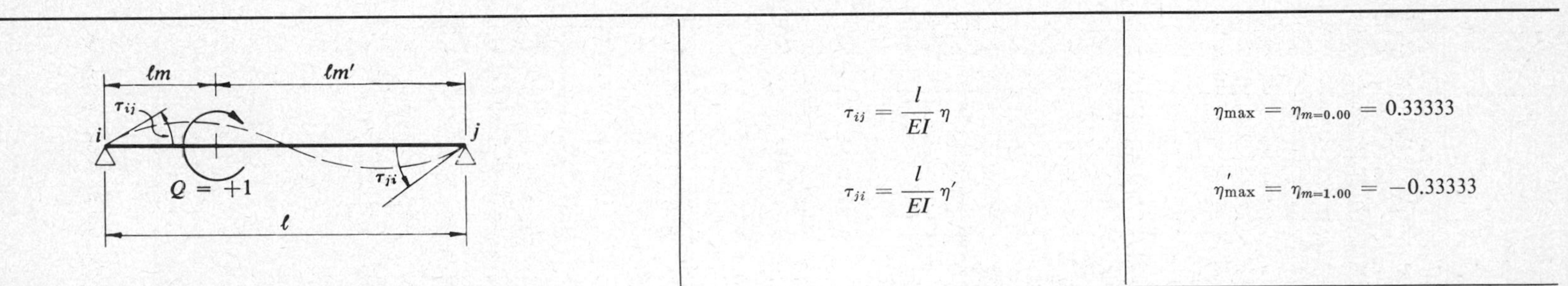

$$\tau_{ij} = \frac{l}{EI}\eta$$

$$\tau_{ji} = \frac{l}{EI}\eta'$$

$$\eta_{max} = \eta_{m=0.00} = 0.33333$$

$$\eta'_{max} = \eta_{m=1.00} = -0.33333$$

100 Point Table of End Slope Coefficients η and η'

m	0	1	2	3	4	5	6	7	8	9	m
0.0	0.33333+ 0.16666+	0.32338+ 0.16661+	0.31353+ 0.16646+	0.30378+ 0.16621+	0.29413+ 0.16586+	0.28458+ 0.16541+	0.27413+ 0.16486+	0.26578+ 0.16421+	0.25653+ 0.16346+	0.24738+ 0.16261+	0.0
0.1	0.23833+ 0.16166+	0.29938+ 0.16061+	0.22053+ 0.15946+	0.21178+ 0.15821+	0.20313+ 0.15686+	0.19458+ 0.15541+	0.18613+ 0.15386+	0.17778+ 0.15221+	0.16953+ 0.15046+	0.16138+ 0.14861+	0.1
0.2	0.15333+ 0.14666+	0.14538+ 0.14461+	0.13753+ 0.14246+	0.12978+ 0.14021+	0.12213+ 0.13786+	0.11458+ 0.13541+	0.10713+ 0.13286+	0.09978+ 0.13021+	0.09253+ 0.12746+	0.08538+ 0.12461+	0.2
0.3	0.07833+ 0.12166+	0.07238+ 0.11861+	0.06453+ 0.11546+	0.05778+ 0.11221+	0.05113+ 0.10886+	0.04458+ 0.10541+	0.03813+ 0.10186+	0.03178+ 0.09821+	0.02553+ 0.09446+	0.01938+ 0.09061+	0.3
0.4	0.01333+ 0.08666+	0.00738+ 0.09261+	0.00153+ 0.07846+	0.00421− 0.07421+	0.00986− 0.06986+	0.01541− 0.06541+	0.02086− 0.06086+	0.02621− 0.05621+	0.03146− 0.05146+	0.03661− 0.04661+	0.4
0.5	0.04166− 0.04166+	0.04661− 0.03661+	0.05146− 0.03146+	0.05621− 0.02621+	0.06086− 0.02086+	0.06541− 0.01541+	0.06986− 0.00986+	0.07421− 0.00421+	0.07846− 0.00153−	0.08261− 0.00738−	0.5
0.6	0.08666− 0.01333−	0.09061− 0.01938−	0.09446− 0.02553−	0.09821− 0.03178−	0.10186− 0.03813−	0.10541− 0.04458−	0.10886− 0.05113−	0.11221− 0.05778−	0.11546− 0.06453−	0.11861− 0.07138−	0.6
0.7	0.12166− 0.07833−	0.12461− 0.08538−	0.12746− 0.09253−	0.13021− 0.09978−	0.13286− 0.10713−	0.13541− 0.11458−	0.13786− 0.12213−	0.14021− 0.12978−	0.14246− 0.13753−	0.14461− 0.14538−	0.7
0.8	0.14666− 0.15333−	0.14861− 0.16138−	0.15046− 0.16953−	0.15221− 0.17778−	0.15386− 0.18613−	0.15541− 0.19458−	0.15686− 0.20313−	0.15821− 0.21178−	0.15946− 0.22053−	0.16061− 0.22938−	0.8
0.9	0.16166− 0.23833−	0.16261− 0.24783−	0.16346− 0.25653−	0.16421− 0.26578−	0.16486− 0.27513−	0.16541− 0.28458−	0.16586− 0.29413−	0.16621− 0.30378−	0.16646− 0.31353−	0.16661− 0.32338−	0.9

*Source: J. J. Tuma, Flexibilities, Vol. I, School of Civil Engineering, Research Publication No. 9, Oklahoma State University, p. 37, 1963.

Table 7-3. Load Terms τ_{ij} and τ_{ji}

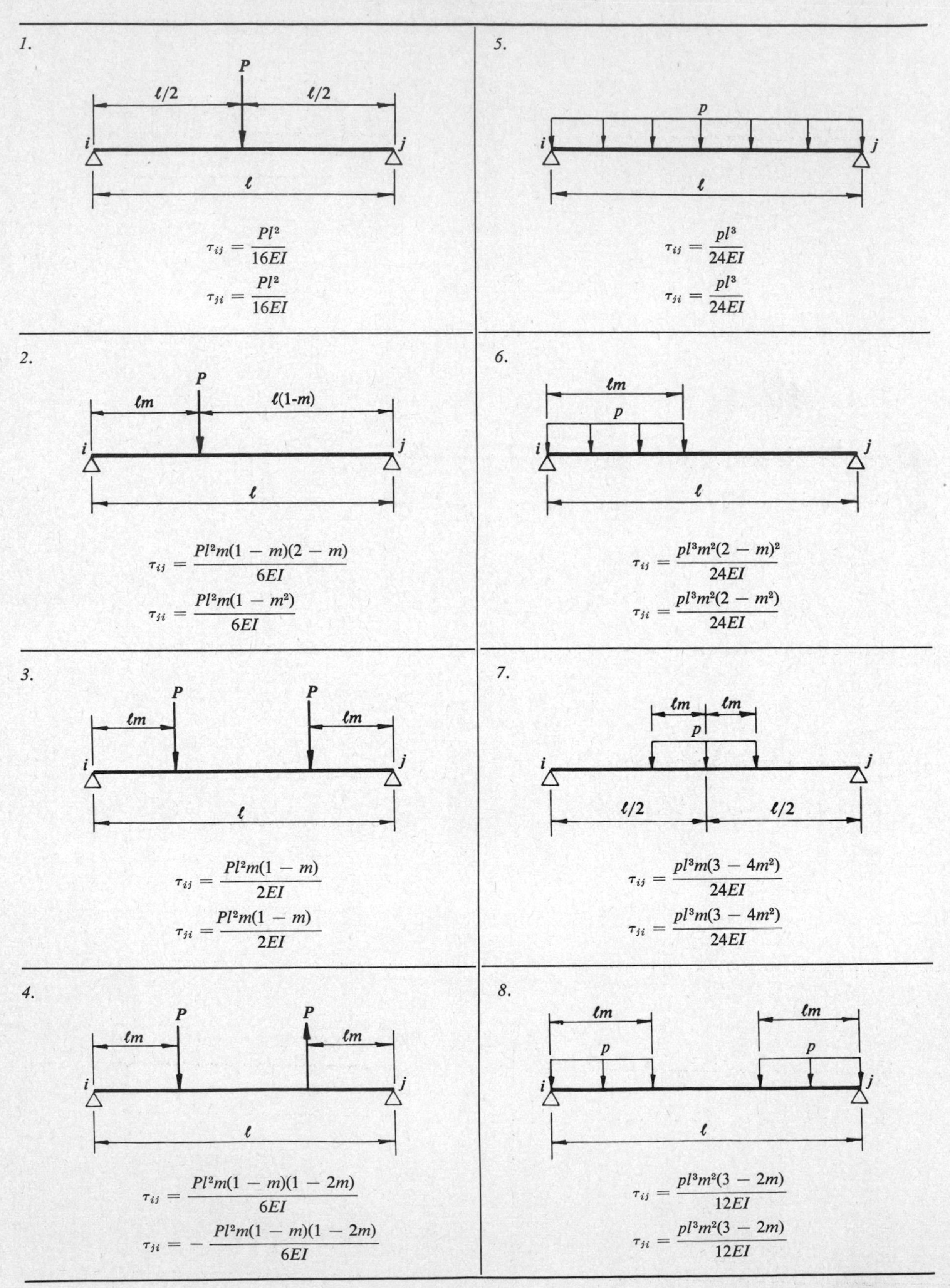

1.

$$\tau_{ij} = \frac{Pl^2}{16EI}$$

$$\tau_{ji} = \frac{Pl^2}{16EI}$$

2.

$$\tau_{ij} = \frac{Pl^2m(1-m)(2-m)}{6EI}$$

$$\tau_{ji} = \frac{Pl^2m(1-m^2)}{6EI}$$

3.

$$\tau_{ij} = \frac{Pl^2m(1-m)}{2EI}$$

$$\tau_{ji} = \frac{Pl^2m(1-m)}{2EI}$$

4.

$$\tau_{ij} = \frac{Pl^2m(1-m)(1-2m)}{6EI}$$

$$\tau_{ji} = -\frac{Pl^2m(1-m)(1-2m)}{6EI}$$

5.

$$\tau_{ij} = \frac{pl^3}{24EI}$$

$$\tau_{ji} = \frac{pl^3}{24EI}$$

6.

$$\tau_{ij} = \frac{pl^3m^2(2-m)^2}{24EI}$$

$$\tau_{ji} = \frac{pl^3m^2(2-m^2)}{24EI}$$

7.

$$\tau_{ij} = \frac{pl^3m(3-4m^2)}{24EI}$$

$$\tau_{ji} = \frac{pl^3m(3-4m^2)}{24EI}$$

8.

$$\tau_{ij} = \frac{pl^3m^2(3-2m)}{12EI}$$

$$\tau_{ji} = \frac{pl^3m^2(3-2m)}{12EI}$$

Table 7-3 (Cont'd)

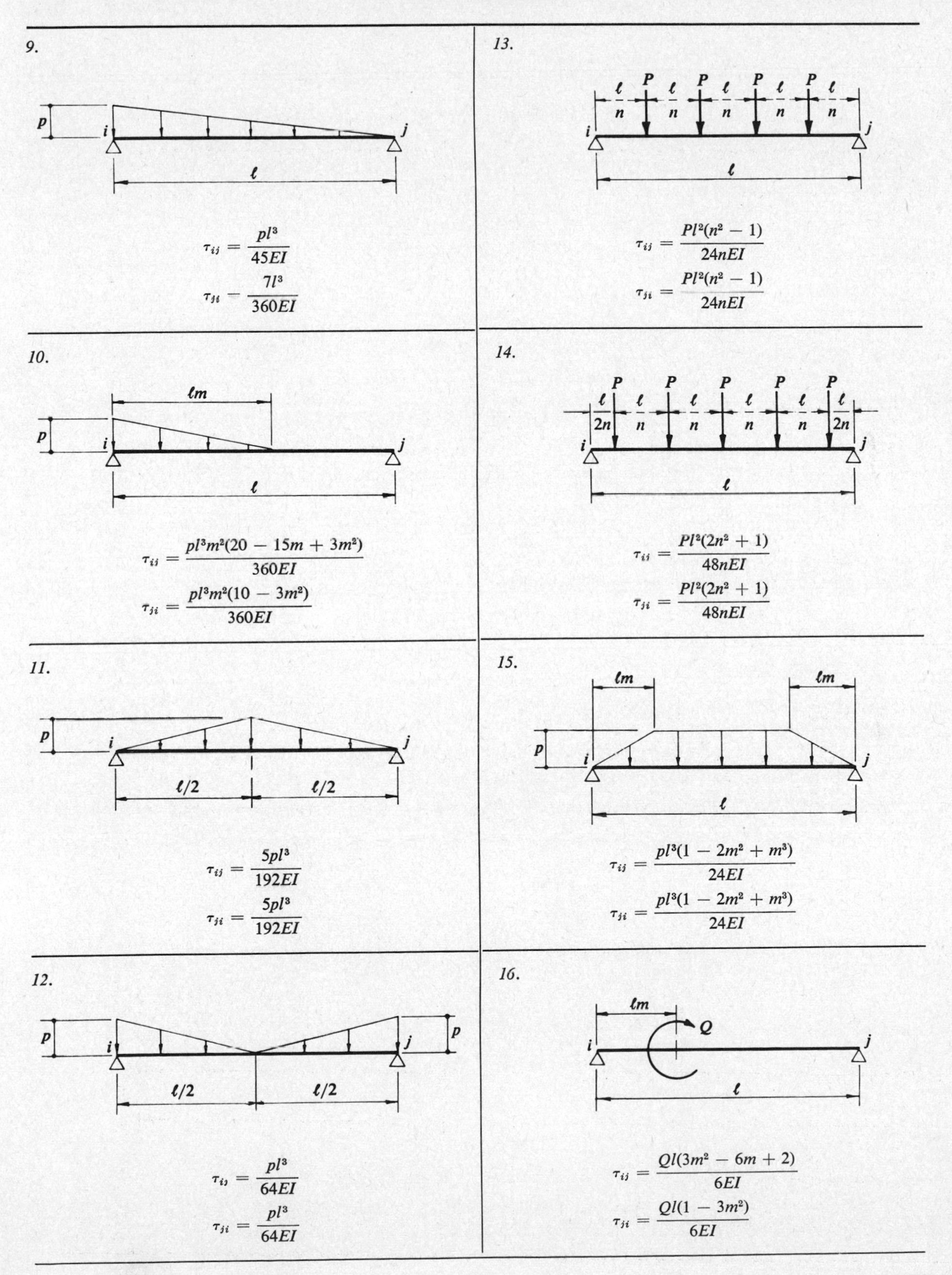

The *nonuniform change in temperature* or *in moisture content* introduces moments which in some cases must be considered. If the variation is linear from the top to the bottom of the bar,

$$\tau_{ji} = \int_0^{l_j} \frac{(\epsilon_B - \epsilon_T)\, x\, dx}{l_j h_j} \qquad \tau_{jk} = \int_0^{l_k} \frac{(\epsilon_B - \epsilon_T)(l_k - x)\, dx}{l_k h_k} \tag{7.5}$$

where ϵ_B, ϵ_T are the strains due to this change at the bottom and top respectively and h_j, h_k is the depth of beam in the respective span.

If the *displacements of supports* are prescribed or obtained from field measurements, the corresponding end angular deviations are

$$-\tau_{ji} = (\delta_j - \delta_i)/l_i \qquad -\tau_{jk} = (\delta_j - \delta_k)/l_k \tag{7.6}$$

where δ_i, δ_j, δ_k are these displacements at i, j, k respectively.

(d) End Conditions

Three end conditions may occur in the analysis of continuous beams: (*a*) fixed end, (*b*) hinged end and (*c*) overhanging end.

If the *end 0 is fixed*, (*7.2*) becomes

$$F_0 M_0 + F_{0i} M_i + \tau_0 = 0$$

where $F_0 = F_{00,i}$ and $\tau_0 = \tau_{0i}$.

If the *end 0 is simply supported* (roller or hinge), the bending moment at 0 is zero and (*7.2*) written for i is

$$F_i M_i + F_{ij} M_j + \tau_i = 0$$

Finally, if the *end 0 is free* and the *span l_i overhangs the support i*, the bending moment at i is statically determinate (cantilever beam bending moment).

7.4 FOUR-MOMENT EQUATION

(a) Governing Equation

A special case arises when the continuous beam of Fig. 7-3*a* is also *restrained angularly* at the intermediate supports. These new constraints represented by *angular springs* at i, j, k introduce additional redundants and cause a discontinuity of the bending moment at supports. Whereas the beam of Fig. 7-2*a* is statically indeterminate to the third degree, the new beam is indeterminate to the sixth degree.

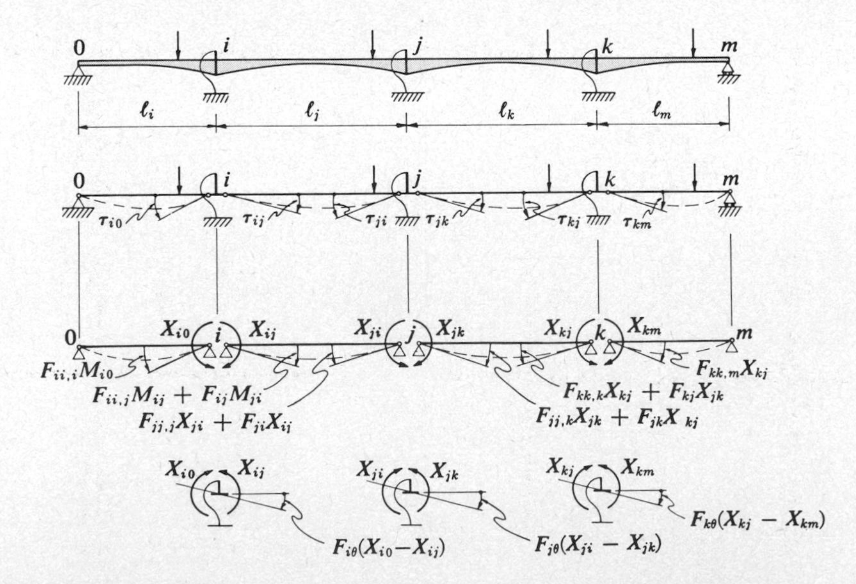

Fig. 7-3. Continuous Beam Angularly Restrained at Intermediate Supports

Two compatibility equations written at j in terms of deformations of basic system (Fig. 7-3*b*) and those of complementary system (Fig. 7-3*c*) are

$$F_{ji}X_{ij} + (F_{jj,j} + F_{j\theta})\,X_{ji} - F_{j\theta}X_{jk} + \tau_{ji} = 0 \tag{7.7a}$$

$$-F_{j\theta}X_{ji} + (F_{j\theta} + F_{jj,k})\,X_{jk} + F_{jk}X_{kj} + \tau_{jk} = 0 \tag{7.7b}$$

where $F_{j\theta}$ is the *flexibility of the angular spring* at j defined as the rotation caused by unit moment. The sum of (7.7*a*) and (7.7*b*) yields the *general four-moment equation* (7.8):

$$F_{ji}X_{ij} + F_{jj,j}X_{ji} + F_{jj,k}X_{jk} + F_{jk}X_{kj} + \tau_j = 0 \tag{7.8}$$

Since *two* and *only two* of these three equations (7.7*a*, *b* and 7.8) are *independent*, the system flexibility matrix can be constructed in three different ways. The most common form obtained using (7.7*a*, *b*) is

$$\begin{bmatrix} (F_{ii,i}+F_{i\theta}) & -F_{i\theta} & & & & \\ -F_{i\theta} & (F_{i\theta}+F_{ii,j}) & F_{ij} & & & \\ & F_{ji} & (F_{jj,j}+F_{j\theta}) & -F_{j\theta} & & \\ & & -F_{j\theta} & (F_{j\theta}+F_{jj,k}) & F_{jk} & \\ & & & F_{kj} & (F_{kk,k}+F_{k\theta}) & -F_{k\theta} \\ & & & & -F_{k\theta} & (F_{k\theta}+F_{kk,m}) \end{bmatrix} \begin{bmatrix} X_{i0} \\ X_{ij} \\ X_{ji} \\ X_{jk} \\ X_{kj} \\ X_{km} \end{bmatrix} + \begin{bmatrix} \tau_{i0} \\ \tau_{ij} \\ \tau_{ji} \\ \tau_{jk} \\ \tau_{kj} \\ \tau_{km} \end{bmatrix} = 0$$

This matrix equation preserves the character of a three-term band matrix and its construction is facilitated by overlapping recurrently the following matrices:

$$f_{(i\theta)} = \begin{bmatrix} F_{i\theta} & -F_{i\theta} \\ -F_{i\theta} & F_{i\theta} \end{bmatrix} \qquad f_{(ij)} = \begin{bmatrix} F_{ii,j} & F_{ij} \\ F_{ji} & F_{jj,j} \end{bmatrix} \qquad f_{(j\theta)} = \begin{bmatrix} F_{j\theta} & -F_{j\theta} \\ -F_{j\theta} & F_{j\theta} \end{bmatrix} \tag{7.9}$$

where $f_{(ij)}$ is the segmental flexibility matrix (Table 5-2) and $f_{(i\theta)}$, $f_{(j\theta)}$ are the angular spring flexibility matrices at i, j respectively. For complete derivation of (7.7) refer to Problem 7.2.

(b) Angular Spring

The substitute model (Fig. 7-3*a*) represents a large family of physical situations, the most important of which are given as real models in Fig. 7-4.

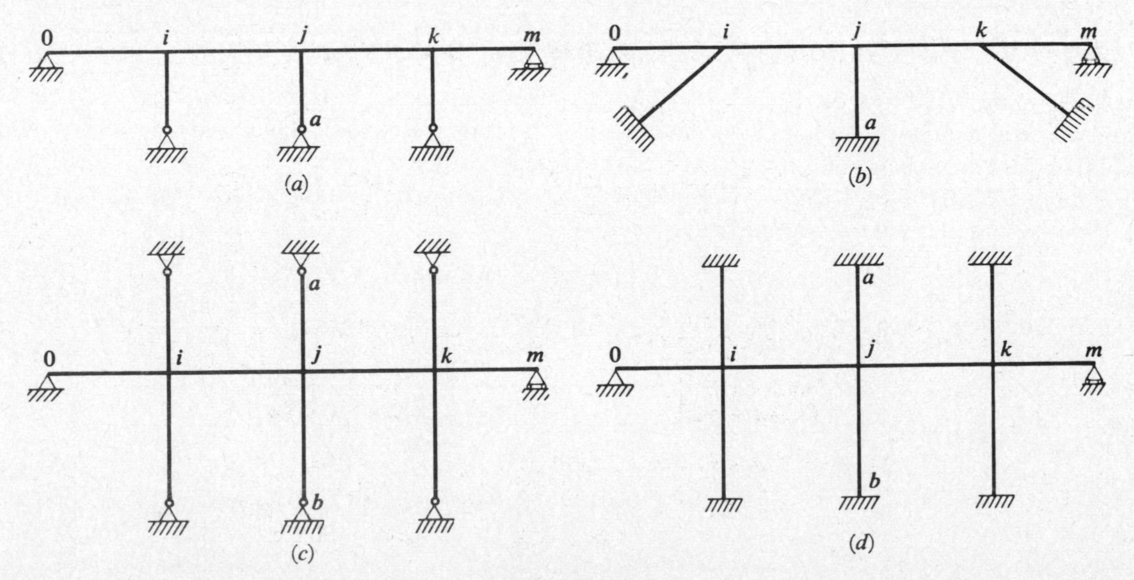

Fig. 7-4. Real Models

Typical angular spring flexibilities for each case of Fig. 7-4 are given analytically in the respective case of Fig. 7-5.

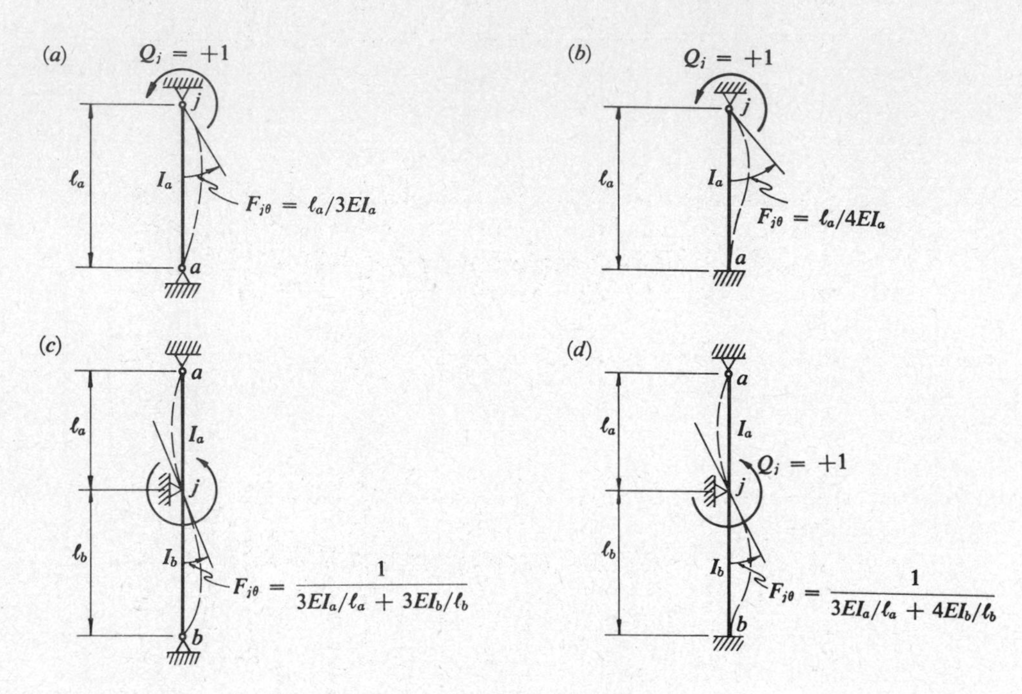

Fig. 7-5. Angular Spring Flexibilities

7.5 FIVE-MOMENT EQUATION

(a) Governing Equation

A special but not uncommon case arises when the continuous beam is *supported on elastic piers* (supports) so that the *displacement* of supports is *proportional to the reactive force R*. Thus for example, at j,

$$\delta_j = F_{j\delta} R_j \tag{7.10}$$

where $F_{j\delta}$ is the flexibility of the linear spring at j defined as the deflection caused by $R_j = +1$. The introduction of elastic supports (Fig. 7-6*a*) does not affect the degree of statical indeterminacy of the system but influences considerably the construction of the system flexibility matrix.

From (*5.25*) the *compatibility requirement* at j in terms of deformations of basic system (Fig. 7-6*b*) and those of complementary system (Fig. 7-6*c*) is

$$-\delta_i/l_j + \delta_j(1/l_j + 1/l_k) - \delta_k/l_k = F_{ji}X_i + F_jX_j + F_{jk}X_k + \tau_j \tag{7.11}$$

in which from Fig. 7-6*b*, *c*

$$\left.\begin{aligned}
\delta_i = R_iF_{i\delta} &= (R_{i0} + R_{ii})\,F_{i\delta} \\
&= [R_{i0} + X_h(1/l_i) - X_i(1/l_i + 1/l_j) + X_j(1/l_j)]\,F_{i\delta} \\
\delta_j = R_jF_{j\delta} &= (R_{j0} + R_{jj})\,F_{j\delta} \\
&= [R_{j0} + X_i(1/l_j) - X_j(1/l_j + 1/l_k) + X_k(1/l_k)]\,F_{j\delta} \\
\delta_k = R_kF_{k\delta} &= (R_{k0} + R_{kk})\,F_{k\delta} \\
&= [R_{k0} + X_j(1/l_k) - X_k(1/l_k + 1/l_l) + X_l(1/l_l)]\,F_{k\delta}
\end{aligned}\right\} \tag{7.12}$$

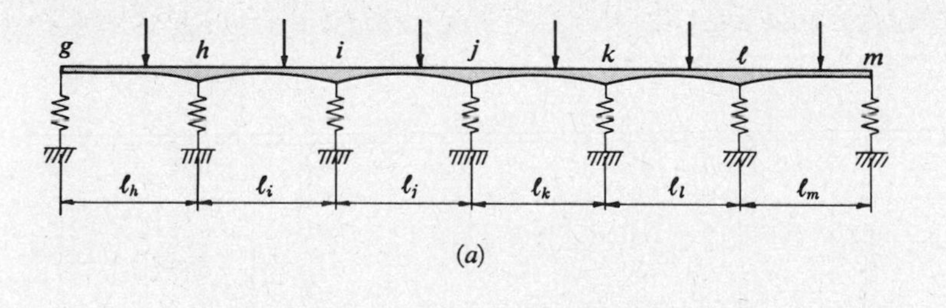

(a)

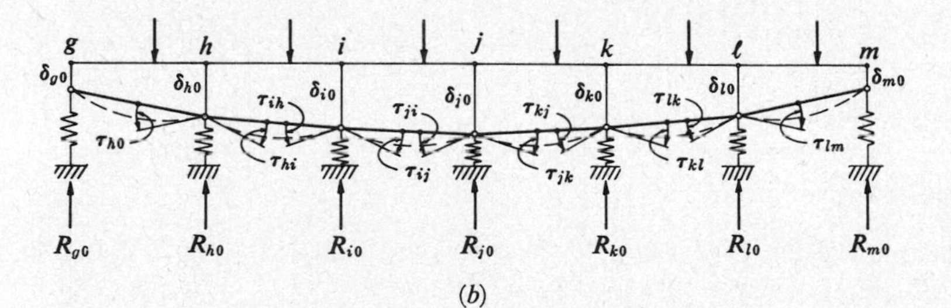

(b)

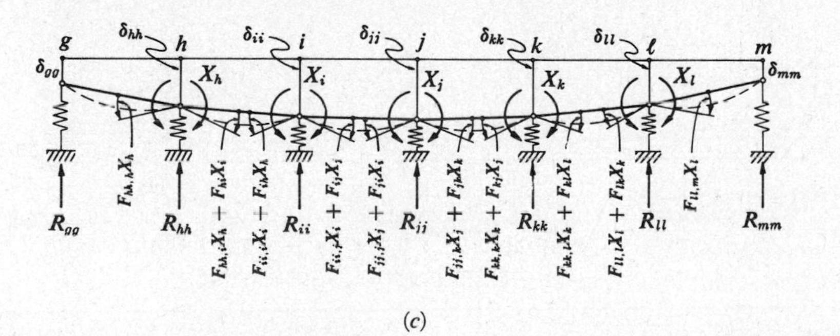

(c)

Fig. 7-6. Continuous Beam on Elastic Supports

After combining (*7.11*) and (*7.12*), the *governing equation* becomes

$$F_{jh}^* X_h + F_{ji}^* X_i + F_j^* X_j + F_{jk}^* X_k + F_{jl}^* X_l + \tau_j^* = 0 \tag{7.13}$$

where

$$\left.\begin{aligned}
F_{jh}^* &= \frac{F_{i\delta}}{l_i l_j} \\
F_{ji}^* &= -\frac{F_{i\delta}(l_i + l_j)}{l_i l_j^2} - \frac{F_{j\delta}(l_j + l_k)}{l_j^2 l_k} + F_{ji} \\
F_j^* &= \frac{F_{i\delta}}{l_j^2} + \frac{F_{j\delta}(l_j + l_k)^2}{l_j^2 l_k^2} + \frac{F_{k\delta}}{l_k^2} + F_j \\
F_{jk}^* &= -\frac{F_{j\delta}(l_j + l_k)}{l_j l_k^2} - \frac{F_{k\delta}(l_k + l_l)}{l_k^2 l_l} + F_{jk} \\
F_{jl}^* &= \frac{F_{k\delta}}{l_k l_l} \\
\tau_j^* &= R_{i0}\,\frac{F_{i\delta}}{l_j} - R_{j0}\,\frac{F_{j\delta}(l_j + l_k)}{l_j l_k} + R_{k0}\,\frac{F_{k\delta}}{l_k} + \tau_j
\end{aligned}\right\} \tag{7.14}$$

are the *new flexibilities*.

Equation (*7.13*) is known as the *general five-moment equation*, which used as a *recurrent formula* yields the system flexibility matrix given below.

$$\begin{bmatrix} F_h^* & F_{hi}^* & F_{hj}^* & & \\ F_{ih}^* & F_i^* & F_{ij}^* & F_{ik}^* & \\ F_{jh}^* & F_{ji}^* & F_j^* & F_{jk}^* & F_{jl}^* \\ & F_{ki}^* & F_{kj}^* & F_k^* & F_{kl}^* \\ & & F_{lj}^* & F_{lk}^* & F_l^* \end{bmatrix} \begin{bmatrix} X_h \\ X_i \\ X_j \\ X_k \\ X_l \end{bmatrix} + \begin{bmatrix} \tau_h^* \\ \tau_i^* \\ \tau_j^* \\ \tau_k^* \\ \tau_l^* \end{bmatrix} = 0$$

Alternate construction of this matrix is introduced in Problem 7.9.

(b) Linear Spring

The substitute model (Fig. 7-6*a*) represents again a large family of physical situations, the most important of which are given as real models in Problem 7.11.

Solved Problems

DERIVATIONS

7.1. Using the Virtual Forces Method derive the general three-moment equation (*7.2*) and interpret verbally (by definitions) and physically (by sketches) F_{ji}, F_j, F_{jk} and τ_j.

The four span continuous beam of Fig. 7-2*a* is resolved into the basic system (Fig. *b*) and the complementary system (Fig. *c, d, e*) by placing mechanical hinges at *i, j, k* and selecting the bending moments over supports *i, j, k* as the redundants X_i, X_j, X_k respectively.

The compatibility condition requiring the continuity of the elastic curve over the support *j* (any support) is

$$\theta_{ji} = -\theta_{jk} \qquad \text{or} \qquad \theta_{ji} + \theta_{jk} = 0$$

By virtual work (*1.8*),

$$(1) \cdot \theta_{ji} + (1) \cdot \theta_{jk} = \int_0^{l_j} \frac{\bar{M}M\,dx}{EI} + \int_0^{l_k} \frac{\bar{M}M\,dx}{EI} = 0$$

where $\bar{M}$ = the internal virtual moment induced at any typical section,
M = the internal real moment at that section.
Substituting proper values of these moments and using $x' = l - x$ gives

$$\int_0^{l_j} \frac{(x/l_j)(X_i(x'/l_j) + X_j(x/l_j) + BM)\,dx}{EI} + \int_0^{l_k} \frac{(x'/l_k)(X_j(x'/l_k) + X_k(x/l_k) + BM)\,dx}{EI} = 0$$

where BM = bending moment in the simple beam due to loads.
Thus the compatibility equation becomes

$$X_i \int_0^{l_j} \frac{xx'\,dx}{l_j^2EI} + X_j \int_0^{l_j} \frac{x^2\,dx}{l_j^2EI} + \int_0^{l_j} \frac{BMx\,dx}{l_jEI} + X_j \int_0^{l_k} \frac{x'^2\,dx}{l_k^2EI} + X_k \int_0^{l_k} \frac{x'x\,dx}{l_k^2EI} + \int_0^{l_k} \frac{BMx'\,dx}{l_kEI} = 0$$

Each integral in the equation above represents an end slope induced at *j* in span *ij* or *jk* by the end moments or the loads. Using the flexibility notations defined in Table 5-2 and recognizing the load terms as τ values, the compatibility equation becomes

$$X_iF_{ji} + X_jF_{jj(\text{left})} + \tau_{ji} + X_jF_{jj(\text{right})} + X_kF_{jk} + \tau_{jk} = 0$$

which when rearranged becomes equation (*7.2*),

$$F_{ji}X_i + F_jX_j + F_{jk}X_k + \tau_j = 0$$

where

$$F_j = F_{jj(\text{left})} + F_{jj(\text{right})} \quad \text{and} \quad \tau_j = \tau_{ji} + \tau_{jk}$$

The physical interpretation of F_{ji}, $F_{jj(\text{left})}$, $F_{jj(\text{right})}$, F_{jk}, τ_{jk} and τ_{jk} is given in Table 5-2. The physical meaning of F_j and τ_j is shown in Fig. 7-2*d* and 7-2*b* respectively.

7.2. Using Engesser's Theorem (*1.10*) derive the general four-moment equation (*7.8*) and its component equations (*7.7a, b*).

The four span continuous beam of Fig. 7-3*a* is resolved into the basic system (Fig. *b*) and the complementary system (Fig. *c*) by placing a mechanical hinge on each side of each internal support *i, j, k*. The bending moments at these releases designated as X_{i0}, X_{ij}, X_{ji}, X_{jk}, X_{kj}, X_{km} are the redundants of the initial system.

The continuity of the elastic curve at each release adjacent to *j* (any support) is the compatibility condition which can be formulated analytically by Engesser's Theorem (*1.10*) as

$$\frac{\partial U}{\partial X_{ji}} = 0 \quad \text{and} \quad \frac{\partial U}{\partial X_{jk}} = 0$$

The strain energy *U* stored in the system is due to the bending of beam and the deformation of the springs. Thus

$$\frac{\partial U}{\partial X_{ji}} = \frac{\partial}{\partial X_{ji}}\left[\int_0^{l_j} \frac{M^2\,dx}{2EI} + \frac{1}{2}M_j^2F_{j0}\right] \quad \text{and} \quad \frac{\partial U}{\partial X_{jk}} = \frac{\partial}{\partial X_{jk}}\left[\int_0^{l_k} \frac{M^2\,dx}{2EI} + \frac{1}{2}M_j^2F_{j0}\right]$$

where M = the bending moment in the beam span, M_j = the moment acting on the spring at *j*, and $F_{j\theta}$ = the flexibility of the angular spring at *j*. These equations can be written as follows:

$$\int_0^{l_j} \frac{M(\partial M/\partial X_{ji})\,dx}{EI} + M_j\frac{\partial M_j}{\partial X_{ji}}F_{j\theta} = 0; \qquad \int_0^{l_k} \frac{M(\partial M/\partial X_{jk})\,dx}{EI} + M_j\frac{\partial M_j}{\partial X_{jk}}F_{j\theta} = 0$$

Substituting proper values of M and M_j gives

$$\int_0^{l_j} \frac{(X_{ij}(x'/l_j) + X_{ji}(x/l_j) + BM)(x/l_j)\,dx}{EI} + (X_{ji} - X_{jk})(1)\,F_{j\theta} = 0$$

and

$$\int_0^{l_k} \frac{(X_{jk}(x'/l_k) + X_{kj}(x/l_k) + BM)(x'/l_k)\,dx}{EI} + (X_{ji} - X_{jk})(-1)\,F_{j\theta} = 0$$

where BM = the bending moment in the basic system due to applied loads. On simplifying, these become

$$X_{ij}\underbrace{\int_0^{l_j}\frac{x'x\,dx}{l_j^2EI}}_{F_{ji}} + X_{ji}\underbrace{\int_0^{l_j}\frac{x^2\,dx}{l_j^2EI}}_{F_{jj,j}} + \underbrace{\int_0^{l_j}\frac{BMx\,dx}{l_jEI}}_{\tau_{ji}} + (X_{ji} - X_{jk})\,F_{j\theta} = 0$$

$$X_{jk}\underbrace{\int_0^{l_k}\frac{x'^2\,dx}{l_k^2EI}}_{F_{jj,k}} + X_{kj}\underbrace{\int_0^{l_k}\frac{xx'\,dx}{l_k^2EI}}_{F_{jk}} + \underbrace{\int_0^{l_k}\frac{BMx'\,dx}{l_kEI}}_{\tau_{jk}} - (X_{ji} - X_{jk})\,F_{j\theta} = 0$$

where the integrals are the segmental flexibilities given in Table 5-2.

The rearrangement of these equations leads to (7.7*a, b*) and their sum gives the four-moment equation (*7.8*).

7.3. Using the Virtual Forces Method derive the general five-moment equation (*7.13*) and interpret physically F_{jh}^*, F_{ji}^*, F_j^*, F_{jk}^*, F_{jl}^* and τ_j^*.

For the beam on elastic supports shown in Fig. 7-6*a*, the moments over the supports of which are chosen as the redundants, the conditions of compatibility basically remain the same as for the continuous beam on rigid supports discussed in Problem 7.1. Thus for a typical support j the condition of compatibility is

$$\theta_{ji} + \theta_{jk} = 0$$

The angular deformations in the equation above can be computed using the Virtual Forces Principle (*1.8*) by applying a unit internal moment $M_j = +1$ at j as in Problem 7.1. Equating the total external virtual work to the total internal virtual work done, however, in this case

$$(1)\cdot\theta_{ji} + (1)\cdot\theta_{jk} = \int_0^{l_j}\frac{\bar{M}M\,dx}{EI} + \int_0^{l_k}\frac{\bar{M}M\,dx}{EI} + \bar{R}_iR_iF_{i\delta} + \bar{R}_jR_jF_{j\delta} + \bar{R}_kR_kF_{k\delta} = 0$$

where $\bar{M}$ = the internal virtual moment induced at any typical section in the beam spans,
M = the internal real moment at that section in the beam spans,
$\bar{R}$ = the internal virtual force induced in an elastic support,
R = the internal real force in that elastic support,
$F_{i\delta}, F_{j\delta}, F_{k\delta}$ = the flexibilities of linear springs at i, j, k respectively.

In this case, two spans ij and jk and three supports i, j, and k are affected by the virtual moment.

In terms of the real and virtual forces and moments obtained from statics of the respective free bodies, the compatibility condition becomes

$$\int_0^{l_j}\frac{(x/l_j)(X_i(x'/l_j) + X_j(x/l_j) + BM)\,dx}{EI} + \int_0^{l_k}\frac{(x'/l_k)(X_j(x'/l_k) + X_k(x/l_k) + BM)\,dx}{EI}$$
$$+ \left[R_{i0} + X_h\frac{1}{l_i} - X_i\left(\frac{1}{l_i}+\frac{1}{l_j}\right) + X_j\frac{1}{l_j}\right]\left(\frac{1}{l_j}\right)F_{i\delta}$$
$$+ \left[R_{j0} + X_i\frac{1}{l_j} - X_j\left(\frac{1}{l_j}+\frac{1}{l_k}\right) + X_k\frac{1}{l_k}\right]\left(\frac{-1}{l_j}+\frac{-1}{l_k}\right)F_{j\delta}$$
$$+ \left[R_{k0} + X_j\frac{1}{l_k} - X_k\left(\frac{1}{l_k}+\frac{1}{l_l}\right) + X_l\frac{1}{l_l}\right]\left(\frac{1}{l_k}\right)F_{k\delta} = 0$$

On simplifying, this becomes

$$X_i\int_0^{l_j}\frac{xx'\,dx}{l_j^2EI} + X_j\int_0^{l_j}\frac{x^2\,dx}{l_j^2EI} + \int_0^{l_j}\frac{BMx\,dx}{l_jEI} + X_j\int_0^{l_k}\frac{x'^2\,dx}{l_k^2EI} + X_k\int_0^{l_k}\frac{x'x\,dx}{l_k^2EI} + \int_0^{l_k}\frac{BMx'\,dx}{l_kEI}$$
$$+ X_h\frac{F_{i\delta}}{l_il_j} - X_i\left(\frac{l_i+l_j}{l_il_j}\frac{F_{i\delta}}{l_j} + \frac{l_j+l_k}{l_jl_k}\frac{F_{j\delta}}{l_j}\right)$$
$$+ X_j\left[\frac{F_{i\delta}}{l_j^2} + \left(\frac{l_j+l_k}{l_jl_k}\right)^2F_{j\delta} + \frac{F_{k\delta}}{l_k^2}\right] - X_k\left(\frac{l_j+l_k}{l_jl_k}\frac{F_{j\delta}}{l_k} + \frac{l_k+l_l}{l_kl_l}\frac{F_{k\delta}}{l_k}\right)$$
$$+ X_l\frac{F_{k\delta}}{l_kl_l} + \left[R_{i0}\frac{F_{i\delta}}{l_j} - R_{j0}\frac{l_j+l_k}{l_jl_k}F_{j\delta} + R_{k0}\frac{F_{k\delta}}{l_k}\right] = 0$$

In terms of the notations already established in (*7.14*) and Table 5-2, it reduces to (*7.13*):

$$F_{jh}^*X_h + F_{ji}^*X_i + F_j^*X_j + F_{jk}^*X_k + F_{jl}^*X_l + \tau_j^* = 0$$

The new flexibilities appearing in this equation have the following physical meanings:

F_{jh}^* = relative angular deviation (slope discontinuity) induced at j in the complementary structure due to $X_h = +1$.
F_{ji}^* = relative angular deviation induced at j in the complementary structure due to $X_i = +1$.
F_j^* = relative angular deviation induced at j in the complementary structure due to $X_j = +1$.
F_{jk}^* = relative angular deviation induced at j in the complementary structure due to $X_k = +1$.
F_{jl}^* = relative angular deviation induced at j in the complementary structure due to $X_l = +1$.
τ_j^* = relative angular deviation induced at j in the complementary structure due to the loads applied on the spans.

THREE-MOMENT EQUATION

7.4. Compute the moments over supports i, j and k in the four span continuous beam shown in Fig. P-7.4. The beam has a constant section and is loaded by a stationary system of transverse loads. The supports are unyielding.

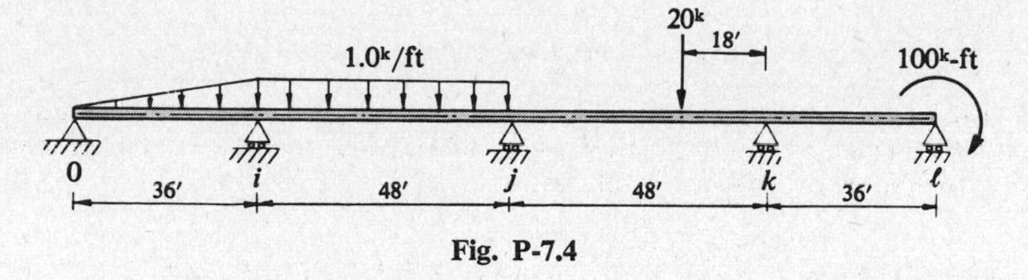

Fig. P-7.4

The three-moment equations written out for the compatibility of slopes over the supports i, j and k of the given beam and arranged in a matrix form are

$$\begin{bmatrix} F_i & F_{ij} & 0 \\ F_{ji} & F_j & F_{jk} \\ 0 & F_{kj} & F_k \end{bmatrix} \begin{bmatrix} X_i \\ X_j \\ X_k \end{bmatrix} + \begin{bmatrix} \tau_i \\ \tau_j \\ \tau_k \end{bmatrix} = 0$$

The flexibilities computed using Table 5-2 and Table 7-3 are

$$F_{ii(\text{left})} = F_{kk(\text{right})} = \frac{s}{3EI} = \frac{36}{3EI} = \frac{12}{EI}$$

$$F_{ii(\text{right})} = F_{jj(\text{left})} = F_{jj(\text{right})} = F_{kk(\text{left})} = \frac{s}{3EI} = \frac{48}{3EI} = \frac{16}{EI}$$

$$F_{ij} = F_{ji} = F_{jk} = F_{kj} = \frac{s}{6EI} = \frac{48}{6EI} = \frac{8}{EI}$$

$$F_i = F_{ii(\text{left})} + F_{ii(\text{right})} = 28/EI = F_k$$

$$F_j = F_{jj(\text{left})} + F_{jj(\text{right})} = 32/EI$$

$$\tau_{io} = \frac{pl^3}{45EI} = \frac{(1)(36)^3}{45EI} = 1{,}036.8/EI$$

$$\tau_{ij} = \tau_{ji} = \frac{pl^3}{24EI} = \frac{(1)(48)^3}{24EI} = 4{,}608.0/EI$$

$$\tau_{jk} = \frac{Pl^2m(1-m)(2-m)}{6EI} = \frac{20(48)^2\,(30/48)(18/48)(66/48)}{6EI} = 2{,}475.0/EI$$

$$\tau_{kj} = \frac{Pl^2m(1-m^2)}{6EI} = \frac{20(48)^2\,(30/48)(1-(30/48)^2)}{6EI} = 2{,}925.0/EI$$

and considering the 100 k-ft moment given at m as an applied load,

$$\tau_{km} = \frac{Ql(3m^2-6m+2)}{6EI} = \frac{100(36)(3(1)^2-6(1)+2)}{6EI} = -600/EI$$

$$\tau_i = \tau_{io} + \tau_{ij} = 5{,}644.8/EI, \qquad \tau_j = \tau_{ji} + \tau_{jk} = 7{,}083.0/EI$$

$$\tau_k = \tau_{kj} + \tau_{km} = 2{,}325.0/EI$$

Substituting in the matrix equation above gives

$$\frac{1}{EI}\begin{bmatrix} 28 & 8 & 0 \\ 8 & 32 & 8 \\ 0 & 8 & 28 \end{bmatrix} \begin{bmatrix} X_i \\ X_j \\ X_k \end{bmatrix} + \frac{1}{EI}\begin{bmatrix} 5{,}644.8 \\ 7{,}083.0 \\ 2{,}325.0 \end{bmatrix} = 0$$

the solution of which gives the required moments

$$X_i = -151.53 \text{ k-ft}, \qquad X_j = -175.21 \text{ k-ft}, \qquad X_k = -32.97 \text{ k-ft}$$

7.5. Compute the moments over supports 1 and 2 of the three span variable section continuous beam shown in Fig. P-7.5. The supports are rigid and the load condition shown is for producing maximum negative moment at 1.

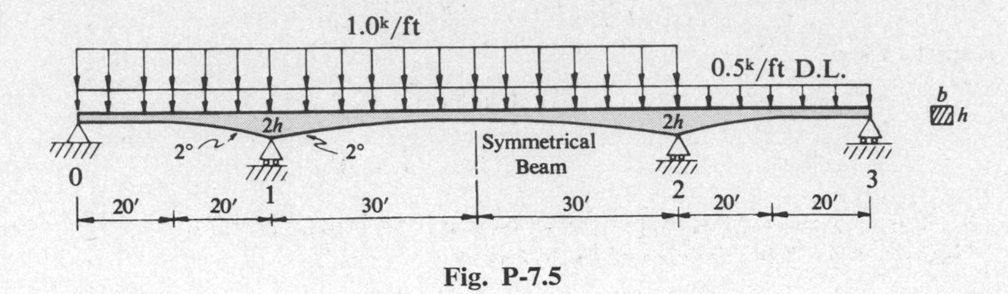

Fig. P-7.5

The flexibilities for variable cross section beams can be computed using the methods described in Chapter 6. The values thus computed are, for $I_0 = I_{\min}$,

$$F_{11(\text{left})} = F_{22(\text{right})} = 0.1689s/EI_0 = 0.1689(40)/EI_0 = 6.7560/EI_0$$
$$F_{11(\text{right})} = F_{22(\text{left})} = 0.1607s/EI_0 = 0.1607(60)/EI_0 = 9.6420/EI_0$$
$$F_{12} = F_{21} = 0.1116s/EI_0 = 0.1116(60)/EI_0 = 6.6960/EI_0$$
$$F_1 = F_{11(\text{left})} + F_{11(\text{right})} = 16.3980/EI_0 = F_2$$
$$\tau_{10} = 0.0309pl^3/EI_0 = 0.0309(1.5)(40)^3/EI_0 = 2{,}966.4/EI_0$$
$$\tau_{12} = \tau_{21} = 0.0279pl^3/EI_0 = 0.0279(1.5)(60)^3/EI_0 = 9{,}039.6/EI_0$$
$$\tau_{23} = 0.0309pl^3/EI_0 = 0.0309(0.5)(40)^3/EI_0 = 988.8/EI_0$$
$$\tau_1 = \tau_{10} + \tau_{12} = 12{,}006.0/EI_0\,, \qquad \tau_2 = \tau_{21} + \tau_{23} = 10{,}028.4/EI_0\,.$$

The matrix of compatibility equations therefore becomes

$$\frac{1}{EI_0}\begin{bmatrix} 16.3980 & 6.6960 \\ 6.6960 & 16.3980 \end{bmatrix}\begin{bmatrix} X_1 \\ X_2 \end{bmatrix} + \frac{1}{EI_0}\begin{bmatrix} 12{,}006.0 \\ 10{,}028.4 \end{bmatrix} = 0$$

which, upon solving, gives the required support moments

$$X_1 = -579.0 \text{ k-ft} \qquad \text{and} \qquad X_2 = -375.1 \text{ k-ft}$$

7.6. Prepare the influence lines for the bending moments over supports i, j and k in the four span continuous beam $0ijkm$ of Problem 7.4 (Fig. P-7.6a).

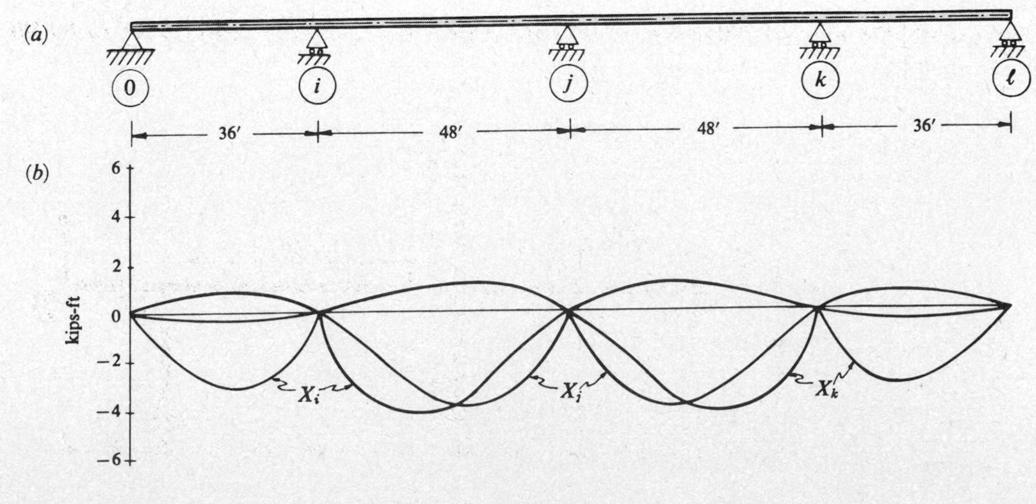

Fig. P-7.6

The compatibility matrix equation for the beam of Problem 7.4 was shown to be

$$\begin{bmatrix} F_i & F_{ij} & 0 \\ F_{ij} & F_j & F_{jk} \\ 0 & F_{kj} & F_k \end{bmatrix} \begin{bmatrix} X_i \\ X_j \\ X_k \end{bmatrix} + \begin{bmatrix} \tau_i \\ \tau_j \\ \tau_k \end{bmatrix} = 0$$

In symbolic form,

$$[F]\{X\} + \{\tau\} = 0 \tag{1}$$

or

$$\{X\} = -[F]^{-1}\{\tau\} \tag{2}$$

where $[F]$ remains constant and $\{\tau\}$ varies as the unit load changes position.

The system flexibility matrix and its inverse are

$$[F] = \frac{1}{EI}\begin{bmatrix} 28 & 8 & 0 \\ 8 & 32 & 8 \\ 0 & 8 & 28 \end{bmatrix} \quad \text{and} \quad [F]^{-1} = \frac{EI}{100}\begin{bmatrix} 3.869 & -1.042 & 0.2976 \\ -1.042 & 3.646 & -1.042 \\ 0.2976 & -1.042 & 3.869 \end{bmatrix} \tag{3, 4}$$

$$\left.\begin{array}{llll} \text{For the unit load in } 0i: & \tau_i = \tau_{i0}, & \tau_j = 0, & \tau_k = 0 \\ \text{For the unit load in } ij: & \tau_i = \tau_{ij}, & \tau_j = \tau_{ji}, & \tau_k = 0 \\ \text{For the unit load in } jk: & \tau_i = 0, & \tau_j = \tau_{jk}, & \tau_k = \tau_{kj} \\ \text{For the unit load in } kl: & \tau_i = 0, & \tau_j = 0, & \tau_k = \tau_{kl} \end{array}\right\} \tag{5}$$

The influence line matrix equation (2) in terms of (4) and (5) then becomes

$$\begin{bmatrix} X_i \\ X_j \\ X_k \end{bmatrix} = -\frac{EI}{100}\begin{bmatrix} 3.869 & -1.042 & 0.2976 \\ -1.042 & 3.646 & -1.042 \\ 0.2976 & -1.042 & 3.869 \end{bmatrix}\begin{bmatrix} \tau_{i0} & \tau_{ij} & 0 & 0 \\ 0 & \tau_{ji} & \tau_{jk} & 0 \\ 0 & 0 & \tau_{kj} & \tau_{kl} \end{bmatrix} \tag{6}$$

The problem of determining the influence values of the redundant moments thus reduces to finding the influence values of the end slopes of the simple beams. According to the reciprocal theorem (C1 and C5), however, the influence line of an end slope of a simple span is the deflection curve of that span due to a unit moment applied at that end. Thus the redundant moments can be expressed in terms of the equations of deflection curves of the basic spans due to unit end moments applied on them.

The τ values in (6) can be expressed analytically by means of Table 7-3, Case 2, as functions of the position coordinate of the unit load or evaluated for a discrete number of positions in each span. The 100 point influence values, Table 7-1, gives such values. The resulting influence lines for the given beam are plotted in Fig. b.

FOUR-MOMENT EQUATION

7.7. Compute the end moments in the rigid frame of Fig. P-7.7a. Assume EI to be the same for all members.

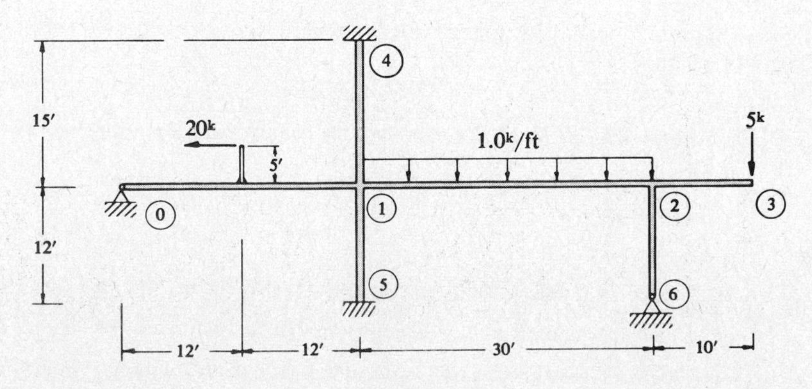

Fig. P-7.7a

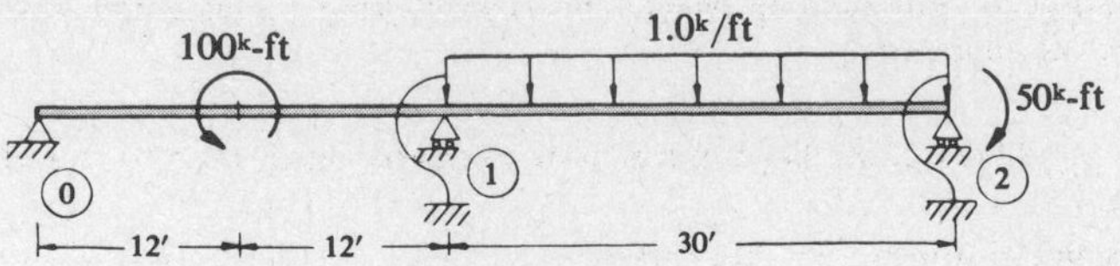

100k-ft 1.0k/ft 50k-ft
0 1 2
12' 12' 30'

Fig. P-7.7b

Girder 0123 of the given frame can be considered as a continuous beam supported and restrained by angular springs as shown in Fig. P-7.7*b*. The equivalent angular spring flexibilities can be computed as described in Section 7.4(b) and as shown in Fig. 7-5.

The compatibility equations (7.7*a*, *b*) written for the sections of release become

$$F_{10}X_{01} + (F_{11,1} + F_{1\theta})\,X_{10} - F_{1\theta}X_{12} + \tau_{10} = 0$$

$$-F_{1\theta}X_{10} + (F_{1\theta} + F_{11,2})\,X_{12} + F_{12}X_{21} + \tau_{12} = 0$$

$$F_{21}X_{12} + (F_{22,2} + F_{2\theta})\,X_{21} - F_{2\theta}X_{23} + \tau_{21} = 0$$

In the matrix form,

$$\begin{bmatrix} F_{11,1} + F_{1\theta} & -F_{1\theta} & 0 \\ -F_{1\theta} & F_{11,2} + F_{1\theta} & F_{12} \\ 0 & F_{21} & F_{22,2} + F_{2\theta} \end{bmatrix} \begin{bmatrix} X_{10} \\ X_{12} \\ X_{21} \end{bmatrix} + \begin{bmatrix} \tau_{10} \\ \tau_{12} \\ -F_{2\theta}X_{23} + \tau_{21} \end{bmatrix} = 0$$

where $F_{11,1} = s/3EI = 24/3EI = 8/EI, \quad F_{11,2} = s/3EI = 30/3EI = 10/EI$

$$F_{12} = F_{21} = s/6EI = 30/6EI = 5/EI$$

$$F_{1\theta} = \frac{1}{4EI/l_1 + 4EI/l_2} = \frac{1}{4EI/15 + 4EI/12} = 1.667/EI, \qquad F_{2\theta} = l/3EI = 12/3EI = 4/EI$$

$$\tau_{10} = Ql(1 - 3m^2)/6EI = -100(24)(1 - 3(0.5)^2)/6EI = -100/EI$$

$$\tau_{12} = \tau_{21} = pl^3/24EI = (1)(30)^3/24EI = 1{,}125/EI \qquad \text{and} \qquad X_{23} = -50.$$

Substitution of these values gives

$$\frac{1}{EI}\begin{bmatrix} 9.667 & -1.667 & 0 \\ -1.667 & 11.667 & 5 \\ 0 & 5 & 14 \end{bmatrix} \begin{bmatrix} X_{10} \\ X_{12} \\ X_{21} \end{bmatrix} + \frac{1}{EI}\begin{bmatrix} -100 \\ 1{,}125 \\ 1{,}325 \end{bmatrix} = 0$$

from which $X_{10} = -1.06$ k-ft, $X_{12} = -66.1$ k-ft, $X_{21} = -71.0$ k-ft.

7.8. Construct the system flexibility matrix for the rigid frame of Fig. P-7.7*a* by means of the transfer matrix q.

In the flexibility analysis, the governing system flexibility matrix has been shown to be $lW + fX = 0$ (5.6). The same equation was also shown expanded in terms of the general transfer matrix q in Problems 5.1 and 5.2,

$$q_X{}^T\lambda_s q_0 W + q_X{}^T\lambda_s q_X X = 0$$

It was further shown in Problems 5.7 and 5.8 that for applied loads of general type the load term in the equation above should be modified to be

$$q_X{}^T\lambda_s q_0 W + q_X{}^T\tau$$

When only flexural deformations are considered, the compatibility equations reduce to a more familiar form

$$\int \frac{m_i m_0\, ds}{EI_s} + \sum_j X_j \int \frac{m_i m_j\, ds}{EI_s} = 0 \qquad i = 1, 2, \ldots, n$$

in which

m_i = bending moment at any section in the basic structure due to $X_i = +1$

m_j = bending moment at any section in the basic structure due to $X_j = +1$

m_0 = bending moment at any section in the basic structure due to applied loads

have replaced the corresponding q influence values.

The integrals cited above can be evaluated easily by a semigraphical method, according to which, for constant EI over the range of an integral,

$$\int \frac{m_p m_q\, ds}{EI} = \frac{1}{EI}\text{(Area of } m_q \text{ diagram)(ordinate of the } m_p \text{ diagram at the centroid of the } m_q \text{ diagram)}$$

wherein m_p is a linear function in that range.

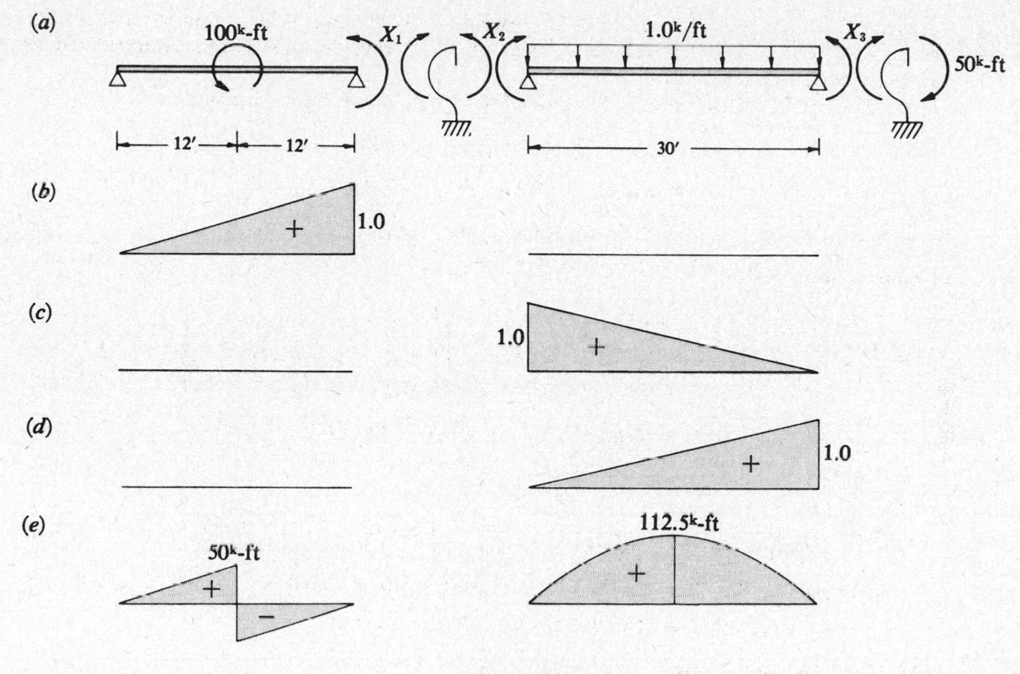

Fig. P-7.8

Fig. P-7.8a shows the basic structure (same as for Problem 7.7) with applied loads and redundants. Figures b, c, d and e respectively show the moment diagrams m_1, m_2, m_3 and m_0 due to $X_1 = +1$, $X_2 = +1$, $X_3 = +1$ and the applied loads. Accordingly, evaluating the integrals over proper ranges and including the elastic spring deformations,

$$\int \frac{m_1 m_1\, ds}{EI} = \frac{1}{EI}\left(\frac{1}{2}(24)(1)\right)\left(\frac{2}{3}\right) + \left(\frac{5}{3EI}\right)(1)(1) = \frac{29}{3EI}$$

$$\int \frac{m_1 m_2\, ds}{EI} = \int \frac{m_2 m_1\, ds}{EI} = \frac{1}{EI}(0) + \left(\frac{5}{3EI}\right)(1)(-1) = -\frac{5}{3EI}$$

$$\int \frac{m_1 m_3\, ds}{EI} = \int \frac{m_3 m_1\, ds}{EI} = \frac{1}{EI}(0) + \left(\frac{5}{3EI}\right)(0) + \left(\frac{4}{EI}\right)(0) = 0$$

$$\int \frac{m_2 m_2\, ds}{EI} = \frac{1}{EI}\left(\frac{1}{2}(30)(1)\right)\left(\frac{2}{3}\right) + \left(\frac{5}{3EI}\right)(1)(1) = \frac{35}{3EI}$$

$$\int \frac{m_2 m_3\, ds}{EI} = \int \frac{m_3 m_2\, ds}{EI} = \frac{1}{EI}\left(\frac{1}{2}(30)(1)\right)\left(\frac{1}{3}\right) + \left(\frac{5}{3EI}\right)(0) + \left(\frac{4}{EI}\right)(0) = \frac{5}{EI}$$

$$\int \frac{m_3 m_3\, ds}{EI} = \frac{1}{EI}\left(\frac{1}{2}(30)(1)\right)\left(\frac{2}{3}\right) + \left(\frac{4}{EI}\right)(1)(1) = \frac{14}{EI}$$

$$\int \frac{m_1 m_0\, ds}{EI} = \frac{1}{EI}\left[\left(\frac{1}{2}(12)(50)\right)\left(\frac{1}{3}\right) + \left(\frac{1}{2}(12)(-50)\right)\left(\frac{2}{3}\right)\right] + \left(\frac{5}{3EI}\right)(0) = -\frac{100}{EI}$$

$$\int \frac{m_2 m_0\, ds}{EI} = \frac{1}{EI}\left(\frac{2}{3}(30)\frac{900}{8}\right)\left(\frac{1}{2}\right) + \left(\frac{5}{3EI}\right)(0) = \frac{1{,}125}{EI}$$

$$\int \frac{m_3 m_0\, ds}{EI} = \frac{1}{EI}\left(\frac{2}{3}(30)\frac{900}{8}\right)\left(\frac{1}{2}\right) + \left(\frac{4}{EI}\right)(1)(50) = \frac{1{,}325}{EI}$$

Substitution in the compatibility equations gives, in the matrix form, the same result as in Problem 7.7:

$$\frac{1}{EI}\begin{bmatrix} \frac{29}{3} & -\frac{5}{3} & 0 \\ -\frac{5}{3} & \frac{35}{3} & 5 \\ 0 & 5 & 14 \end{bmatrix}\begin{bmatrix} X_1 \\ X_2 \\ X_3 \end{bmatrix} + \frac{1}{EI}\begin{bmatrix} -100 \\ 1{,}125 \\ 1{,}325 \end{bmatrix} = 0$$

7.9. Construct the governing matrix equation for the continuous beam on elastic supports of Fig. P-7.9a by means of the transfer matrix q and solve for the bending moments over the supports. Assume EI to be constant for the beam and linear flexibility of each spring to be $1{,}600/EI$ ft/k.

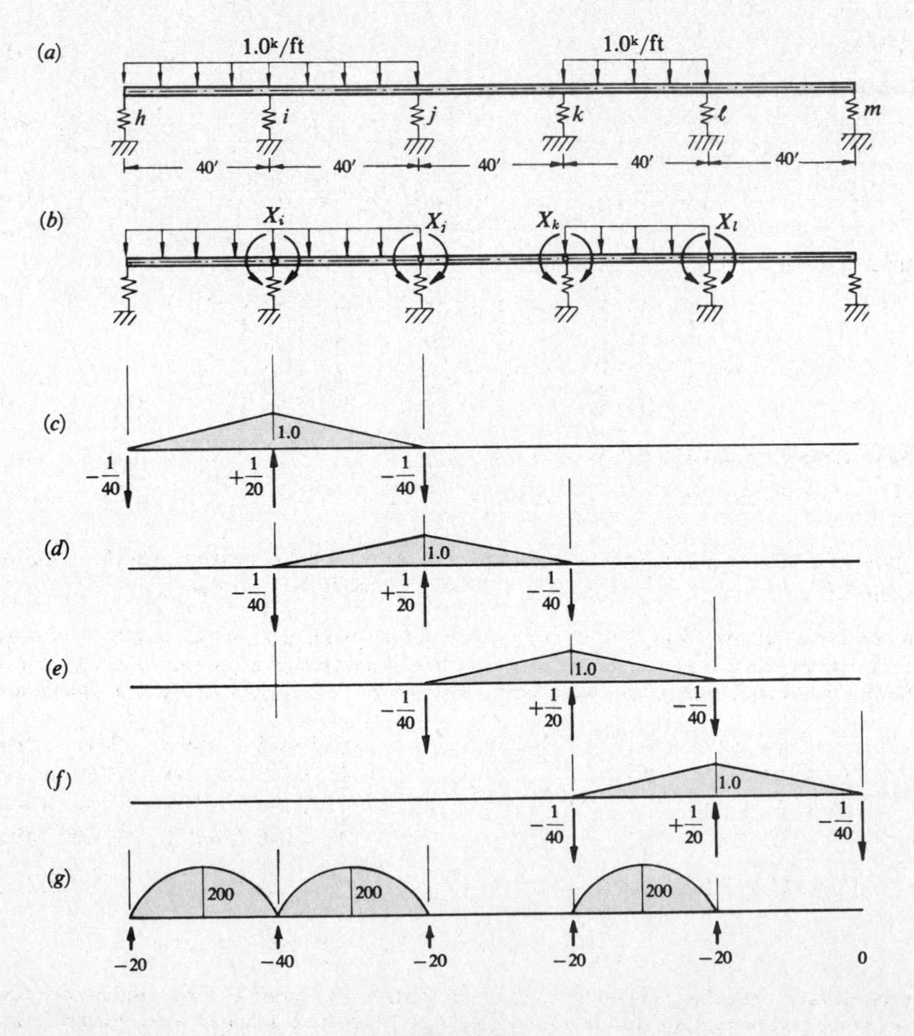

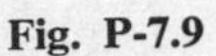
Fig. P-7.9

Figure b shows the releases and the redundants. Figures c, d, e, f and g show the moment diagrams for the basic structure and the spring forces due to unit redundants $X_i = +1$, $X_j = +1$, $X_k = +1$, $X_l = +1$ and the applied loads. The following integrals are computed from these using the semigraphical method explained in Problem 7.8.

$$\int \frac{m_i m_i\, ds}{EI} = \frac{1}{EI}\left[\left\{\frac{1}{2}(40)(1)\right\}\left(\frac{2}{3}\right)\right](2) + \frac{1{,}600}{EI}\left[\left(-\frac{1}{40}\right)\left(-\frac{1}{40}\right) + \left(\frac{1}{20}\right)\left(\frac{1}{20}\right) + \left(-\frac{1}{40}\right)\left(-\frac{1}{40}\right)\right] = \frac{98}{3EI}$$

By inspection of the diagrams it is noted that

$$\int \frac{m_j m_j\, ds}{EI} = \int \frac{m_k m_k\, ds}{EI} = \int \frac{m_l m_l\, ds}{EI} = \int \frac{m_i m_i\, ds}{EI} = \frac{98}{3EI}$$

$$\int \frac{m_i m_j\, ds}{EI} = \int \frac{m_j m_i\, ds}{EI} = \frac{1}{EI}\left[\left\{\frac{1}{2}(40)(1)\right\}\left(\frac{1}{3}\right)\right] + \frac{1{,}600}{EI}\left[\left(\frac{1}{20}\right)\left(-\frac{1}{40}\right) + \left(-\frac{1}{40}\right)\left(\frac{1}{20}\right)\right] = \frac{8}{3EI}$$

Also $$\int \frac{m_j m_k\, ds}{EI} = \int \frac{m_k m_j\, ds}{EI} = \int \frac{m_k m_l\, ds}{EI} = \int \frac{m_l m_k\, ds}{EI} = \int \frac{m_i m_j\, ds}{EI} = \frac{8}{3EI}$$

$$\int \frac{m_i m_k\, ds}{EI} = \int \frac{m_k m_i\, ds}{EI} = \frac{1{,}600}{EI}\left[\left(-\frac{1}{40}\right)\left(-\frac{1}{40}\right)\right] = \frac{1}{EI} = \int \frac{m_j m_l\, ds}{EI} = \int \frac{m_l m_j\, ds}{EI}$$

$$\int \frac{m_i m_l\, ds}{EI} = \int \frac{m_l m_i\, ds}{EI} = 0$$

$$\int \frac{m_i m_0\, ds}{EI} = \frac{1}{EI}\left[\left\{\frac{2}{3}(40)(200)\right\}\left(\frac{1}{2}\right)\right](2) + \frac{1{,}600}{EI}\left[\left(-\frac{1}{40}\right)(-20) + \left(\frac{1}{20}\right)(-40) + \left(-\frac{1}{40}\right)(-20)\right] = \frac{11{,}200}{3EI}$$

$$\int \frac{m_j m_0\, ds}{EI} = \frac{1}{EI}\left[\left\{\frac{2}{3}(40)(200)\right\}\left(\frac{1}{2}\right)\right] + \frac{1{,}600}{EI}\left[\left(-\frac{1}{40}\right)(-40) + \left(\frac{1}{20}\right)(-20) + \left(-\frac{1}{40}\right)(-20)\right] = \frac{10{,}400}{3EI}$$

$$\int \frac{m_k m_0\, ds}{EI} = \frac{1}{EI}\left[\left\{\frac{2}{3}(40)(200)\right\}\left(\frac{1}{2}\right)\right] + \frac{1{,}600}{EI}\left[\left(-\frac{1}{40}\right)(-20) + \left(\frac{1}{20}\right)(-20) + \left(-\frac{1}{40}\right)(-20)\right] = \frac{8{,}000}{3EI}$$

$$\int \frac{m_l m_0\, ds}{EI} = \frac{1}{EI}\left[\left\{\frac{2}{3}(40)(200)\right\}\left(\frac{1}{2}\right)\right] + \frac{1{,}600}{EI}\left[\left(-\frac{1}{40}\right)(-20) + \left(\frac{1}{20}\right)(-20) + \left(-\frac{1}{40}\right)(0)\right] = \frac{5{,}600}{3EI}$$

Substitution in the compatibility equations gives

$$\frac{1}{3EI}\begin{bmatrix} 11{,}200 \\ 10{,}400 \\ 8{,}000 \\ 5{,}600 \end{bmatrix} + \frac{1}{3EI}\begin{bmatrix} 98 & 8 & 3 & 0 \\ 8 & 98 & 8 & 3 \\ 3 & 8 & 98 & 8 \\ 0 & 3 & 8 & 98 \end{bmatrix}\begin{bmatrix} X_i \\ X_j \\ X_k \\ X_l \end{bmatrix} = 0$$

Solving this gives the redundant support moments

$$X_i = -104.87\text{ k-ft}, \qquad X_j = -90.60\text{ k-ft}, \qquad X_k = -67.04\text{ k-ft}, \qquad X_l = -48.91\text{ k-ft}$$

7.10. Compute the influence line for the bending moment over the support j in the continuous beam of Problem 7.9.

As demonstrated in Problem 7.6, the influence line for a redundant moment can be constructed from the governing matrix equation of a system, in terms of the variation of the load functions τ's due to a unit moving load.

For the continuous beam on elastic supports, of Problem 7.9, the system flexibility matrix $[F]$ and its inverse are

$$[F] = \frac{1}{3EI}\begin{bmatrix} 98 & 8 & 3 & 0 \\ 8 & 98 & 8 & 3 \\ 3 & 8 & 98 & 8 \\ 0 & 3 & 8 & 98 \end{bmatrix} \quad \text{and} \quad [F]^{-1} = \frac{3EI}{1{,}000}\begin{bmatrix} 10.279 & -0.820 & -0.251 & 0.046 \\ -0.820 & 10.344 & -0.799 & -0.251 \\ -0.251 & -0.799 & 10.344 & -0.820 \\ 0.046 & -0.251 & -0.820 & 10.279 \end{bmatrix}$$

Therefore from $\{X\} = -[F]^{-1}\{\tau\}$ in which $\{X\} = \{X_i, X_j, X_k, X_l\}$,

$$X_j = -\frac{3EI}{1{,}000}(-0.820\tau_i + 10.344\tau_j - 0.799\tau_k - 0.251\tau_l)$$

The τ values (and then the value of X_j) can now be described in terms of load position in various spans. These τ values, in the case of beams on elastic supports, are (*a*) due to the bending of basic spans as in the case of beams on rigid supports and (*b*) due to the displacements of supports because of the spring deformations.

The τ values on a basic span pq of constant cross section due to flexural deformation have been noted to be

$$\tau_{pq} = (2l^2x - 3lx^2 + x^3)/6lEI$$

$$\tau_{qp} = (l^2x - x^3)/6lEI$$

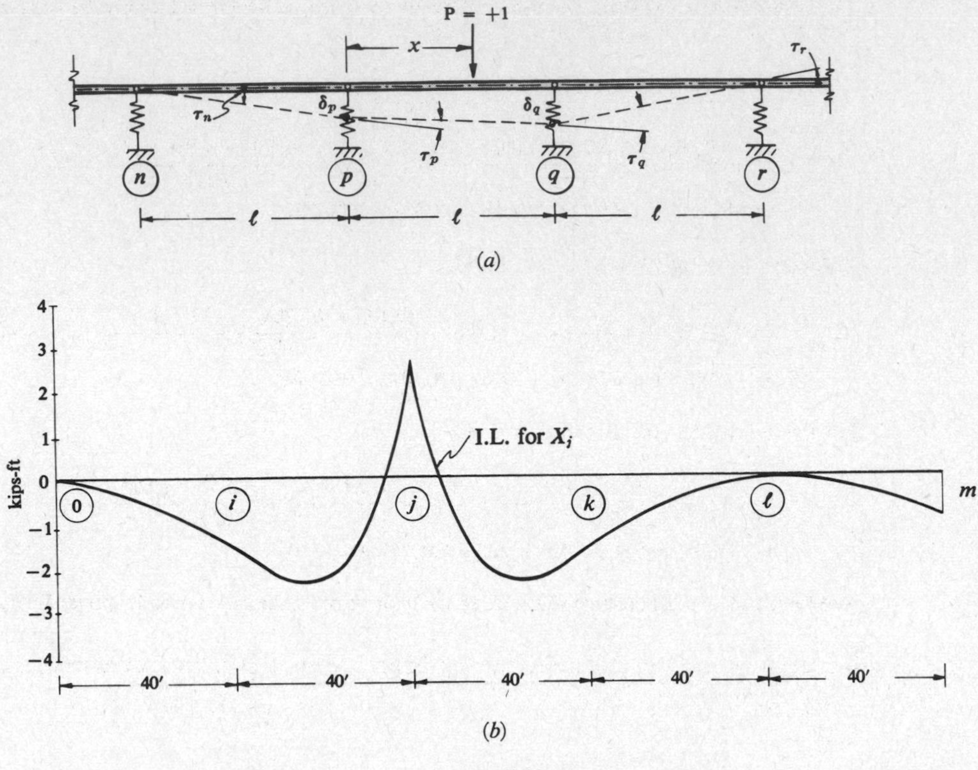

Fig. P-7.10

The τ values due to spring deformations can be computed by examining Fig. P-7.10*a*. For a unit load in the span *pq* of any basic structure ... *npqr* ... with equal spans and identical spring supports,

$$\tau_n = \tau_{np} = \frac{\delta_p}{l} - \frac{l - x}{l^2} F_\delta$$

$$\tau_p = \tau_{pn} + \tau_{pq} = -\frac{\delta_p}{l} + \frac{\delta_q - \delta_p}{l} = \frac{\delta_q - 2\delta_p}{l} = \frac{x - 2(l - x)}{l^2} F_\delta = \frac{3x - 2l}{l^2} F_\delta$$

$$\tau_q = \tau_{qp} + \tau_{qr} = -\frac{\delta_q - \delta_p}{l} - \frac{\delta_q}{l} = \frac{\delta_p - 2\delta_q}{l} = \frac{(l - x) - 2x}{l^2} F_\delta = \frac{l - 3x}{l^2} F_\delta$$

$$\tau_r = \frac{\delta_q}{l} = \frac{x}{l^2} F_\delta$$

For the unit load in span $0i$ $(0 < x < 40)$,

$$\tau_i = \frac{(l^2 x - x^3)}{6lEI} + \frac{l - 3x}{l^2} F_\delta = \frac{1{,}600x - x^3}{240EI} + \frac{40 - 3x}{1{,}600} \frac{1{,}600}{EI} = \frac{9{,}600 + 880x - x^3}{240EI}$$

$$\tau_j = \frac{x}{l^2} F_\delta = \frac{x}{1{,}600} \frac{1{,}600}{EI} = \frac{x}{EI}, \qquad \tau_k = \tau_m = 0$$

$$X_j = (984 - 220.1x - 0.1025x^3)/10{,}000$$

For the unit load in span ij $(0 < x < 40)$,

$$\tau_i = \frac{(2l^2 x - 3lx^2 + x^3)}{6lEI} + \frac{3x - 2l}{l^2} F_\delta = \frac{3{,}200x - 120x^2 + x^3}{240EI} + \frac{3x - 80}{1{,}600} \frac{1{,}600}{EI}$$

$$= \frac{-19{,}200 + 3{,}920x - 120x^2 + x^3}{240EI}$$

$$\tau_j = \frac{l^2 x - x^3}{6lEI} + \frac{l - 3x}{l^2} F_\delta = \frac{1{,}600x - x^3}{240EI} + \frac{40 - 3x}{1{,}600} \frac{1{,}600}{EI} = \frac{9{,}600 + 880x - x^3}{240EI}$$

$$\tau_k = \frac{x}{l^2} F_\delta = \frac{x}{1{,}600} \frac{1600}{EI} = \frac{x}{EI}, \qquad \tau_l = 0$$

$$X_j = (-14{,}381 - 712.1x - 12.3x^2 + 1.3955x^3)/10{,}000$$

The recurrence of τ expressions can be observed and the remaining values can be written down by inspection. For the unit load in span jk $(0 < x < 40)$,

$$\tau_i = \frac{l - x}{l^2} F_\delta = \frac{40 - x}{1{,}600} \frac{1{,}600}{EI} = \frac{40 - x}{EI}$$

$$\tau_j = \frac{-19{,}200 + 3{,}920x - 120x^2 + x^3}{240EI}, \qquad \tau_k = \frac{9{,}600 + 880x - x^3}{240EI}, \qquad \tau_l = \frac{x}{EI}$$

$$X_j = (26{,}768 - 4{,}998x + 155.2x^2 - 1.3928x^3)/10{,}000$$

For the unit load in span kl $(0 < x < 40)$,

$$\tau_i = 0, \qquad \tau_j = \frac{40 - x}{EI}, \qquad \tau_k = \frac{-19{,}200 + 3{,}920x - 120x^2 + x^3}{240EI}, \qquad \tau_l = \frac{9{,}600 + 880x - x^3}{240EI}$$

$$X_j = (-14{,}029 + 729x - 11.99x^2 + 0.0685x^3)/10{,}000$$

For the unit load in span lm $(0 < x < 40)$,

$$\tau_i = \tau_j = 0, \qquad \tau_k = \frac{40 - x}{EI}, \qquad \tau_l = \frac{-19{,}200 + 3{,}920x - 120x^2 + x^3}{240EI}$$

$$X_j = (356 + 99x - 3.77x^2 + 0.03138x^3)/10{,}000$$

The influence line for X_j computed using the expressions obtained above is shown in Fig. P-7.10*b*.

7.11. Derive the analytical expressions for the linear spring flexibilities of the members shown in Fig. P-7.11*a*, *b*, *c*, *d*, *e*.

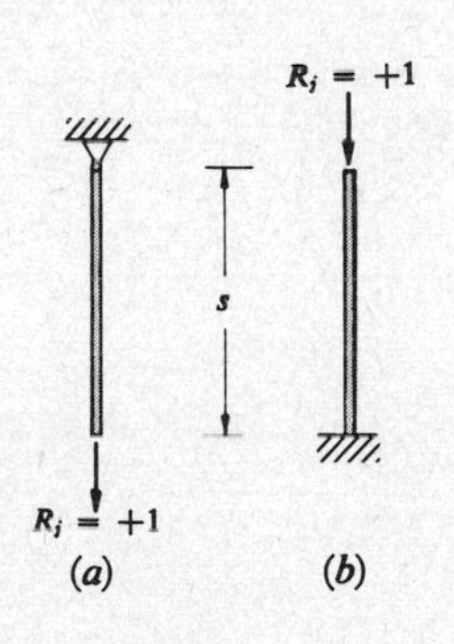

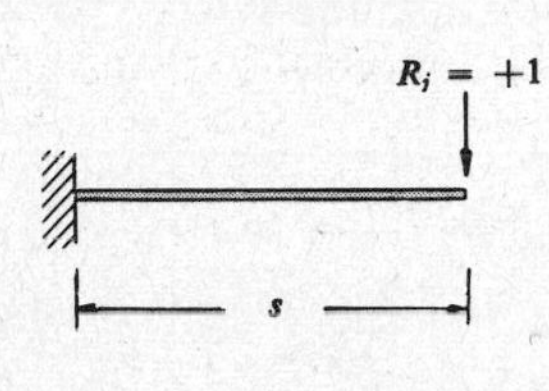

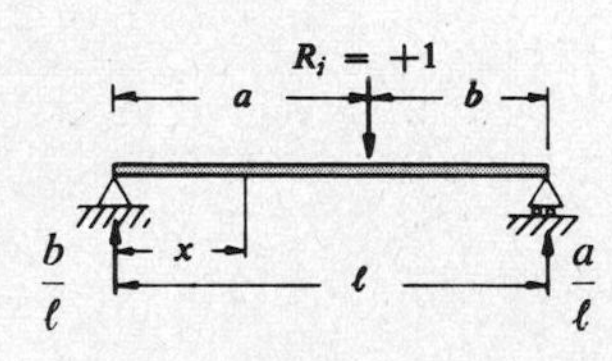

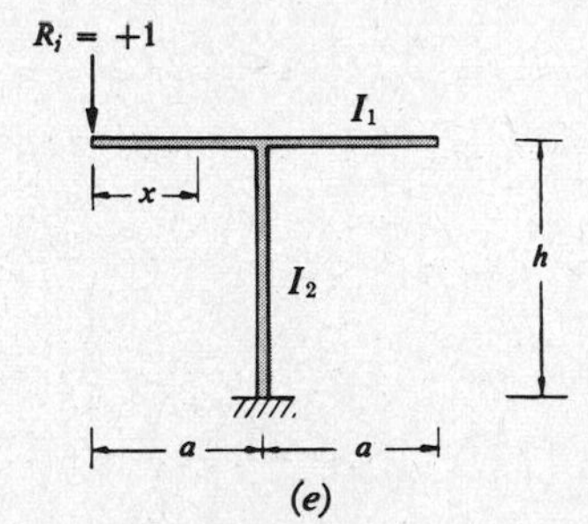

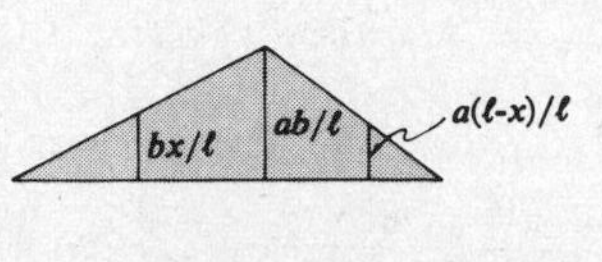

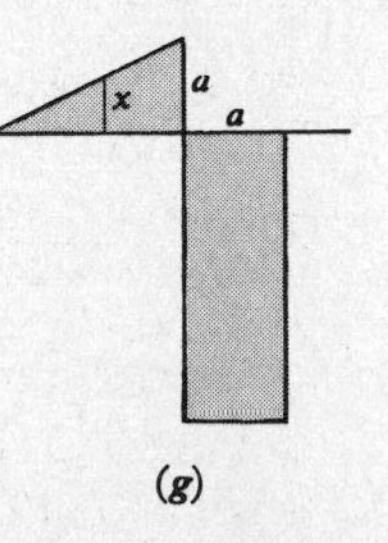

Fig. P-7.11

The cases shown in Fig. (*a*) and (*b*) are virtually the same. In both, linear axial flexibilities are required which have already been calculated in Table 5-1, as was the linear flexibility of the cantilever bar of Fig. (*c*) under an applied transverse end force. Thus from Table 5-1, for (*a*) and (*b*),

$$F_{\delta j} = s/EA$$

and for (*c*),

$$F_{\delta j} = s^3/3EI$$

For cases (*d*) and (*e*), by (*5.8*) (considering only flexural deformations),

$$F_{\delta j} = \int \frac{M_s M_s \, ds}{EI_s}$$

where M_s = bending moment induced at a section due to a unit force applied at j.

Figures (*f*) and (*g*) show the moment diagrams for the members shown in (*d*) and (*e*), induced by forces $R_j = +1$. Then for the member shown in (*d*),

$$F_{\delta j} = \int_0^a \left(\frac{bx}{l}\right)^2 \frac{dx}{EI} + \int_a^l \left(\frac{a(l-x)}{l}\right)^2 \frac{dx}{EI} = \frac{a^2b^2}{3lEI}, \qquad \text{for } EI = \text{constant}$$

And for the member shown in (*e*),

$$F_{\delta j} = \int_0^a x^2 \frac{dx}{EI_1} + \int_0^h a^2 \frac{dx}{EI_2} = \frac{a^3}{3EI_1} + \frac{a^2h}{EI_2}$$

7.12. Compute the moments over the supports due to prestress in the three span continuous prestressed concrete girder of constant section shown in Fig. P-7.12. The prestressing force is 660 k and the cable profile is parabolic.

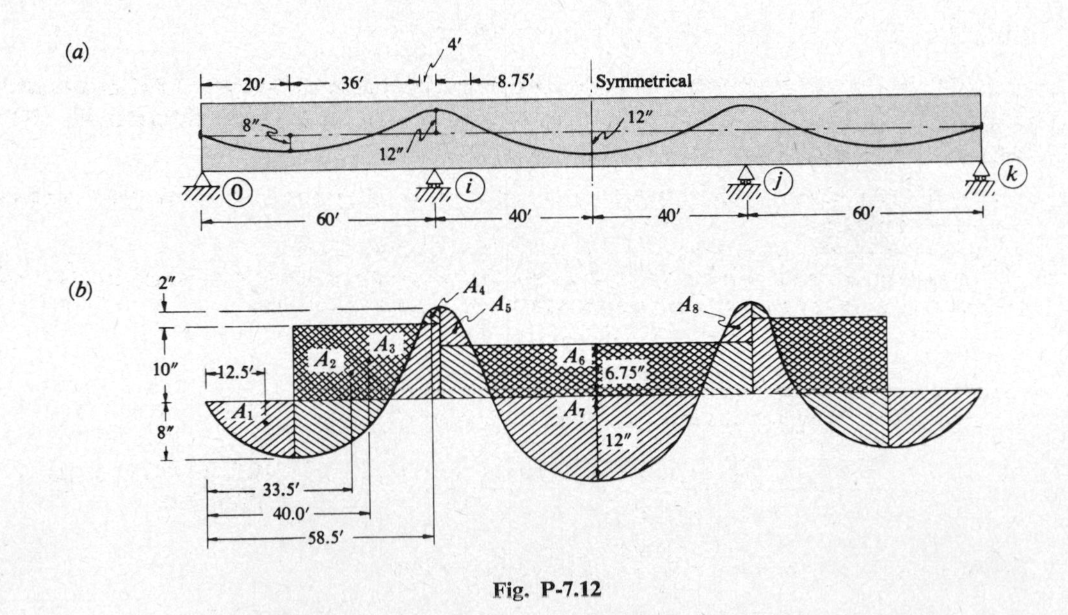

Fig. P-7.12

The effect of an eccentric cable profile in a prestressed girder causes internal moments on sections and thus induces deformations similar to those caused by transverse loads. Redundant moments can be found in exactly the same manner as for any other causes, using (*7.2*).

The end slopes of a simple span ij developed by the prestressing force H and the eccentricity of the cable, e, are

$$\tau_{ij} = \int_0^{l_j} \frac{Hex'\,dx}{l_jEI} \qquad \text{and} \qquad \tau_{ji} = \int_0^{l_j} \frac{Hex\,dx}{l_jEI}$$

Alternately,

$$\tau_{ij} = \text{(static moment about } j \text{ of the } He/EI \text{ diagram of span } ij)/l_j$$

$$\tau_{ji} = \text{(static moment about } i \text{ of the } He/EI \text{ diagram of span } ij)/l_j$$

In this problem the τ values are computed accordingly using the e diagram (cable profile diagram), since H and EI are constant. Advantage is taken of known properties of standard shapes of areas obtained by regrouping the cable profile diagram as shown in Fig. P-7.12(b). Thus

$$\tau_{i0} = \tau_{jk} = \frac{H}{EI}(A_1x_1 + A_2x_2 + A_3x_3 + A_4x_4)/l_i$$

$$= \frac{660}{60EI}\left[-\frac{2}{3}(20)\left(\frac{8}{12}\right)(12.5) - \frac{2}{3}(36)\left(\frac{18}{12}\right)(33.5) + (40)\left(\frac{10}{12}\right)(40) + \frac{2}{3}(4)\left(\frac{2}{12}\right)(58.5)\right] = 464.44/EI$$

$$\tau_{ij} = \tau_{ji} = \frac{H}{EI}(A_5x_5 + A_6x_6 + A_7x_7 + A_8x_8)/l_i = \frac{H}{EI}\left[\frac{1}{2}(A_5 + A_6 + A_7 + A_8)\right]$$

$$= \frac{660}{2EI}\left[\frac{2}{3}(8.75)\left(\frac{5.25}{12}\right) + (80)\left(\frac{6.75}{12}\right) - \frac{2}{3}(62.5)\left(\frac{18.75}{12}\right) + \frac{2}{3}(8.75)\left(\frac{5.25}{12}\right)\right] = -4{,}950/EI$$

$$\tau_i = \tau_{i0} + \tau_{ij} = -4{,}485.56/EI = \tau_j$$

By Table 5-2,

$$F_{ii(\text{Left})} = F_{jj(\text{Right})} = s/3EI = 60/3EI = 20/EI$$

$$F_{ii(\text{Right})} = F_{jj(\text{Left})} = s/3EI = 80/3EI = 26.67/EI$$

$$F_{ij} = F_{ji} = s/6EI = 80/6EI = 13.33/EI$$

$$F_i = F_{ii(\text{Left})} + F_{ii(\text{Right})} = 46.67/EI = F_j$$

In terms of these constants,

$$\frac{1}{EI}\begin{bmatrix} 46.67 & 13.33 \\ 13.33 & 46.67 \end{bmatrix}\begin{bmatrix} X_i \\ X_j \end{bmatrix} + \frac{1}{EI}\begin{bmatrix} -4{,}485.56 \\ -4{,}485.56 \end{bmatrix} = 0$$

from which

$$X_i = X_j = 74.76 \text{ k-ft}$$

7.13. Compute the moments developed at the supports in the beam of Problem 7.4 due to a linear temperature variation of 40° F between the bottom side and the top side of the beam. The beam is of W 21X55 steel section.

For the given beam, $E = 29 \times 10^3$ k/in², $I = 1{,}140.7$ in⁴, $h = 20.8$ in and the coefficient of thermal expansion $\alpha = 6.5 \times 10^{-6}$ in/in/°F.

In k-ft units, $EI = 29 \times 10^3 \times 144 \times 1{,}140.7/(12)^4 = 229{,}724.3$ k-ft².

The governing matrix equation for the beam remains the same as in Problem 7.4 except that the τ values due to loads are replaced by the τ values due to temperature effect. In symbolic form,

$$[F]\{X\} + \{\tau\} = 0$$

and $[F]$ remains unchanged.

The τ values due to temperature effect are computed using (7.5). Thus

$$\tau_{i0} = \tau_{km} = \int_0^{l_i} \frac{(\epsilon_B - \epsilon_T)\,x\,dx}{l_i h_i} = \int_0^{l_k} \frac{(\alpha T_B - \alpha T_T)\,x\,dx}{l_i h_i} = \int_0^{36} \frac{40(6.5)\,10^{-6} x\,dx}{36(20.8/12)} = 0.0027$$

Similarly $\tau_{ij} = \tau_{ji} = \tau_{jk} = \tau_{kj} = \displaystyle\int_0^{48} \frac{40(6.5)\,10^{-6} x\,dx}{48(20.8/12)} = 0.0036$

$$\tau_i = \tau_{i0} + \tau_{ij} = 0.0063 = \tau_k \quad \text{and} \quad \tau_j = \tau_{ji} + \tau_{jk} = 0.0072.$$

Substituting in the governing matrix equation gives

$$\frac{1}{229{,}724.3}\begin{bmatrix} 28 & 8 & 0 \\ 8 & 32 & 8 \\ 0 & 8 & 28 \end{bmatrix}\begin{bmatrix} X_i \\ X_j \\ X_k \end{bmatrix} + \begin{bmatrix} 0.0063 \\ 0.0072 \\ 0.0063 \end{bmatrix} = 0$$

from which

$$X_i = X_k = -43.07 \text{ k-ft} \quad \text{and} \quad X_j = -30.15 \text{ k-ft}.$$

7.14. Compute the influence of unit settlements of supports i and j on the moments at the supports for the beam of Problem 7.13.

As in Problem 7.13, the governing matrix equation for the beam remains the same. The τ values, however, are due to the settlement of supports. Figures P-7.14a and b respectively show the τ values generated by a unit settlement of support i and of support j.

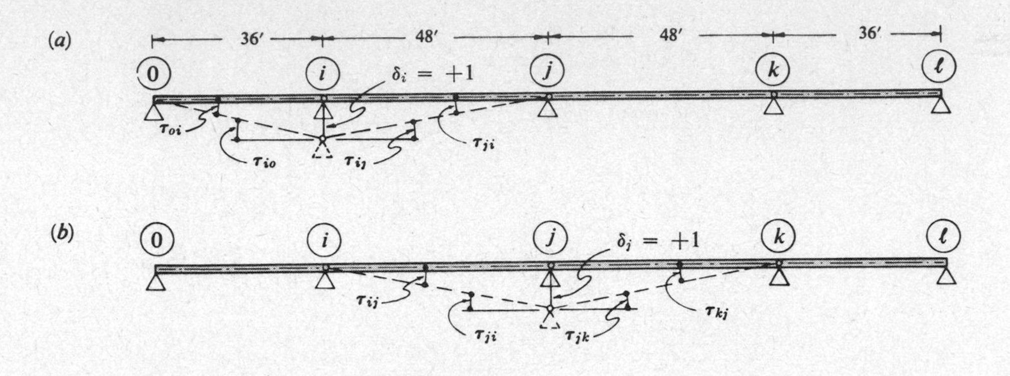

Fig. P-7.14

From these figures, for a unit settlement of support at i,

$$\tau_{io} = -1/36, \qquad \tau_{ij} = -\tau_{ji} = -1/48, \qquad \tau_{jk} = \tau_{kj} = \tau_{km} = 0$$

$$\tau_i = \tau_{io} + \tau_{ij} = -7/144, \qquad \tau_j = \tau_{ji} + \tau_{jk} = 1/48, \qquad \tau_k = \tau_{kj} + \tau_{km} = 0, \qquad \tau = \{-7/144, 1/48, 0\}$$

Substitution in the governing matrix equation gives

$$\frac{1}{229{,}724.3}\begin{bmatrix} 28 & 8 & 0 \\ 8 & 32 & 8 \\ 0 & 8 & 28 \end{bmatrix}\begin{bmatrix} X_i \\ X_j \\ X_k \end{bmatrix} + \begin{bmatrix} -7/144 \\ 1/48 \\ 0 \end{bmatrix} = 0$$

from which, for $\delta_i = +1$,

$$X_i = +481.9 \text{ k-ft}, \qquad X_j = -290.8 \text{ k-ft}, \qquad X_k = +83.1 \text{ k-ft}$$

Similarly for a unit settlement of support at j,

$$\tau_{io} = \tau_{km} = 0, \qquad \tau_{ij} = -\tau_{ji} = -\tau_{jk} = \tau_{kj} = 1/48$$

$$\tau_i = 1/48, \qquad \tau_j = -2/48 \quad \text{and} \quad \tau_k = 1/48$$

The τ vector for $\delta_j = +1$ becomes $\{1/48, -2/48, 1/48\}$ which when substituted in the governing matrix equation in the same way as shown above for $\delta_i = +1$, gives

$$X_i = X_k = -299.1 \text{ k-ft} \quad \text{and} \quad X_j = +448.7 \text{ k-ft} \quad \text{for} \quad \delta_j = +1$$

Supplementary Problems

7.15. Using the three-moment equation (*7.2*) compute the moments over the supports in the four span continuous beam of Fig. P-7.15. The beam has a constant section.

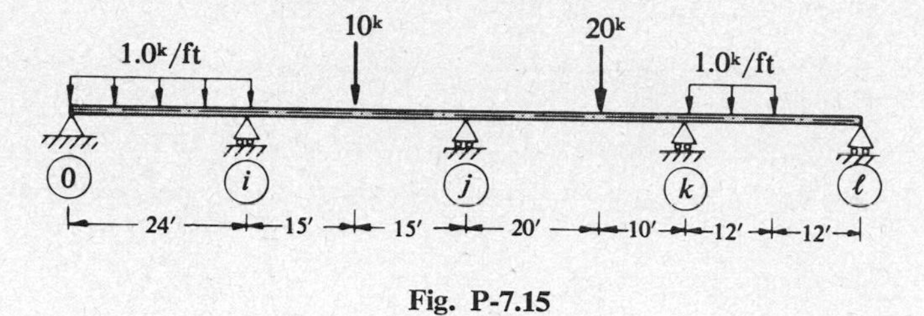

Fig. P-7.15

7.16. Use the three-moment equation (*7.2*) to compute the moments over the supports in the continuous beam of Fig. P-7.16. EI = constant.

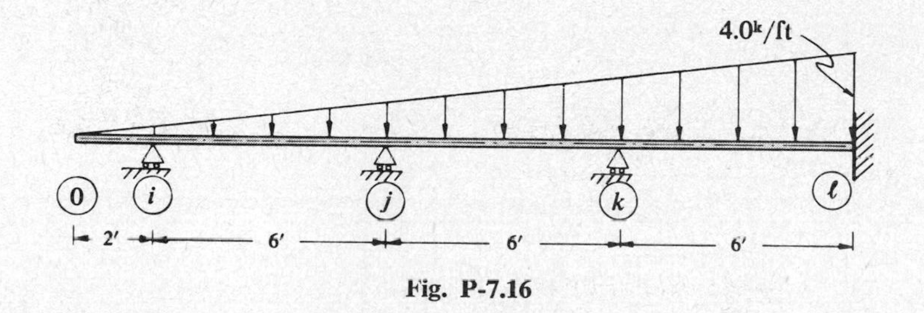

Fig. P-7.16

7.17. Compute the moments over the supports in the three span continuous beam shown in Fig. P-7.17. Use $EI_1 = 1.5EI$.

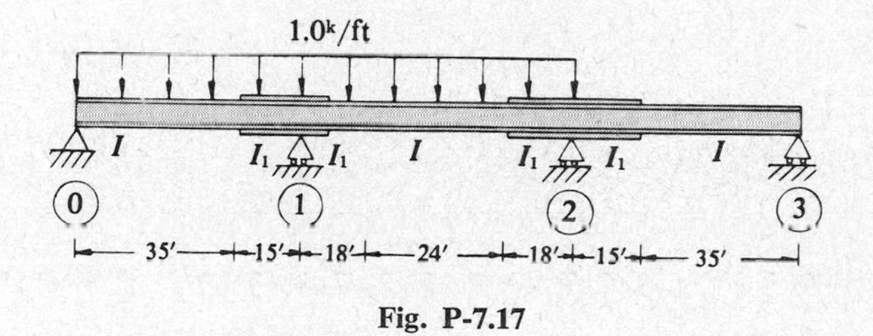

Fig. P-7.17

7.18. For the beam of Problem 7.16 compute the influence on the moments over supports of (*a*) a unit settlement of support at *j*, (*b*) 5° counterclockwise rotation of the fixed end at *l*.

7.19. Compute the moments over the supports of the three span continuous beam of variable cross section in Fig. P-7.19.

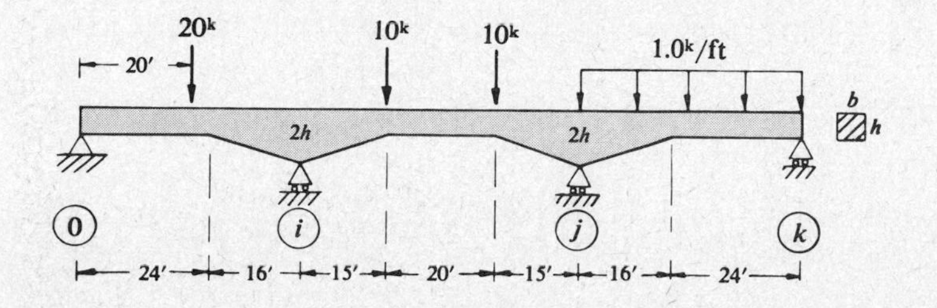

Fig. P-7.19

7.20. Compute and plot the influence line for the moment over support 1 of the three span variable cross section beam of Problem 7.5.

7.21. Use (*7.7a, b*) to compute the end moments in the girder of the frame shown in Fig. P-7.21. Assume EI to be constant for the entire frame.

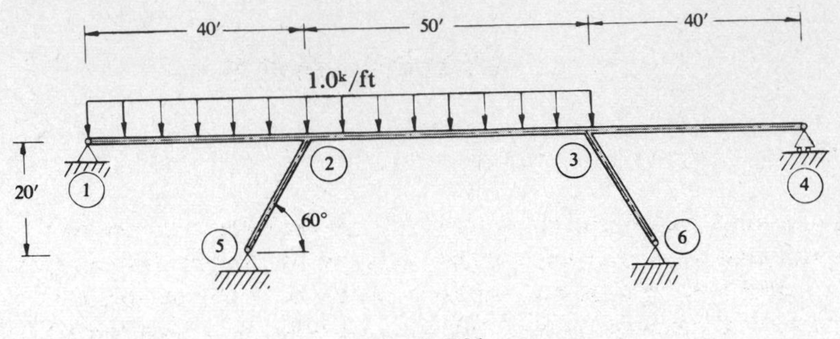

Fig. P-7.21

7.22. Compute the end moments in the girder of the frame shown in Fig. P-7.22. EI = constant.

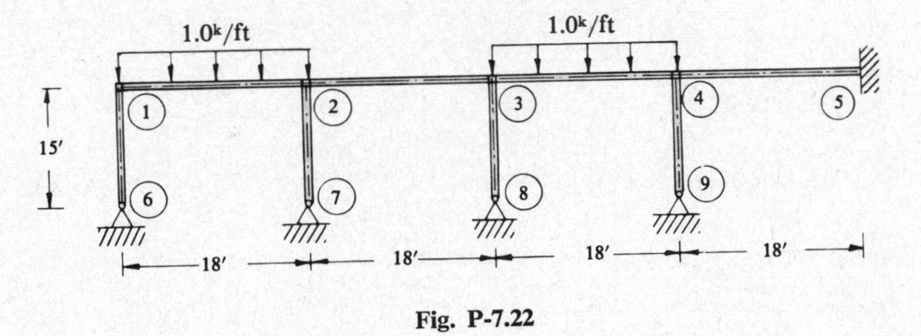

Fig. P-7.22

7.23. Using the five-moment equation compute the moments over the supports i and j in the girder $0ijk$ of the system shown in Fig. P-7.23. Assume that EI for the supporting girders mn and pq is twice that of the girder $0ijk$.

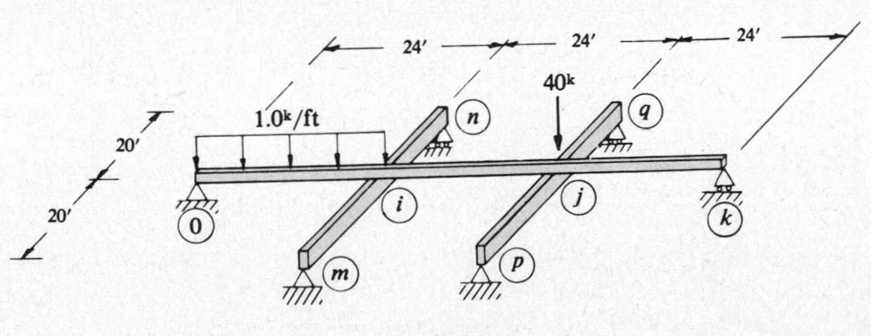

Fig. P-7.23

Chapter 8

Elastic Arch

8.1 SYSTEM

Although the designation *arch* is, in general, reserved for a curved bar capable of developing a horizontal thrust (when acted upon by vertical loads), in this volume (for convenience) *all curved bars are called arches*. Furthermore they are assumed to be *slender* (flexible) members and denoted as *elastic arches*. On the basis of statical behavior, planar arches are classified as *statically determinate* (Fig. 8-1*a*, *b*, *c*) or *statically indeterminate* (Fig. 8-1*d*, *e*, *f*). Frequently they are parts of a complex structure, in which case the designation of *elastically restrained arches* is used.

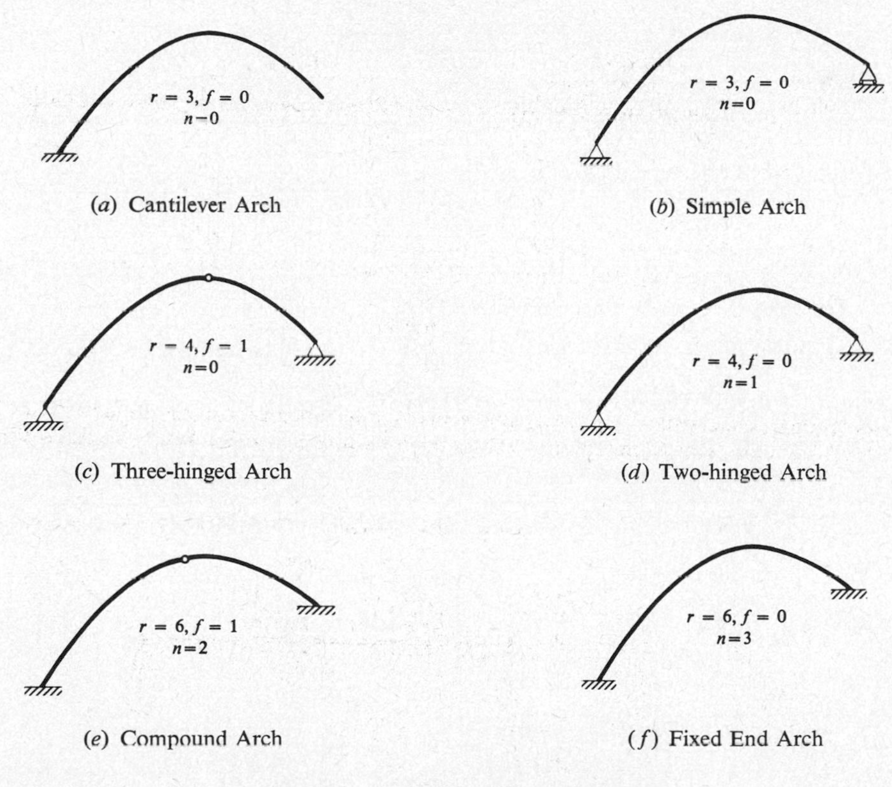

(*a*) Cantilever Arch (*b*) Simple Arch

(*c*) Three-hinged Arch (*d*) Two-hinged Arch

(*e*) Compound Arch (*f*) Fixed End Arch

Fig. 8-1. Single Span Elastic Arches

Their *degree of statical indeterminacy* is governed by the *number of redundants n*,

$$n = r - f - 3 > 0 \tag{8.1}$$

where as in (*7.1*), r = number of independent reactions, f = number of special conditions. If $n = 0$ the arch is *statically determinate*, and if $n < 0$ the arch is *geometrically unstable* and unsuitable to carry loads.

The object of this chapter is the development of the *segmental flexibility matrix* for a planar arch of general shape and the application of this matrix in the analysis of *single span* and *continuous arches*. The general application of this matrix in the analysis of *rigid frames* with curved members follows in the next chapter.

8.2 SEGMENTAL FLEXIBILITY MATRIX

The coefficients of the segmental flexibility matrix for a planar arch are again derived by means of (*5.10*) and (*5.11*) from the segmental basic structures of which the most typical ones are the cantilever arch and the simple arch (however, a three-hinged arch can also be used for this purpose).

(a) Segmental Flexibilities, Cantilever Arch

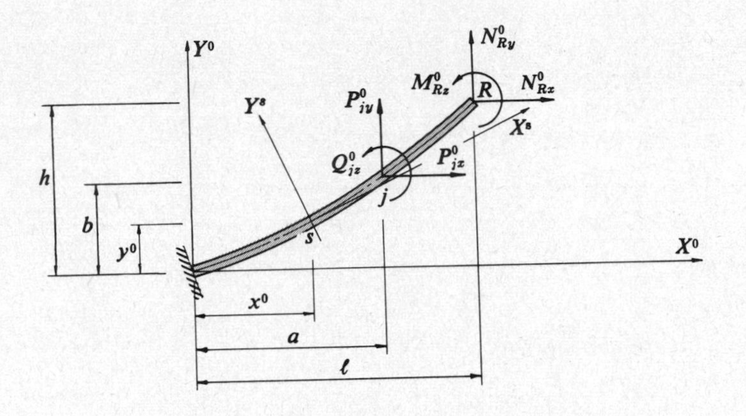

Fig. 8-2. Segmental Basic Structure, Cantilever Arch

For the cantilever arch of Fig. 8-2 the *unit stress flexibility matrix* is

$$f = \int_L^R q_X^{)T} \lambda_s q_X = \begin{bmatrix} C_{RRxx} & C_{RRxy} & B_{RRxz} \\ C_{RRyx} & C_{RRyy} & B_{RRyz} \\ B_{RRzx} & B_{RRzy} & A_{RRzz} \end{bmatrix} \tag{8.2}$$

where $$q_X = \begin{bmatrix} 1 & 0 & 0 \\ 0 & 1 & 0 \\ -(h-y) & l-x & 1 \end{bmatrix} \quad \text{and} \quad \lambda_s = \begin{bmatrix} \lambda_{sxx} & \lambda_{sxy} & 0 \\ \lambda_{syx} & \lambda_{syy} & 0 \\ 0 & 0 & \lambda_{szz} \end{bmatrix}$$

Similarly, the *unit load flexibility matrix* is

$$l = \int_L^R q_X^{)T} \lambda_s q_0 = \begin{bmatrix} C_{RPxx} & C_{RPxy} & B_{RQxz} \\ C_{RPyx} & C_{RPyy} & B_{RQyz} \\ B_{RPzx} & B_{RPzy} & A_{RQzz} \end{bmatrix} \tag{8.3}$$

where $$q_0(x = 0 \to a) = \begin{bmatrix} 1 & 0 & 0 \\ 0 & 1 & 0 \\ -(b-y) & a-x & 1 \end{bmatrix} \quad \text{and} \quad q_0(x = a \to l) = \begin{bmatrix} 0 & 0 & 0 \\ 0 & 0 & 0 \\ 0 & 0 & 0 \end{bmatrix}$$

The analytical expressions for coefficients of (*8.2*) and (*8.3*) are given in Table 8-1. The coefficients of λ_s are already known (*3.4*). The superscript 0 is omitted in all terms.

Table 8-1. Segmental Flexibilities, Cantilever Arch

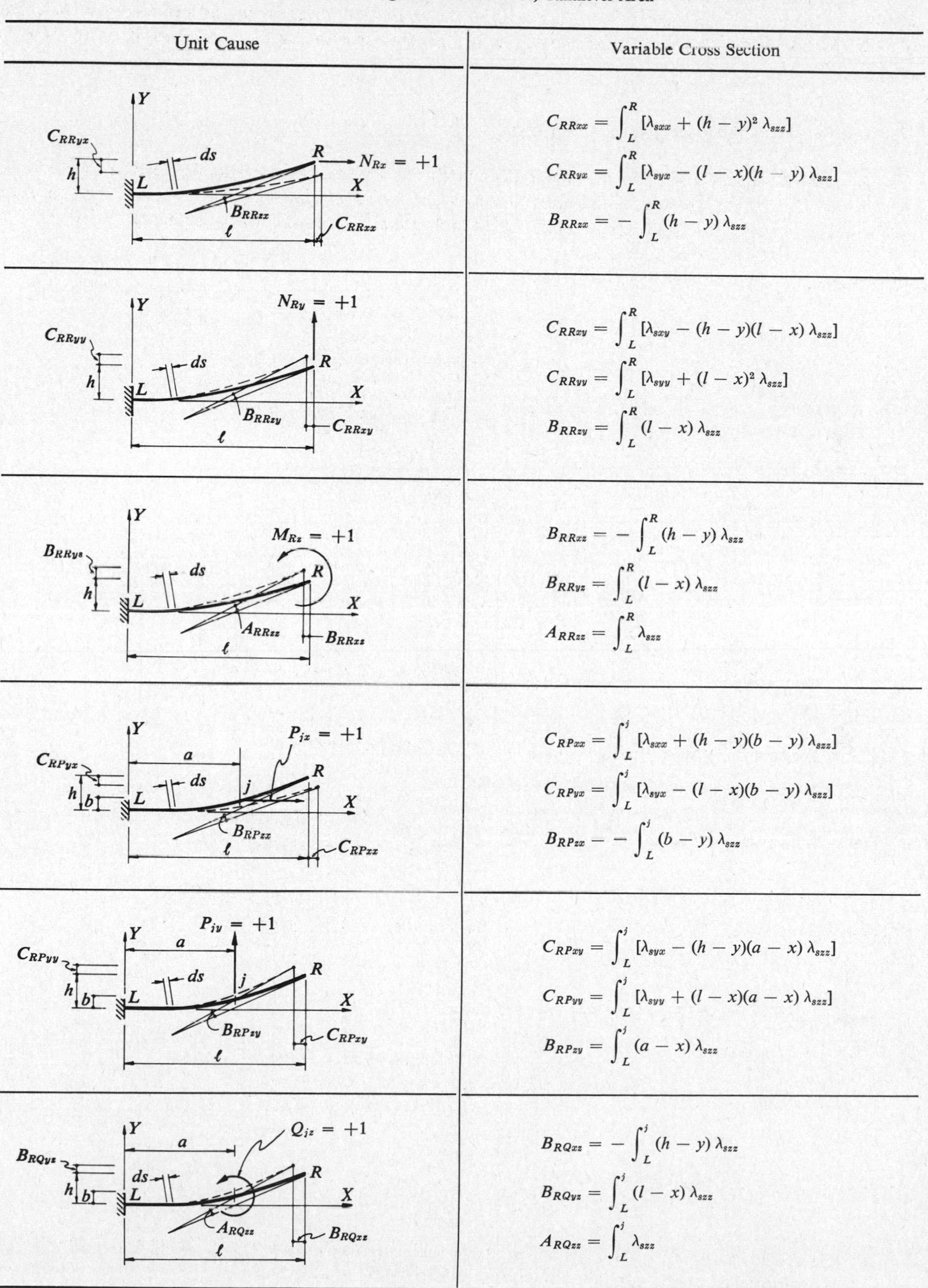

Unit Cause	Variable Cross Section
$N_{Rx} = +1$	$C_{RRxx} = \int_L^R [\lambda_{sxx} + (h-y)^2 \lambda_{szz}]$ $C_{RRyx} = \int_L^R [\lambda_{syx} - (l-x)(h-y) \lambda_{szz}]$ $B_{RRzx} = -\int_L^R (h-y) \lambda_{szz}$
$N_{Ry} = +1$	$C_{RRxy} = \int_L^R [\lambda_{sxy} - (h-y)(l-x) \lambda_{szz}]$ $C_{RRyy} = \int_L^R [\lambda_{syy} + (l-x)^2 \lambda_{szz}]$ $B_{RRzy} = \int_L^R (l-x) \lambda_{szz}$
$M_{Rz} = +1$	$B_{RRxz} = -\int_L^R (h-y) \lambda_{szz}$ $B_{RRyz} = \int_L^R (l-x) \lambda_{szz}$ $A_{RRzz} = \int_L^R \lambda_{szz}$
$P_{jx} = +1$	$C_{RPxx} = \int_L^j [\lambda_{sxx} + (h-y)(b-y) \lambda_{szz}]$ $C_{RPyx} = \int_L^j [\lambda_{syx} - (l-x)(b-y) \lambda_{szz}]$ $B_{RPzx} = -\int_L^j (b-y) \lambda_{szz}$
$P_{jy} = +1$	$C_{RPxy} = \int_L^j [\lambda_{syx} - (h-y)(a-x) \lambda_{szz}]$ $C_{RPyy} = \int_L^j [\lambda_{syy} + (l-x)(a-x) \lambda_{szz}]$ $B_{RPzy} = \int_L^j (a-x) \lambda_{szz}$
$Q_{jz} = +1$	$B_{RQxz} = -\int_L^j (h-y) \lambda_{szz}$ $B_{RQyz} = \int_L^j (l-x) \lambda_{szz}$ $A_{RQzz} = \int_L^j \lambda_{szz}$

(b) Segmental Flexibilities, Simple Arch

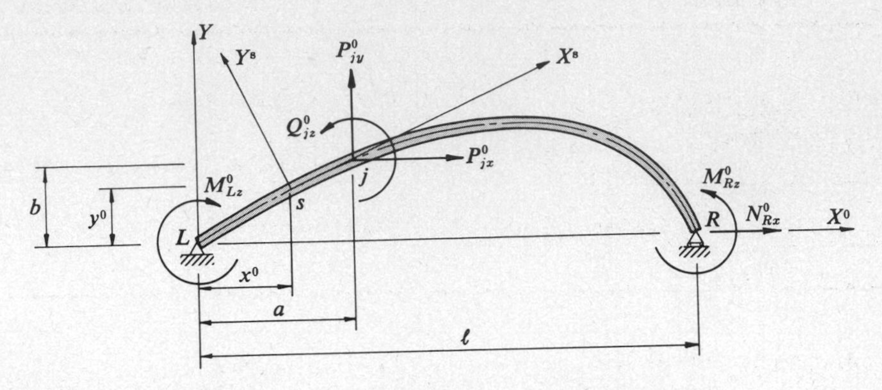

Fig. 8-3. Segmental Basic Structure, Simple Arch

For the simple arch of Fig. 8-3, the *unit stress flexibility matrix* is

$$f = \int_L^R q_X)^T \lambda_s q_X = \left[\begin{array}{c|cc} E_{RR} & G_{RR} & G_{RL} \\ \hline G_{RR} & F_{RR} & F_{RL} \\ G_{LR} & F_{LR} & F_{LL} \end{array}\right] \tag{8.4}$$

where $$q_X = \left[\begin{array}{c|cc} 1 & 0 & 0 \\ 0 & -\dfrac{1}{l} & \dfrac{1}{l} \\ \hline y & \dfrac{x}{l} & \dfrac{l-x}{l} \end{array}\right] \quad \text{and} \quad \lambda_s = \left[\begin{array}{cc|c} \lambda_{sxx} & \lambda_{sxy} & 0 \\ \lambda_{syx} & \lambda_{syy} & 0 \\ \hline 0 & 0 & \lambda_{szz} \end{array}\right]$$

Similarly, the *unit load flexibility matrix* is

$$l = \int_L^R q_X)^T \lambda_s q_0 = \left[\begin{array}{c|cc} E_{RH} & G_{RV} & G_{RQ} \\ \hline G_{RH} & F_{RV} & F_{RQ} \\ G_{LH} & F_{LV} & F_{LQ} \end{array}\right] \tag{8.5}$$

where $$q_0(x = 0 \rightarrow a) = \left[\begin{array}{c|cc} 1 & 0 & 0 \\ \hline \dfrac{b}{l} & \dfrac{l-a}{l} & -\dfrac{1}{l} \\ \dfrac{ly - bx}{l} & \dfrac{-(l-x)\,x}{l} & \dfrac{x}{l} \end{array}\right]$$

and $$q_0(x = a \rightarrow l) = \left[\begin{array}{c|cc} 0 & 0 & 0 \\ \hline \dfrac{b}{l} & -\dfrac{a}{l} & -\dfrac{1}{l} \\ \dfrac{b\,(l-x)}{l} & -\dfrac{a(l-x)}{a} & -\dfrac{(l-x)}{l} \end{array}\right]$$

The analytical expressions for coefficients of (*8.4*) and (*8.5*) are given in Table 8-2.

Table 8-2. Segmental Flexibilities, Simple Arch

Unit Cause	Variable Cross Section
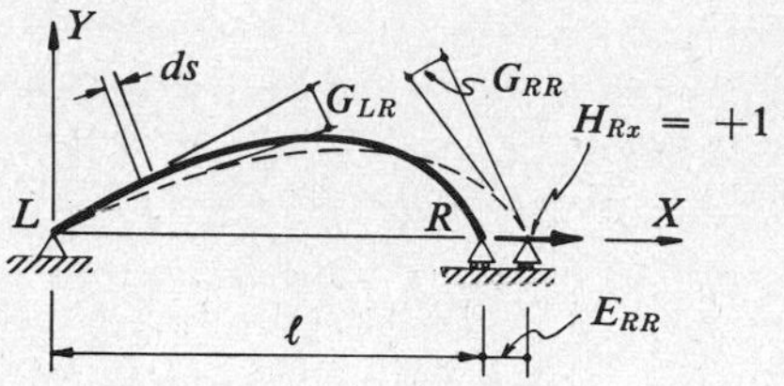 $H_{Rx} = +1$	$E_{RR} = \int_L^R [\lambda_{sxx} + y^2\lambda_{szz}]$ $G_{RR} = \int_L^R \frac{xy}{l}\lambda_{szz}$ $G_{LR} = \int_L^R \frac{(l-x)\,y}{l}\lambda_{szz}$
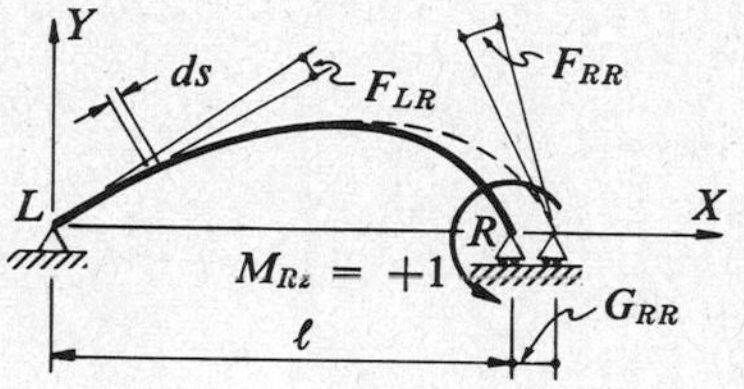 $M_{Rz} = +1$	$G_{RR} = \int_L^R \frac{yx}{l}\lambda_{szz}$ $F_{RR} = \int_L^R \frac{x^2}{l^2}\lambda_{szz}$ $F_{LR} = \int_L^R \frac{(l-x)\,x}{l^2}\lambda_{szz}$
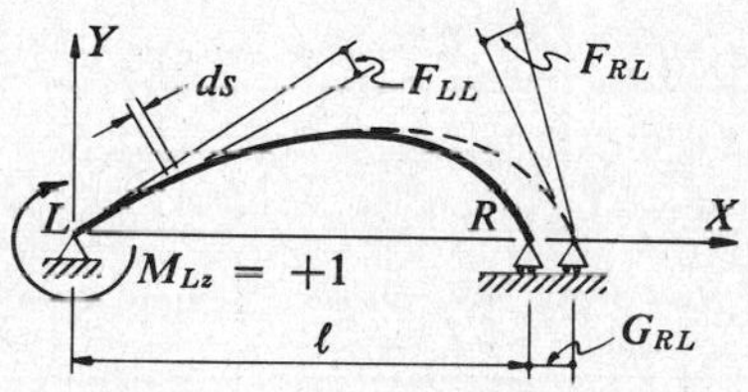 $M_{Lz} = +1$	$G_{RL} = \int_L^R \frac{y(l-x)}{l}\lambda_{szz}$ $F_{RL} = \int_L^R \frac{x(l-x)}{l^2}\lambda_{szz}$ $F_{LL} = \int_L^R \frac{(l-x)^2}{l^2}\lambda_{szz}$
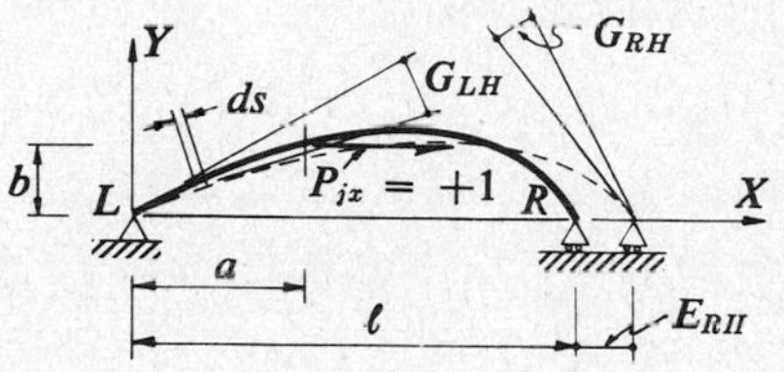 $P_{jx} = +1$	$E_{RH} = \int_L^j \lambda_{sxx} + \int_L^j \frac{y(ly-bx)}{l}\lambda_{szz} + \int_j^R \frac{yb(l-x)}{l}\lambda_{szz}$ $G_{RH} = \int_L^j \frac{x(ly-bx)}{l^2}\lambda_{szz} + \int_j^R \frac{xb(l-x)}{l^2}\lambda_{szz}$ $G_{LH} = \int_L^j \frac{(l-x)(ly-bx)}{l^2}\lambda_{szz} + \int_j^R \frac{(l-x)\,b(l-x)}{l^2}\lambda_{szz}$
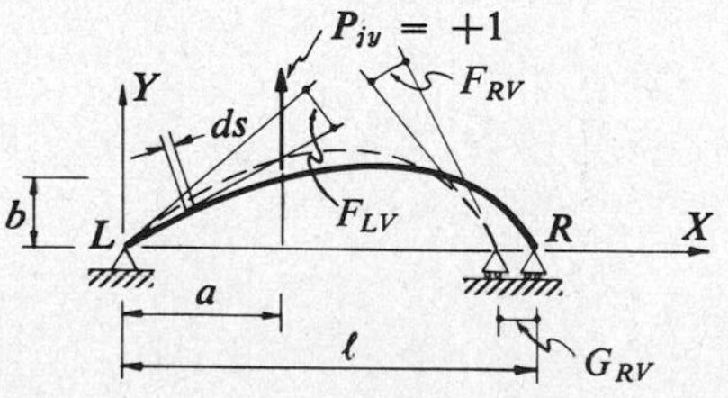 $P_{jy} = +1$	$G_{RV} = -\int_L^j \frac{y(l-a)\,x}{l}\lambda_{szz} - \int_j^R \frac{ya(l-x)}{l}\lambda_{szz}$ $F_{RV} = -\int_L^j \frac{x(l-a)\,x}{l^2}\lambda_{szz} - \int_j^R \frac{xa(l-x)}{l^2}\lambda_{szz}$ $F_{LV} = -\int_L^j \frac{(l-x)(l-a)\,x}{l^2}\lambda_{szz} - \int_j^R \frac{(l-x)\,a(l-x)}{l^2}\lambda_{szz}$
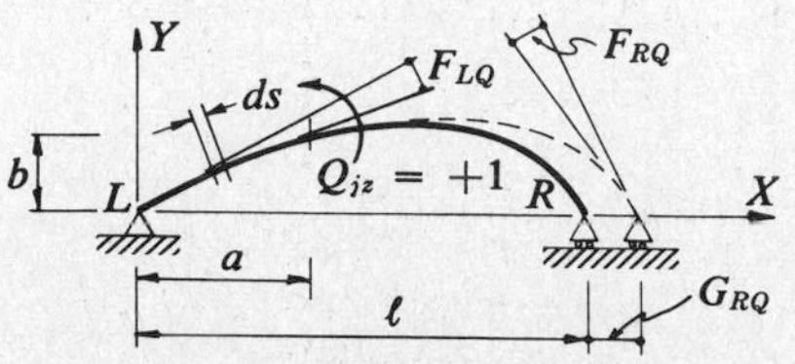 $Q_{jz} = +1$	$G_{RQ} = \int_L^j \frac{yx}{l}\lambda_{szz} - \int_j^R \frac{y(l-x)}{l}\lambda_{szz}$ $F_{RQ} = \int_L^j \frac{x^2}{l^2}\lambda_{szz} - \int_j^R \frac{x(l-x)}{l^2}\lambda_{szz}$ $F_{LQ} = \int_L^j \frac{(l-x)\,x}{l^2}\lambda_{szz} + \int_j^R \frac{(l-x)(l-x)}{l^2}\lambda_{szz}$

8.3 INTEGRATION METHODS

Flexibility integrals recorded in Tables 8-1 and 8-2 take various forms depending on the geometry of the arch. Similarly as in Chapter 6, for certain arches a closed evaluation of these integrals is possible. In other cases, a substitute function or a substitute model must be introduced.

For reasons of appearance, economy and convenience, two geometric shapes, the *parabolic arch* and the *circular arch*, are most common. Their segmental flexibilities are given in Tables 8-3 to 8-6. In the calculation of these matrices, the following simplifications have been made:

$$\int_L^R \lambda_{sxy}^0 \cong 0 \qquad \int_L^R \lambda_{syy}^0 \cong 0$$

The introduction of substitute functions similar to those given in Chapter 6 is shown in Problem 8.10.

Whenever the algebraic integration or the substitute integration is not feasible, the numerical value of the flexibility integrals can be computed by means of the *quadrature formulas* introduced in (*6.5*).

Table 8-3

Segmental Flexibilities, Cantilever Parabolic Arch

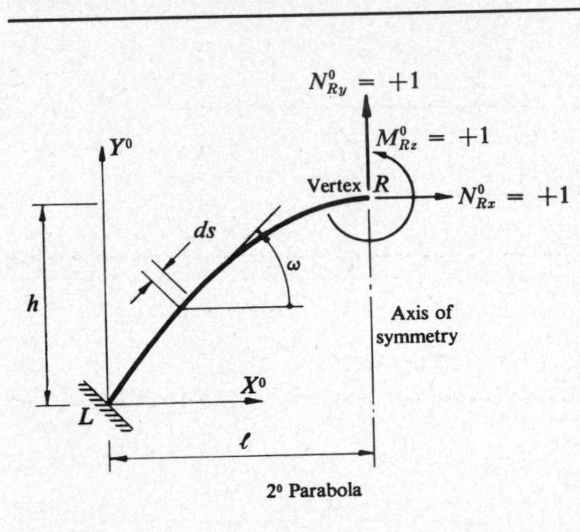

Geometry:

$$y - h = -\frac{h}{l^2}(x - l)^2$$

$$\tan\omega = -\frac{2h}{l^2}(x - l)$$

$$A = A_R \cos\omega$$

$$I = I_R/\cos\omega$$

$$\alpha = I_R/A_R$$

Unit Stress Flexibility Matrix (*8.2*):

$$\frac{l}{EI_R}\begin{bmatrix} \alpha + h^2/5 & -lh/4 & -h/3 \\ -lh/4 & l^2/3 & l/2 \\ -h/3 & l/2 & 1 \end{bmatrix}$$

Note: For unit load flexibility matrix, refer to Problem 8.5.

Table 8-4.

Segmental Flexibilities, Simple Parabolic Arch

Geometry:

$$y = \frac{4h}{l^2}x(l - x)$$

$$\tan\omega = \frac{4h}{l^2}(l - 2x)$$

$$A = A_C \cos\omega$$

$$I = I_C/\cos\omega$$

$$\alpha = I_C/A_C$$

Unit Stress Flexibility Matrix (*8.4*):

$$\frac{l}{EI_C}\begin{bmatrix} \alpha + 8h^2/15 & h/3 & h/3 \\ h/3 & 1/3 & 1/6 \\ h/3 & 1/6 & 1/3 \end{bmatrix}$$

Note: For unit load flexibility matrix, refer to Problem 8.6.

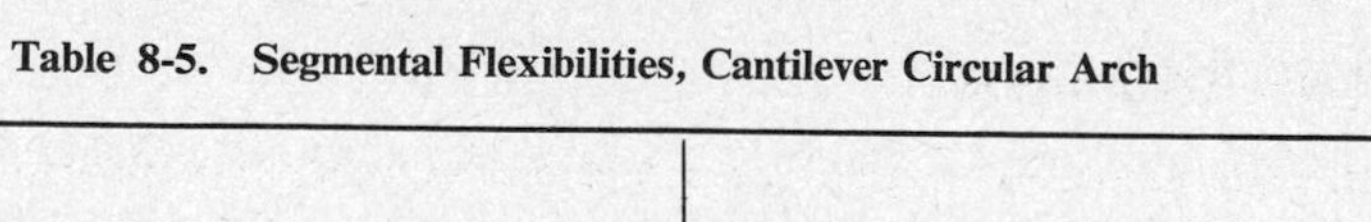

Table 8-5. Segmental Flexibilities, Cantilever Circular Arch

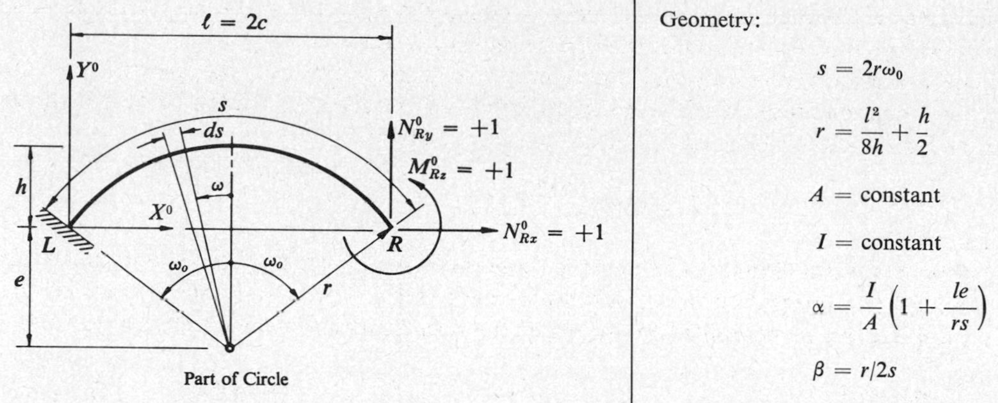

Geometry:

$$s = 2r\omega_0$$

$$r = \frac{l^2}{8h} + \frac{h}{2}$$

$$A = \text{constant}$$

$$I = \text{constant}$$

$$\alpha = \frac{I}{A}\left(1 + \frac{le}{rs}\right)$$

$$\beta = r/2s$$

Unit Stress Flexibility Matrix (*8.2*):

$$\frac{s}{EI}\begin{bmatrix} (\alpha + r^2)/2 + e^2 - 3el\beta & l^2\beta - ce & 2l\beta - e \\ l^2\beta - ce & c^2 + 2s^2\beta^2 - le\beta & c \\ 2l\beta - c & c & 1 \end{bmatrix}$$

Note: For unit load flexibility matrix, refer to Problem 8.7.

Table 8-6. Segmental Flexibilities, Simple Circular Arch

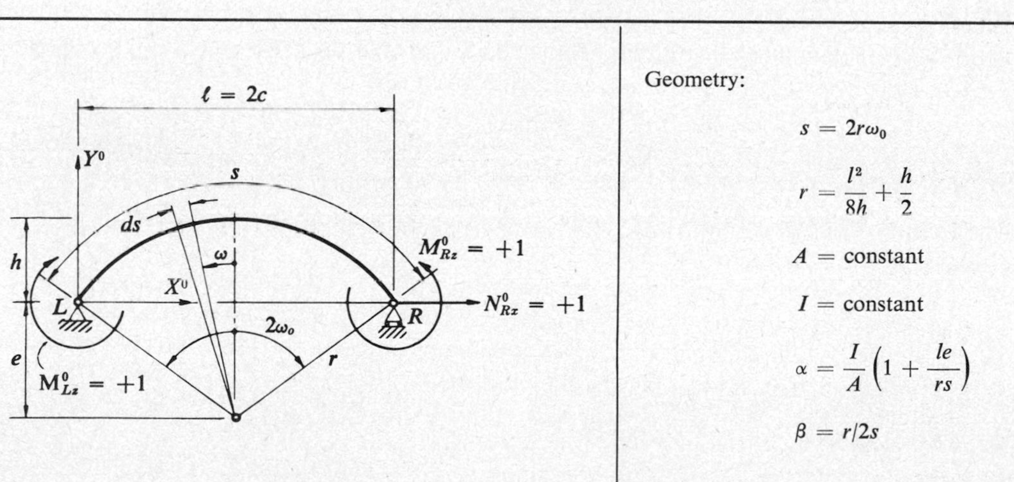

Geometry:

$$s = 2r\omega_0$$

$$r = \frac{l^2}{8h} + \frac{h}{2}$$

$$A = \text{constant}$$

$$I = \text{constant}$$

$$\alpha = \frac{I}{A}\left(1 + \frac{le}{rs}\right)$$

$$\beta = r/2s$$

Unit Stress Flexibility Matrix (*8.4*):

$$\frac{s}{EI}\begin{bmatrix} (\alpha + r^2 + s^2 - 3el\beta)/2 & l\beta - e/2 & l\beta - e/2 \\ l\beta - e/2 & 1/4 + r^2/2l^2 - 4e\beta/l & 1/4 - r^2/2l^2 + 4e\beta/l \\ l\beta - e/2 & 1/4 - r^2/2l^2 + 4e\beta/l & 1/4 + r^2/2l^2 - 4e\beta/l \end{bmatrix}$$

Note: For unit load flexibility matrix, refer to Problem 8.8.

8.4 MATRIX METHODS

The segmental flexibility matrix for an arch of variable cross section and/or curvature can be again constructed by *general transport equations* [(*6.6*) and (*6.7*)] or by *general transfer equations* [(*6.8*) and (*6.9*)]. Because of arch geometry, the segmental matrices for each finite element must be first taken in the element system and then transformed to 0-system.

For example:

In (*6.6*) and (*6.7*), $f^0_{(jj)} = \omega^{0s} f^s_{(jj)} \omega^{s0}$

In (*6.8*) and (*6.9*), $f^0_{(ij)} = \mu^{0s} f^s_{(ij)} \mu^{s0}$

$$\text{where} \quad \mu^{0s} = \begin{bmatrix} \cos\omega_{s0} & 0 & 0 \\ \sin\omega_{s0} & 0 & 0 \\ 0 & 1 & 0 \\ 0 & 0 & 1 \end{bmatrix} \quad \text{and} \quad \mu^{s0} = \begin{bmatrix} \cos\omega_{s0} & \sin\omega_{s0} & 0 & 0 \\ 0 & 0 & 1 & 0 \\ 0 & 0 & 0 & 1 \end{bmatrix} \qquad (8.6)$$

These new matrices are essentially ω^{0s} and ω^{s0} matrices adjusted to accommodate the transformation of stress vectors (components of which are two forces and two moments) and to produce a displacement vector (components of which are two linear and two angular displacements).

8.5 SINGLE SPAN ARCH

The *displacement vector matrix* (*5.6*) for a single span planar arch is

$$\Delta = \Delta_\sigma + \Delta_0 + \Delta_T \qquad (8.7)$$

where $\Delta_\sigma = f\sigma$, $\Delta_0 = lW$ and Δ_T = secondary effect displacement vector. This matrix equation is written in terms of (*8.2*) and (*8.3*) or (*8.4*) and (*8.5*).

Six particular applications are given in Table 8-7. Note the *relationship* of Δ^0 and σ^0. For a zero value in Δ^0-column there is an unknown value in σ^0-column and vice versa (Problems 8.11 to 8.13).

8.6 INTERMEDIATE CONDITIONS

Intermediate *hinges, guides or hangers* located within the span of the arch cause no particular difficulties in the construction of the system flexibility matrix. If matrix forms introduced in Section 8.4 are applied, the respective transport matrix or transfer matrix adjacent to the given discontinuity must be modified to meet the imposed condition. This usually requires setting *certain coefficients* in the respective matrix equal to *zero*.

8.7 ELASTIC CENTER

As known from the elementary theory of linear structures, the existing stress vector of an arbitrarily selected cross section in a given arch can be replaced by a *statically equivalent stress vector* acting at another arbitrarily selected station (not necessarily lying on the arch). This new station must be connected to the initial point of action by a *rigid arm*, the shape of which is immaterial. Since the position of this equivalent vector is given by *two coordinates* and *angle of inclination*, three conditions define uniquely this transformation. Two forms of this matrix transformation follow.

(a) Cantilever Arch (Fig. 8-4)

The *unit stress segmental flexibility matrix* of the cantilever arch LR at the end C of a rigid arm attached to this arch at R is

$$f^C_{CC} = t^{0C)T}_{RC} f^0_{RR} t^{0C}_{RC} \qquad (8.8)$$

where f^0_{RR} is the unit stress segmental flexibility matrix of LR at R in 0-system (*8.2*) and $t^{0C)T}_{RC}$, t^{0C}_{RC} are the respective transport matrices.

If the C-system is so selected as to make the off-diagonal terms equal zero, the unit stress flexibility matrix at C reduces to a diagonal matrix.

$$f^C_{CC} = \begin{bmatrix} C^C_{CCxx} & 0 & 0 \\ 0 & C^C_{CCyy} & 0 \\ 0 & 0 & A^C_{CCzz} \end{bmatrix} \qquad (8.9)$$

Table 8-7. Single Span Arches, Continuous between Supports

System	Flexibilities	Δ^0	σ^0
1. Cantilever Arch	Solution I: Matrices (*8.2*), (*8.3*)	$\{\delta^0_{Rx}, \delta^0_{Ry}, \theta^0_{Rz}\}$	$\{0, 0, 0\}$
2. Simple Arch	Solution II: Matrices (*8.4*), (*8.5*)	$\{\delta^0_{Rx}, \theta^0_{Rz}, \theta^0_{Lz}\}$	$\{0, 0, 0\}$
3. Two-hinged Arch	Solution II: Matrices (*8.4*), (*8.5*)	$\{0, \theta^0_{Rz}, \theta^0_{Lz}\}$	$\{N^0_{Rx}, 0, 0\}$
4. Fixed End Arch	Solution I: Matrices (*8.2*), (*8.3*)	$\{0, 0, 0\}$	$\{N^0_{Rx}, N^0_{Ry}, M^0_{Rz}\}$
	Solution II: Matrices (*8.4*), (*8.5*)	$\{0, 0, 0\}$	$\{N^0_{Rx}, M^0_{Rz}, M^0_{Lz}\}$

The analytical expressions for the coefficients of f^C_{CC} bear a resemblance to the *functions of a plane section*, and the conditions

$$C^C_{CCxy} = C^C_{CCyx} = 0, \qquad B^C_{CCxz} = B^C_{CCzx} = 0, \qquad B^C_{CCyz} = B^C_{CCzy} = 0$$

are similar to those defining the position of *principal axes* and *centroid* of a plane section. For this reason, the point C is frequently called the *elastic center* or *neutral point*.

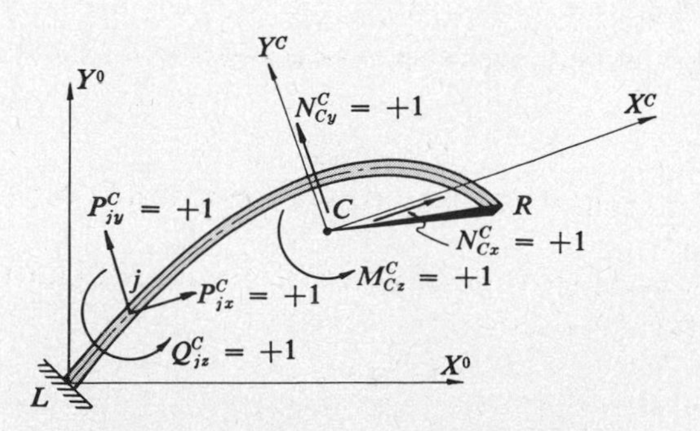

Fig. 8-4. Neutral Point, Cantilever Arch

The latter designation is more appropriate, since C is the only point in the plane of arch through which a unit stress acting along one of the C-system axes produces displacement along the same axis, *unaffected* by the unit stresses acting through the same point along the remaining two axes. The diagonal matrix (*8.9*) is the analytical representation of this property.

Similarly, the unit load segmental flexibility matrix at C is

$$l_{CC}^{C} = t_{RL}^{(0L)T} l_{RR}^{0} \omega^{0C} \tag{8.10}$$

where l_{RR}^{0} is the *unit load segmental flexibility matrix* of LR at R in 0-system (*8.3*).

(b) Simple Arch (Fig. 8-5)

The *unit stress segmental flexibility matrix* of the simple arch LR produced by unit stresses acting at the ends A and B of rigid arms LA and RB attached to this arch at L and R respectively is

$$f_{(AB)}^{C} = q_{(LR,AB)}^{0C)T} f_{(LR)}^{0} q_{(LR,AB)}^{0C} \tag{8.11}$$

where $f_{(LR)}^{0}$ is the unit stress segmental flexibility matrix of LR in 0-system (*8.4*) and $q_{(LR,AB)}^{0C)T}$, $q_{(LR,AB)}^{0C}$ are the respective transfer matrices.

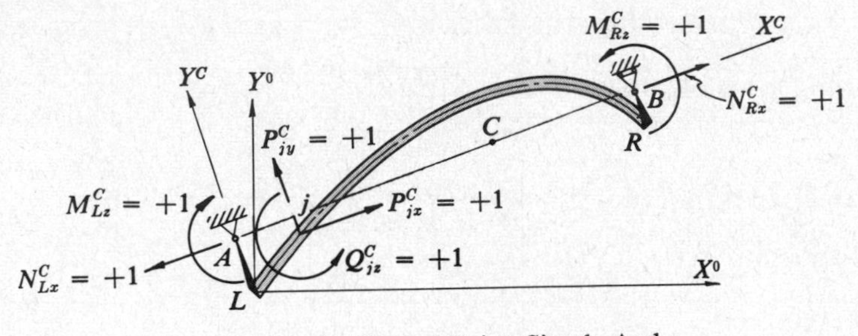

Fig. 8-5. Neutral Point, Simple Arch

If the C-system is so selected as to make zero the off-diagonal terms of the first row and first column, matrix (*8.11*) reduces to matrix (*8.12*):

$$f_{(AB)}^{C} = \begin{bmatrix} E_{BB}^{C} & 0 & 0 \\ 0 & F_{BB}^{C} & F_{BA}^{C} \\ 0 & F_{AB}^{C} & F_{AA}^{C} \end{bmatrix} \tag{8.12}$$

Since two components of unit stress vector are moments, a *complete diagonalization* of matrix (*8.11*) is *not possible*.

Similarly, the *unit load segmental flexibility matrix* representing displacements at A and B is

$$l_{(AB)}^{C} = q_{(LR,AB)}^{0C)T} l_{(LR)}^{0} \mu^{0C} \tag{8.13}$$

where μ^{0C} is defined by (*8.6*).

These *two relocations* of segmental flexibilities [(*8.8*), (*8.10*) and (*8.11*), (*8.13*)] are the most typical ones. Other frequently used relocations are shown in Figs. 8-6, 8-7, and 8-8. For applications refer to Problems 8.15 and 8.16.

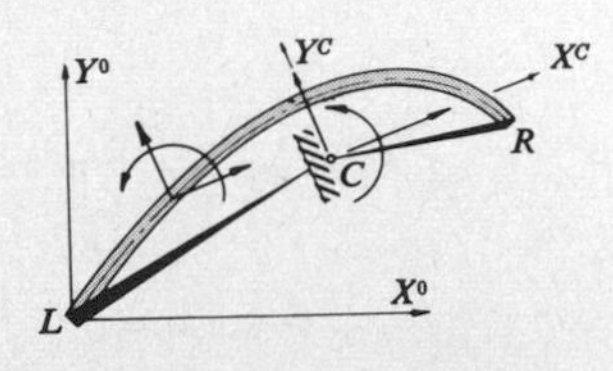

Fig. 8-6. Neutral Point, Cantilever Arch

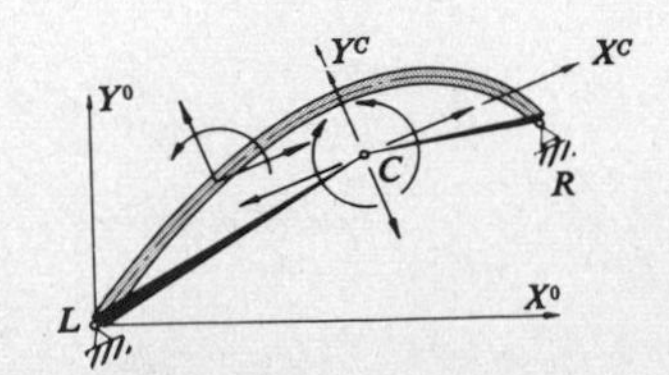

Fig. 8-7. Neutral Point, Simple Arch

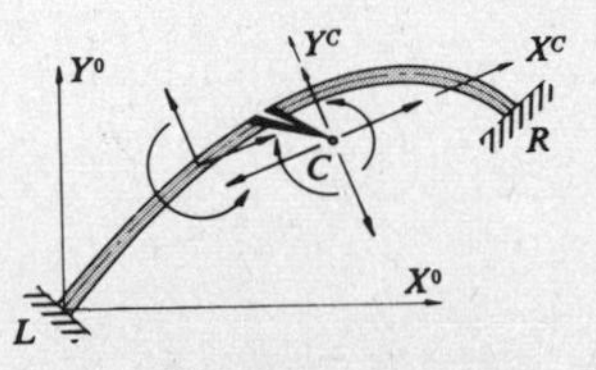

Fig. 8-8. Neutral Point, Two Cantilever Arches

8.8 ELASTIC RING

The elastic arches of Fig. 8-1 can be always visualized as *rings* of Fig. 8-9 with or without intermediate conditions and with external constraints satisfying geometric stability. If statically equivalent constraints are applied, the addition of a *rigid bar* shown in all six cases has no material influence on the stress and deformation state of the elastic arch. Systems shown in Figs. 8-4 to 8-8 are only special cases of those given in Fig. 8-9.

Elastic
Rigid

(*a*) Cantilever Arch

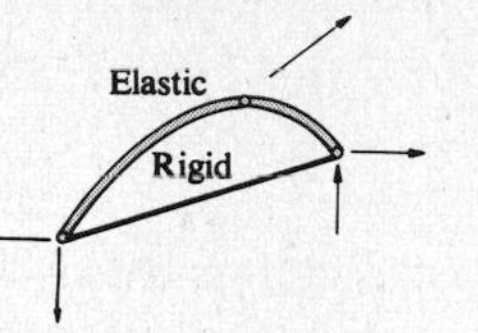

(*c*) Three-hinged Arch

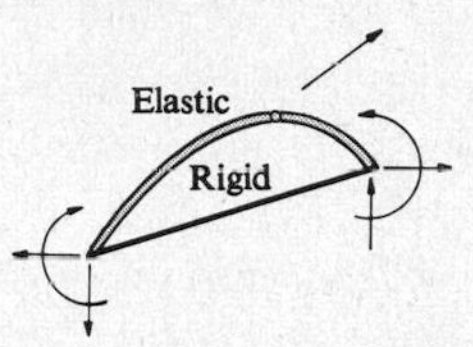

(*e*) Compound Arch

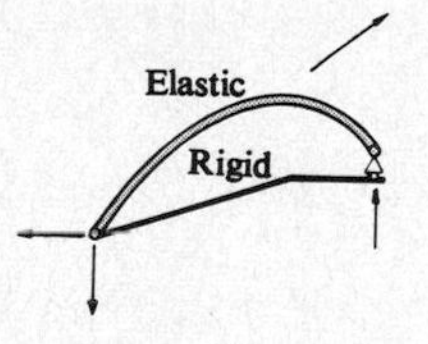

(*b*) Simple Arch

Elastic
Rigid

(*d*) Two-hinged Arch

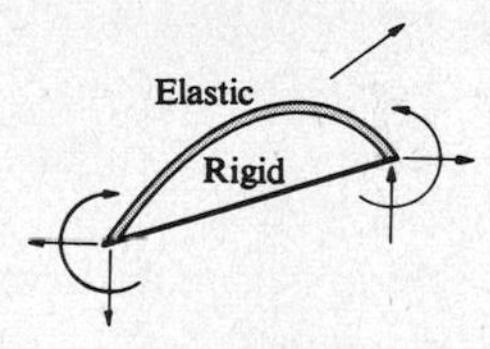

(*f*) Fixed End Arch

Fig. 8-9. Equivalent Rings

The elastic generalization of Fig. 8-9 are the elastic rings of Fig. 8-10 which may have any arbitrary shape. For the analysis of these rings *two criteria of statics* are necessary.

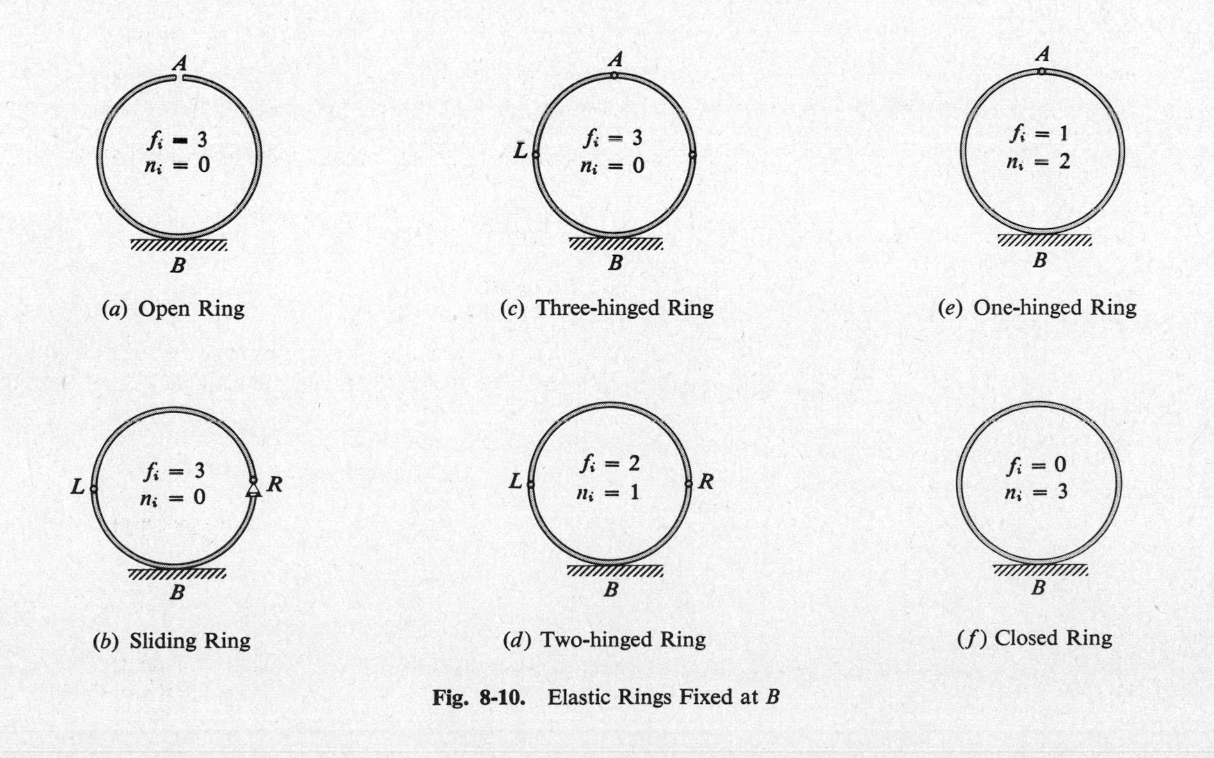

(*a*) Open Ring (*c*) Three-hinged Ring (*e*) One-hinged Ring

(*b*) Sliding Ring (*d*) Two-hinged Ring (*f*) Closed Ring

Fig. 8-10. Elastic Rings Fixed at *B*

Internally, the ring is statically indeterminate if

$$n_i = 3 - f_i > 0 \tag{8.14}$$

where n_i = number of internal redundants, f_i = number of internal releases. If $n_i = 0$ the ring is internally statically determinate, and if $n_i < 0$ the ring is geometrically unstable.

Externally, the ring is statically indeterminate if

$$n_e = r_e - f_i - 3 > 0 \tag{8.15}$$

where n_e = number of external redundants, r_e = number of independent external reactions. If $n_e = 0$ the ring is externally statically determinate, and if $n_e < 0$ the ring is geometrically unstable.

Restricting the study to the case of an externally statically determinate elastic ring of Fig. 8-11, the *conditions of compatibility* are given by

$$f^A_{AA} X_A{}^A + l^A_{AA} W^A = 0 \tag{8.16}$$

where f^A_{AA} = unit stress segmental flexibility matrix (*8.2*), l^A_{AA} = unit load segmental flexibility matrix (*8.3*), $X_A{}^A$ = stress redundant vector at A, W^A = load vector, all in A-system (or any given system).

Obviously, if the concept of *neutral point* is adopted, f^A_{AA} becomes a *diagonal matrix*.

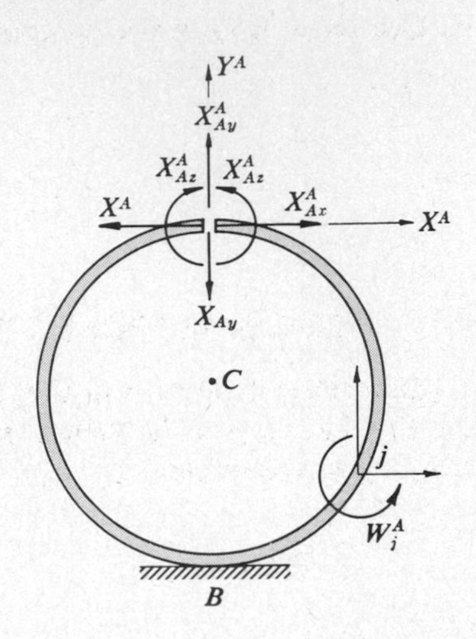

Fig. 8-11. Elastic Ring Fixed at B

8.9 ARCH ON ELASTIC SUPPORTS

A more general case arises when the supports of a planar arch are elastic (Fig. 8-12*a*). The introduction of *elastic supports*, usually represented by two linear and one angular spring at each end, does not affect the degree of statical indeterminacy of the system, but influences considerably the construction of the system flexibility matrix.

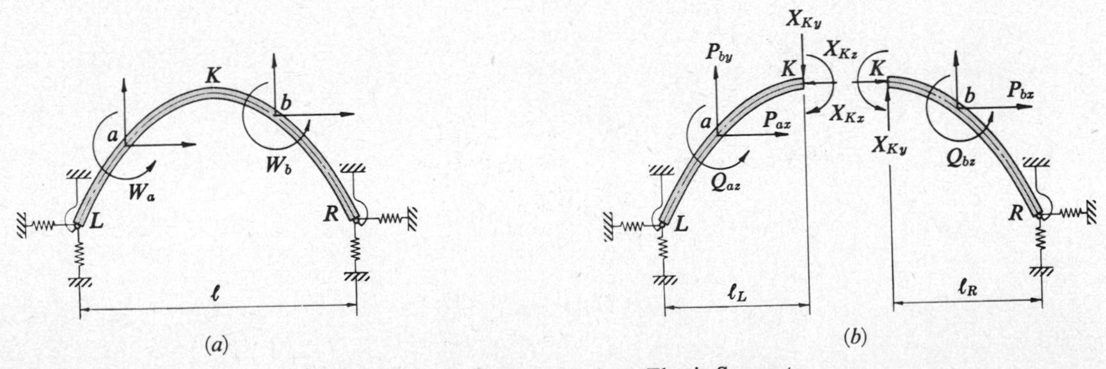

Fig. 8-12. Single Span Arch on Elastic Supports

Selecting the stresses at K as the internal redundants and decomposing this structure into *two cantilever arches* (Fig. 8-12*b*), the segmental flexibilities at K of the left and right branch respectively become

$$f^*_{KK,L} = f_{KK,L} + t^{)T}_{LK} f_{L\Delta} t_{LK} \qquad f^*_{KK,R} = f_{KK,R} + t^{)T}_{RK} f_{R\Delta} t_{RK} \tag{8.17}$$

$$l^*_{Ka} = l_{Ka} + t^{)T}_{LK} f_{L\Delta} t_{La} \qquad l^*_{Kb} = l_{Kb} - t^{)T}_{KR} f_{R\Delta} t_{Rb}$$

where $f_{KK,L}$, $f_{KK,R}$ are the unit stress segmental flexibilities of the respective cantilevers, l_{Ka}, l_{Kb} are the unit load segmental flexibilities and $f_{L\Delta}$, $f_{R\Delta}$ are the unit stress flexibilities of the respective elastic support. The designation of system is omitted in all terms.

The *condition of continuity* at K is satisfied by

$$\underbrace{(f^*_{KK,L} + f^*_{KK,R})}_{f^*_{KK}} X_K + \underbrace{l^*_{Ka} W_a + l^*_{Kb} W_b}_{\Delta^*_{K0}} = 0 \tag{8.18}$$

If the concept of *neutral point* is employed, f^*_{KK} reduces to a diagonal matrix and the compatibility matrix splits into *three independent equations*:

$$f^*_{KKxx} X_{Kx} + \Delta^*_{K0x} = 0$$

$$f^*_{KKyy} X_{Ky} + \Delta^*_{K0y} = 0$$

$$f^*_{KKzz} X_{Kz} + \Delta^*_{K0z} = 0$$

8.10 CONTINUOUS ARCHES ON ELASTIC SUPPORTS

The most general case in this class of problems is the continuous arch on elastic supports of Fig. 8-13*a*. For the analysis, the structure is decomposed into a *series of free-body cantilevers* (Fig. 8-13*b*, *c*, *d*, *e*) with the stress redundants X_I, X_J, X_K selected as the unknowns.

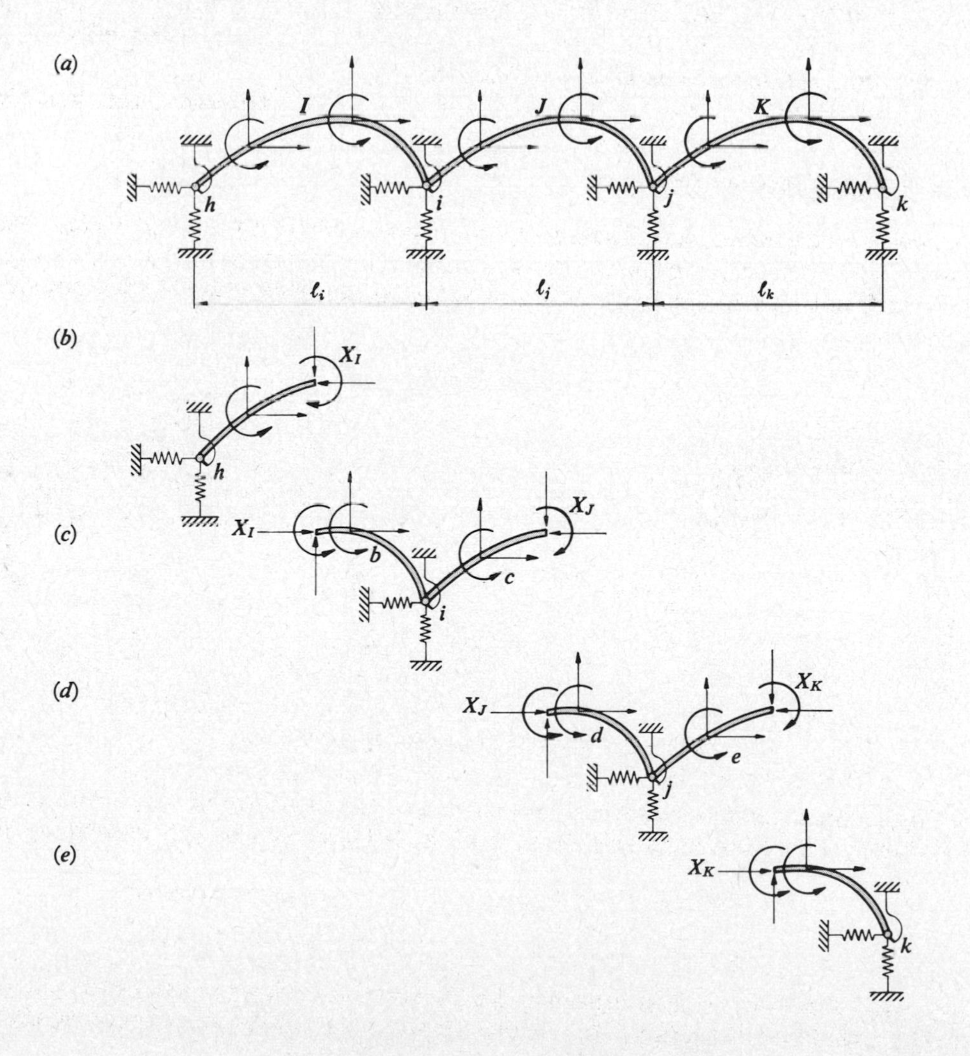

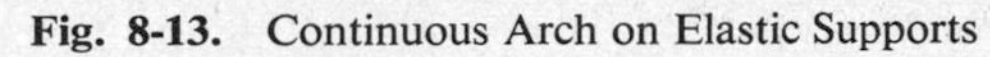

Fig. 8-13. Continuous Arch on Elastic Supports

Choosing the *double cantilevers* of Fig. 8-13*c*, *d* as typical models, the respective *end displacement vectors* at J are

$$\Delta^*_{JJ,i} = f^*_{JI}X_I + f^*_{JJ,i}X_J + l^*_{Jb}W_b + l^*_{Jc}W_c$$
$$\Delta^*_{JJ,j} = f^*_{JJ,j}X_J + f^*_{JK}X_K + l^*_{Jd}W_d + l^*_{Je}W_e \qquad (8.19)$$

where

$$f^*_{JI} = -t_{iJ}^{)T} f_{i\Delta} t_{iI} \qquad f^*_{JK} = -t_{jJ}^{)T} f_{j\Delta} t_{jK}$$
$$l^*_{Jb} = -t_{iJ}^{)T} f_{i\Delta} t_{ib} \qquad l^*_{Je} = -t_{jJ}^{)T} f_{j\Delta} t_{je}$$

are the displacements at J due to unit cause acting at I and K or b and e respectively.

In terms of (*8.18*) the *compatibility condition* yields

$$f^*_{JI}X_I + \underbrace{(f^*_{JJ,i} + f^*_{JJ,j})}_{f^*_J} X_J + f^*_{JK}X_K + \underbrace{l^*_{Jb}W_b + l^*_{Jc}W_c + l^*_{Jd}W_d + l^*_{Je}W_e}_{\Delta^*_{J0}} = 0 \qquad (8.20)$$

Matrix equation (*8.20*) is a *three-vector equation* consisting of *three nine-stress algebraic equations.* Equation (*8.20*) can be used *recurrently* for the construction of the system flexibility matrix given below.

$$\begin{bmatrix} f^*_I & f^*_{IJ} & \\ f^*_{JI} & f^*_J & f^*_{JK} \\ & f^*_{KJ} & f^*_K \end{bmatrix} \begin{bmatrix} X_I \\ X_J \\ X_K \end{bmatrix} + \begin{bmatrix} \Delta^*_{I0} \\ \Delta^*_{J0} \\ \Delta^*_{K0} \end{bmatrix} = 0$$

Solved Problems

SEGMENTAL FLEXIBILITIES

8.1. Using the Virtual Forces Method, derive the coefficients of the unit stress segmental flexibility matrix (*8.2*) for the cantilever arch given in Table 8-1.

The expression for the unit stress flexibility, $f = \int_L^R q_x^{)T} \lambda_s q_x$, in (*8.2*) is a direct result of the method of virtual forces. Substituting the values of q_x and λ_s introduced in (*8.2*),

$$f = \int_L^R q_x^{)T} \lambda_s q_x = \int_L^R \begin{bmatrix} 1 & 0 & -(h-y) \\ 0 & 1 & l-x \\ 0 & 0 & 1 \end{bmatrix} \begin{bmatrix} \lambda_{sxx} & \lambda_{sxy} & 0 \\ \lambda_{syx} & \lambda_{syy} & 0 \\ 0 & 0 & \lambda_{szz} \end{bmatrix} \begin{bmatrix} 1 & 0 & 0 \\ 0 & 1 & 0 \\ -(h-y) & l-x & 1 \end{bmatrix}$$

$$= \int_L^R \left[\begin{array}{c|c|c} \lambda_{sxx} + (h-y)^2 \lambda_{szz} & \lambda_{sxy} - (h-y)(l-x)\lambda_{szz} & -(h-y)\lambda_{szz} \\ \hline \lambda_{syx} - (l-x)(h-y)\lambda_{szz} & \lambda_{syy} + (l-x)^2 \lambda_{szz} & (l-x)\lambda_{szz} \\ \hline -(h-y)\lambda_{szz} & (l-x)\lambda_{szz} & \lambda_{szz} \end{array}\right]$$

A comparison of the elements of this matrix with corresponding elements of the flexibility matrix of (*8.2*) gives the values shown in Table 8-1.

8.2. Using the procedure and results of the preceding problem derive the coefficients of the unit load segmental flexibility matrix (*8.3*) for the cantilever arch given in Table 8-1.

The expression for the unit load flexibility matrix, $l = \int_L^R q_x^T \lambda_s q_0$, follows directly from the Virtual Forces Method. The coefficients of this matrix can be derived by direct substitution of the values of q_x, λ_s and q_0 established on page 126. Accordingly,

$$l = \int_L^R q_x^T \lambda_s q_0 = \int_L^j \begin{bmatrix} 1 & 0 & -(h-y) \\ 0 & 1 & (l-x) \\ 0 & 0 & 1 \end{bmatrix} \begin{bmatrix} \lambda_{sxx} & \lambda_{sxy} & 0 \\ \lambda_{syx} & \lambda_{syy} & 0 \\ 0 & 0 & \lambda_{szz} \end{bmatrix} \begin{bmatrix} 1 & 0 & 0 \\ 0 & 1 & 0 \\ -(b-y) & a-x & 1 \end{bmatrix}$$

$$= \int_L^j \left[\begin{array}{c|c|c} \lambda_{sxx} + (h-y)(b-y)\,\lambda_{szz} & \lambda_{sxy} - (h-y)(a-x)\,\lambda_{szz} & -(h-y)\,\lambda_{szz} \\ \hline \lambda_{syx} - (l-x)(b-y)\,\lambda_{szz} & \lambda_{syy} + (l-x)(a-x)\,\lambda_{szz} & (l-x)\,\lambda_{szz} \\ \hline -(b-y)\,\lambda_{szz} & (a-x)\,\lambda_{szz} & \lambda_{szz} \end{array} \right]$$

The unit load flexibility matrix coefficients of (*8.3*) are obtained on comparison with the corresponding elements of the matrix above.

8.3. Using Engesser's First Theorem, derive the coefficients of the unit stress segmental flexibility matrix (*8.4*) for the simple arch given in Table 8-2.

The total strain energy stored in an elastic bar in terms of the internal stress vector σ and elemental flexibility matrix λ_s is

$$U = \int \tfrac{1}{2}\sigma^T \lambda_s \sigma$$

The internal stresses at any section can be expressed in terms of the end forces P and applied loads W by the general transfer matrices q. Thus at any section, $\sigma = q_x P + q_0 W$.

$$\therefore \quad U = \int \tfrac{1}{2}(P^T q_x^T + W^T q_0^T)\,\lambda_s (q_x P + q_0 W) = U^* \qquad \text{for a } \textit{linearly} \text{ elastic bar}$$

The segmental unit stress flexibilities and the unit load flexibilities are the end deformations due to unit end forces and unit applied load, and can be found by applying Engesser's Theorem I (*1.10*) to the energy expression above. Thus the end deformations

$$\Delta = \frac{\partial U}{\partial P} = \frac{1}{2}\frac{\partial}{\partial P}\int [P^T q_x^T \lambda_s q_x P + W^T q_0^T \lambda_s q_x P + P^T q_x^T \lambda_s q_0 W + W^T q_0^T \lambda_s q_0 W]$$

The differentiation above can be effected for each end force successively and Δ vector constructed. The resulting expression can be shown to be

$$\Delta = \int q_x^T \lambda_s q_x P + \int q_x^T \lambda_s q_0 W$$

The unit stress flexibility matrix $f = \int q_x^T \lambda_s q_x$ and the unit load flexibility matrix $l = \int q_x^T \lambda_s q_0$ can be identified above. The required elements of the f matrix can be easily derived by substituting the values of q_x and λ_s shown on page 128. Thus

$$= \int_L^R q_x^T \lambda_s q_x = \int_L^R \begin{bmatrix} 1 & 0 & y \\ 0 & -\frac{1}{l} & \frac{x}{l} \\ 0 & \frac{1}{l} & \frac{l-x}{l} \end{bmatrix} \begin{bmatrix} \lambda_{sxx} & \lambda_{sxy} & 0 \\ \lambda_{syx} & \lambda_{syy} & 0 \\ 0 & 0 & \lambda_{szz} \end{bmatrix} \begin{bmatrix} 1 & 0 & 0 \\ 0 & -\frac{1}{l} & \frac{1}{l} \\ y & \frac{x}{l} & \frac{l-x}{l} \end{bmatrix}$$

Using the simplifications $\lambda_{sxy} = \lambda_{syx} = 0$ and $\lambda_{syy} = 0$ and evaluating the matrix product gives

$$f = \int_L^R \left[\begin{array}{c|c|c} \lambda_{sxx} + y^2\lambda_{szz} & \dfrac{yx}{l}\lambda_{szz} & \dfrac{y(l-x)}{l}\lambda_{szz} \\ \hline \dfrac{xy}{l}\lambda_{szz} & \dfrac{x^2}{l^2}\lambda_{szz} & \dfrac{x(l-x)}{l}\lambda_{szz} \\ \hline \dfrac{(l-x)\,y}{l}\lambda_{szz} & \dfrac{(l-x)\,x}{l^2}\lambda_{szz} & \dfrac{(l-x)^2}{l^2}\lambda_{szz} \end{array}\right]$$

A comparison of the matrix above with that of (*8.4*) gives the unit stress flexibility coefficients listed in Table 8-2.

8.4. **Using the procedure and results of the preceding problem, derive the coefficients of the unit load segmental flexibility matrix (*8.5*) for the simple arch given in Table 8-2.**

It was shown in the preceding problem, using Engesser's Theorem I, that the unit load flexibility of a linearly elastic bar is

$$l = \int_L^R q_x^T \lambda_s q_0$$

For a simple arch, using the values of q_x, λ_s and q_0 stated on page 128, this matrix becomes

$$l = \int_L^j \begin{bmatrix} 1 & 0 & y \\ 0 & -\dfrac{1}{l} & \dfrac{x}{l} \\ 0 & \dfrac{1}{l} & \dfrac{l-x}{l} \end{bmatrix} \begin{bmatrix} \lambda_{sxx} & \lambda_{sxy} & 0 \\ \lambda_{syx} & \lambda_{syy} & 0 \\ 0 & 0 & \lambda_{szz} \end{bmatrix} \begin{bmatrix} 1 & 0 & 0 \\ \dfrac{b}{l} & \dfrac{l-a}{l} & -\dfrac{1}{l} \\ \dfrac{ly-bx}{l} & -\dfrac{(l-a)\,x}{l} & \dfrac{x}{l} \end{bmatrix}$$

$$+ \int_j^R \begin{bmatrix} 1 & 0 & y \\ 0 & -\dfrac{1}{l} & \dfrac{x}{l} \\ 0 & \dfrac{1}{l} & \dfrac{l-x}{l} \end{bmatrix} \begin{bmatrix} \lambda_{sxx} & \lambda_{sxy} & 0 \\ \lambda_{syx} & \lambda_{syy} & 0 \\ 0 & 0 & \lambda_{szz} \end{bmatrix} \begin{bmatrix} 0 & 0 & 0 \\ \dfrac{b}{l} & -\dfrac{a}{l} & -\dfrac{1}{l} \\ \dfrac{b(l-x)}{l} & -\dfrac{a(l-x)}{l} & -\dfrac{(l-x)}{l} \end{bmatrix}$$

Assuming $\lambda_{sxy} = \lambda_{syx} \simeq 0$ and $\lambda_{syy} \simeq 0$ and simplifying gives the coefficients of the unit load matrix:

$$E_{RH} = \int_L^j \lambda_{sxx} + \int_L^j \frac{y(ly-bx)}{l}\lambda_{szz} + \int_j^R \frac{yb(l-x)}{l}\lambda_{szz}$$

$$G_{RH} = \int_L^j \frac{x(ly-bx)}{l^2}\lambda_{szz} + \int_j^R \frac{xb(l-x)}{l^2}\lambda_{szz}$$

$$G_{LH} = \int_L^j \frac{(l-x)(ly-bx)}{l^2}\lambda_{szz} + \int_j^R \frac{(l-x)\,b(l-x)}{l^2}\lambda_{szz}$$

$$G_{RV} = -\int_L^j \frac{y(l-a)\,x}{l}\lambda_{szz} - \int_j^R \frac{ya(l-x)}{l}\lambda_{szz}$$

$$F_{RV} = -\int_L^j \frac{x(l-a)\,x}{l^2}\lambda_{szz} - \int_j^R \frac{xa(l-x)}{l^2}\lambda_{szz}$$

$$F_{LV} = -\int_L^j \frac{(l-x)(l-a)\,x}{l^2}\lambda_{szz} - \int_j^R \frac{(l-x)\,a(l-x)}{l^2}\lambda_{szz}$$

$$G_{RQ} = \int_L^j \frac{yx}{l}\lambda_{szz} - \int_j^R \frac{y(l-x)}{l}\lambda_{szz}$$

$$F_{RQ} = \int_L^j \frac{x^2}{l^2}\lambda_{szz} - \int_j^R \frac{x(l-x)}{l^2}\lambda_{szz}$$

$$F_{LQ} = \int_L^j \frac{(l-x)\,x}{l^2}\lambda_{szz} - \int_j^R \frac{(l-x)(l-x)}{l^2}\lambda_{szz}$$

These coefficients are listed in Table 8-2.

8.5. Using the general expressions derived in Problem 8.2 and given in Table 8-1, compute the unit load segmental flexibilities for the cantilever parabolic arch shown in Table 8-3.

The simplifying assumption made in evaluating the unit stress flexibilities shown in Table 8-3 will be made here too, i.e. $\lambda_{sxy} = \lambda_{syx} \simeq 0$ and $\lambda_{syy} \simeq 0$.

$$\lambda_{sxx} = \frac{\cos^2 \omega \, ds}{EA_s} = \frac{dx}{EA_R}, \qquad \lambda_{szz} = \frac{ds}{EI_s} = \frac{dx}{EI_R}$$

The following integrals will be needed and hence they are evaluated first:

$$\int_0^a dx = a, \qquad \int_0^a x\,dx = \frac{a^2}{2}, \qquad \int_0^a x^2\,dx = \frac{a^3}{3}$$

$$\int_0^a y\,dx = \int_0^a \frac{h}{l^2}(2lx - x^2)\,dx = \frac{h}{l^2}\left(la^2 - \frac{a^3}{3}\right)$$

$$\int_0^a y^2\,dx = \int_0^a \frac{h^2}{l^4}(2lx - x^2)^2\,dx = \frac{h^2}{l^4}\left(\frac{4l^2a^3}{3} - la^4 + \frac{a^5}{5}\right)$$

$$\int_0^a xy\,dx = \int_0^a \frac{h}{l^2}(2lx^2 - x^3)\,dx = \frac{h}{l^2}\left(\frac{2la^3}{3} - \frac{a^4}{4}\right)$$

The required coefficients, on evaluating the integrals and simplifying, are as follows:

$$C_{RPxx} = \int_0^a \left[\frac{dx}{EA_R} + \{hb - (h+b)\,y + y^2\}\frac{dx}{EI_R}\right]$$

$$= \frac{1}{EI_R}\left[\alpha a + hba - \frac{ha^2}{l}(h+b) + \frac{ha^3}{3l^2}(5h+b) - \frac{h^2a^4}{5l^4}(5l-a)\right]$$

$$C_{RPyx} = \int_0^a (-lb + bx + ly - xy)\frac{dx}{EI_R}$$

$$= \frac{1}{EI_R}\left[-lba + \frac{ba^2}{2} + ha^2 - \frac{ha^3}{l} + \frac{ha^4}{4l^2}\right]$$

$$B_{RPzx} = -\int_0^a (b - y)\frac{dx}{EI_R} = -\frac{1}{EI_R}\left[ba - \frac{h}{l^2}\left(la^2 - \frac{a^3}{3}\right)\right]$$

$$C_{RPxy} = \int_0^a (-ha + ay + hx - xy)\frac{dx}{EI_R} = \frac{-ha^2}{12l^2EI_R}[6l^2 - 4la + a^2]$$

$$C_{RPyy} = \int_0^a \{la - (l+a)\,x + x^2\}\frac{dx}{EI_R} = \frac{a^2}{6EI_R}(3l - a)$$

$$B_{RPzy} = \int_0^a (a - x)\frac{dx}{EI_R} = \frac{1}{EI_R}\left(a^2 - \frac{a^2}{2}\right) = \frac{a^2}{2EI_R}$$

$$B_{RQxz} = -\int_0^a (h - y)\frac{dx}{EI_R} = -\frac{ha}{3l^2EI_R}(3l^2 - 3al + a^2)$$

$$B_{RQyz} = \int_0^a (l - x)\frac{dx}{EI_R} = \frac{a}{2EI_R}(2l - a)$$

$$A_{RQzz} = \int_0^a \frac{dx}{EI_R} = \frac{a}{EI_R}$$

It may be verified that for $a = l$ and $b = h$, these expressions reduce to those for the unit stress flexibilities given in Table 8-3.

8.6. Using the general expressions derived in Problem 8.4 and given in Table 8-2, compute the unit load segmental flexibilities for the simple parabolic arch shown in Table 8-4.

For a simple parabolic arch with $A_x = A_c \cos \omega$ and $I_s = I_c/\cos \omega$,

$$\lambda_{sxx} = \frac{\cos^2 \omega \, ds}{EA_s} = \frac{dx}{EA_c} \qquad \text{and} \qquad \lambda_{szz} = \frac{dx}{EI_s} = \frac{dx}{EI_c}$$

The following integrals are evaluated first:

$$\int_0^a dx = a, \qquad \int_0^a x\,dx = \frac{a^2}{2}, \qquad \int_0^a x^2\,dx = \frac{a^3}{3}$$

$$\int_0^a y\,dx = \int_0^a \frac{4h}{l^2} x(l-x)\,dx = \frac{2ha^2}{3l^2}(3l-2a)$$

$$\int_0^a y^2\,dx = \int_0^a \frac{16h^2}{l^4} x^2(l^2-2lx+x^2)\,dx = \frac{8h^2a^3}{15l^4}(10l^2-15la+6a^2)$$

$$\int_0^a xy\,dx = \int_0^a \frac{4h}{l^2} x^2(l-x)\,dx = \frac{ha^3}{3l^2}(4l-3a)$$

Also,

$$\int_a^l dx = l-a, \qquad \int_a^l x\,dx = \tfrac{1}{2}(l^2-a^2), \qquad \int_a^l x^2\,dx = \tfrac{1}{3}(l^3-a^3)$$

$$\int_a^l y\,dx = \int_a^l \frac{4h}{l^2} x(l-x)\,dx = \frac{2h}{3l^2}(l^3-3la^2+2a^3)$$

$$\int_a^l y^2\,dx = \int_a^l \frac{16h^2}{l^4} x^2(l-x)^2\,dx = \frac{8h^2}{15l^4}(l^5-10l^2a^3+15la^4-6a^5)$$

$$\int_a^l xy\,dx = \int_a^l \frac{4h}{l^2} x^2(l-x)\,dx = \frac{h}{3l^2}(l^4-4la^3+3a^4)$$

The required unit load flexibility constants then, on evaluating the integrals and simplifying, are as follows:

$$E_{RH} = \int_0^a \frac{dx}{EA_c} + \int_0^a \frac{y(ly-bx)}{l}\frac{dx}{EI_c} + \int_a^l \frac{yb(l-x)}{l}\frac{dx}{EI_c}$$

$$= \frac{1}{EI_c}\left[\alpha a + \frac{8h^2a^3}{15l^4}(10l^2-15la+6a^2) + \frac{hb}{3l^2}(l^3-6la^2+4a^3)\right]$$

$$G_{RH} = \int_0^a \frac{x(ly-bx)}{l^2}\frac{dx}{EI_c} + \int_a^l \frac{xb(l-x)}{l^2}\frac{dx}{EI_c} = \frac{1}{l^2EI_c}\left[\frac{ha^3}{3l}(4l-3a) + \frac{bl}{6}(l^2-3a^2)\right]$$

$$G_{LH} = \int_0^a \frac{(l-x)(ly-bx)}{l^2}\frac{dx}{EI_c} + \int_a^l \frac{(l-x)\,b(l-x)}{l^2}\frac{dx}{EI_c}$$

$$= \frac{1}{l^2EI_c}\left[\frac{ha^2}{3l}(6l^2-8la+3a^2) + \frac{bl}{6}(2l^2-6la+3a^2)\right]$$

$$G_{RV} = -\int_0^a \frac{y(l-a)\,x}{l}\frac{dx}{EI_c} - \int_a^l \frac{ya(l-x)}{l}\frac{dx}{EI_c} = -\frac{ah}{3l^2EI_c}(l^3-2la^2+a^3)$$

$$F_{RV} = -\int_0^a \frac{x(l-a)\,x}{l^2}\frac{dx}{EI_c} - \int_a^l \frac{xa(l-x)}{l^2}\frac{dx}{EI_c} = -\frac{a}{6lEI_c}(l^2-a^2)$$

$$F_{LV} = -\int_0^a \frac{(l-x)(l-a)\,x}{l^2}\frac{dx}{EI_c} - \int_a^l \frac{(l-x)\,a(l-x)}{l^2}\frac{dx}{EI_c} = -\frac{a}{6lEI_c}(2l^2-3la+a^2)$$

$$G_{RQ} = \int_0^a \frac{yx}{l}\frac{dx}{EI_c} - \int_a^l \frac{y(l-x)}{l}\frac{dx_c}{EI_c} = -\frac{h}{3l^2EI_c}(l^3-6la^2+4a^3)$$

$$F_{RQ} = \int_0^a \frac{x^2}{l^2}\frac{dx}{EI_c} - \int_a^l \frac{x(l-x)}{l^2}\frac{dx}{EI_c} = -\frac{1}{6lEI_c}(l^2-3a^2)$$

$$F_{LQ} = \int_0^a \frac{(l-x)\,x}{l^2}\frac{dx}{EI_c} - \int_a^l \frac{(l-x)(l-x)}{l^2}\frac{dx}{EI_c} = -\frac{1}{6lEI_c}(2l^2-6la+3a^2)$$

For $a = l$, these unit load flexibilities reduce to the appropriate unit stress flexibilities of Table 8-4, as can be easily verified.

8.7. Using the general expressions derived in Problem 8.2 and given in Table 8-1, compute the unit load segmental flexibilities for the cantilever circular arch given in Table 8-5.

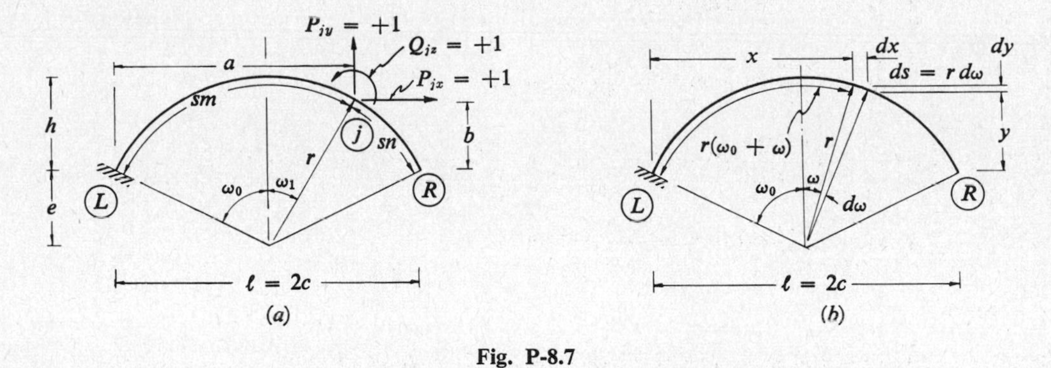

Fig. P-8.7

Figures P-8.7*a*, *b* show the constant and variable quantities of the cantilever arch.

From Fig. *a*, $sm = r(\omega_0 + \omega_1) = 2r\omega_0 m, \quad s = 2r\omega_0, \quad \beta = r/2s$

$a = r(\sin\omega_1 + \sin\omega_0), \quad b = r(\cos\omega_1 - \cos\omega_0), \quad x = c + r\sin\omega, \quad y = -e + r\cos\omega$

and $\gamma = (\sin 2\omega_0 + \sin 2\omega_1)/2$ is a simplifying equivalent.

Since the unit load flexibility integrals consist of several basic types, these basic integrals are computed first. They are:

$$u_{00} = \int_L^j ds = \int_{-\omega_0}^{\omega_1} r\,d\omega - r(\omega_0 + \omega_1) = sm$$

$$u_{01} = \int_L^j x\,ds = \int_{-\omega_0}^{\omega_1} (c + r\sin\omega)\,r\,d\omega = s(cm - 2\beta b)$$

$$u_{02} = -\int_L^j y\,ds = \int_{-\omega_0}^{\omega_1} (e - r\cos\omega)\,r\,d\omega = s(em - 2\beta a)$$

$$u_{11} = \int_L^j x^2\,ds = \int_{-\omega_0}^{\omega_1} (c + r\sin\omega)^2\,r\,d\omega = sc(cm - 4\beta b) + sr^2(m/2 - \beta\gamma)$$

$$u_{22} = \int_L^j y^2\,ds = \int_{-\omega_0}^{\omega_1} (e - r\cos\omega)^2\,r\,d\omega = se(em - 4\beta a) + sr^2(m/2 + \beta\gamma)$$

$$u_{12} = -\int_L^j xy\,ds = \int_{-\omega_0}^{\omega_1} (c + r\sin\omega)(e - r\cos\omega)r\,d\omega = s(cem - 2\beta be - \beta a^2) = u_{21}$$

$$u_{33} = \int_L^j \cos^2\omega\,ds = \int_{-\omega_0}^{\omega_1} (\cos^2\omega)\,r\,d\omega = s(m/2 + \beta\gamma)$$

Once these basic integrals are known, the remaining task consists of evaluation of Table 8-1 in terms of the results obtained above. In the subsequent calculations,

$$\lambda_{sxx} = (\cos^2\omega)r\,d\omega/EA, \quad \lambda_{szz} = r\,d\omega/EI, \quad \lambda_{sxy} = \lambda_{syx} \simeq 0 \quad \text{and} \quad \lambda_{syy} \simeq 0$$

From Table 8-1,

$$C_{RPxx} = u_{33}/EA + (blu_{02} + u_{22})/EI$$
$$C_{RPyx} = (-blu_{00} + blu_{01} - lu_{02} + u_{12})/EI$$
$$B_{RPzx} = (-blu_{00} - u_{02})/EI$$
$$C_{RPxy} = (-alu_{02} - u_{12})/EI$$
$$C_{RPyy} = (alu_{00} - alu_{01} - lu_{01} + u_{11})/EI$$
$$B_{RPzy} = (alu_{00} - u_{01})/EI$$
$$B_{RQxz} = -u_{02}/EI$$
$$B_{RQyz} = (lu_{00} - u_{01})/EI$$
$$A_{RQzz} = u_{00}/EI$$

8.8. Using the general expressions derived in Problem 8.4 and given in Table 8-2, compute the unit load segmental flexibilities for the simple circular arch given in Table 8-6.

The geometric relations and the basic integrals established in the previous problem are usable in this problem too. In addition the following values are defined:

$$v_{00} = \int_{\omega_1}^{\omega_0} ds = \int_{\omega_1}^{\omega_0} r\,d\omega = r(\omega_0 - \omega_1) = sn$$

$$v_{01} = \int_{\omega_1}^{\omega_0} x\,ds = \int_{\omega_1}^{\omega_0} (c + r\sin\omega)\,r\,d\omega = s(cn + 2\beta d)$$

$$v_{02} = -\int_{\omega_1}^{\omega_0} y\,ds = \int_{\omega_1}^{\omega_0} (e - r\cos\omega)\,r\,d\omega = s(en - 2\beta(l-a))$$

$$v_{11} = \int_{\omega_1}^{\omega_0} x^2\,ds = \int_{\omega_1}^{\omega_0} (c + r\sin\omega)^2\,r\,d\omega = sc(cn + 4\beta b - 2\beta e) + sr^2(n/2 + \beta\gamma)$$

$$v_{22} = \int_{\omega_1}^{\omega_0} y^2\,ds = \int_{\omega_1}^{\omega_0} (e - r\cos\omega)^2\,r\,d\omega = se(en + 4\beta a - 6\beta c) + sr^2(n/2 - \beta\gamma)$$

$$v_{12} = -\int_{\omega_1}^{\omega_0} xy\,ds = \int_{\omega_1}^{\omega_0} (c + r\sin\omega)(e - r\cos\omega)\,r\,d\omega = s(cen + 2\beta be - \beta(l^2 - a^2)) = v_{21}$$

Using these results in Table 8-2 gives

$$\begin{aligned}
E_{RH} &= u_{33}/EA + (lu_{22} + bu_{12} - blv_{02} + bv_{12})/lEI \\
G_{RH} &= (-lu_{12} - bu_{11} + blv_{01} - bv_{11})/l^2EI \\
G_{LH} &= (-l^2u_{02} - blu_{01} + lu_{12} + bu_{11} + bl^2v_{00} - 2blv_{01} + bv_{11})/l^2EI \\
G_{RV} &= ((l-a)u_{12} + alv_{02} - av_{12})/lEI \\
F_{RV} &= -((l-a)\,u_{11} + alv_{01} - av_{11})/l^2EI \\
F_{LV} &= -((l-a)(lu_{01} - u_{11}) + a(l^2v_{00} - 2lv_{01} + v_{11}))/l^2EI \\
G_{RQ} &= (-u_{12} + lv_{02} - v_{12})/lEI \\
F_{RQ} &= (u_{11} - lv_{01} + v_{11})/l^2EI \\
F_{LQ} &= (lu_{01} - u_{11} + l^2v_{00} - 2lv_{01} + v_{11})/l^2EI
\end{aligned}$$

8.9. Derive the matrix relationship between (*8.2*) and (*8.4*).

The relationship between the stress vector σ_1 in the cantilever arch (Fig. P-8.9*a*) and the stress vector σ_2 in the simple arch (Fig. *b*) is given as

$$\sigma_1 = q_{12}\sigma_2 \qquad \sigma_2 = q_{21}\sigma_1 \tag{1, 2}$$

where

$$\sigma_1 = \{N^0_{Rx},\, N^0_{Ry},\, M^0_{Rz}\} \qquad \sigma_2 = \{N^0_{Rx},\, M^0_{Rz},\, M^0_{Lz}\}$$

and

$$q_{12} = \begin{bmatrix} 1 & 0 & 0 \\ h/l & -1/l & 1/l \\ 0 & 1 & 0 \end{bmatrix} \qquad q_{21} = \begin{bmatrix} 1 & 0 & 0 \\ 0 & 0 & 1 \\ -h & l & 1 \end{bmatrix} \tag{3,4}$$

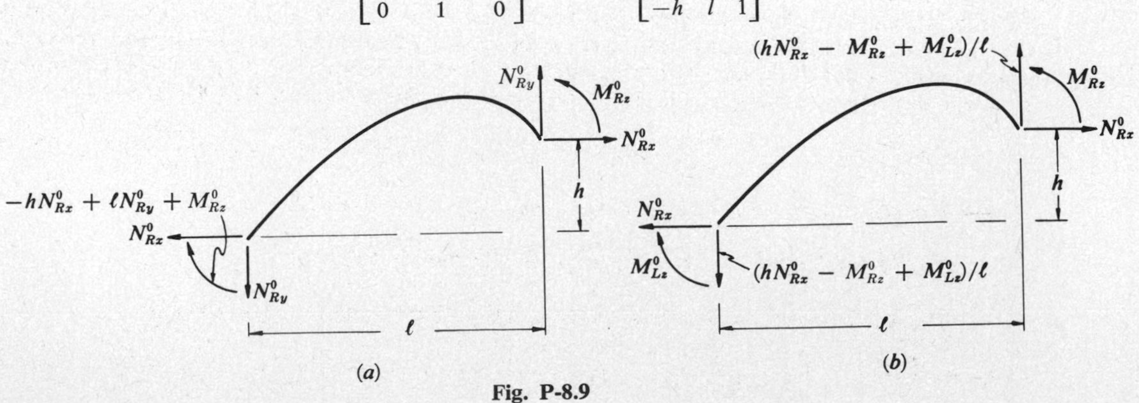

Fig. P-8.9

Similarly, the relationships between the end displacement vectors Δ_1 and Δ_2 produced by σ_1 and σ_2 respectively are

$$\Delta_1 = q_{21}^{)T}\Delta_2 \qquad \Delta_2 = q_{12}^{)T}\Delta_1 \tag{5,6}$$

where $\qquad \Delta_1 = \{\delta^0_{Rx}, \delta^0_{Ry}, \theta^0_{Rz}\} \qquad \Delta_2 = \{\delta^0_{Rx}, \theta^0_{Rz}, \theta^0_{Lz}\}$

and $q_{12}^{)T}$ and $q_{21}^{)T}$ are the transposes of (3, 4) respectively.

The relationships between the displacement vectors and the stress vectors are, by definition,

$$\Delta_1 = f_1\sigma_1 \qquad \Delta_2 = f_2\sigma_2 \tag{7, 8}$$

where f_1, f_2 are given by (8.2), (8.4) respectively.

Then (7) and (8) in terms of (1) and (2) become

$$\Delta_1 = f_1 q_{12}\sigma_2 \qquad \Delta_2 = f_2 q_{21}\sigma_1 \tag{9, 10}$$

Further, (5) and (6) in terms of (10) and (9) become

$$\Delta_1 = q_{21}^{)T} f_2 q_{21}\sigma_1 \qquad \Delta_2 = q_{12}^{)T} f_1 q_{12}\sigma_2 \tag{11,12}$$

If σ_1 and σ_2 are unit stress vectors, then $\Delta_1 = f_1$ and $\Delta_2 = f_2$ and (11, 12) reduce to typical congruent transformations

$$f_1 = q_{21}^{)T} f_2 q_{21} \qquad f_2 = q_{12}^{)T} f_1 q_{12}$$

which are perfectly general and valid for all flexibility transformations.

VARIABLE CROSS SECTION

8.10. For the symmetrical 2° parabolic arch of Fig. P-8.10, compute the unit stress segmental flexibility constants E_{RR}, F_{RR}, F_{LL}, F_{RL} and F_{LR} of Table 8-2. The depth of the 1/2″ thick web of the I-cross section varies parabolically with $d_L = d_R = 3d_c = 30''$ and each flange has a constant section $15'' \times 1''$. $E = 29 \times 10^3$ k/in².

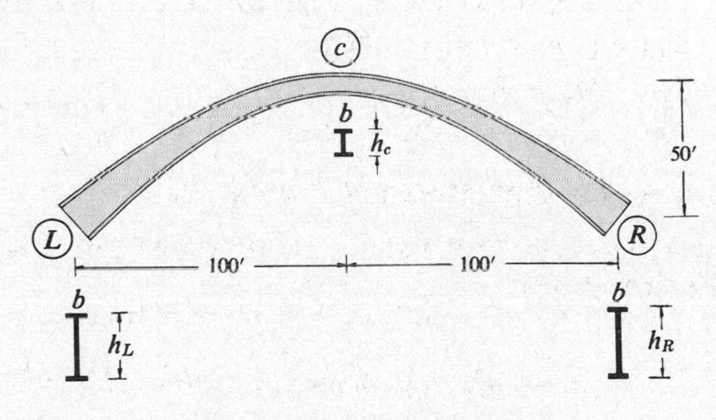

Fig. P-8.10

The required flexibility constants are computed using numerical integration. Quadrature formula (6.5b) (Simpson's Rule) is used with the arch divided in ten segments using $\Delta x = 20'$. The integrands of the flexibility integrals of Table 8-2 are computed as functions of position x before Simpson's Rule is applied. These calculations and those for the geometric and elastic properties of sections at selected stations can be performed efficiently in a tabular form as shown in Table P-8.10 below. The following relations are used in the computation.

$$y = \frac{4h}{l^2}(x)(l-x) = \frac{200}{(4)\,10^4}(x)(200-x)\text{ ft}, \qquad y' = \tan\omega = \frac{4h}{l^2}(l-2x) = \frac{200}{(4)\,10^4}(200-2x)$$

$$\cos\omega = 1/(1+\tan^2\omega)^{1/2}, \qquad \text{depth of the web} = d_\omega = 10 + 0.002(100-x)^2\text{ in.}$$

$$A_i = 30 + 0.5(d_\omega)_i\text{ in}^2, \qquad I_i = \frac{1}{12}(0.5)(d_\omega)_i^3 + 2(15)(d_\omega/2 + 0.5)^2\text{ in}^4$$

$$\alpha_i = A_i/A_c \quad\text{and}\quad \beta_i = I_i/I_c \quad\text{where}\quad A_c = 35\text{ in}^2 \quad\text{and}\quad I_c = 949.2\text{ in}^4$$

$$\phi_{1i} = \frac{\cos\omega_i}{\alpha_i}, \qquad \phi_{2i} = \frac{x_i^2}{\beta_i\cos\omega_i}, \qquad \phi_{3i} = \frac{y_i^2}{\beta_i\cos\omega_i}, \qquad \phi_{4i} = \frac{x_i\,y_i}{\beta_i\cos\omega_i}, \qquad \phi_{5i} = \frac{x_i(l-x_i)}{\beta_i\cos\omega_i}$$

Table P-8.10

Station	x_i ft	y_i ft	$\tan \omega_i$	$\cos \omega_i$	$(d_\omega)_i$ in.	A_i in^2	I_i in^4	α_i	β_i	ϕ_{1i}	ϕ_{2i}	ϕ_{3i}	ϕ_{4i}	ϕ_{5i}	Station
0	0	0	1.0	0.707	30.0	45.0	8,333	1.286	8.779	0.550	0	0	0	0	0
1	20	18	0.8	0.781	22.8	41.4	4,742	1.183	4.996	0.660	103	83	92	923	1
2	40	32	0.6	0.857	17.2	38.6	2,692	1.103	2.836	0.777	658	421	527	2,633	2
3	60	42	0.4	0.928	13.2	36.6	1,608	1.046	1.694	0.887	2,290	1,122	1,603	5,344	3
4	80	48	0.2	0.981	10.8	35.4	1,097	1.011	1.156	0.970	5,644	2,032	3,386	8,466	4
5	100	50	0.0	1.000	10.0	35.0	949	1.000	1.000	1.000	10,000	2,500	5,000	10,000	5
6	120	48	−0.2	0.981	10.8	35.4	1,097	1.011	1.156	0.970	12,698	2,032	5,079	8,466	6
7	140	42	−0.4	0.928	13.2	36.6	1,608	1.046	1.694	0.887	12,468	1,122	3,740	5,344	7
8	160	32	−0.6	0.857	17.2	38.6	2,692	1.103	2.836	0.777	10,533	421	2,107	2,633	8
9	180	18	−0.8	0.781	22.8	41.4	4,742	1.183	4.996	0.660	8,304	83	830	923	9
10	200	0	−1.0	0.707	30.0	45.0	8,333	1.286	8.779	0.550	6,445	0	0	0	10

The unit stress flexibilities are now computed as follows: For reasons of symmetry of the arch, $F_{RR} = F_{LL}$ and $G_{RR} = G_{LR}$. Also, because of reciprocal deformation relationship, $F_{RL} = F_{LR}$ and $G_{RL} = G_{LR}$. Therefore

$$F_{RR} = F_{LL} = \int_L^R \frac{x^2}{l^2}\lambda_{szz} = \int_L^R \frac{x^2\,ds}{l^2EI_s} = \frac{1}{l^2EI_c}\int_0^l \frac{x^2\,dx}{\beta\cos\omega} = \frac{1}{l^2EI_c}\int_0^l \phi_2\,dx$$

$$E_{RR} = \int_L^R [\lambda_{sxx} + y^2\lambda_{szz}] = \int_L^R \left[\frac{\cos^2\omega\,ds}{EA_s} + \frac{y^2\,ds}{EI_s}\right] = \frac{1}{EA_c}\int_0^l \frac{\cos\omega\,dx}{\alpha} + \frac{1}{EI_c}\int_0^l \frac{y^2\,dx}{\beta\cos\omega}$$

$$= \frac{1}{EA_c}\int_0^l \phi_1\,dx + \frac{1}{EI_c}\int_0^l \phi_3\,dx$$

$$G_{RR} = G_{LR} = G_{RL} = \int_L^R \frac{xy}{l}\lambda_{szz} = \int_L^R \frac{xy\,ds}{lEI_s} = \frac{1}{lEI_c}\int_0^l \frac{xy\,dx}{\beta\cos\omega} = \frac{1}{lEI_c}\int_0^l \phi_4\,dx$$

$$F_{RL} = F_{LR} = \int_L^R \frac{x(l-x)}{l^2}\lambda_{szz} = \int_L^R \frac{x(l-x)\,ds}{l^2EI_s} = \frac{1}{l^2EI_c}\int_0^l \frac{x(l-x)\,dx}{\beta\cos\omega} = \frac{1}{l^2EI_c}\int_0^l \phi_5\,dx$$

Evaluated using the Simpson's Rule (*6.5b*), these functions become

$$F_{RR} = F_{LL} = \frac{\Delta x}{3l^2EI_c}[0 + 4(103) + 2(658) + 4(2{,}290) + 2(5{,}644) + 4(10{,}000)$$
$$+ 2(12{,}698) + 4(12{,}468) + 2(10{,}533) + 4(8{,}304) + 6{,}445]$$
$$= \frac{20(198{,}171)(144)}{3(200)^2\,(29\times10^3)(949.2)} = 1.728\times10^{-4}\text{ rad/k-ft}$$

$$E_{RR} = \frac{\Delta x}{3EA_c}[0.550 + 4(0.660) + 2(0.777) + 4(0.887) + 2(0.970) + 4(1.000)$$
$$+ 2(0.970) + 4(0.887) + 2(0.777) + 4(0.660) + 0.550]$$
$$+ \frac{\Delta x}{3EI_c}[0 + 4(83) + 2(421) + 4(1{,}122) + 2(2{,}032) + 4(2{,}500) + 2(2{,}032) + 4(1{,}122) + 2(421) + 4(83) + 0]$$
$$= \frac{20(24.464)}{3(29\times10^3)(35)} + \frac{20(29{,}452)(144)}{3(29\times10^3)(949.2)} = 1.6068\times10^{-4} + 10{,}271\times10^{-4} = 10{,}273\times10^{-4}\text{ ft/k}$$

$$G_{RR} = G_{LR} = G_{RL} = \frac{\Delta x}{3lEI_c}[0 + 4(92) + 2(527) + 4(1{,}603) + 2(3{,}386) + 4(5{,}000)$$
$$+ 2(5{,}079) + 4(3{,}740) + 2(2{,}107) + 4(830) + 0]$$
$$= \frac{20(67{,}258)(144)}{3(200)(29\times10^3)(949.2)} = 1.1728\times10^{-2}\text{ rad/k or ft/k-ft}$$

$$F_{RL} = F_{LR} = \frac{\Delta x}{3l^2EI}[0 + 4(923) + 2(2{,}633) + 4(5{,}344) + 2(8{,}466) + 4(10{,}000)$$
$$+ 2(8{,}466) + 4(5{,}344) + 2(2{,}633) + 4(923) + 0]$$
$$= \frac{20(134{,}532)(144)}{3(200)^2(29\times10^3)(949.2)} = 1.1730\times10^{-4}\text{ rad/k-ft}$$

8.11. Compute the reactions and end deformations of the symmetrical two-hinged parabolic arch of Fig. P-8.11 in terms of the segmental flexibilities (Table 8-4, Problem 8.6). Assume $A = A_c\cos\omega$, $I = I_c\sec\omega$ and $\alpha = 1.0$ ft².

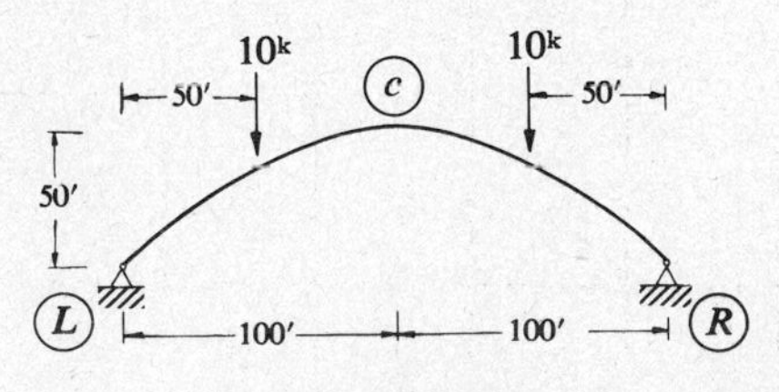

Fig. P-8.11

From (*8.7*), $\Delta = \Delta_\sigma + \Delta_0 = f\sigma + l_1W_1 + l_2W_2$ in which $\Delta = \{0, \theta^0_{Rz}, \theta^0_{Lz}\}$, $\sigma = \{N^0_{Rx}, 0, 0\}$, $W_1 = \{0, -10, 0\}$, $W_2 = \{0, -10, 0\}$, f is computed from Table 8-4 and l_1 and l_2 are constructed from coefficients derived in Problem 8.6 using $l = 200'$, $h = 50'$, $a_1 = 50'$, $b_1 = 37.5'$, $a_2 = 150'$ and $b_2 = 37.5'$. Using these values the equation stated above becomes

$$\begin{bmatrix} 0 \\ \theta^0_{Rz} \\ \theta^0_{Lz} \end{bmatrix} = \frac{200}{15EI_c}\begin{bmatrix} 20,015 & 250 & 250 \\ 250 & 5 & 2.5 \\ 250 & 2.5 & 5 \end{bmatrix}\begin{bmatrix} N^0_{Rx} \\ 0 \\ 0 \end{bmatrix} + \frac{1}{EI_c}\begin{bmatrix} 36,248 & -148,438 & -2,291.7 \\ 1,185 & -1,562.5 & -27.083 \\ 1,732 & -2,187.5 & -22.917 \end{bmatrix}\begin{bmatrix} 0 \\ -10 \\ 0 \end{bmatrix}$$

$$+\frac{1}{EI_c}\begin{bmatrix} 153,275 & -148,438 & 2,291.7 \\ 1,601.6 & -2,187.5 & 22.917 \\ 2,148.4 & -1,562.5 & 27.083 \end{bmatrix}\begin{bmatrix} 0 \\ -10 \\ 0 \end{bmatrix}$$

which reduces to a set of three scalar equations

$$0 = (266,866N^0_{Rx} + 1,484,380 + 1,484,380)/EI_c$$

$$\theta^0_{Rz} = (3,333.3N^0_{Rx} + 15,625 + 21,875)/EI_c$$

$$\theta^0_{Lz} = (3,333.3N^0_{Rx} + 21,875 + 15,625)/EI_c$$

Hence

$$N^0_{Rx} = -11.12 \text{ k}, \qquad \theta^0_{Rz} = +418.4/EI_c = \theta^0_{Lz}$$

8.12. If the parabolic arch of Problem 8.11 had a hinge at the crown and if the ends L and R were fully fixed (Fig. P-8.12), compute the end reactions induced by the loads. Use Table 8-3 and Problem 8.5.

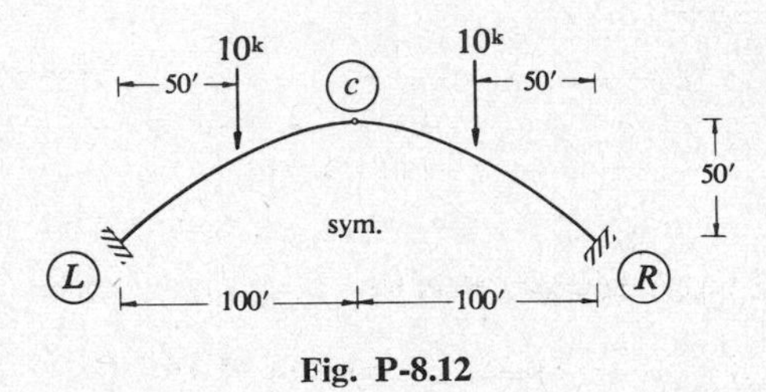

Fig. P-8.12

For reasons of symmetry, only half of the given arch may be analyzed. Also because of symmetry,

$$V_c = 0 \qquad \Delta_{cx} = 0$$

Also, $M_{cz} = 0$ at the hinge.
For the left half of the structure, (8.7) becomes

$$\Delta = f\sigma + lW$$

where $\Delta = \{0, \Delta_{cy}, \theta_{cz}\}$, $\sigma = \{N_{cx}, 0, 0\}$ and the load vector $W = \{0, -10, 0\}$ applied at $a = 50'$ and $b = 37.5'$. The matrices f and l are computed using Table 8-3 and Problem 8-5 respectively. The displacement vector thus becomes

$$\begin{bmatrix} 0 \\ \Delta_{cy} \\ \theta_{cz} \end{bmatrix} = \frac{100}{60EI_c}\begin{bmatrix} 30,090 & -75,000 & -1,000 \\ -75,000 & 200,000 & 3,000 \\ -1,000 & 3,000 & 60 \end{bmatrix}\begin{bmatrix} N_{cx} \\ 0 \\ 0 \end{bmatrix} + \frac{1}{EI_c}\begin{bmatrix} 30,283.3 & -44,270.8 & -1,458.3 \\ -70,312.5 & 104,166.7 & 3,750 \\ -833.3 & 1,250 & 50 \end{bmatrix}\begin{bmatrix} 0 \\ -10 \\ 0 \end{bmatrix} \qquad (1)$$

from which

$$(100/60)(30,090)\,N_{cx} + 442,708 = 0$$

$$\therefore\ N_{cx} = -8.828 \text{ k}$$

$$\therefore \quad \sigma_L = r_{Lc}\sigma_c + r_{Lj}W_j = \begin{bmatrix} 1 & 0 & 0 \\ 0 & 1 & 0 \\ -50 & 100 & 1 \end{bmatrix}\begin{bmatrix} -8.828 \\ 0 \\ 0 \end{bmatrix} + \begin{bmatrix} 1 & 1 & 0 \\ 0 & 1 & 0 \\ -37.5 & 50 & 0 \end{bmatrix}\begin{bmatrix} 0 \\ -10 \\ 0 \end{bmatrix} = \begin{bmatrix} -8.828 \\ -10 \\ -58.6 \end{bmatrix}$$

It may be noted that the values of Δ_{cy} and θ_{cz}, if desired, can be computed by substituting the value of N_{cx} in (1).

8.13. Find the forces transmitted by the hinge at the crown in the arch of Fig. P-8.12, if only the 10 k load on the left side were applied.

Unlike in Problem 8.12, advantage of symmetry cannot be taken and a more general setup is necessary. Choosing the forces transmitted by the hinge as redundants, the equation of compatibility of displacements at the hinge can be written in terms of known properties of each half of the arch. Thus

$$\Delta_{cL} + \Delta_{cR} = \{0, 0, \theta_c\}$$

$$\Delta_{cL} = f_{ccL}\sigma_c + l_{cL}W_L \qquad \text{and} \qquad \Delta_{cR} = f_{ccR}\sigma_c + l_{cR}W_R$$

where $f_{ccL} = f$, $l_{cL} = l$ and $W_L = W$ as for Problem 8.12 and $W_R = 0$. Then f_{ccR} is obtained by slightly modifying f_{ccL} to be consistent with the directions of the forces at the hinge (Fig. P-8.13). Thus

$$\text{for} \quad f_{ccL} = \begin{bmatrix} C_{RRxx} & C_{RRxy} & B_{RRxz} \\ C_{RRyx} & C_{RRyy} & B_{RRyz} \\ B_{RRzx} & B_{RRzy} & A_{RRzz} \end{bmatrix}, \quad \text{we have} \quad f_{ccR} = \begin{bmatrix} C_{RRxx} & -C_{RRxy} & B_{RRxz} \\ -C_{RRyx} & C_{RRyy} & -B_{RRyz} \\ B_{RRzx} & -B_{RRzy} & A_{RRzz} \end{bmatrix}$$

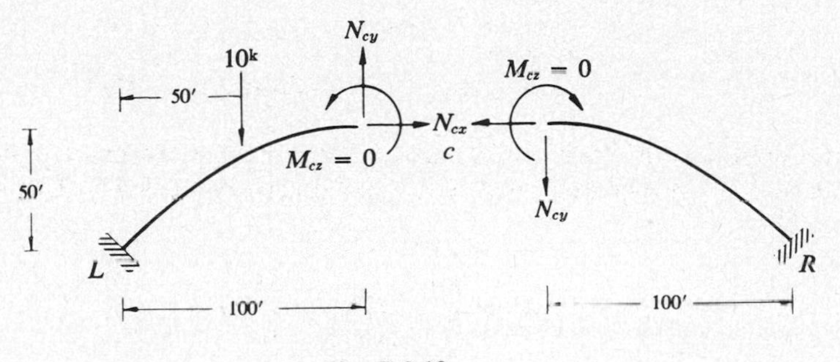

Fig. P-8.13

The compatibility equation therefore becomes

$$(f_{ccL} + f_{ccR})\,\sigma_c + lW = \{0, 0, \theta_c\}$$

$$\therefore \quad \frac{200}{60EI_c}\begin{bmatrix} 30{,}090 & 0 & -1{,}000 \\ 0 & 200{,}000 & 0 \\ -1{,}000 & 0 & 60 \end{bmatrix}\begin{bmatrix} N_{cx} \\ N_{cy} \\ 0 \end{bmatrix} + \frac{1}{EI_c}\begin{bmatrix} 30{,}283.3 & -44{,}270.8 & 1{,}458.3 \\ -70{,}312.5 & 104{,}166.7 & 3{,}750 \\ -833.3 & 1{,}250 & 50 \end{bmatrix}\begin{bmatrix} 0 \\ -10 \\ 0 \end{bmatrix} = \begin{bmatrix} 0 \\ 0 \\ \theta_c \end{bmatrix}$$

i.e.

$$100{,}300N_{cx} + 442{,}708 = 0$$

$$666{,}667N_{cy} - 1{,}041{,}667 = 0$$

from which $N_{cx} = -4.414$ k and $N_{cy} = 1.5625$ k.

It may be noted that θ_c, the angular change induced at c, can also be computed, if desired, by substituting in the matrix equation above the values of N_{cx} and N_{cy}.

8.14. Using the procedure shown in Problem 8.13, compute the forces and the moment at the crown D in the unsymmetrical fixed end parabolic arch shown in Fig. P-8.14. Assume $I = I_D \sec \omega$ and $\alpha \simeq 0$.

To use the properties established in Table 8-3, the redundants are selected at the point D. The compatibility equation is

$$\Delta_{DDL} + \Delta_{DDR} = 0$$

where $\Delta_{DDL} = f_{DDL}\sigma_D + l_{DL}W_L$ and $\Delta_{DDR} = f_{DDR}\sigma_D + l_{DR}W_R$. Therefore

$$(f_{DDL} + f_{DDR})\,\sigma_D + (l_{DL}W_L + l_{DR}W_R) = 0$$

and

$$\sigma_D = -(f_{DDL} + f_{DDR})^{-1}(l_{DL}W_L + l_{DR}W_R)$$

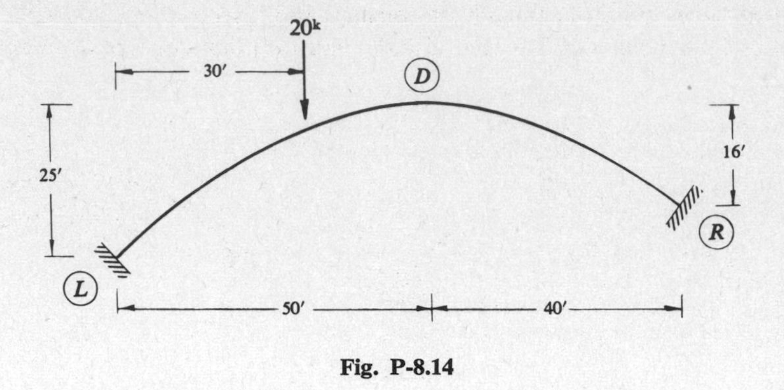

Fig. P-8.14

Using the given dimensions and Table 8-3 and the results of Problem 8.5,

$$f_{DDL} = \frac{1}{EI_D}\begin{bmatrix} 6{,}250 & -15{,}625 & -416.7 \\ -15{,}625 & 41{,}667 & 1{,}250 \\ -416.7 & 1{,}250 & 50 \end{bmatrix}, \qquad f_{DDR} = \frac{1}{EI_D}\begin{bmatrix} 2{,}048 & 6{,}400 & -213.3 \\ 6{,}400 & 21{,}333 & -800 \\ -213.3 & -800 & 40 \end{bmatrix}$$

$$l_{DL} = \frac{1}{EI_D}\begin{bmatrix} 4{,}626 & -7{,}425 & -390 \\ -11{,}025 & 18{,}000 & 1{,}050 \\ -270 & 450 & 30 \end{bmatrix} \qquad \text{for } a = 30', \ b = 21'$$

$$W_L = \{0,\ -20,\ 0\} \qquad \text{and} \qquad W_R = \{0,\ 0,\ 0\}$$

Substituting these values in the expression for σ_D,

$$\sigma_D = \{-16.461,\ 3.539,\ -32.923\}$$

ELASTIC CENTER

8.15. Explain how the location of the elastic center of the unsymmetrical parabolic arch of Fig. P-8.14 can be computed.

To take advantage of the properties established in Table 8-3, the arch must be cut at D and the free ends of the two cantilever bars connected to the neutral point C by two rigid arms as shown in Fig. 8-8. Then from (8.7),

$$f_{CC}^{C} = t_{DC}^{0C)T} f_{DD}^{0} t_{DC}^{0C}$$

where $f_{DD}^{0} = f_{DDL}^{0} + f_{DDR}^{0}$ as established in Prob. 8.14 and $t_{DC}^{0C} = r_{DC}^{0}\omega^{0C}$ in which

$$r_{DC}^{0} = \begin{bmatrix} 1 & 0 & 0 \\ 0 & 1 & 0 \\ -y_{DC} & x_{DC} & 1 \end{bmatrix} \qquad \text{and} \qquad \omega^{0C} = \begin{bmatrix} \cos\omega_{0C} & \sin\omega_{0C} & 0 \\ -\sin\omega_{0C} & \cos\omega_{0C} & 0 \\ 0 & 0 & 1 \end{bmatrix}$$

The three unknown quantities (x_{DC}, y_{DC} and ω_{0C}) relating to the location of the elastic center appear in the matrix product for f_{CC}^{C}. They are to be solved for simultaneously from the conditions

$$C_{CCxy}^{C} = C_{CCyx}^{C} = 0$$

$$B_{CCxz}^{C} = B_{CCzx}^{C} = 0$$

$$B_{CCyz}^{C} = B_{CCzy}^{C} = 0$$

enforced upon evaluating the matrix product.

For unsymmetrical arches this results into a set of complex simultaneous equations. For symmetrical arches it can be shown that the elastic center lies on the axis of symmetry, and $\omega = 0$.

8.16. A symmetrical fixed end circular arch of constant cross section is acted upon by a concentrated load of 50 k at the crown, Fig. P-8.16*a*. Use the neutral point concept (*8.7*) and compute the reactions.

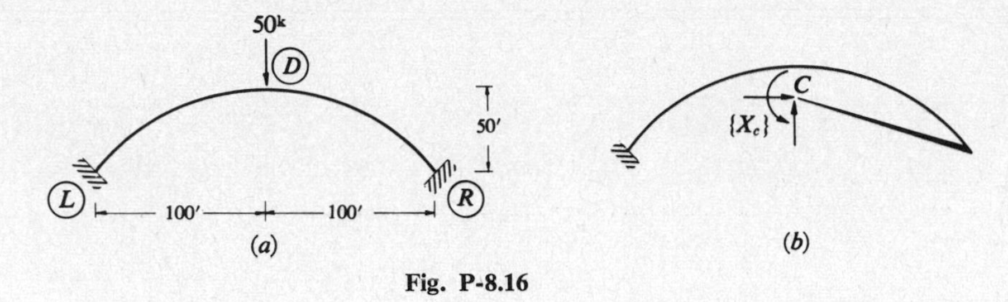

Fig. P-8.16

The location of the neutral point will be first established.

$$f_{CC}^{C} = t_{RC}^{0C)T} f_{RR}^{0} t_{RC}^{0C} \qquad t_{RC}^{0C} = r_{RC}^{0} \omega^{0C}$$

where
$$\omega^{0C} = \begin{bmatrix} \cos \omega_{0C} & \sin \omega_{0C} & 0 \\ -\sin \omega_{0C} & \cos \omega_{0C} & 0 \\ 0 & 0 & 1 \end{bmatrix} \quad \text{and} \quad r_{RC}^{0} = \begin{bmatrix} 1 & 0 & 0 \\ 0 & 1 & 0 \\ -y_{RC}^{0} & x_{RC}^{0} & 1 \end{bmatrix}$$

as discussed before. Also, using the given dimensions and the properties established in Table 8-5,

$$f_{RR}^{0} = \frac{231.8}{EI} \begin{bmatrix} 1,306 & 3,283 & 32.83 \\ 3,283 & 13,769 & 100 \\ 32.83 & 100 & 1 \end{bmatrix}$$

Substituting in the expression for f_{CC}^{C} and applying the conditions $C_{CCxy}^{C} = 0$, $B_{CCxz}^{C} = 0$ and $B_{CCyz}^{C} = 0$ gives

$$x_{RC} = -100', \qquad y_{RC} = 32.83' \qquad \text{and} \qquad \omega_{0C} = 0$$

Substituting these values back, (*8.9*) becomes

$$f_{CC}^{C} = \frac{231.8}{EI} \begin{bmatrix} 228 & 0 & 0 \\ 0 & 3,769 & 0 \\ 0 & 0 & 1 \end{bmatrix}$$

The unit load flexibility matrix at C can be computed by (*8.10*) wherein l_{RR}^{0} is evaluated using $a = 100'$ and $b = 50'$ in the results obtained in Problem 8-7. However, in this case the total deformation vector due to load can be calculated simply as follows:

$$\Delta_0{}^C = l_{CC}^{C} W^C = r_{RC}^{0)T} l_{RR}^{0} W^0$$

which for $W = \{0, -50, 0\}$ is equal to

$$-50 r_{RC}^{0)T} \begin{bmatrix} C_{RPxy} \\ C_{RPyy} \\ B_{RPzy} \end{bmatrix} = -\frac{50}{EI} \begin{bmatrix} 1 & 0 & -32.83 \\ 0 & 1 & -100 \\ 0 & 0 & 1 \end{bmatrix} \begin{bmatrix} 156,250 \\ 1,061,852 \\ 6,250 \end{bmatrix} = -\frac{50}{EI} \begin{bmatrix} -48,950 \\ 436,852 \\ 6,250 \end{bmatrix}$$

The conditions of compatibility at C are

$$f_{CC}^{C} X_C{}^C + \Delta_0{}^C = 0$$

Substituting the above values of f_{CC}^{C} and $\Delta_0{}^C$, we find

$$X_C{}^C = X_C{}^0 = \{-46.21, 25.0, 1,347.9\}$$

Then the end reactions can easily be computed from $\sigma_L{}^0 = r_{LC}^{0} X_C{}^0 + r_{LD}^{0} W_D^{0}$ and $\sigma_R{}^0 = r_{RC}^{0} X_C{}^0$.

ELASTIC RING

8.17. A circular ring of constant cross section is acted upon by a system of forces in equilibrium as shown in Fig. P-8.17*a*. Derive the general expressions for the stress vectors.

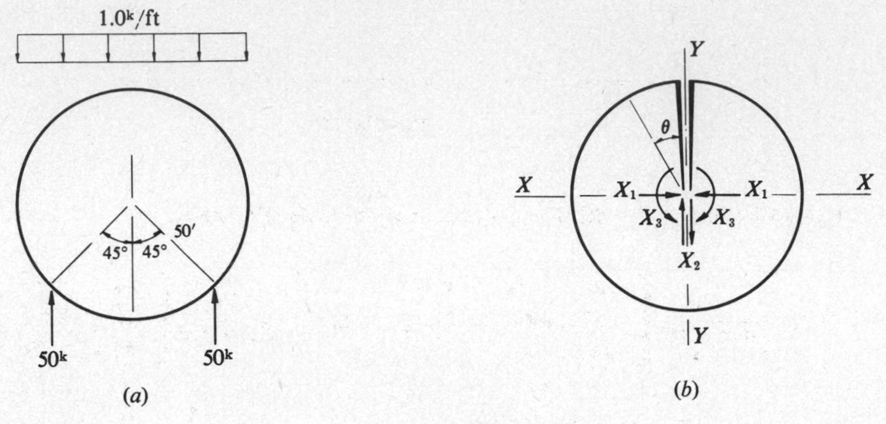

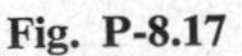

Fig. P-8.17

The ring is statically indeterminate to the third degree. The three internal redundants are chosen at the elastic center which is the center of the circle, the point of intersection of the two axes of symmetry shown in Fig. P-8.17*b*.

The unit stress flexibilities and load flexibilities at the elastic center are established as discussed in Section 8.7. These can also be done by applying the virtual work method directly to the case in hand. The total effect of the distributed load is found by integrating the effect of a differential load. The compatibility equation thus becomes

$$\frac{1}{EI}\begin{bmatrix} 392{,}699 & 0 & 0 \\ 0 & 392{,}699 & 0 \\ 0 & 0 & 314.16 \end{bmatrix}\begin{bmatrix} X_1 \\ X_2 \\ X_3 \end{bmatrix} + \frac{1}{EI}\begin{bmatrix} 1{,}039{,}767 \\ 0 \\ -217{,}394 \end{bmatrix} = 0$$

from which $X_1 = -2.648$ k, $X_2 = 0$, $X_3 = 692.0$ k-ft.

The required stress vectors are computed by superimposing the effects of the redundants and of the loads on typical sections taken in appropriate regions. Thus in the left half of the ring, the following σ^0 vectors are obtained.

$$0 \leqslant \theta \leqslant \pi/2 \qquad \pi/2 \leqslant \theta \leqslant 3\pi/4 \qquad 3\pi/4 \leqslant \theta \leqslant \pi$$

$$\begin{bmatrix} -2.648 \\ -50 \sin \theta \\ 559.6 - 1{,}250 \sin^2 \theta \end{bmatrix} \qquad \begin{bmatrix} -2.648 \\ -50 \\ 1{,}809.6 - 2{,}500 \sin \theta \end{bmatrix} \qquad \begin{bmatrix} -2.648 \\ 0 \\ 42.1 \end{bmatrix}$$

ELASTIC SUPPORTS

8.18. A two-span continuous arch consisting of two symmetrical parabolically curved bars loaded as shown in Fig. P-8.18 is supported by elastic springs of given flexibilities. Compute the reactions at i, j and k. Neglect axial deformation in the arches and use $I_s = I_c \sec \theta_s$, $I_c = 1.0$ ft^4, $E = 3 \times 10^3$ k/in^2, $F_{\delta x} = F_{\delta y} = 5 \times 10^{-3}$ ft/k and $F_{\theta z} = 5 \times 10^{-5}$ rad/k-ft, common for all supports.

Equations (*8.20*) in matrix form, for the given structure, are

$$\begin{bmatrix} f_J^* & f_{JK}^* \\ f_{KJ}^* & f_K^* \end{bmatrix}\begin{bmatrix} X_J \\ X_K \end{bmatrix} + \begin{bmatrix} \Delta_{J0}^* \\ \Delta_{K0}^* \end{bmatrix} = 0$$

in which $f_J^* = f^*_{JJ,i} + f^*_{JJ,j} = f_{JJ,i} + t)^T_{iJ} f_{i\Delta} t_{iJ} + f_{JJ,j} + t)^T_{jJ} f_{j\Delta} t_{jJ}$.

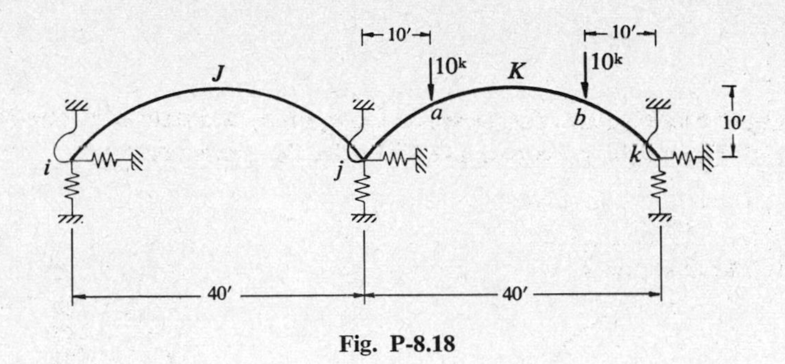

Fig. P-8.18

Using Table 8-3, for $l = 20'$, $h = 10'$ and the given values of E and I_c,

$$f_{JJ,i} = \frac{20}{432 \times 10^3}\begin{bmatrix} 20 & -50 & -10/3 \\ -50 & 400/3 & 10 \\ -10/3 & 10 & 1 \end{bmatrix}, \quad f_{JJ,j} = \frac{20}{432 \times 10^3}\begin{bmatrix} 20 & 50 & -10/3 \\ 50 & 400/3 & -10 \\ -10/3 & -10 & 1 \end{bmatrix}$$

$$t_{iJ} = r_{iJ} = \begin{bmatrix} 1 & 0 & 0 \\ 0 & 1 & 0 \\ -10 & 20 & 1 \end{bmatrix} = t_{jK}, \quad t_{jJ} = r_{jJ} = \begin{bmatrix} 1 & 0 & 0 \\ 0 & 1 & 0 \\ -10 & -20 & 1 \end{bmatrix} = t_{kK}$$

$$f_{i\Delta} = f_{j\Delta} = 10^{-4}\begin{bmatrix} 50 & 0 & 0 \\ 0 & 50 & 0 \\ 0 & 0 & 0.5 \end{bmatrix}$$

Hence,

$$f_J{}^* = 10^{-4}\begin{bmatrix} 218.52 & 0 & -13.09 \\ 0 & 623.46 & 0 \\ -13.09 & 0 & 1.926 \end{bmatrix} = f_K{}^* \text{ because of symmetry}$$

$$f_{JK}^* = t_{jJ}^{)T} f_{j\Delta} t_{jK} = 10^{-4}\begin{bmatrix} -100 & 100 & 5 \\ -100 & 150 & 10 \\ 5 & -10 & -0.5 \end{bmatrix}$$

Also $f_{KJ}^* = f_{JK}^{*)T}$ because of the reciprocal deformation relationship.

$$\Delta_{J0}^* = l_{Ja}^* W_a = t_{jJ}^{)T} f_{j\Delta} t_{ja} W_a = 10^{-4}\begin{bmatrix} -87.5 & 50 & 5 \\ -75 & 50 & 10 \\ 3.75 & -5 & -0.5 \end{bmatrix}\begin{bmatrix} 0 \\ -10 \\ 0 \end{bmatrix} = 10^{-4}\begin{bmatrix} -500 \\ -500 \\ 50 \end{bmatrix}$$

where

$$t_{ja} = \begin{bmatrix} 1 & 0 & 0 \\ 0 & 1 & 0 \\ -7.5 & 10 & 0 \end{bmatrix}$$

$$\Delta_{K0}^* = l_{Ka}^* W_a + l_{Kb}^* W_b = t_{jK}^{)T} f_{j\Delta} t_{ja} W_a + t_{kK}^{)T} f_{k\Delta} t_{kb} W_b$$

$$= 10^{-4}\begin{bmatrix} 87.5 & -50 & -5 \\ -75 & 150 & 10 \\ -3.75 & 5 & 0.5 \end{bmatrix}\begin{bmatrix} 0 \\ -10 \\ 0 \end{bmatrix} + 10^{-4}\begin{bmatrix} -87.5 & -50 & 5 \\ -75 & -150 & 10 \\ 3.75 & 5 & -0.5 \end{bmatrix}\begin{bmatrix} 0 \\ -10 \\ 0 \end{bmatrix} = 10^{-4}\begin{bmatrix} 1,000 \\ 0 \\ -100 \end{bmatrix}$$

It may be noted that algebraic signs were reversed in f^*_{JK}, l^*_{Ja} and l_{Kb} to be consistent with the directions of the redundants.

Substituting all values in the compatibility matrix equations and solving,

$$X_J = \{-0.418, -0.090, -14.54\} \qquad X_K = \{-2.529, -0.144, 32.52\}$$

The support reactions then can easily be computed from

$$\sigma_i = r_{iJ}X_J, \qquad \sigma_j = -r_{jJ}X_J + r_{jK}X_K + r_{ja}W_a \qquad \text{and} \qquad \sigma_k = -r_{kK}X_K + r_{kb}W_b$$

Supplementary Problems

8.19. Verify that, for $a = l$, the unit load segmental flexibilities computed in Problem 8.6 reduce to appropriate unit stress segmental flexibilities of Table 8-4, as stated in the solution of that problem.

8.20. Show that a 2° parabolic two-hinge arch acted upon by a uniformly distributed load (Fig. P-8.20) is in a state of pure compression, if axial deformations are neglected. Use the results of Problem 8.6 and Table 8-4.

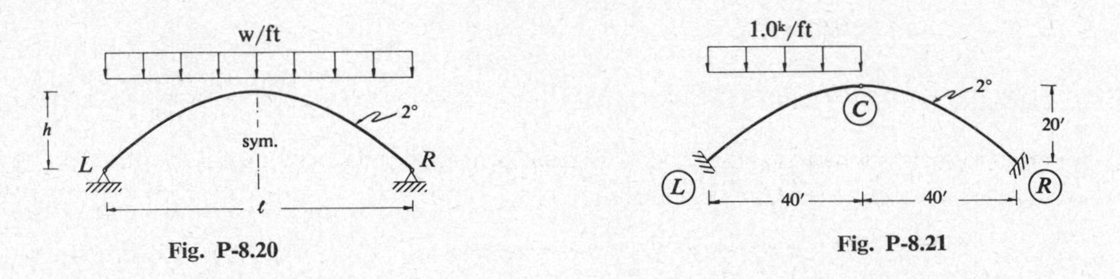

Fig. P-8.20

Fig. P-8.21

8.21. Using the procedure shown in Problem 8.13, compute the end reactions of the one-hinge parabolic arch shown in Fig. P-8.21. Integrate the results of Problem 8.5 to compute the effect of the load. $I_s = I_c \sec \omega$ and $\alpha \simeq 0$.

8.22. Compute the end reactions and deformations of a two-hinge circular arch loaded as shown in Fig. P-8.22. Use the results of Problem 8.8 and Table 8-6.

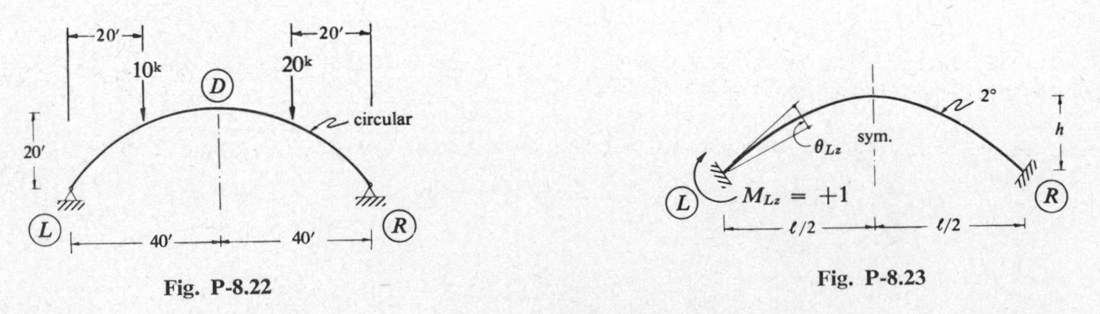

Fig. P-8.22

Fig. P-8.23

8.23. Compute the end angular flexibility of a symmetrical 2° parabolic fixed ended arch (end rotation/unit end moment, all other constraints being maintained). $I_s = I_c \sec \omega$ and $\alpha \simeq 0$. See Fig. P-8.23.

8.24. If the arch of Problem 8.10 were pin supported at L and R, compute the reactions developed due to a 100 k downward force applied at the crown C.

8.25. Using the results of Problem 8.9, compute the unit stress flexibilities of a 3-hinge arch shown in Fig. P-8.25 from those of the simple parabolic arch of Table 8-4.

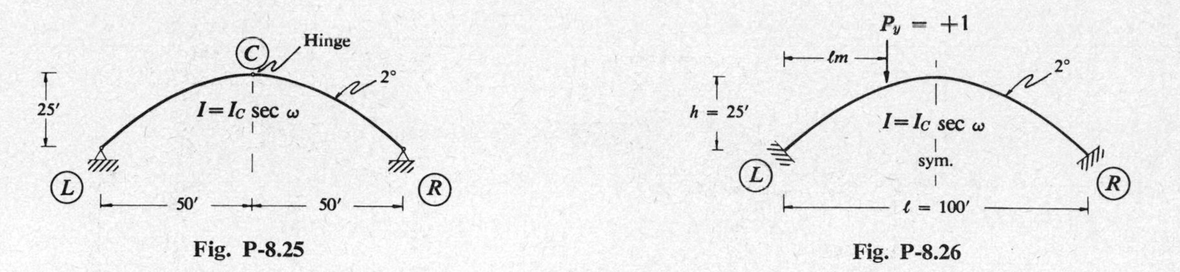

Fig. P-8.25

Fig. P-8.26

8.26. Compute and sketch the influence lines for the reactions at R for a fixed ended 2° parabolic arch, due to $P_y = +1$ (Fig. P-8.26).

8.27. Show that the elastic center of a symmetrical 2° parabolic arch of span l and rise h, with $I_s = I_c \sec \omega$ and $\alpha \simeq 0$, is located at $x = l/2$ and $y = 2h/3$ with respect to the origin at the left support.

8.28. Considering the curved member of the frame shown in Fig. P-8.28 as an arch on elastic supports, find the reactions at the supports.

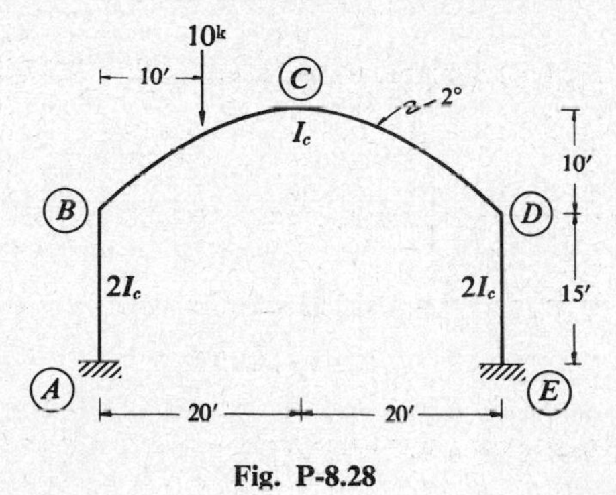

Fig. P-8.28

Chapter 9

Rigid Frame

9.1 SYSTEM

A *planar rigid frame* is defined as a planar system of bars connected together by joints, some or all of which are rigid. The *rigid joint* is capable of transmitting forces and moments from one member to another member connected at the joint. By definition this *joint displaces as a unit* and all members framed into it retain their relative angular positions to each other (angle between two members at the joint before and after deformation remains unchanged).

According to their *shapes*, planar frames are classified as *single span* or *multispan*, *one story* or *multistory* frames (Fig. 9-1). In general, they are statically indeterminate systems. If the rigid frame is in a state of static equilibrium, each of its members and joints must be in the same state. Thus the total number of independent *conditions of static equilibrium* is

$$e = 3m + 3j + f \tag{9.1}$$

where m = number of members, j = number of joints, f = number of special conditions.

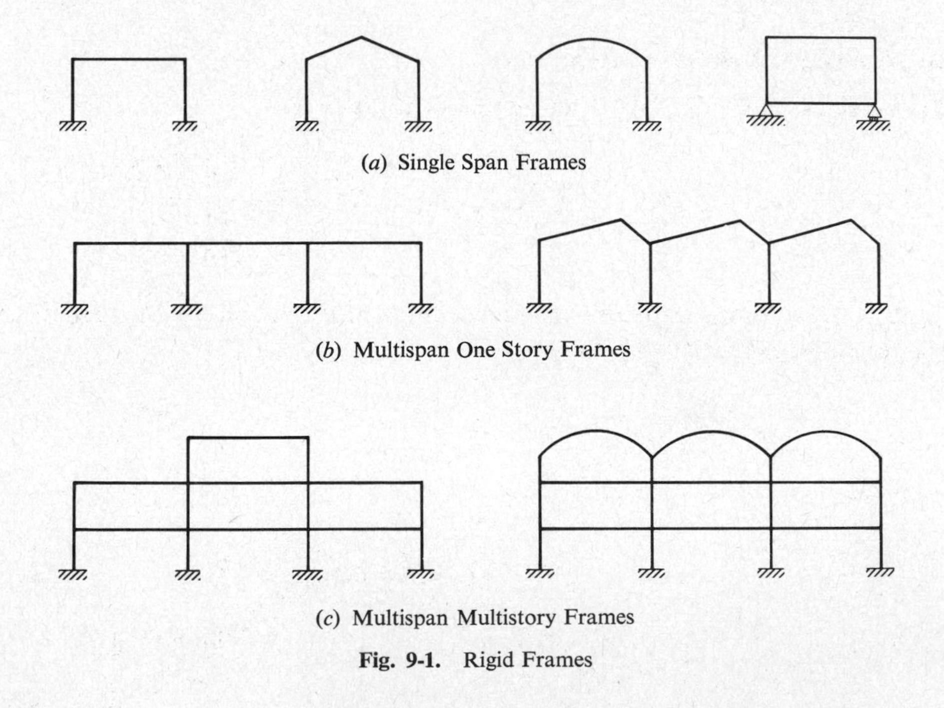

(*a*) Single Span Frames

(*b*) Multispan One Story Frames

(*c*) Multispan Multistory Frames

Fig. 9-1. Rigid Frames

Since there are six unknown end stresses in each member and r unknown reactions at the supports, the number of *redundants* is

$$n = 6m + r - e = 3m + r - 3j - f > 0 \tag{9.2}$$

If $n = 0$ the frame is statically determinate, and if $n < 0$ the frame is geometrically unstable. The number of joints j in (*9.1*) and (*9.2*) includes all internal joints and all points of support.

Although (*9.2*) is perfectly general and suitable for the accounting of redundants in frames of all kinds, for systems with a large number of members and joints, an alternate formula (*9.3*) is more convenient. Since a planar rigid frame can be considered as a *system of polygonal rings*, the number of redundants n can be expressed as

$$n = 3p - f \tag{9.3}$$

where p = number of polygonal rings. The number p includes all internal rings and also all support rings. For the concept of support rings and the application of (*9.2*) and (*9.3*) refer to Problem 9.1.

9.2 ANALYSIS

Although all three classes of methods (Sec. 1.6) are suitable for the analysis of rigid frames, the *flexibility method* and the *stiffness method* are the most commonly used. The object of this chapter is the general application of the segmental flexibility matrices (Tables 5-1, 5-2 and 8-1, 8-2) in the analysis of single span and continuous rigid frames, with single branch ring topology (Fig. 9-1*a*, *b*). The analysis of complex rigid frames with general ring topology (Fig. 9-1*c*) by segmental stiffness matrices follows in the following chapters.

9.3 GROUP FLEXIBILITY MATRIX

The coefficients of the flexibility matrix for a planar bar consisting of straight and/or curved segments are derived by means of (*5.10*) and (*5.11*) in terms of the respective segmental flexibilities given in Tables 5-1, 5-2 and 8-1, 8-2. Because a group of segments is involved, the designation of *group flexibility* is introduced.

(a) Group Flexibilities, Cantilever Frame

For the cantilever frame of Fig. 9-2 the *unit stress flexibility* is

$$f^S_{RR,L} = \begin{bmatrix} (t^{RS}_{RR})^T & (t^{JS}_{JR})^T & (t^{IS}_{IR})^T \end{bmatrix} \begin{bmatrix} f^R_{RR,J} & & \\ & f^J_{JJ,I} & \\ & & f^I_{II,L} \end{bmatrix} \begin{bmatrix} t^{RS}_{RR} \\ t^{JS}_{JR} \\ t^{IS}_{IR} \end{bmatrix} \tag{9.4}$$

where $f^R_{RR,J}$, $f^J_{JJ,I}$, $f^I_{II,L}$ are the segmental unit stress flexibilities of cantilever bars JR, IJ, LI at the free ends R, J, I respectively (Problem 9.2).

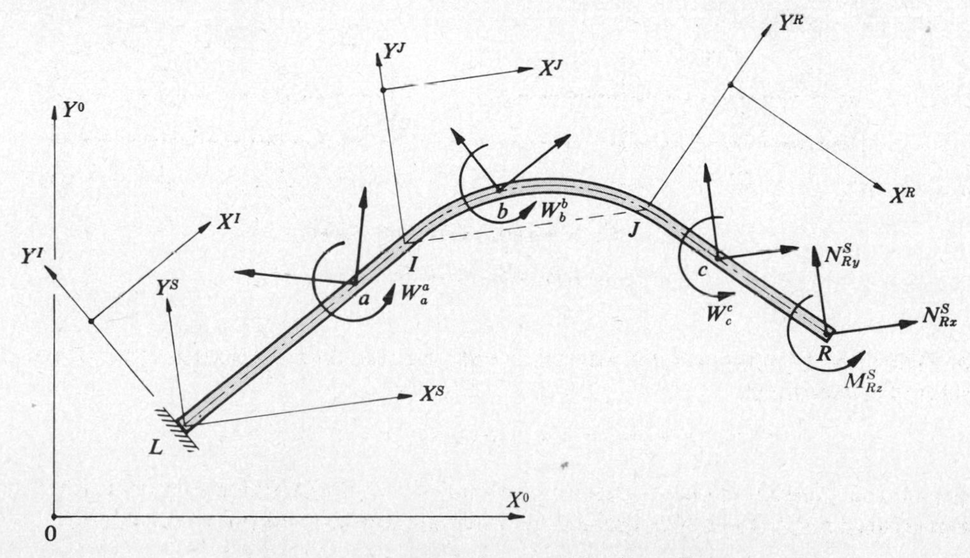

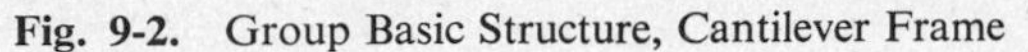
Fig. 9-2. Group Basic Structure, Cantilever Frame

The *unit load flexibility* of the same frame is

$$l^S_{RR,L} = [t^{RS)T}_{RR} \quad t^{JS)T}_{JR} \quad t^{IS)T}_{IR}] \begin{bmatrix} f^R_{RR,J} & & \\ & f^J_{JJ,I} & \\ & & f^I_{II,L} \end{bmatrix} \begin{bmatrix} \bar{\sigma}_R{}^R \\ \bar{\sigma}_J{}^J \\ \bar{\sigma}_I{}^I \end{bmatrix}$$

$$+ [t^{RS)T}_{RR} \quad t^{JS)T}_{JR} \quad t^{IS)T}_{IR}] \begin{bmatrix} l^R_{RR,J} & & \\ & l^J_{JJ,I} & \\ & & l^I_{II,L} \end{bmatrix} \begin{bmatrix} \omega^{Rc} & & \\ & \omega^{Jb} & \\ & & \omega^{Ia} \end{bmatrix} \tag{9.5}$$

where

$$\begin{bmatrix} \bar{\sigma}_R{}^R \\ \bar{\sigma}_J{}^J \\ \bar{\sigma}_I{}^I \end{bmatrix} = \begin{bmatrix} 0 & 0 & 0 \\ t^{Jc}_{Jc} & 0 & 0 \\ t^{Ic}_{Ic} & t^{Ib}_{Ib} & 0 \end{bmatrix} \tag{9.6}$$

are the *stress influence values* at R, J, I due to unit loads acting at c, b, a respectively and $l^R_{RR,J}$, $l^J_{JJ,I}$, $l^I_{II,L}$ are the segmental unit load flexibilities of the respective cantilevers (Problem 9.3).

(b) Group Flexibilities, Simple Frame

For the simple frame of Fig. 9-3 the *unit stress flexibility* is

$$f^S_{(LR)} = [q^{RS)T}_{(JR)} \quad q^{JS)T}_{(IJ)} \quad q^{IS)T}_{(LI)}] \begin{bmatrix} f^R_{(JR)} & & \\ & f^J_{(IJ)} & \\ & & f^I_{(LI)} \end{bmatrix} \begin{bmatrix} q^{RS}_{(JR)} \\ q^{JS}_{(IJ)} \\ q^{IS}_{(LI)} \end{bmatrix} \tag{9.7}$$

where $f^R_{(JR)}$, $f^J_{(IJ)}$, $f^I_{(LI)}$ are the segmental unit stress flexibilities of the respective simple beams (JR), (IJ), (LI) (Problem 9.4).

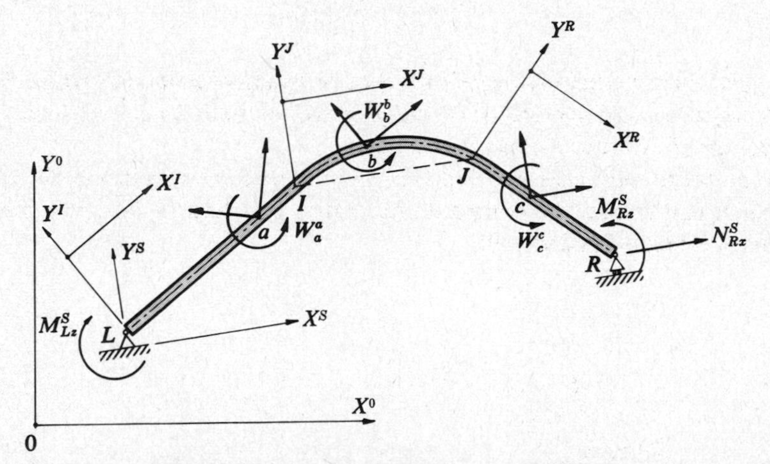

Fig. 9-3. Group Basic Structure, Simple Frame

The *unit load flexibility* of the same frame is

$$l^S_{(LR)} = [q^{RS)T}_{(JR)} \quad q^{JS)T}_{(IJ)} \quad q^{IS)T}_{(LI)}] \begin{bmatrix} f^R_{(JR)} & & \\ & f^J_{(IJ)} & \\ & & f^I_{(LI)} \end{bmatrix} \begin{bmatrix} \bar{\sigma}^R_{(JR)} \\ \bar{\sigma}^J_{(IJ)} \\ \bar{\sigma}^I_{(LI)} \end{bmatrix}$$

$$+ [q^{RS)T}_{(JR)} \quad q^{JS)T}_{(IJ)} \quad q^{IS)T}_{(LI)}] \begin{bmatrix} l^R_{(JR)} & & \\ & l^J_{(IJ)} & \\ & & l^I_{(LI)} \end{bmatrix} \begin{bmatrix} \mu^{Rc} & & \\ & \mu^{Jb} & \\ & & \mu^{Ia} \end{bmatrix} \tag{9.8}$$

where

$$\begin{bmatrix} \bar{\sigma}^R_{(JR)} \\ \bar{\sigma}^J_{(IJ)} \\ \bar{\sigma}^I_{(LI)} \end{bmatrix} = \begin{bmatrix} q^{Rc}_{(JR)c} & q^{Rb}_{(JR)b} & q^{Ra}_{(JR)a} \\ q^{Jc}_{(IJ)c} & q^{Jb}_{(IJ)b} & q^{Ja}_{(IJ)a} \\ q^{Ic}_{(LI)c} & q^{Ib}_{(LI)b} & q^{Ia}_{(LI)a} \end{bmatrix} \tag{9.9}$$

are the *stress influence values* at (*JR*), (*IJ*), (*LI*) due to unit loads acting at *c*, *b*, *a* respectively and $l^R_{(JR)}$, $l^J_{(IJ)}$, $l^I_{(LI)}$ are the segmental unit load flexibilities of the respective simple beams (*JR*), (*IJ*), (*LI*) (Problem 9.5).

9.4 SINGLE SPAN FRAME

Once the group flexibilities (*9.4*), (*9.5*) or (*9.7*), (*9.8*) are available for the entire frame, they can be inserted in the displacement vector matrix (*8.7*) and used as indicated in Table 8-7, where the notion of arch is to be replaced by that of rigid frame. The analytical expressions for the effect of cross-sectional variation (Sec. 8.3), the treatment of end and intermediate conditions (Sec. 8.5 and 8.6), neutral point concept (Sec. 8.7) and the influence of elastic supports (Sec. 8.10), developed for the elastic arch in the preceding chapter, are applicable in the analysis of single span rigid frames (Problems 9.6 and 9.7).

9.5 POLYGONAL RING

Rigid frames of Fig. 9-1*a* can be always visualized as *polygonal rings* analogous to the equivalent rings of Fig. 8-9 or to the real rings of Fig. 8-10. For closed polygonal rings, the *criteria of statics* (*8.14*) and (*8-15*) apply without modification.

For *externally statically determinate rings* (Fig. 9-4*a*), the *condition of compatibility* is again

$$f^J_{JJ} X_J{}^J + l^J_{JJ} W^J = 0 \tag{9.10}$$

where f^J_{JJ} = unit stress group flexibility matrix (*9.4*) or (*9.7*), l^J_{JJ} = unit load group flexibility matrix (*9.5*) or (*9.8*), $X_J{}^J$ = stress redundant vector, W^J = load vector, all in *J*-system related (with exception of *W*) to the section of release *J* (arbitrarily selected section).

If the *concept of neutral point* is employed (Fig. 9-4*b*), the unit stress group flexibility matrix in (9.10) reduces to a diagonal matrix and the compatibility matrix equation (*9.10*) splits into three independent algebraic equations (Problems 9.8 and 9.9).

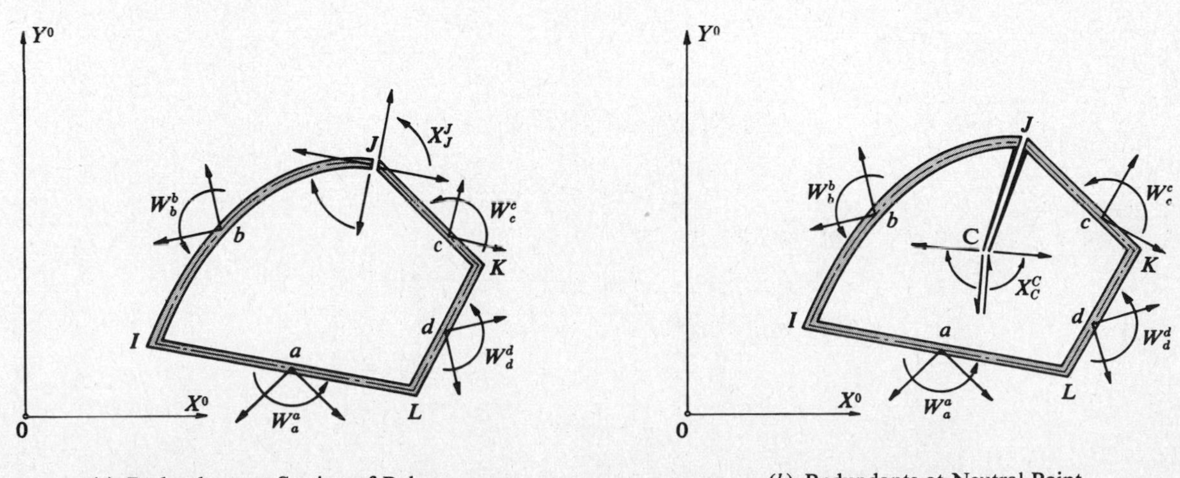

(*a*) Redundants at Section of Release

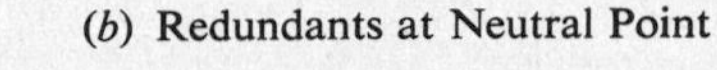
(*b*) Redundants at Neutral Point

Fig. 9-4. Polygonal Ring

9.6 STRING POLYGON

In the majority of frames, the axial deformations are small compared with the flexural deformations and can be disregarded. In such cases the angle change of the finite element Δs_j of the elastic curve is

$$\Delta\gamma_j = \Lambda_j M_j \tag{9.11}$$

where $\Lambda_j = \Delta s_j / EI_j$ and M_j = bending moment at j. The bending moment is the linear combination of the effect of redundant stress vector X and the load vector W.

For the polygonal ring of Fig. 9-5*a*, the length of which is divided into m finite elements, the compatibility condition (*9.10*) written for the section of release J is

$$\Delta_J^J = \underbrace{m_{JX}^{J)T} \Lambda m_{JX}^J}_{f_{JJ}^J} X_J^J + \underbrace{m_{JX}^{J)T} \Lambda m_{J0}^J}_{l_{JJ}^J} W^J \tag{9.12}$$

where X_J^J = stress redundant vector at J, $[3 \times 1]$, W^J = load vector, $[3m \times 1]$, some terms of which may equal zero if loads are not applied at some of the finite elements, Λ = finite element flexibility matrix, diag. $[m \times m]$, m_{JX}^J = moment influence value matrix due to $X_J^J = +1$, $[m \times 3]$, m_{J0}^J = moment influence value matrix due to $W^J = +1$ (Problem 9.10).

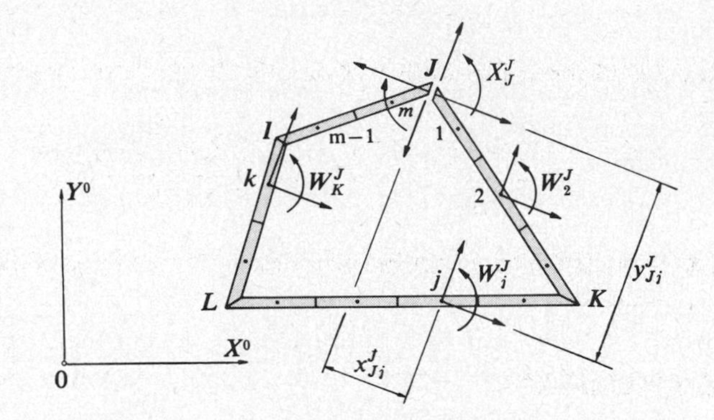

(*a*) Finite Elements 1, 2,..., *j*,..., *m* — 1, *m*

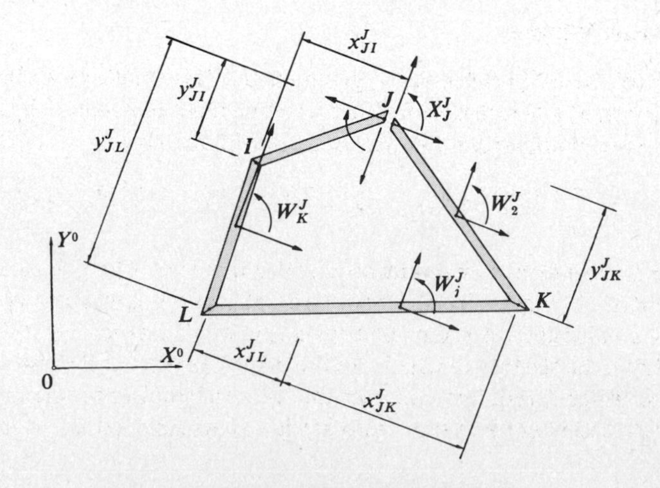

(*b*) Finite Segments *IJ*, *JK*, *KL*, *LI*

Fig. 9-5. Polygonal Ring

When instead of finite elements, finite segments *IJ, JK, KL, LI* are used (Fig. 9-5*b*), the joint angle change vector becomes

$$\underbrace{\begin{bmatrix} \gamma_I^{\ J} \\ \gamma_J^{\ J} \\ \gamma_K^{\ J} \\ \gamma_L^{\ J} \end{bmatrix}}_{\gamma^J} = \underbrace{\begin{bmatrix} F_I^{\ J} & F_{IJ}^J & 0 & F_{IL}^J \\ F_{JI}^J & F_J^{\ J} & F_{JK}^J & 0 \\ 0 & F_{KJ}^J & F_K^{\ J} & F_{KL}^J \\ F_{LI}^J & 0 & F_{LK}^J & F_L^{\ J} \end{bmatrix}}_{F^J} \underbrace{\begin{bmatrix} M_I^{\ J} \\ M_J^{\ J} \\ M_K^{\ J} \\ M_L^{\ J} \end{bmatrix}}_{M^J} + \underbrace{\begin{bmatrix} \tau_I^{\ J} \\ \tau_J^{\ J} \\ \tau_K^{\ J} \\ \tau_L^{\ J} \end{bmatrix}}_{\tau^J} \tag{9.13}$$

which is a generalization of (*5.25*). The bending moment matrix M^J consists of the bending moments caused by the redundants and loads. Thus

$$M^J = m_{JX}^J X_J^{\ J} + m_{J0}^J W^J \tag{9.14}$$

where

$$m_{JX}^J = \begin{bmatrix} -y_{IJ}^J & x_{IJ}^J & +1 \\ -y_{JJ}^J & x_{JJ}^J & +1 \\ -y_{KJ}^J & x_{KJ}^J & +1 \\ -y_{LJ}^J & x_{LJ}^J & +1 \end{bmatrix} \qquad m_{J0}^J = \left[\begin{array}{ccc|ccc|ccc} -y_{Ii}^J & x_{Ii}^J & +1 & -y_{Ij}^J & x_{Ij}^J & +1 & -y_{Ik}^J & x_{Ik}^J & +1 \\ 0 & 0 & 0 & 0 & 0 & 0 & 0 & 0 & 0 \\ -y_{Ki}^J & x_{Ki}^J & +1 & 0 & 0 & 0 & 0 & 0 & 0 \\ -y_{Li}^J & x_{Li}^J & +1 & y_{Lj}^J & x_{Lj}^J & +1 & 0 & 0 & 0 \end{array}\right]$$

In terms of (*9.13*) and (*9.14*) the compatibility condition (*9.10*) written again for the section of release *J* is

$$\Delta_J^{\ J} = \underbrace{m_{JX}^{J)T} F^J m_{JX}^J}_{f_{JJ}^J} X_J^{\ J} + \underbrace{m_{JX}^{J)T} F^J m_{J0}^J W^J + m_{JX}^{J)T} \tau^J}_{l_{JJ}^J W^J} \tag{9.15}$$

This relationship is perfectly general and it can be extended to the analysis of polygonal rings of all kinds (Problem 9.11).

9.7 ELASTO-STATIC ANALOGY*

The analogy between the equations of elasto-kinematics (geometry of small angle changes) and those of stereostatics (ordinary statics) of the same segment introduced in Sections 5.8-5.10 can be extended to a polygonal ring as shown in two forms in this section.

(a) Finite Element Elastic Weights

If the angle change of the finite element Δs_j given by (*9.11*) is small, it can be treated as a force-vector normal to the plane of ring at j and denoted as the finite element elastic weight $\bar{P}_j = \Delta\gamma_j$.

Then the conditions of compatibility of the ring can be stated as

$$-\sum_m y_{Jj}^J \bar{P}_j^{\ J} = \delta_{Jx}^J \qquad \sum_m x_{Jj}^J \bar{P}_j^{\ J} = \delta_{Jy}^J \qquad \sum_m \bar{P}_j^{\ J} = \theta_{Jz}^J \tag{9.16}$$

where δ_{Jx}^J, δ_{Jy}^J, θ_{Jz}^J are the prescribed or unknown displacements at J (which for a closed ring equal zero).

The formal similarity of (*9.16*) with the equations of static equilibrium is the source of the elasto-static analogy. The line connecting the points of application of all elastic weights is known as the conjugate structure (Fig. 9-6*a* below), the stresses in which are the displacements of the real structure. The application of finite element elastic weights requires considerable labor: bending moments and moments of inertia must be calculated for each element and the elasto-static equations used are in terms of a large number of elastic weights.

* Source: J. J. Tuma and J. T. Oden, String Polygon Analysis of Frames with Straight Members, *Journal of the Structural Division, ASCE,* Vol. 87, No. ST 7, Proc. Paper 2956, October, 1961, p. 63.

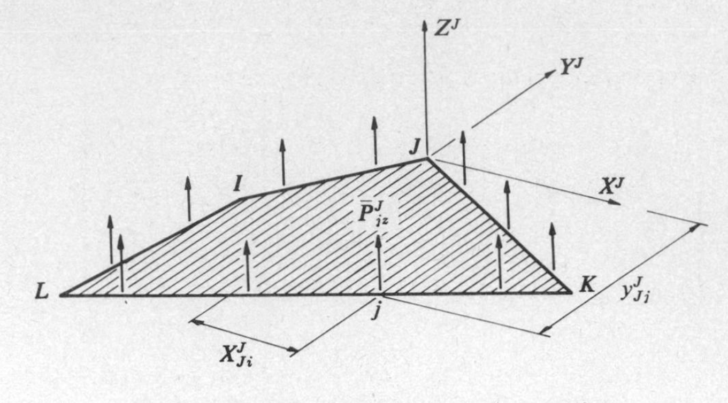

(*a*) Elemental Elastic Weights, Conjugate Ring

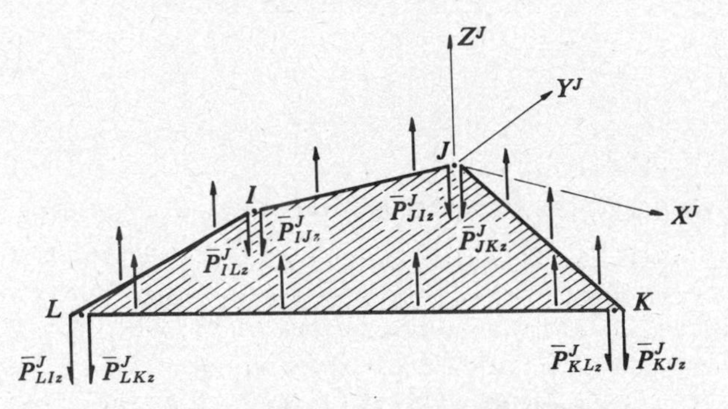

(*b*) Elemental Elastic Weights, Conjugate Beams

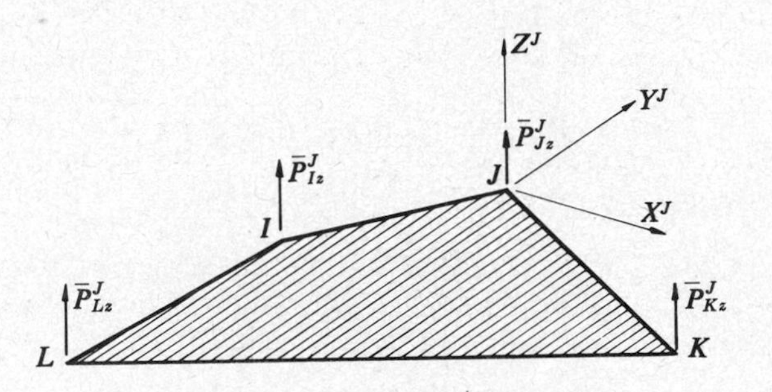

(*c*) Joint Elastic Weights, Conjugate Ring

Fig. 9-6. Conjugate Structure

(b) Segmental Elastic Weights

To circumvent this difficulty, it is always possible to remove some or all members of the ring, consider them as separate conjugate beams, calculate their reactions (Fig. 9-6*b*) and apply these reactions as new loads on the initial conjugate structure (Fig. 9-6*c*). Since the reactions of the separate conjugate beams are the end angular deviations of real beams (*5.24*), their sum at the respective joint becomes the joint elastic weight given by (*5.25*).

For the joint J (any joint),

$$\bar{P}_J{}^J = \bar{P}^J_{JI} + \bar{P}^J_{JK} = F^J_{JI} M_I{}^J + F_J{}^J M_J{}^J + F^J_{JK} M_K{}^J + \tau_J{}^J \qquad (9.17)$$

which is identical to $\gamma_J{}^J$ in (*9.13*).

These joint elastic weights represent a new set of force-vectors again necessarily in a state of elastostatic equilibrium and equivalent to the initial set of finite element elastic weights. Consequently (*9.16*) can be written in terms of $\bar{P}_j$ or $\bar{P}_J$ as (*9.12*) or (*9.15*) respectively (Problem 9.13).

(c) Elastic Area

As known from the elementary analysis (Problem 1.16, page 7),

$$f_{JJ}^{J} = m_{JX}^{J)T} F^{J} m_{JX}^{J} = \begin{bmatrix} \bar{I}_{Jxx}^{J} & -\bar{I}_{Jxy}^{J} & -\bar{Q}_{Jxz}^{J} \\ -\bar{I}_{Jyx}^{J} & \bar{I}_{Jyy}^{J} & \bar{Q}_{Jyz}^{J} \\ -\bar{Q}_{Jzx}^{J} & \bar{Q}_{Jzy}^{J} & \bar{A}_{Jzz}^{J} \end{bmatrix} \tag{9.18}$$

where $\bar{I}_{Jxx}^{J}$, $\bar{I}_{Jyy}^{J}$ are the moments of inertia, $\bar{I}_{Jxy}^{J}$, $\bar{I}_{Jyx}^{J}$ are the products of inertia, $\bar{Q}_{Jxz}^{J}$, $\bar{Q}_{Jzx}^{J}$, $\bar{Q}_{Jyz}^{J}$, $\bar{Q}_{Jzy}^{J}$ are the static moments of the elastic area

$$\bar{A}_{Jzz}^{J} = \sum_{I}^{L} (F_{JI}^{J} + F_{J}{}^{J} + F_{JK}^{J}) \tag{9.19}$$

which is the algebraic sum of all coefficients of F^J in (*9.13*). If the concept of neutral point is introduced, (*9.18*) reduces to a diagonal matrix and (*9.15*) becomes the matrix formulation of the column analogy method (Problem 9.12).

9.8 SERIES OF POLYGONAL RINGS

A more general case is encountered, when polygonal rings are combined to form a horizontal, vertical or closed ring series. Although the numerical work becomes more involved, the underlying principles remain the same. By (*9.3*) each panel (ring) generates $3 - f_i$ redundants (where f_i is the number of special conditions in that panel) and an equal number of compatibility conditions. Similarly as in continuous beams (which can be considered as degenerated one story multispan frames), the compatibility conditions of all panels yield a set of $3p - f$ equations (where f is the total number of special conditions) involving successively the deformations of three adjacent panels and only three corresponding redundant vectors.

Three typical cases in this class of problems are shown in Tables 9-1, 9-2 and 9-3, where X_I, X_J, X_R are the stress redundant vectors at the sections of release in the respective panels, $[3 \times 1]$, f_I, f_J, f_K are

Table 9-1. Horizontal Series of Rings

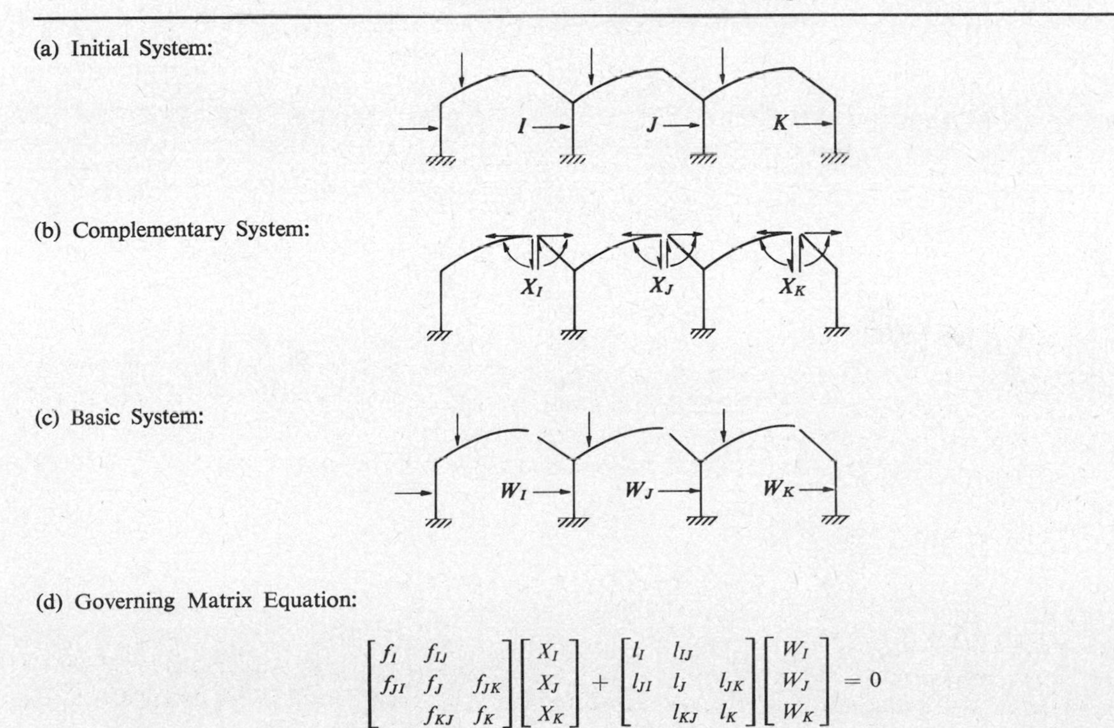

$$\begin{bmatrix} f_I & f_{IJ} & \\ f_{JI} & f_J & f_{JK} \\ & f_{KJ} & f_K \end{bmatrix} \begin{bmatrix} X_I \\ X_J \\ X_K \end{bmatrix} + \begin{bmatrix} l_I & l_{IJ} & \\ l_{JI} & l_J & l_{JK} \\ & l_{KJ} & l_K \end{bmatrix} \begin{bmatrix} W_I \\ W_J \\ W_K \end{bmatrix} = 0$$

Table 9-2. Vertical Series of Rings

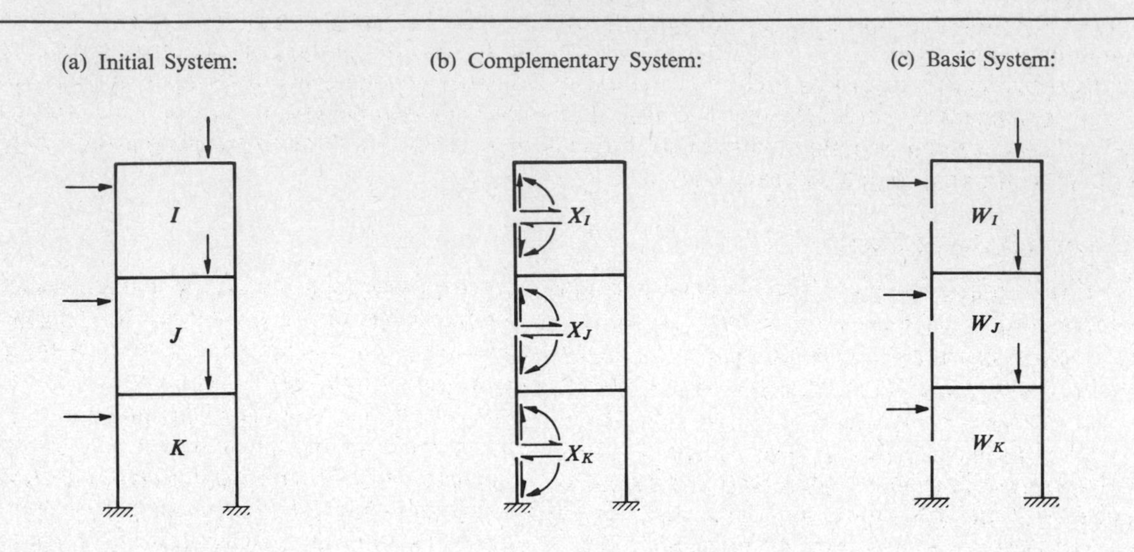

(d) Governing Matrix Equation:

$$\begin{bmatrix} f_I & f_{IJ} & \\ f_{JI} & f_J & f_{JK} \\ & f_{KJ} & f_K \end{bmatrix} \begin{bmatrix} X_I \\ X_J \\ X_K \end{bmatrix} + \begin{bmatrix} l_I & l_{IJ} & \\ l_{JI} & l_J & l_{JK} \\ l_{KI} & l_{KJ} & l_K \end{bmatrix} \begin{bmatrix} W_I \\ W_J \\ W_K \end{bmatrix} = 0$$

Table 9-3. Closed Series of Rings

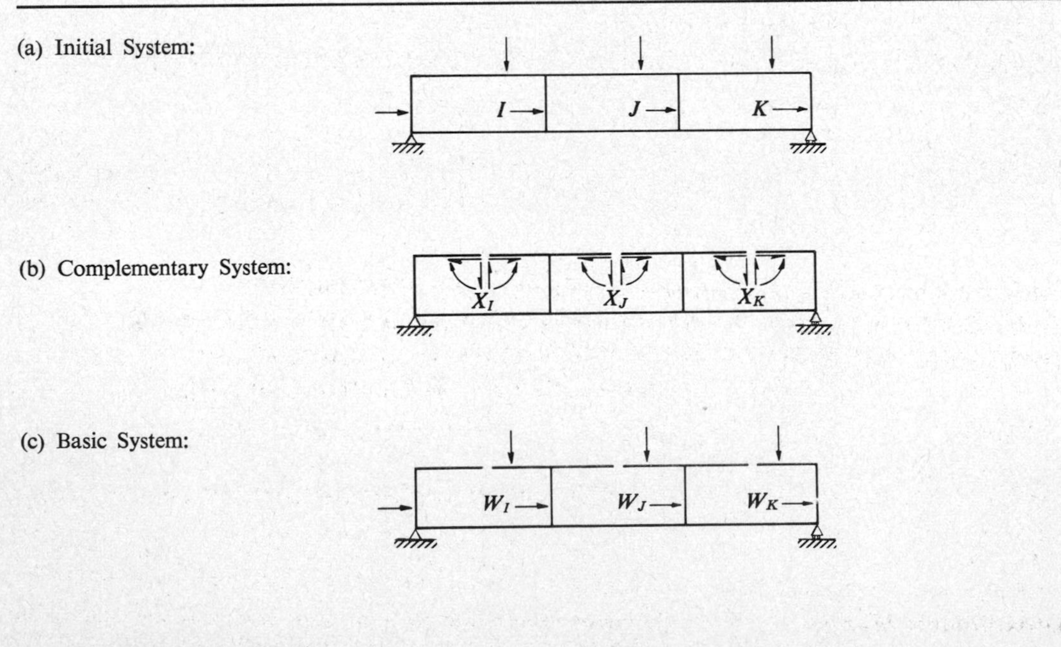

(d) Governing Matrix Equation:

$$\begin{bmatrix} f_I & f_{IJ} & \\ f_{JI} & f_J & f_{JK} \\ & f_{KJ} & f_K \end{bmatrix} \begin{bmatrix} X_I \\ X_J \\ X_K \end{bmatrix} + \begin{bmatrix} l_I & l_{IJ} & l_{IK} \\ l_{JI} & l_J & l_{JK} \\ l_{KI} & l_{KJ} & l_K \end{bmatrix} \begin{bmatrix} W_I \\ W_J \\ W_K \end{bmatrix} = 0$$

the direct unit stress flexibilities of the respective panel, [3 × 3], f_{IJ}, f_{IK},..., f_{KI}, f_{KJ}, are the indirect unit stress flexibilities expressing the influence of unit redundant causes acting in one panel on the deformation of another panel, [3 × 3]; similarly, l_I, l_J, l_K and l_{IJ}, l_{IK},..., l_{KI}, l_{KJ}, are the direct and indirect unit load flexibilities, consisting each of three rows and number of columns corresponding to the number of load components involved. Finally, W_I, W_J, W_K are the load vectors in the respective panel. Although the unit stress system flexibility matrices are formally identical in all three cases, the unit load system flexibility matrices take different shapes (Problem 9.13).

9.9 GENERAL METHOD

Three-, four-, five-redundant moment equations and three-redundant vector equations developed in the preceding chapters for particular structures are special forms of the general flexibility method, applicable to structures of all kinds. The underlying principles of this method and the procedure of application have been discussed in the first part of Chapter 5; the formulation of this procedure in terms of segmental matrices is introduced here as a *final summary and conclusion of the flexibility analysis.*

(1) *Component Systems.* The degree of statical indeterminacy of the initial system is determined by the respective formula (*9.2*) or (*9.3*) and the initial system is resolved into a complementary system and basic system, the definitions and qualifications of which are given in Sec. 5.1. The requirement of statical determinacy is customary but not mandatory. The selection of a statically indeterminate structure as a complementary and/or basic structure is useful in many special situations. Furthermore, the complementary and basic structure may or may not be necessarily the same structure (Problems 9.14 and 9.15).

(2) *Complementary System.* By cutting the initial structures at selected points, removing given causes and applying redundants at the sections of release as loads of unknown magnitude, the complementary system and its stress redundant vector $X = \{X_i, X_j, ..., X_p\}$ are defined. The displacement vector at these cuts is

$$\Delta_X = q_X^{)T} f q_X X = \Phi_X X \tag{9.20}$$

where Φ_X is the *unit stress redundant system flexibility matrix.* For the construction of this matrix, the complementary structure is resolved in a series of segments ($a, b, ..., m$), the segmental or group flexibilities of which are given by (*5.12*), (*8.2*), and (*9.4*) or (*5.14*), (*8.4*), and (*9.7*).

The diagonal assembly of these segmental matrices, known as the *unit stress segmental flexibility chain,* is

$$f = \begin{bmatrix} f_a & & & \\ & f_b & & \\ & & \ddots & \\ & & & f_m \end{bmatrix} \tag{9.21}$$

where all diagonal terms are [3 × 3] matrices and all off-diagonal terms are zero.

The transfer of the static effect of X from the points of action to the respective segments ($a, b, ..., m$) is accomplished by the *general transfer matrix* q_X, which is

$$q_X = \begin{array}{c} \begin{matrix} X_i = +1 & X_j = +1 & \cdots & X_p = +1 \\ \downarrow & \downarrow & & \downarrow \end{matrix} \\ \left[\begin{matrix} q_{ai} & q_{aj} & \cdots & q_{ap} \\ q_{bi} & q_{bj} & \cdots & q_{bp} \\ \cdots & \cdots & \cdots & \cdots \\ q_{mi} & q_{mj} & \cdots & q_{mp} \end{matrix}\right] \end{array} \tag{9.22}$$

where each column consists of m matrices of influence values caused by the respective unit redundant.

The matrix product $fq_X X$ gives the displacement vector due to X at $a, b, ..., m$, the effect of which must be now transferred back to the sections of release $i, j, ..., p$. The transpose of q_X produces the necessary transfer vehicle, making

$$\Phi_X = q_X^{)T} f q_X \tag{9.23}$$

With Φ_X known, Δ_X becomes a linear combination of the computed coefficients of Φ_X and the unknown components of X.

(3) *Basic System.* By cutting the initial structure at selected points, removing redundants at the sections of release and retaining applied loads, the basic system and its load vector $W = \{W_a, W_b, ..., W_m\}$ are defined. The displacement vector at these cuts is

$$\Delta_W = q_X^{)T} f q_W W + q_X^{)T} l W = \Phi_W W \tag{9.24}$$

where Φ_W is the *unit load system flexibility matrix*. For the construction of this matrix, the basic structure is resolved in a series of segments $(a, b, ..., m)$, the segmental or group flexibilities of which are given by (*5.13*), (*8.3*) and (*9.5*) or (*5.15*), (*8.5*) and (*9.8*).

The diagonal assembly of these segmental matrices, known as the *unit load segmental flexibility chain*, is

$$l = \begin{bmatrix} l_a & & & \\ & l_b & & \\ & & \ddots & \\ & & & l_m \end{bmatrix} \tag{9.25}$$

where all diagonal terms are [3 × 3] matrices and all off-diagonal terms are zero. This form of construction, of course, allows only one load vector per segment.

The transfer of the static effect of W from the points of action to the respective segments $(a, b, ..., m)$ is accomplished by the *general transfer matrix* q_W, which is

$$\begin{array}{c} \begin{array}{cccc} W_a = +1 & W_b = +1 & \cdots & W_m = +1 \\ \downarrow & \downarrow & & \downarrow \end{array} \\ q_W = \begin{bmatrix} q_{aa} & q_{ab} & \cdots & q_{am} \\ q_{ba} & q_{bb} & \cdots & q_{bm} \\ \cdots & \cdots & \cdots & \cdots \\ q_{ma} & q_{mb} & \cdots & q_{mm} \end{bmatrix} \end{array} \tag{9.26}$$

where each of these columns consists of m matrices of influence values caused by the respective unit load vector, which precludes that only one load vector acts in each segment.

The sum of matrix products $(f q_W + l)W$ gives the displacement vector due to W at $a, b, ..., m$, the effect of which is transferred to the sections of release $i, j, ..., p$ by $q_X^{)T}$ as before.

With

$$\Phi_W = q_X^{)T}(f q_W + l) \tag{9.27}$$

known, the displacement vector Δ_W is determined.

(4) *Secondary Effects.* The displacement vector Δ_T at the cuts of the basic structure due to secondary causes such as volume change, prestressing, etc., is determined in resultant form or can be obtained by superposition of transferred segmental effects as

$$\Delta_T = q_X^{)T}\{\Delta_{aT}, \Delta_{bT}, ..., \Delta_{mT}\} \tag{9.28}$$

where $\Delta_{aT}, \Delta_{bT}, ..., \Delta_{mT}$ are the segmental displacements due to these secondary causes.

(5) *Governing Equation.* The superposition of displacement vectors Δ_X, Δ_W and Δ_T must satisfy the condition of compatibility, namely, the algebraic sum of displacements at $i, j, ..., p$ must either equal zero or equal the prescribed displacement. Thus

$$\Delta_X + \Delta_W + \Delta_T = \Delta$$

and in terms of (*9.20*) and (*9.24*)

$$\Phi_X X + \Phi_W W + \Delta_T = \Delta \tag{9.29}$$

Since there are p redundant vectors and p matrix compatibility equations,

$$X = -\Phi_X^{)-1}[\Phi_W W + \Delta_T - \Delta] \tag{9.30}$$

If $\Delta_T = 0$, $\Delta = 0$, (*9.30*) in terms of (*9.23*) and (*9.24*) becomes

$$X = -[q_X^{)T} f q_X]^{-1} [q_X^{)T} f q_W + q_X^{)T} l] W \qquad (9.31)$$

If loads act at the segment boundaries, (*9.31*) reduces to the *standard form*

$$X = -[q_X^{)T} f q_X]^{-1} [q_X^{)T} f q_W] W \qquad (9.32)$$

which occurs in the literature in *three different forms*:

Argyris[1]: $X = -[b_1^{)T} f b_1]^{-1} [b_1^{)T} f b_0] R$

Gallagher[2]: $X = -[b_1^{)T} f b_1]^{-1} [b_1^{)T} f b_0] P$

Denke[3]: $X = -[f_X^{)T} D f_X]^{-1} [f_X^{)T} D f_0] \Phi$

Although the symbols differ their physical *meaning is the same.*

(6) *Stress Vector.* With the redundants known, the *true stress vector* at $a, b, \ldots, m$ is

$$\sigma = q_W W + q_X X = \underbrace{[q_W - q_X \Phi_X^{)-1} \Phi_W]}_{q} W \qquad (9.33)$$

where q is the *true unit load system transfer matrix* in the initial system.

(7) *Displacement vector* at $a, b, \ldots, m$ in terms of (*9.33*) is

$$\Delta = \underbrace{q^{)T} f q}_{\Phi} W$$

where Φ is the *true unit load system flexibility matrix* in the initial system.

Once the true stress vector and the true displacement vectors are known, the objective of the analysis is accomplished (Problem 9.16).

9.10 GENERAL PROPERTIES

The general procedure described in the preceding section deals with *three classes of basic matrices*:

(*a*) State vectors W, X, σ,
(*b*) Transfer matrices q_W, q_X,
(*c*) Flexibility chain matrices f, l,

and *two system matrices* Φ_W, Φ_X.

The coefficients of flexibility matrices of all kinds exhibit certain *characteristic properties* useful in their construction.

(1) *Symmetry*

By Maxwell-Mohr's Theorem $f_{ij} = f_{ji}^{)T}$ and consequently all flexibility matrices (elemental, segmental, group and system) are symmetrical, which reduces the number of coefficients to be determined.

(2) *Positive Definiteness*

Since the displacement due to a unit cause cannot move against the direction of the cause, the principal diagonal coefficients (direct flexibilities) cannot be negative.

(3) *Superposition of Coefficients*

Since the displacement due to a unit cause is a sum of component displacement, each flexibility can be treated as a set of springs in series.

---

[1] J. H. Argyris, "Recent Advances in Matrix Methods of Structural Analysis," Macmillan Company, New York, 1964.
[2] R.H. Gallagher," A Correlation Study of Methods of Matrix Structural Analysis," Macmillan Company, New York, 1964.
[3] P. H. Denke, "A General Digital Computer Analysis of Statically Indeterminate Structures," AGARD Structures and Materials Panel Meeting, Aachen, Germany, 1959.

Solved Problems

REDUNDANTS

9.1. Classify the frames of Fig. P-9.1 according to (*9.2*) and (*9.3*) as statically determinate or indeterminate. If applicable, determine the number of redundants.

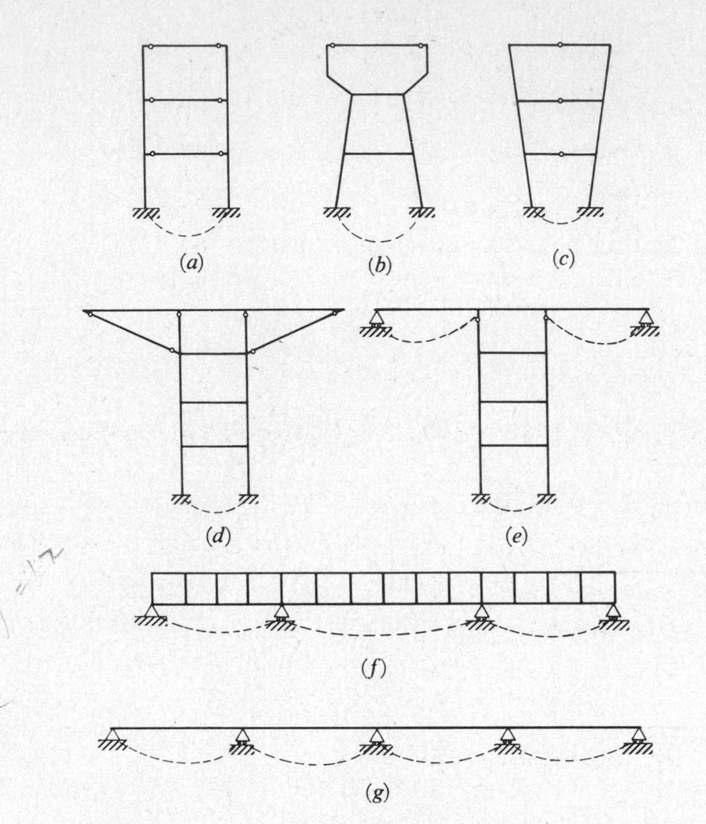

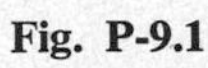

Fig. P-9.1

Case	By (*9.2*)	By (*9.3*)	Number of Redundants
(a)	$m = 9,\ r = 6,\ j = 8,\ f = 6$ $n = 27 + 6 - 24 - 6 = 3$	$p = 3,\ f = 6$ $n = 9 - 6 = 3$	3
(b)	$m = 11,\ r = 6,\ j = 10,\ f = 2$ $n = 33 + 6 - 30 - 2 = 7$	$p = 3,\ f = 2$ $n = 9 - 2 = 7$	7
(c)	$m = 9,\ r = 6,\ j = 8,\ f = 3$ $n = 27 + 6 - 24 - 3 = 6$	$p = 3,\ f = 3$ $n = 9 - 3 = 6$	6
(d)	$m = 16,\ r = 6,\ j = 12,\ f = 6$ $n = 48 + 6 - 36 - 6 = 12$	$p = 6,\ f = 6$ $n = 18 - 6 = 12$	12
(e)	$m = 14,\ r = 8,\ j = 12,\ f = 2$ $n = 42 + 8 - 36 - 2 = 12$	$p = 6,\ f = 6$ $n = 18 - 6 = 12$	12
(f)	$m = 43,\ r = 5,\ j = 30,\ f = 0$ $n = 129 + 5 - 90 - 0 = 44$	$p = 17,\ f = 7$ $n = 51 - 7 = 44$	44
(g)	$m = 4,\ r = 6,\ j = 5,\ f = 0$ $n = 12 + 6 - 15 - 0 = 3$	$p = 4,\ f = 9$ $n = 12 - 9 = 3$	3

All frames are statically indeterminate. Note that the number of special conditions f for a given frame may be a different value for (*9.2*) and (*9.3*).

GROUP FLEXIBILITIES

9.2. For the cantilever frame of Fig. P-9.2 construct (*9.4*) and compute the unit stress group flexibilities.

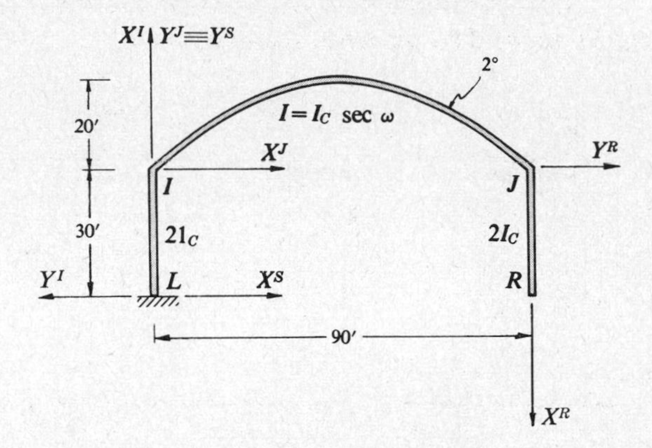

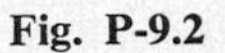
Fig. P-9.2

Geometric values are: $x^S_{RR} = 0$, $y^S_{RR} = 0$, $\omega_{RS} = -90°$; $x^S_{JR} = 0$, $y^S_{JR} = -30'$, $\omega_{JS} = 0$; $x^S_{IR} = 90'$, $y^S_{IR} = -30'$, $\omega_{IS} = 90°$. Hence in (*9.4*),

$$t^{RS}_{RR} = \omega^{RS} r^S_{RR} = \omega^{RS} I = \omega^{RS} = \begin{bmatrix} 0 & -1 & 0 \\ 1 & 0 & 0 \\ 0 & 0 & 1 \end{bmatrix} \qquad t^{JS}_{JR} = \omega^{JS} r^S_{JR} = I r^S_{JR} = r^S_{JR} = \begin{bmatrix} 1 & 0 & 0 \\ 0 & 1 & 0 \\ 30 & 0 & 1 \end{bmatrix}$$

$$t^{IS}_{IR} = \omega^{IS} r^S_{IR} = \begin{bmatrix} 0 & 1 & 0 \\ -1 & 0 & 0 \\ 0 & 0 & 1 \end{bmatrix} \begin{bmatrix} 1 & 0 & 0 \\ 0 & 1 & 0 \\ 30 & 90 & 1 \end{bmatrix} = \begin{bmatrix} 0 & 1 & 0 \\ -1 & 0 & 0 \\ 30 & 90 & 1 \end{bmatrix}$$

Using Table 5-1 and neglecting axial deformations,

$$f^R_{RR,J} = f^I_{II,L} = \frac{1}{EI} \begin{bmatrix} 0 & 0 & 0 \\ 0 & s^3/3 & s^2/2 \\ 0 & s^2/2 & s \end{bmatrix} = \frac{1}{2EI_c} \begin{bmatrix} 0 & 0 & 0 \\ 0 & 9{,}000 & 450 \\ 0 & 450 & 30 \end{bmatrix}$$

Using Table 8-1, for $y = (4h/l^2)(x)(l - x)$ and $I/A \simeq 0$,

$$f^J_{JJ,I} = \frac{1}{EI_c} \begin{bmatrix} 8lh^2/15 & l^2h/3 & 2lh/3 \\ l^2h/3 & l^3/3 & l^2/2 \\ 2lh/3 & l^2/2 & l \end{bmatrix} = \frac{1}{EI_c} \begin{bmatrix} 19{,}200 & 54{,}000 & 1{,}200 \\ 54{,}000 & 243{,}000 & 4{,}050 \\ 1{,}200 & 4{,}050 & 90 \end{bmatrix}$$

Substituting these values in (*9.4*) and reducing gives the required group flexibility matrix

$$f^S_{RR,L} = \frac{1}{EI_c} \begin{bmatrix} 181{,}200 & 195{,}750 & 4{,}350 \\ 195{,}750 & 364{,}500 & 5{,}400 \\ 4{,}350 & 5{,}400 & 120 \end{bmatrix}$$

9.3. For the cantilever frame of Fig. P-9.3 use (*9.5*) and compute the unit load group flexibilities for the given load.

The transport matrices $t^{RS)T}_{RR}$, $t^{JS)T}_{JR}$, $t^{IS)T}_{IR}$ and the segmental unit stress flexibility matrices $f^R_{RR,J}$, $f^J_{JJ,I}$, $f^I_{II,L}$ in (*9.5*), for this frame, are the same as in Problem 9.2.

Also, for loads applied on segment *IJ* only, (*9.5*) degenerates into

$$l^S_{RR,L} = t^{IS)T}_{IR} f^I_{II,L} t^{Ib}_{Ib} + t^{JS)T}_{JR} l^{Jb}_{JJ,I\omega}$$

in which

$$\overset{Jb}{\omega} = I \quad \text{and} \quad \overset{Ib}{t_{Ib}} = \overset{IJ}{t_{Ib}} = \overset{IJ}{\omega}\overset{J}{r_{Ib}} = \begin{bmatrix} 0 & 1 & 0 \\ -1 & 0 & 0 \\ 0 & 0 & 1 \end{bmatrix}\begin{bmatrix} 1 & 0 & 0 \\ 0 & 1 & 0 \\ -\overset{J}{y_{Ib}} & \overset{J}{x_{Ib}} & 1 \end{bmatrix} = \begin{bmatrix} 0 & 1 & 0 \\ 1 & 0 & 0 \\ -\overset{J}{y_{Ib}} & \overset{J}{x_{Ib}} & 1 \end{bmatrix}$$

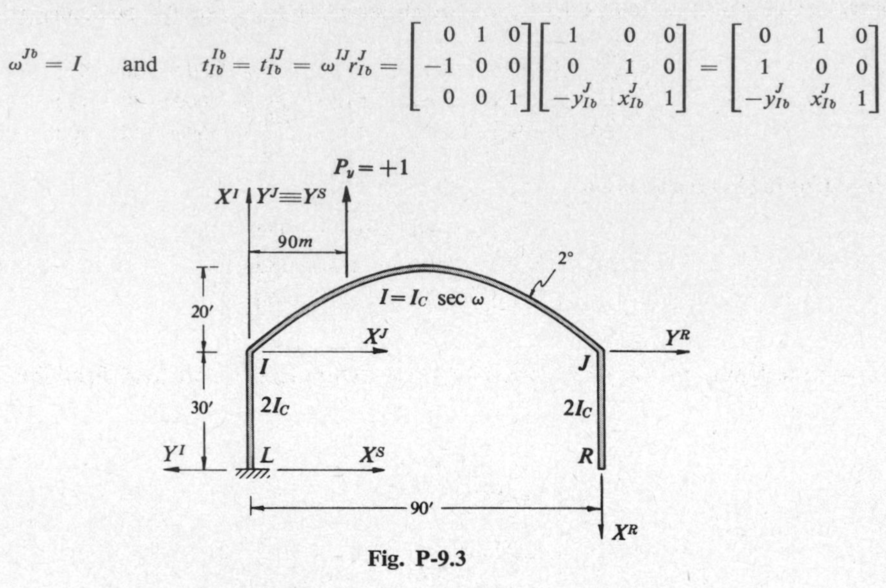

Fig. P-9.3

If only P_y forces on IJ are applied, the unit load group flexibility matrix reduces to

$$\overset{S}{l_{RR,L}} = \overset{IS)T}{t_{IR}}\overset{I}{f_{II,L}}\begin{bmatrix} 1 \\ 0 \\ \overset{J}{x_{Ib}} \end{bmatrix} + \overset{JS)T}{t_{JR}}\begin{bmatrix} C_{RPxy} \\ C_{RPyy} \\ B_{RPzy} \end{bmatrix}$$

$$= \frac{1}{2EI_c}\begin{bmatrix} 0 & -1 & 30 \\ 1 & 0 & 90 \\ 0 & 0 & 1 \end{bmatrix}\begin{bmatrix} 0 & 0 & 0 \\ 0 & 9{,}000 & 450 \\ 0 & 450 & 30 \end{bmatrix}\begin{bmatrix} 1 \\ 0 \\ 90m \end{bmatrix} + \frac{1}{EI_c}\begin{bmatrix} 1 & 0 & 30 \\ 0 & 1 & 0 \\ 0 & 0 & 1 \end{bmatrix}\begin{bmatrix} 5{,}400m^3(2-m) \\ 121{,}500m^2(3-m) \\ 4{,}050m^2 \end{bmatrix}$$

$$\overset{S}{l_{RR,L}} = \frac{1}{EI_c}\begin{bmatrix} 6{,}750(3m + 18m^2 + 16m^3 - 8m^4) \\ 121{,}500(m + 3m^2 - m^3) \\ 1{,}350(m + 3m^2) \end{bmatrix}$$

The coefficients C_{RPxy}, C_{RPyy} and B_{RPzy} above are computed using $y = (4h/l^2)(x)(l - x)$ in Table 8-1.

9.4. For the simple frame of Fig. P-9.4 construct (*9.7*) and compute the unit stress group flexibilities.

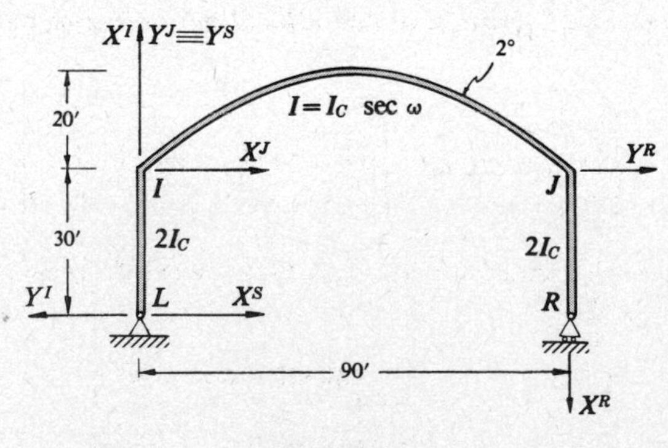

Fig. P-9.4

For the given frame, the stress transfer matrices q's of (*9.7*), established by simple statics, are

$$\overset{RS}{q_{(JR)}} = \begin{bmatrix} 0 & 1/90 & -1/90 \\ 0 & 1 & 0 \\ 30 & 1 & 0 \end{bmatrix}, \quad \overset{JS}{q_{(IJ)}} = \begin{bmatrix} 1 & 0 & 0 \\ 30 & 1 & 0 \\ 30 & 0 & 1 \end{bmatrix} \quad \text{and} \quad \overset{IS}{q_{(LI)}} = \begin{bmatrix} 0 & -1/90 & 1/90 \\ 30 & 0 & 1 \\ 0 & 0 & 1 \end{bmatrix}$$

The segmental unit stress flexibilities are established using Tables 5-2 and 8-4. Neglecting axial deformations,

$$f^R_{(JR)} = f^I_{(LI)} = \frac{1}{2EI_c}\begin{bmatrix} 0 & 0 & 0 \\ 0 & 10 & 5 \\ 0 & 5 & 10 \end{bmatrix} \quad \text{and} \quad f^J_{(IJ)} = \frac{1}{EI_c}\begin{bmatrix} 19{,}200 & 600 & 600 \\ 600 & 30 & 15 \\ 600 & 15 & 30 \end{bmatrix}$$

Substituting in (*9.7*) and reducing,

$$f^S_{(LR)} = \frac{1}{EI_c}\begin{bmatrix} 181{,}200 & 2{,}175 & 2{,}175 \\ 2{,}175 & 45 & 15 \\ 2{,}175 & 15 & 45 \end{bmatrix}$$

9.5. For the simple frame of Fig. P-9.5 use (*9.8*) and compute the unit load flexibilities for the load shown.

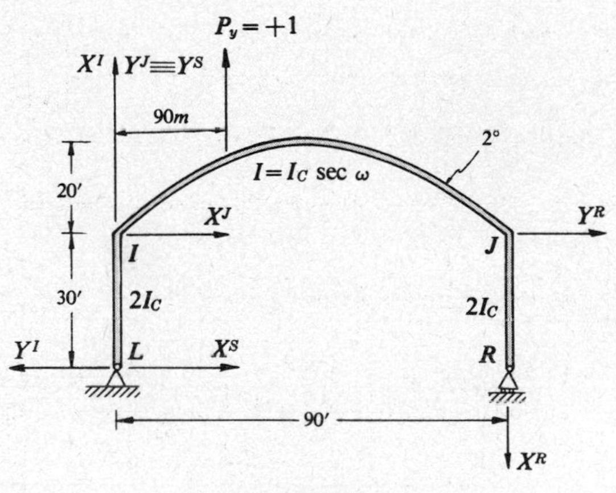

Fig. P-9.5

The transfer matrices $q^{RS)T}_{(JR)}$, $q^{JS)T}_{(IJ)}$, $q^{IS)T}_{(LI)}$ and the segmental unit stress flexibilities of (*9.8*), for the given frame, remain the same as in Problem 9.4.

For applied loads on segment IJ only, the stress matrix (*9.9*) reduces to $\{q^{Rb}_{(JR)b}, q^{Jb}_{(IJ)b}, q^{Ib}_{(LI)b}\}$ and (*9.8*) degenerates into

$$l^S_{(LR)} = q^{RS)T}_{(JR)} f^R_{(JR)} q^{Rb}_{(JR)b} + q^{JS)T}_{(IJ)} f^J_{(IJ)} q^{Jb}_{(IJ)b} + q^{IS)T}_{(LI)} f^I_{(LI)} q^{Ib}_{(LI)b} + q^{JS)T}_{(IJ)} l^J_{(IJ)} \mu^{Jb}$$

If only P_y forces are applied, $l^S_{(LR)}$ can be further reduced by considering only the applicable stress influence coefficients. Thus by statics,

$$q^{Rb}_{(JR)b} = \begin{bmatrix} m \\ 0 \\ 0 \end{bmatrix}, \quad q^{Jb}_{(IJ)b} = \begin{bmatrix} 0 \\ 0 \\ 0 \end{bmatrix} \quad \text{and} \quad q^{Ib}_{(LI)b} = \begin{bmatrix} 1-m \\ 0 \\ 0 \end{bmatrix}$$

Also, $\mu^{Jb} = I$ and $l^J_{(IJ)}$ can be reduced to $\{G_{RV}, F_{RV}, F_{LV}\}$ (Table 8-2). These coefficients G_{RV}, F_{RV} and F_{LV} are computed using results of Problem 8.6:

$$\begin{bmatrix} G_{RV} \\ F_{RV} \\ F_{LV} \end{bmatrix} = -\frac{1{,}350}{EI_c}\begin{bmatrix} 40m(1 - 2m^2 + m^3) \\ m(1 - m^2) \\ m(2 - 3m + m^2) \end{bmatrix}$$

Substituting all values, the unit load group flexibilities due to the applied load become

$$l^S_{(LR)} = -\frac{1{,}350}{EI_c}\begin{bmatrix} 10m(13 - 9m - 8m^2 + 4m^3) \\ m(1 - m^2) \\ m(2 - 3m + m^2) \end{bmatrix}$$

SINGLE SPAN FRAMES

9.6. Using the results of Problems 9.2 and 9.3 and the concept of neutral point, compute the reactions in the frame of Fig. P-9.6*a*.

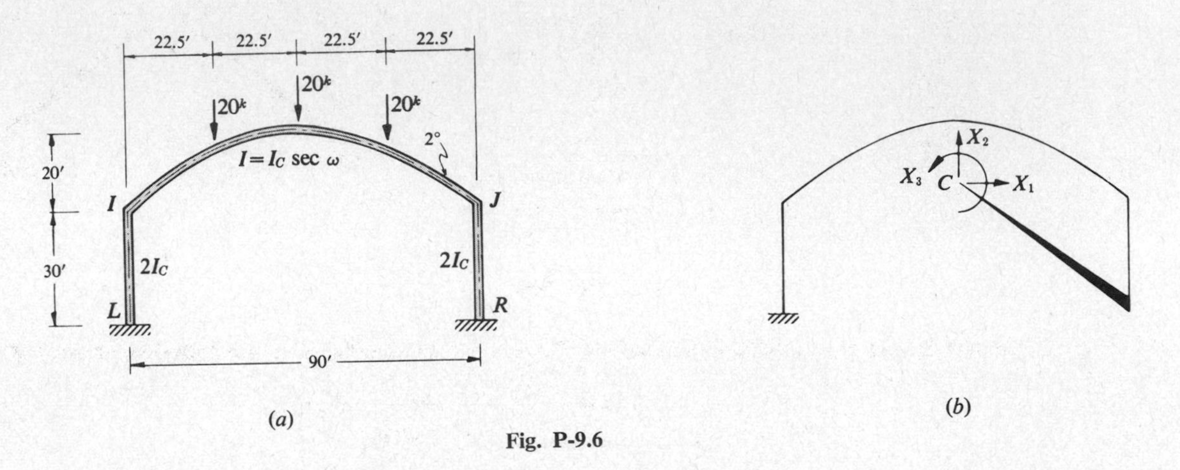

Fig. P-9.6

Using the unit stress flexibilities computed in Problem 9.2 and (*8.8*), the coordinates of neutral point (Fig. *b*) are $x_{RC} = -45.0'$, $y_{RC} = 36.25'$, $\omega_{SC} = 0$.
With respect to the neutral point, the unit stress group flexibility matrix is

$$f_{CC}^{C} = \frac{1}{EI_c}\begin{bmatrix} 23{,}512.5 & 0 & 0 \\ 0 & 121{,}500 & 0 \\ 0 & 0 & 120 \end{bmatrix}$$

The unit load group flexibilities computed in Problem 9.3 are also transferred to the neutral point by (*8.10*). For unit force P_y applied on segment IJ, it becomes

$$l_{CC}^{C} = \frac{1}{EI_c}\begin{bmatrix} -1{,}687.5(17m + 15m^2 - 64m^3 + 32m^4) \\ 60{,}750(m + 3m^2 - 2m^3) \\ 1{,}350(m + 3m^2) \end{bmatrix}$$

For the given frame, the compatibility equation

$$f_{CC}^{C} X_C + \sum_{i=1}^{3} (l_{CC,i}^{C} P_i) = 0$$

in terms of $P_1 = P_2 = P_3 = -20^k$ at $m = 0.25$, 0.5 and 0.75, respectively, becomes

$$\frac{1}{EI_c}\begin{bmatrix} 23{,}512.5 & 0 & 0 \\ 0 & 121{,}500 & 0 \\ 0 & 0 & 120 \end{bmatrix}\begin{bmatrix} X_1 \\ X_2 \\ X_3 \end{bmatrix} - \frac{20}{EI_c}\begin{bmatrix} -25{,}102 \\ 182{,}253 \\ 5{,}569 \end{bmatrix} = 0$$

from which $X_1 = -21.35$ k, $X_2 = 30.0$ k, $X_3 = 928$ k-ft.
The reactions at R and L in the reference system then are

$$R_R = \{-21.35, 30.0, 352\} \quad \text{and} \quad R_L = \{21.35, 30.0, -352\}$$

9.7. Using the results of Problems 9.4 and 9.5 and the concept of neutral point, compute the reactions in the frame of Fig. P-9.7*a*.

The neutral point for the given frame is obviously the same as for the frame of Fig. P-9.6*a*; but it is checked out to be so using (*8.11*) and the results of Problem 9.4. The unit stress group flexibility matrix with respect to the neutral point (Fig. P-9.7*b*) is

$$f_{CC}^{C} = \frac{1}{EI_c}\begin{bmatrix} 23{,}512.5 & 0 & 0 \\ 0 & 121{,}500 & 0 \\ 0 & 0 & 120 \end{bmatrix}$$

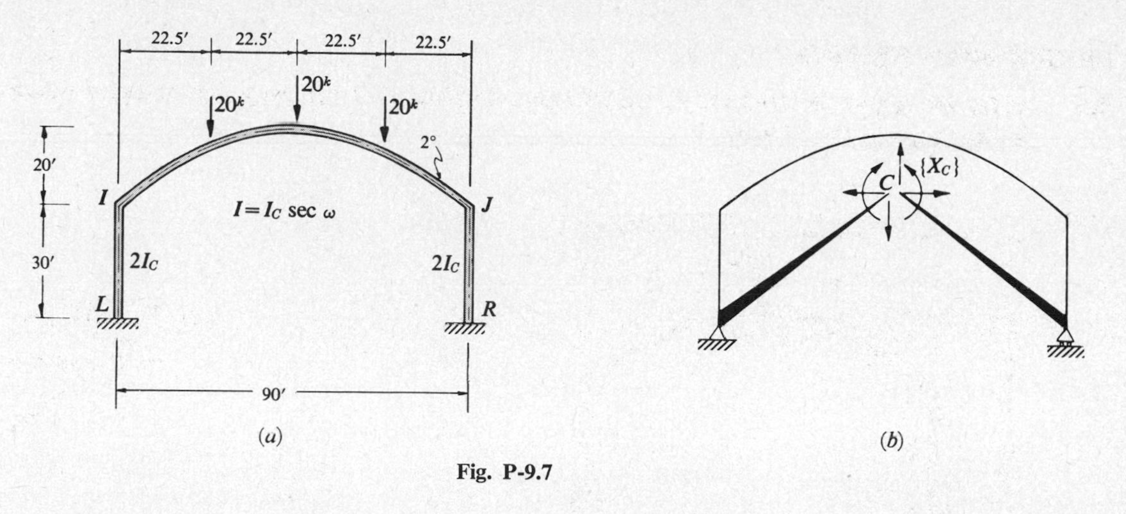

Fig. P-9.7

The unit load group flexibilities computed in Problem 9.5 are transferred to the neutral point using (*8.13*).

$$l_{CC}^{C} = -\frac{1{,}350}{EI_c}\begin{bmatrix} 21.25m \mid 18.75m^2 & 80m^3 \mid 40m^4 \\ & 45m - 135m^2 + 90m^3 \\ & 3m - 3m^2 \end{bmatrix}$$

The compatibility equation

$$f_{CC}^{C} X_C + \sum_{i=1}^{3} (l_{CC,i}^{C} P_i) = 0$$

in which $P_1 = P_2 = P_3 = -20^k$ respectively at $m = 0.25$, 0.5 and 0.75 is solved for X_C:

$$X_C = \{-21.35, 0, -422\}$$

The reactions are computed by adding the effects of the redundants and the given loads and are seen to be the same as in Problem 9.6.

POLYGONAL RINGS

9.8. Using (*9.10*) and the concept of neutral point, analyze the closed ring of Fig. P-9.8*a*.

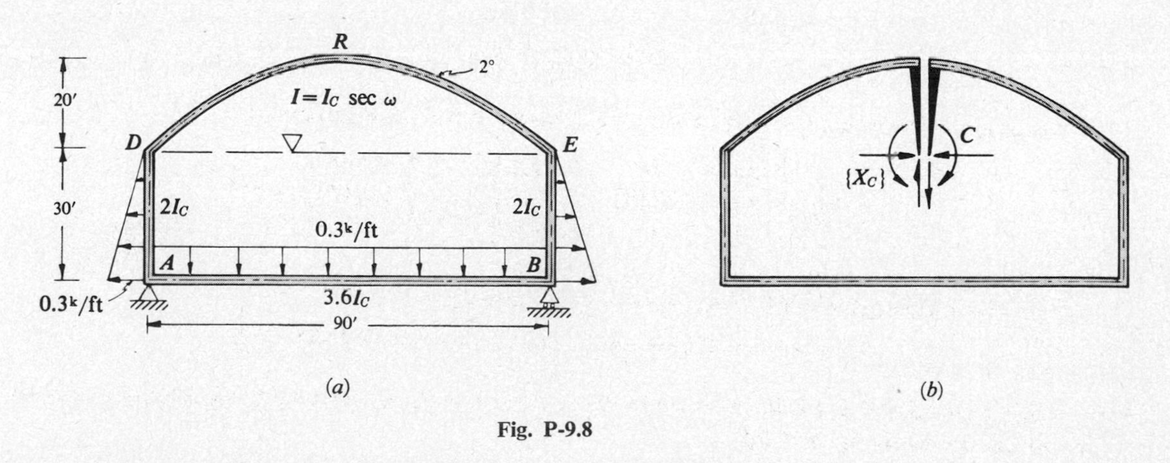

Fig. P-9.8

The ring and the loads are symmetrical about the vertical axis. A cut is introduced at R and the unit stress group flexibility matrix f_{RR}^{0} at R is

$$f_{RR}^{0} = \frac{1}{EI_c}\begin{bmatrix} 108{,}700 & 0 & -2{,}900 \\ 0 & 138{,}375 & 0 \\ -2{,}900 & 0 & 145 \end{bmatrix}$$

The coordinates of the neutral point by (*8.8*) are

$$x_{RC} = 0, \qquad y_{RC} = -20.0', \qquad \omega_{RC} = 0$$

and the unit stress group flexibility matrix transferred to the neutral point (Fig. *b*) becomes

$$f_{CC}^{C} = \frac{1}{EI_c}\begin{bmatrix} 50{,}700 & 0 & 0 \\ 0 & 138{,}375 & 0 \\ 0 & 0 & 145 \end{bmatrix}$$

The total load effect on Δ_c is computed by integrating for the distributed load the unit load flexibilities (*9.5*):

$$l_{CC}^{C} W = \frac{1}{EI_c}\begin{bmatrix} 109{,}688 \\ 0 \\ -3{,}600 \end{bmatrix}$$

Substituting these values in (*9.10*) and solving for X_C gives

$$X_C = \{-2.16, 0, 24.83\}$$

9.9. Using (*9.10*) and the concept of neutral point analyze the closed ring of Fig. P-9.9*a*.

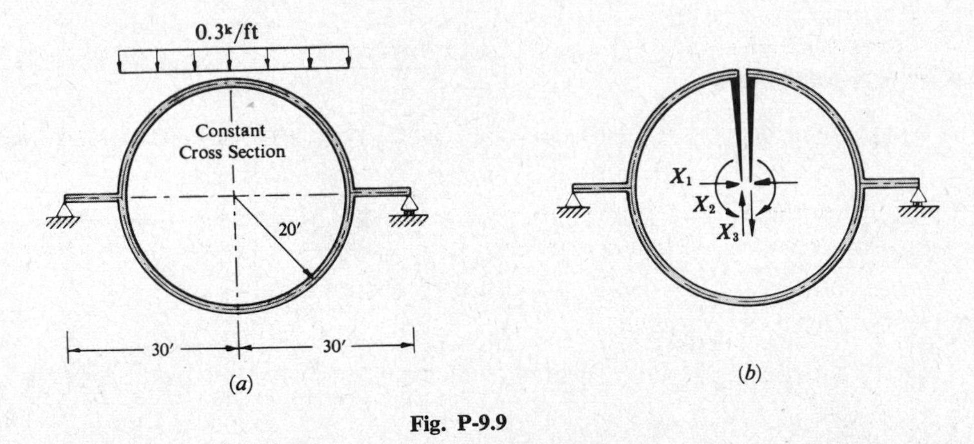

Fig. P-9.9

The neutral point of the system is located at the center of the ring by inspection. The redundants are taken as shown in Fig. *b*. The system flexibilities are computed as discussed in Problem 8.17. The resulting equation of compatibility at C becomes

$$\frac{1}{EI_c}\begin{bmatrix} 8{,}000\pi & 0 & 0 \\ 0 & 8{,}000\pi & 0 \\ 0 & 0 & 80\pi \end{bmatrix}\begin{bmatrix} X_1 \\ X_2 \\ X_3 \end{bmatrix} + \frac{1}{EI_c}\begin{bmatrix} 80{,}000 \\ 0 \\ -3{,}000\pi \end{bmatrix} = 0$$

from which $X_1 = -3.18$ k, $X_2 = 0$, $X_3 = 37.5$ k-ft.

STRING POLYGON

9.10.* Using (*9.11*), (*9.12*) and the concept of neutral point, analyze the frame of Fig. P-9.10*a*.

The frame is divided up into 24 finite elements, the properties of which are available from the source cited below. The flexibility matrix Λ is constructed using these values. The moment influence value matrix m_{JX} due to unit redundants initially chosen at the apex is formulated by computing the moment values at the centers of the elements.

*Source: J. Griffiths, "Single Span Rigid Frames in Steel," American Institute of Steel Construction, Inc., New York, 1948, by permission of the author and publisher.

Element No.	Element Flexibility $\Lambda \times E$
1	65.09
2	15.25
3	12.87
4	24.09
5-20	40.34
21	24.09
22	12.87
23	15.25
24	65.09

$$m_{JX} = \begin{bmatrix} -28.00 & 50.00 & 1 \\ -18.30 & 49.80 & 1 \\ -14.70 & 47.20 & 1 \\ -12.90 & 42.40 & 1 \\ -11.25 & 37.50 & 1 \\ -9.75 & 32.50 & 1 \\ -8.25 & 27.50 & 1 \\ -6.75 & 22.50 & 1 \\ -5.25 & 17.50 & 1 \\ -3.75 & 12.50 & 1 \\ -2.25 & 7.50 & 1 \\ -0.75 & 2.50 & 1 \\ -0.75 & -2.50 & 1 \\ -2.25 & -7.50 & 1 \\ -3.75 & -12.50 & 1 \\ -5.25 & -17.50 & 1 \\ -6.75 & -22.50 & 1 \\ -8.25 & -27.50 & 1 \\ -9.75 & -32.50 & 1 \\ -11.25 & -37.50 & 1 \\ -12.90 & -42.40 & 1 \\ -14.70 & -47.20 & 1 \\ -18.30 & -49.80 & 1 \\ -28.00 & -50.00 & 1 \end{bmatrix}$$

The system flexibility matrix $f_{JJ}^J = m_{JX}^{)T} \Lambda m_{JX}$ is computed and transferred to the neutral point C by (*8.8*), from which

$$x_{JC} = 0, \quad y_{JC} = -10.31', \quad \omega_{JC} = 0 \quad \text{and} \quad f_{CC}^C = 1/E\,\text{Diag.}[63{,}118,\ 1{,}402{,}994,\ 880]$$

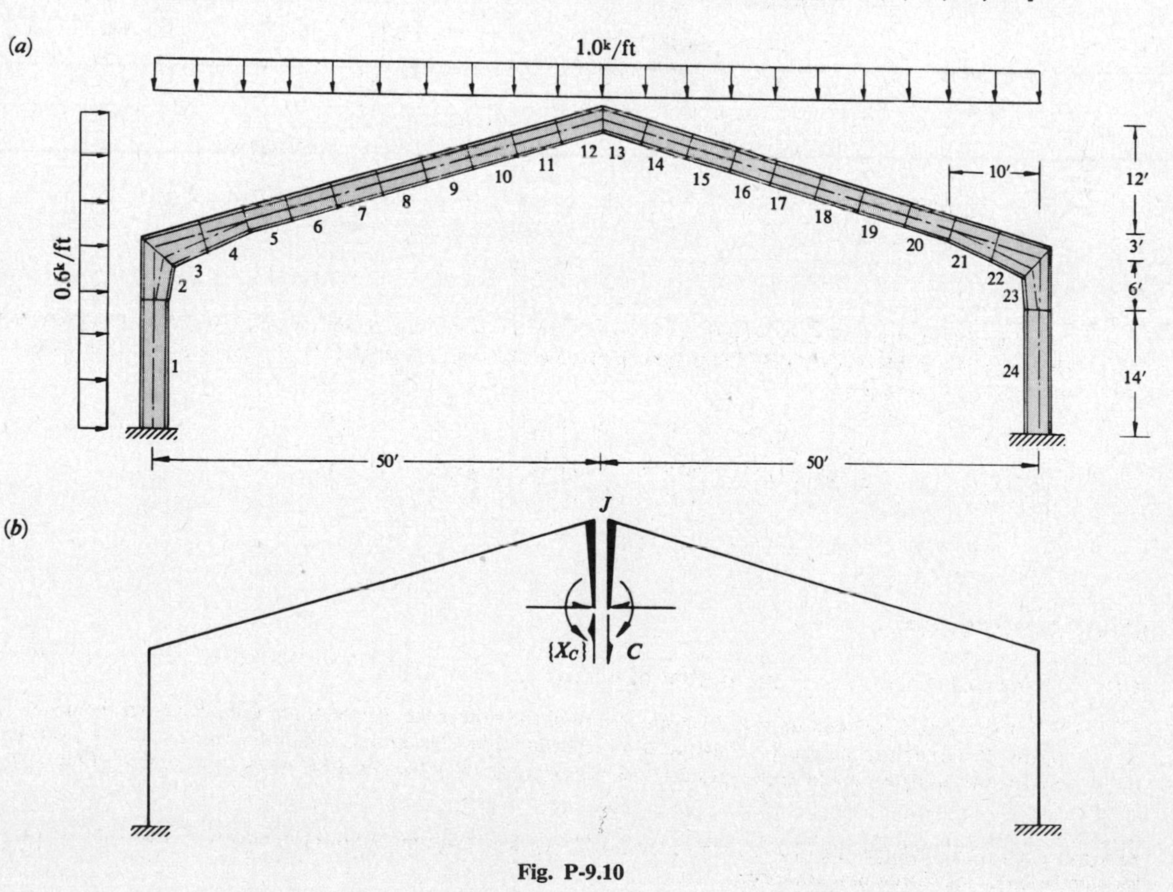

Fig. P-9.10

The moments at the midpoints of the elements due to loads, $M^J_{J0} = m^J_{J0}W^J$, are obtained by statics and inserted in the displacement vector $\Delta^J_{J0} = m^{J)T}_{JX}\Lambda m^J_{J0}W^J$, where

$$M^J_{J0} = \{-1{,}485.20, -1{,}340.49, -1{,}178.75, -948.80, -741.10, -556.65, -398.55, -266.80, -161.40, -82.35, -29.65, -3.30, -3.13, -28.13, -78.13, -153.13, -253.13, -378.13, -528.13, -703.13, -898.88, -1{,}113.92, -1{,}240.02, -1{,}250.00\}$$

With Δ^J_{J0} known,

$$\Delta^C_{C0} = t^{JC)T}_{JC}\Delta^J_{J0} = 1/E\{3{,}470{,}427, -1{,}070{,}465, 31{,}537\}$$

Finally, from the compatibility equation $f^C_{CC}X_C + \Delta^C_{C0} = 0$, the redundant vector at C is

$$X_C = \{-54.98, 0.763, -35.84\}$$

9.11. Using (*9.15*) compute the stresses at C in the frame of Fig. P-9.11*a*.

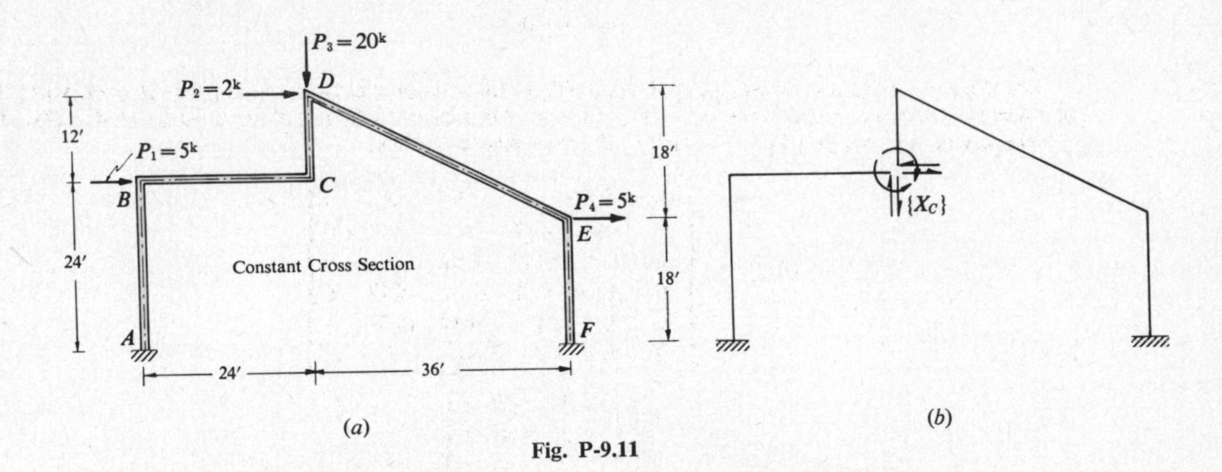

(*a*) (*b*)

Fig. P-9.11

The stresses at C are chosen as redundants. The flexibility matrix F^C and the moment matrix m^C_{CX} are constructed by (*9.13*) and (*9.14*) following the procedure of Sec. 9.6. These matrices, arranged for joints A through F, are

$$F^C = \frac{1}{EI}\begin{bmatrix} 8 & 4 & 0 & 0 & 0 & 0 \\ 4 & 16 & 4 & 0 & 0 & 0 \\ 0 & 4 & 12 & 2 & 0 & 0 \\ 0 & 0 & 2 & 17.415 & 6.707 & 0 \\ 0 & 0 & 0 & 6.707 & 19.415 & 3 \\ 0 & 0 & 0 & 0 & 3 & 6 \end{bmatrix} \qquad m^C_{CX} = \begin{bmatrix} -24 & 24 & 1 \\ 0 & 24 & 1 \\ 0 & 0 & 1 \\ 12 & 0 & 1 \\ -6 & -36 & 1 \\ -24 & -36 & 1 \end{bmatrix}$$

The moment matrix m^C_{C0} due to $W = \{P_1, P_2, P_3, P_4\} = \{5, 2, 20, 5\}$ is

$$m_{C0} = \begin{bmatrix} -24 & 0 & 0 & 0 \\ 0 & 0 & 0 & 0 \\ 0 & 0 & 0 & 0 \\ 0 & 0 & 0 & 0 \\ 0 & 18 & -36 & 0 \\ 0 & 36 & -36 & 18 \end{bmatrix}$$

and since the loads act at joints (and not in spans), the τ vector is zero.

All these values are then substituted in (*9.15*), from which for $\Delta_C{}^C = 0$, the redundant stress vector at C is

$$X_C = \{-9.30, -10.06, 151.10\}$$

ELASTO-STATIC ANALOGY

9.12. Using the concept of joint elastic weights (*9.17*) and the compatibility equation (*9.15*) analyze the frame of Fig. P-9.12*a*. Compute the functions of elastic areas in terms of segmental flexibilities.

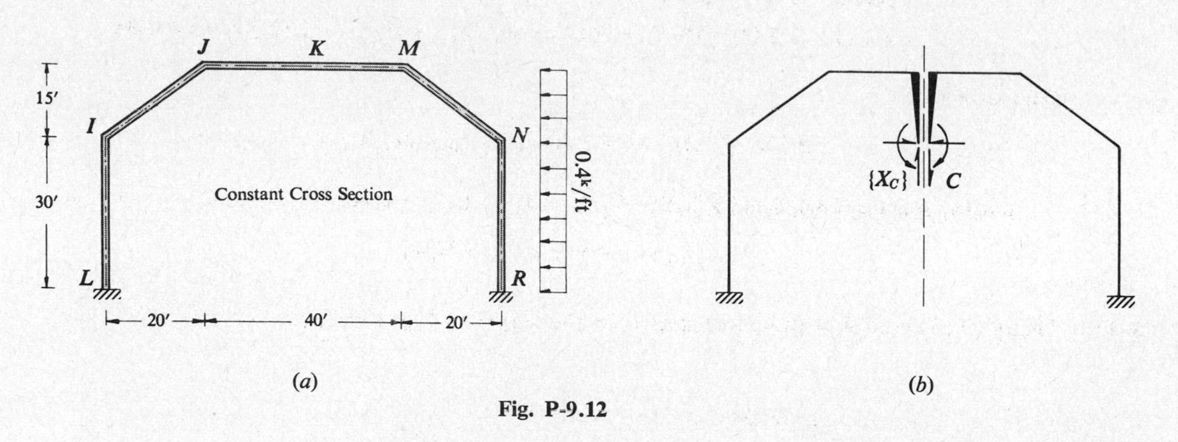

Fig. P-9.12

The frame is released of continuity at K as shown in Fig. P-9.12*b* and the component matrices of (*9.18*), the joint flexibility matrix F^K constructed by (*9.13*) in terms of the angular flexibilities of segments LI, IJ, JM, MN and NR, and the moment matrix m^K_{KX} constructed by (*9.14*) are recorded below.

$$F^K = \frac{1}{EI}\begin{bmatrix} 10 & 5 & 0 & 0 & 0 & 0 \\ 5 & 18.33 & 4.17 & 0 & 0 & 0 \\ 0 & 4.17 & 21.67 & 6.67 & 0 & 0 \\ 0 & 0 & 6.67 & 21.67 & 4.17 & 0 \\ 0 & 0 & 0 & 4.17 & 18.33 & 5 \\ 0 & 0 & 0 & 0 & 5 & 10 \end{bmatrix}$$

$$m^K_{KX} = \begin{bmatrix} -45 & 40 & 1 \\ -15 & 40 & 1 \\ 0 & 20 & 1 \\ 0 & -20 & 1 \\ -15 & -40 & 1 \\ -45 & -40 & 1 \end{bmatrix}$$

By (*9.18*),

$$f^L_{KK} = m^{K)T}_{KX} F^K m^K_{KX} = \frac{1}{EI}\begin{bmatrix} 62{,}250 & 0 & -2{,}175 \\ 0 & 148{,}000 & 0 \\ -2{,}175 & 0 & 150 \end{bmatrix}$$

The effect of the loads is computed by (*9.15*). For this, the joint moments $m^K_{K0}W^K$ and the joint elastic weights τ^K due to loads are calculated respectively by using statics and Table 7-3. The condition of compatibility at K, $\Delta_K{}^K = 0$, identical to the condition of elasto-static equilibrium about a set of axes at K, is

$$\frac{1}{EI}\begin{bmatrix} 62{,}250 & 0 & -2{,}175 \\ 0 & 148{,}000 & 0 \\ -2{,}175 & 0 & 150 \end{bmatrix}\{X_K\} + \frac{1}{EI}\begin{bmatrix} 206{,}719 \\ 247{,}125 \\ -6{,}225 \end{bmatrix} = 0$$

This equation can be solved for X_K, or by (*8.8*), the compatibility equation at the neutral point located at $x_{KC} = 0$, $y_{KC} = -14.5'$, $\omega_{KC} = 0$ becomes

$$\frac{1}{EI}\begin{bmatrix} 30{,}713 & 0 & 0 \\ 0 & 148{,}000 & 0 \\ 0 & 0 & 150 \end{bmatrix}\{X_C\} + \frac{1}{EI}\begin{bmatrix} 116{,}456 \\ 247{,}125 \\ -6{,}225 \end{bmatrix} = 0$$

from which $X_C = \{-3.79, -1.67, 41.5\}$.

SERIES OF POLYGONAL RINGS

9.13.* Using the concept of neutral point for each panel and the procedure outlined in Sec. 9.8, analyze the three span frame of Fig. P-9.13*a*. Consider only flexural deformations.

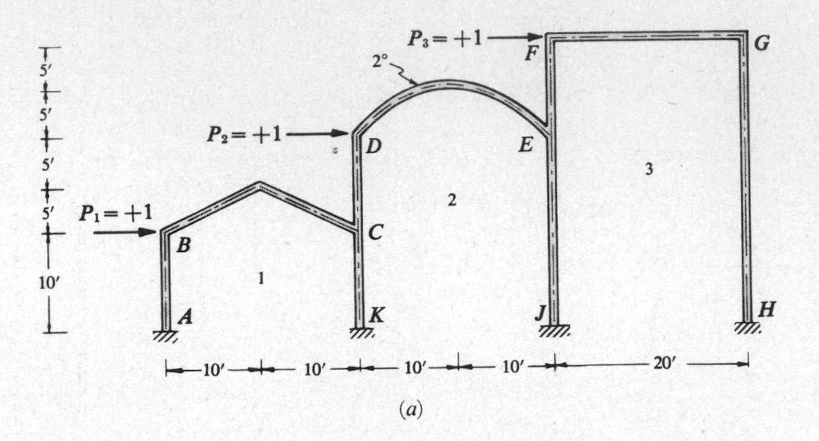

(*a*)

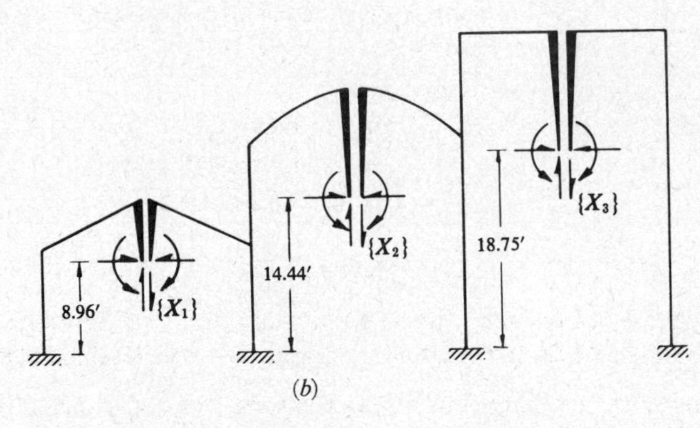

(*b*)

Fig. P-9.13

The procedure of analysis consists of four steps:

1. The initial system of Fig. P-9.13*a* is resolved into the basic system and the complementary system. In this case, the structure of Fig. P-9.13*b* with loads is the basic system and the structure of Fig. P-9.13*b* with redundants at the neutral points is the complementary system.
2. Next, the system unit stress flexibility matrix Φ_X and the system unit load flexibility matrix Φ_W are outlined symbolically from the topology of the respective system. They are

$$\Phi_X{}^C = \begin{bmatrix} f_{11}^C & f_{12}^C & \\ f_{21}^C & f_{22}^C & f_{23}^C \\ & f_{32}^C & f_{33}^C \end{bmatrix} \qquad \Phi_W{}^C = \begin{bmatrix} l_{10,1}^C & l_{10,2}^C & \\ & l_{20,2}^C & l_{20,3}^C \\ & & l_{30,3}^C \end{bmatrix}$$

3. Then the unit stress flexibilities and the unit load flexibilities are computed for each ring as follows.

$$f_{11}^C = \frac{1}{EI}\begin{bmatrix} 807.1 & 0 & 0 \\ 0 & 2{,}745.3 & 0 \\ 0 & 0 & 42.4 \end{bmatrix} \qquad f_{22}^C = \frac{1}{EI}\begin{bmatrix} 3{,}748 & 0 & 0 \\ 0 & 4{,}667 & 0 \\ 0 & 0 & 60 \end{bmatrix} \qquad f_{33}^C = \frac{1}{EI}\begin{bmatrix} 7{,}875 & 0 & 0 \\ 0 & 6{,}667 & 0 \\ 0 & 0 & 80 \end{bmatrix}$$

$$f_{12} = f_{21}^{)T} = \frac{1}{EI}\begin{bmatrix} -457 & 396 & 39.6 \\ -944 & 1{,}000 & 100 \\ 94.4 & -100 & -10 \end{bmatrix} \qquad f_{23} = f_{32}^{)T} = \frac{1}{EI}\begin{bmatrix} -1{,}444 & 889 & 88.9 \\ -1{,}750 & 2{,}000 & 200 \\ 175 & -200 & -20 \end{bmatrix}$$

*Source: J. J. Tuma, K. S. Havner and F. Hedges, Analysis of Frames with Curved and Bent Members, *Journal of the Structural Division, ASCE*, Vol. 84, No. ST 5, Proc. Paper 1764, p. 23.

$$l^C_{10,1} = \frac{1}{EI}\begin{bmatrix} 281 & 0 & 0 \\ -500 & 0 & 0 \\ -50 & 0 & 0 \end{bmatrix} \qquad l^C_{20,2} = \frac{1}{EI}\begin{bmatrix} 1{,}516 & 0 & 0 \\ -2{,}000 & 0 & 0 \\ -200 & 0 & 0 \end{bmatrix} \qquad l^C_{30,3} = \frac{1}{EI}\begin{bmatrix} 3{,}938 & 0 & 0 \\ -4{,}500 & 0 & 0 \\ -450 & 0 & 0 \end{bmatrix}$$

$$l^C_{10,2} = \frac{1}{EI}\begin{bmatrix} -677 & 0 & 0 \\ -1{,}500 & 0 & 0 \\ 150 & 0 & 0 \end{bmatrix} \qquad l^C_{20,3} = \frac{1}{EI}\begin{bmatrix} -2{,}444 & 0 & 0 \\ -4{,}000 & 0 & 0 \\ 400 & 0 & 0 \end{bmatrix}$$

The coefficients of these matrices have been obtained by the group flexibility concept introduced at the beginning of this chapter.

4. Finally the compatibility equation $\Phi_X X + \Phi_W W = 0$ becomes

$$\frac{1}{EI}\left[\begin{array}{ccc|ccc|ccc} 807.1 & 0 & 0 & -457 & 396 & 39.6 & 0 & 0 & 0 \\ 0 & 2{,}745.3 & 0 & -944 & 1{,}000 & 100 & 0 & 0 & 0 \\ 0 & 0 & 42.4 & 94.4 & -100 & -10 & 0 & 0 & 0 \\ \hline -457 & -944 & 94.4 & 3{,}748 & 0 & 0 & -1{,}444 & 889 & 88.9 \\ 396 & 1{,}000 & -100 & 0 & 4{,}667 & 0 & -1{,}750 & 2{,}000 & 200 \\ 39.6 & 100 & -10 & 0 & 0 & 60 & 175 & -200 & -20 \\ \hline 0 & 0 & 0 & -1{,}444 & -1{,}750 & 175 & 7{,}875 & 0 & 0 \\ 0 & 0 & 0 & 889 & 2{,}000 & -200 & 0 & 6{,}667 & 0 \\ 0 & 0 & 0 & 88.9 & 200 & -20 & 0 & 0 & 80 \end{array}\right] \begin{bmatrix} \{X_1\} \\ \\ \{X_2\} \\ \\ \{X_3\} \end{bmatrix} + \frac{1}{EI}\left[\begin{array}{c} -396 \\ -2{,}000 \\ 100 \\ \hline -888 \\ 2{,}000 \\ 200 \\ \hline 3{,}938 \\ -4{,}500 \\ -450 \end{array}\right] = 0$$

the solution of which is

$$X_1 = \{0.343, 0.604, -1.56\}$$
$$X_2 = \{0.187, 0.672, -1.55\}$$
$$X_3 = \{-0.282, 0.402, 3.35\}$$

GENERAL METHOD

9.14. For the three span frame of Fig. P-9.14*a* below select the basic system of Fig. *b*, the complementary system of Fig. *c* and solve for the redundants. Consider only flexural deformations.

The given structure is resolved into seven straight segments *HA*, *AC*, *CI*, *CE*, *EJ*, *EG* and *GK*. Matrix *f* *(9.21)* is constructed using *(5.14)* for flexural deformations only.

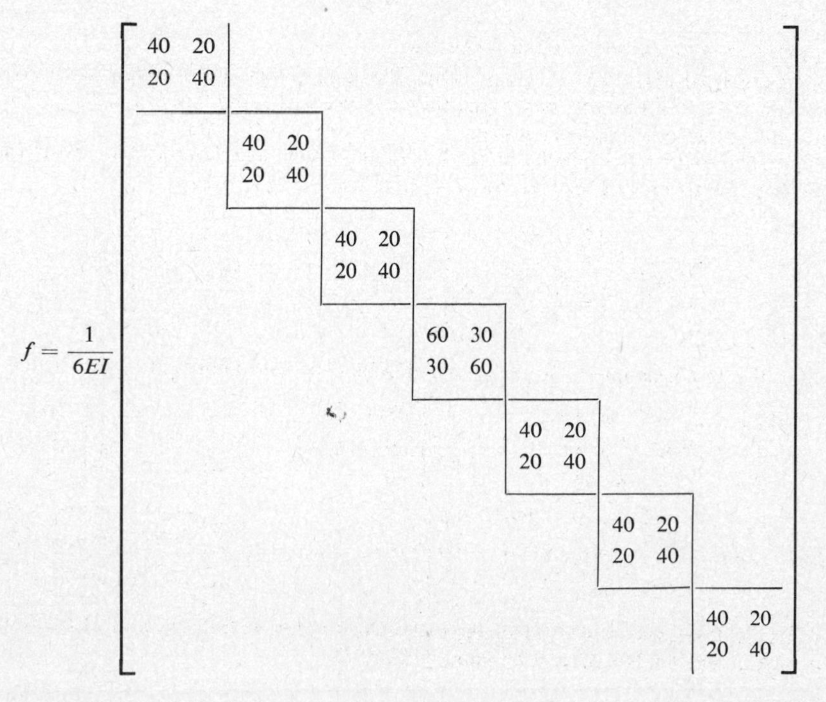

$$f = \frac{1}{6EI}\begin{bmatrix} 40 & 20 & & & & & & & & & & & & \\ 20 & 40 & & & & & & & & & & & & \\ & & 40 & 20 & & & & & & & & & & \\ & & 20 & 40 & & & & & & & & & & \\ & & & & 40 & 20 & & & & & & & & \\ & & & & 20 & 40 & & & & & & & & \\ & & & & & & 60 & 30 & & & & & & \\ & & & & & & 30 & 60 & & & & & & \\ & & & & & & & & 40 & 20 & & & & \\ & & & & & & & & 20 & 40 & & & & \\ & & & & & & & & & & 40 & 20 & & \\ & & & & & & & & & & 20 & 40 & & \\ & & & & & & & & & & & & 40 & 20 \\ & & & & & & & & & & & & 20 & 40 \end{bmatrix}$$

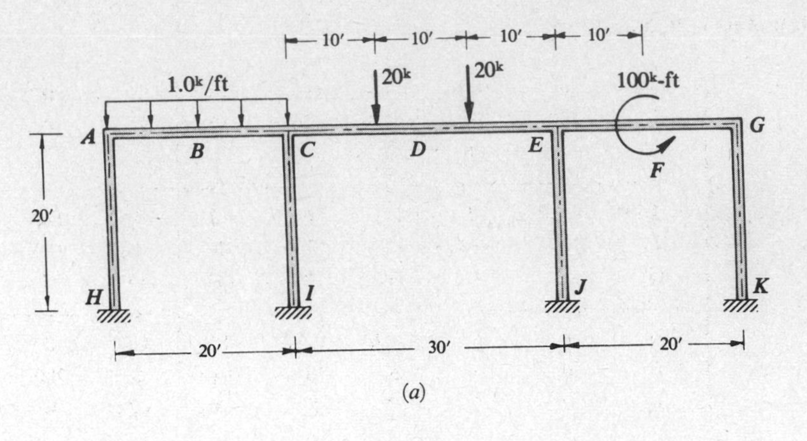

(a)

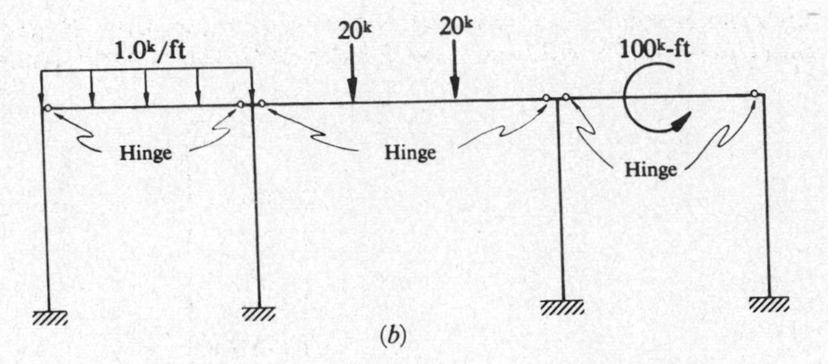

(b)

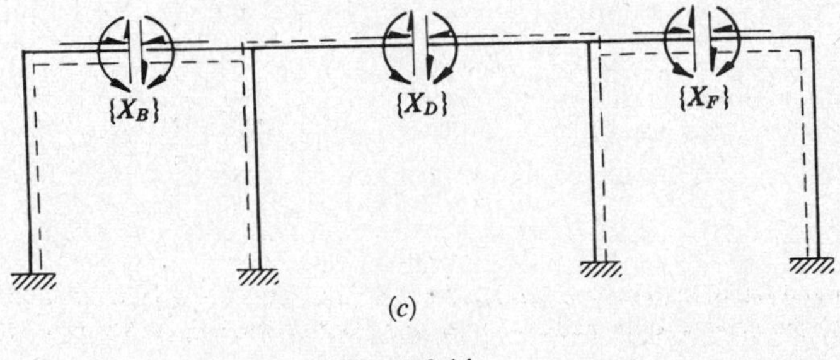

(c)

Fig. P-9.14

The general transfer matrix q_X (9.22) is the moment influence value matrix and is constructed easily by statics of the complementary system. The moments are considered positive if they produce tension on dotted sides of the segments.

$$q_X = \begin{bmatrix} -20 & 10 & 1 & 0 & 0 & 0 & 0 & 0 & 0 \\ 0 & 10 & 1 & 0 & 0 & 0 & 0 & 0 & 0 \\ 0 & 10 & 1 & 0 & 0 & 0 & 0 & 0 & 0 \\ 0 & -10 & 1 & 0 & 0 & 0 & 0 & 0 & 0 \\ 0 & -10 & 1 & 0 & -15 & -1 & 0 & 0 & 0 \\ -20 & -10 & 1 & 20 & -15 & -1 & 0 & 0 & 0 \\ 0 & 0 & 0 & 0 & -15 & -1 & 0 & 0 & 0 \\ 0 & 0 & 0 & 0 & 15 & -1 & 0 & 0 & 0 \\ 0 & 0 & 0 & 0 & 15 & -1 & 0 & 10 & 1 \\ 0 & 0 & 0 & 20 & 15 & -1 & -20 & 10 & 1 \\ 0 & 0 & 0 & 0 & 0 & 0 & 0 & 10 & 1 \\ 0 & 0 & 0 & 0 & 0 & 0 & 0 & -10 & 1 \\ 0 & 0 & 0 & 0 & 0 & 0 & 0 & -10 & 1 \\ 0 & 0 & 0 & 0 & 0 & 0 & -20 & -10 & 1 \end{bmatrix}$$

Substituting in (9.23) gives Φ_X.

$$\Phi_X = \frac{100}{6EI_c}\left[\begin{array}{ccc|ccc|ccc} 320 & 0 & -24 & -160 & 180 & 12 & 0 & 0 & 0 \\ 0 & 280 & 0 & -120 & 180 & 12 & 0 & 0 & 0 \\ -24 & 0 & 3.6 & 12 & -18 & -1.2 & 0 & 0 & 0 \\ \hline -160 & -120 & 12 & 320 & 0 & -24 & -160 & 120 & 12 \\ 180 & 180 & -18 & 0 & 675 & 0 & -180 & 180 & 18 \\ 12 & 12 & -1.2 & 24 & 0 & 4.2 & 12 & -12 & -1.2 \\ \hline 0 & 0 & 0 & -160 & -180 & 12 & 320 & 0 & -24 \\ 0 & 0 & 0 & 120 & 180 & -12 & 0 & 280 & 0 \\ 0 & 0 & 0 & 12 & 18 & -1.2 & -24 & 0 & 3.6 \end{array}\right]$$

The displacement vector due to load (9.24) is computed in two parts. lW representing the displacement vector for the segments is the vector of the end slopes τ due to loads. This is readily computed using Table 7-3.

$$lW = \tau = \frac{1}{EI}\begin{bmatrix} 0 \\ 0 \\ 333.3 \\ 333.3 \\ 0 \\ 0 \\ -2{,}000 \\ -2{,}000 \\ 0 \\ 0 \\ 83.3 \\ 83.3 \\ 0 \\ 0 \end{bmatrix}$$

The general transfer matrix q_W giving the end moments on segments, due to loads, is null and the advantage of the choice of the basic system becomes apparent. Substitution in (9.24) gives Δ_W.

$$\Delta_W = \frac{1}{EI}\begin{bmatrix} 0 \\ 0 \\ 666.7 \\ 0 \\ 0 \\ 4{,}000 \\ 0 \\ 1{,}666.7 \\ 0 \end{bmatrix}$$

The compatibility equation is

$$\Phi_X X + \Delta_W = 0$$

where $X = \{X_B, X_D, X_F\}$. Solving for X,

$$X_B = \{-0.053, 3.96, -42.3\}$$

$$X_D = \{-2.78, -0.163, -117.8\}$$

$$X_F = \{1.49, -4.11, -19.2\}$$

9.15. For the two story frame of Fig. P-9.15a select the basic system of Fig. b, the complementary system of Fig. c and solve for the redundants. Only flexural deformations may be considered.

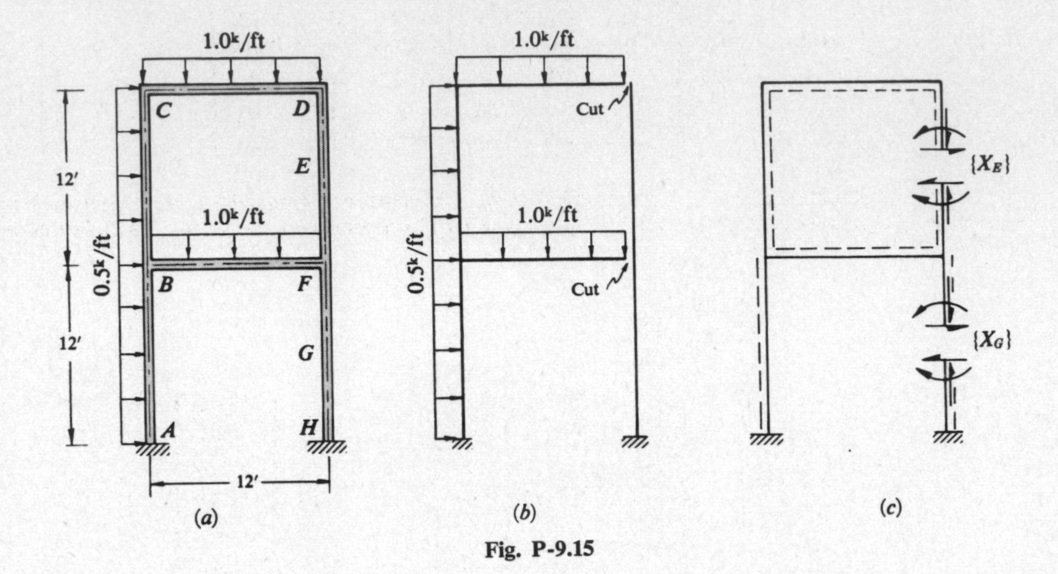

Fig. P-9.15

The frame is resolved into six segments AB, BF, FH, BC, CD and DF. Matrix f (9.21) is constructed using (5.14) for flexural deformations only.

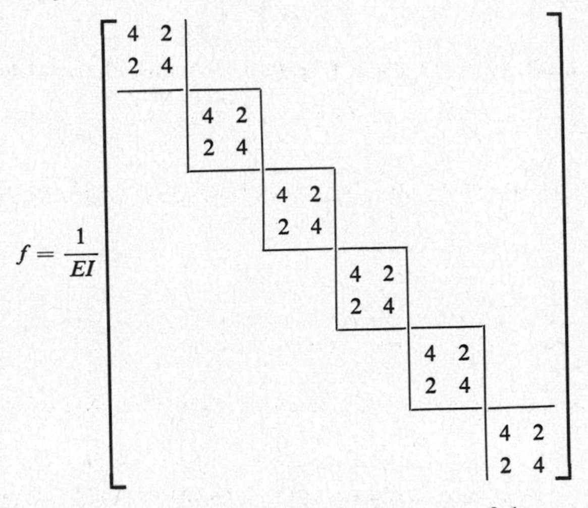

$$f = \frac{1}{EI}\begin{bmatrix} 4 & 2 & & & & & & & & & & \\ 2 & 4 & & & & & & & & & & \\ & & 4 & 2 & & & & & & & & \\ & & 2 & 4 & & & & & & & & \\ & & & & 4 & 2 & & & & & & \\ & & & & 2 & 4 & & & & & & \\ & & & & & & 4 & 2 & & & & \\ & & & & & & 2 & 4 & & & & \\ & & & & & & & & 4 & 2 & & \\ & & & & & & & & 2 & 4 & & \\ & & & & & & & & & & 4 & 2 \\ & & & & & & & & & & 2 & 4 \end{bmatrix}$$

The general transfer matrix q_X (9.22) is constructed using statics of the complementary system. Dotted lines in Fig. c indicate tension sides of segments for positive moments

$$q_X = \begin{bmatrix} 12 & 6 & -1 & 0 & 0 & 0 \\ 12 & -6 & -1 & 0 & 0 & 0 \\ 12 & -6 & -1 & -12 & -6 & 1 \\ 0 & -6 & -1 & 0 & -6 & 1 \\ 0 & -6 & -1 & 0 & 0 & 0 \\ 0 & 6 & -1 & 0 & 0 & 0 \\ 0 & 0 & 0 & -12 & -6 & 1 \\ 0 & 0 & 0 & -12 & 6 & 1 \\ 0 & 0 & 0 & -12 & 6 & 1 \\ 0 & 0 & 0 & 0 & 6 & 1 \\ 0 & 0 & 0 & 0 & 6 & 1 \\ 0 & 0 & 0 & 0 & -6 & 1 \end{bmatrix}$$

With f and q_X defined, (9.23) gives Φ_X.

$$\Phi_X = \frac{1}{EI}\begin{bmatrix} 2{,}304 & -432 & -216 & -576 & -432 & 72 \\ -432 & 720 & 72 & 432 & 432 & -72 \\ -216 & 72 & 36 & 72 & 72 & -12 \\ -576 & 432 & 72 & 2{,}880 & 0 & -288 \\ -432 & 432 & 72 & 0 & 1{,}152 & 0 \\ 72 & -72 & -12 & -288 & 0 & 48 \end{bmatrix}$$

The loads being distributed, their integrated effect on segment end moments, $q_W W$, is computed by statics of the basic system. The segment deformations due to loads, lW, are computed using Table 7-3. Substitution of appropriate values in (9.24) gives Δ_W.

$$q_W W = \begin{bmatrix} 288 \\ 180 \\ 72 \\ 0 \\ 0 \\ 0 \\ -108 \\ -72 \\ -72 \\ 0 \\ 0 \\ 0 \end{bmatrix} \qquad lW = \frac{1}{EI}\begin{bmatrix} -36 \\ -36 \\ -72 \\ -72 \\ 0 \\ 0 \\ 36 \\ 36 \\ 72 \\ 72 \\ 0 \\ 0 \end{bmatrix} \qquad \Delta_W = \frac{1}{EI}\begin{bmatrix} 35{,}424 \\ -432 \\ -3{,}024 \\ 12{,}096 \\ -3{,}024 \\ -1{,}008 \end{bmatrix}$$

The compatibility condition $\Phi_X X + \Delta_W = 0$ in which $X = \{X_G, X_E\}$ is solved for X giving

$$X_G = \{-18.22, -4.98, 3.73\} \qquad X_E = \{-7.53, -2.57, -3.38\}$$

9.16. Using the results of Problem 9.11, determine the true stress vector (9.33) and the true displacement vector (9.34).

The true stress influence value matrix q from (9.33) is

$$q = q_W - q_X \Phi_X^{-1} \Phi_W$$

$q_W = m_{C0}$ and $q_X = m_{CX}$ are readily available from Problem 9.11. Also using other matrices of Problem 9.11,

$$\Phi_W = m_{CX}^T F^C m_{C0} = \frac{1}{EI}\begin{bmatrix} 4{,}608 & -7{,}776 & 9{,}720 & -2{,}916 \\ -6{,}912 & -26{,}189 & 40{,}713 & -5{,}832 \\ -288 & 848 & -1{,}372 & 162 \end{bmatrix}$$

and

$$\Phi_X^{-1} = (m_{CX}^T F^C m_{CX})^{-1} = \frac{EI}{10^5}\begin{bmatrix} 9.986 & -0.217 & 29.912 \\ -0.217 & 1.760 & 6.900 \\ 29.912 & 6.900 & 967.728 \end{bmatrix}$$

Substituting gives

$$q = \begin{bmatrix} -9.141 & -6.005 & 4.467 & -3.771 \\ 5.523 & 5.179 & -6.857 & 1.751 \\ 1.886 & -4.075 & 7.565 & -0.293 \\ -2.782 & 1.517 & 1.903 & 2.468 \\ -1.236 & -2.753 & -3.972 & -4.739 \\ 5.766 & 6.859 & 4.521 & 9.119 \end{bmatrix}$$

The true stress vector (in this case the moment vector) in terms of $W = \{5, 2, 20, 5\}$ is

$$\sigma = qW = \{12.76, -90.42, 151.10, 39.51, -114.83, 178.56\}$$

The true displacement vector is

$$\Delta = \Phi W = (1/EI)\{6{,}234, 476, 25{,}224, 13{,}087\}$$

where
$$\Phi = q)^{T} f q = \frac{1}{EI}\begin{bmatrix} 1{,}225 & 656 & -199 & 556 \\ 656 & 775 & -366 & 592 \\ -199 & -366 & 1{,}279 & 274 \\ 556 & 592 & 274 & 729 \end{bmatrix}$$

Note: $f = F^{C}$ was given in Problem 9.11.

Supplementary Problems

9.17. Using (*9.2*) and (*9.3*) determine the number of redundants in the frames shown in Fig. P-9.17.

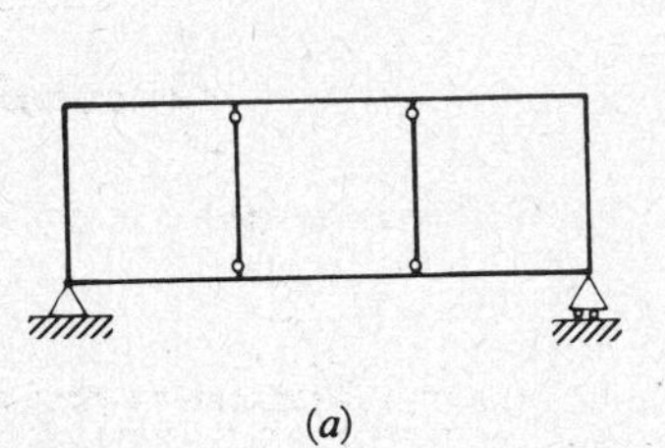

(*a*)

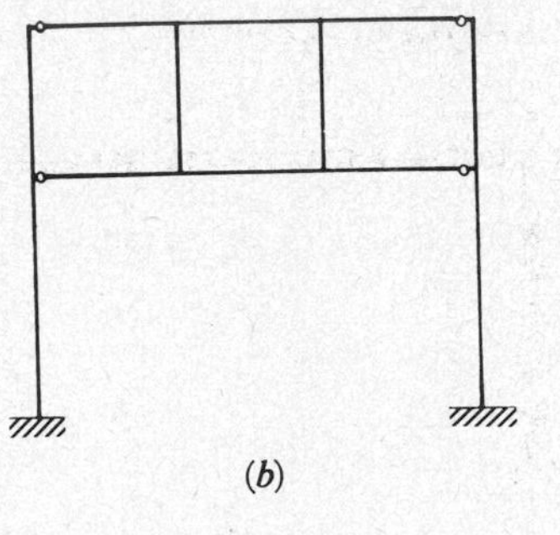

(*b*)

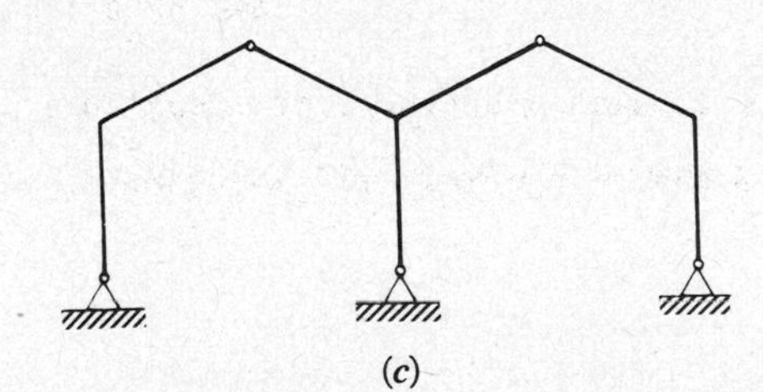

(*c*)

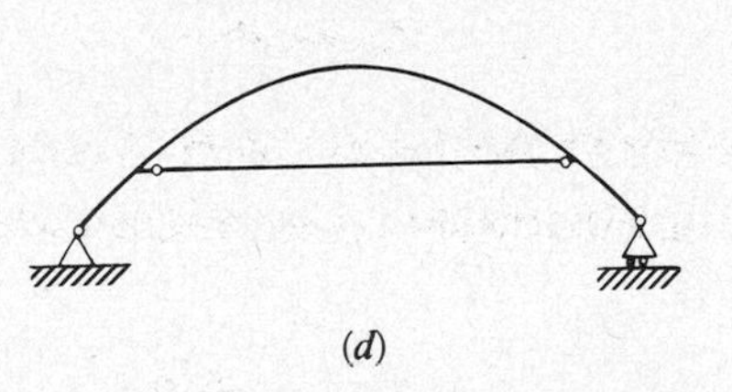

(*d*)

(*e*)

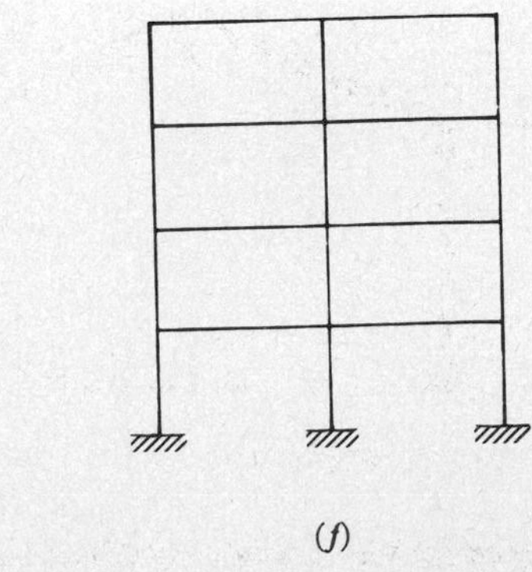

(*f*)

Fig. P-9.17

9.18. Using (*9.4*) compute the unit stress group flexibility matrix $f^S_{RR,L}$ for the cantilever frame of constant cross section shown in Fig. P-9.18.

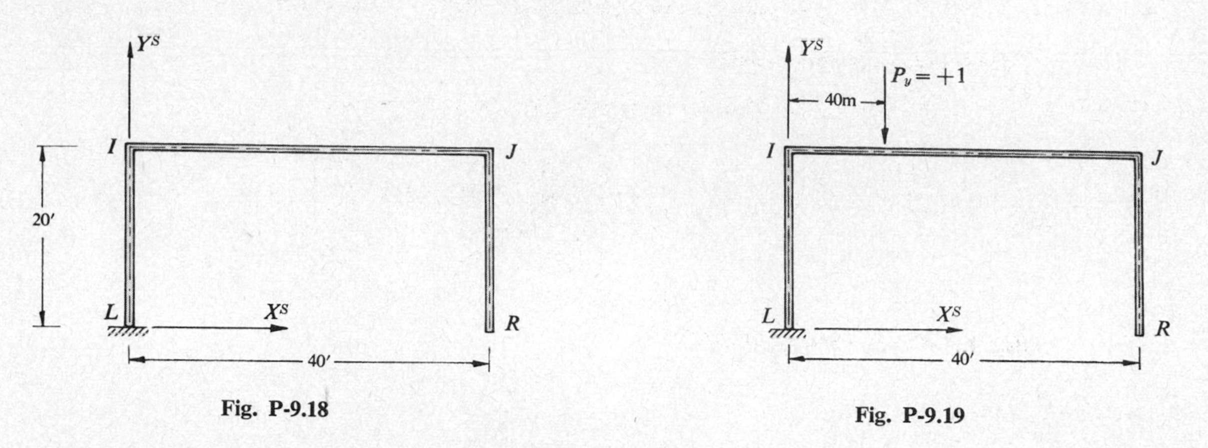

Fig. P-9.18

Fig. P-9.19

9.19. For the frame of Problem 9.18, compute the unit load group flexibility matrix $l^S_{RR,L}$ for the load shown in Fig. P-9.19.

9.20. Using the results of Problems 9.18 and 9.19 and the concept of neutral point, compute and sketch the influence lines for the reactions at *R* in the frame shown in Fig. P-9.20.

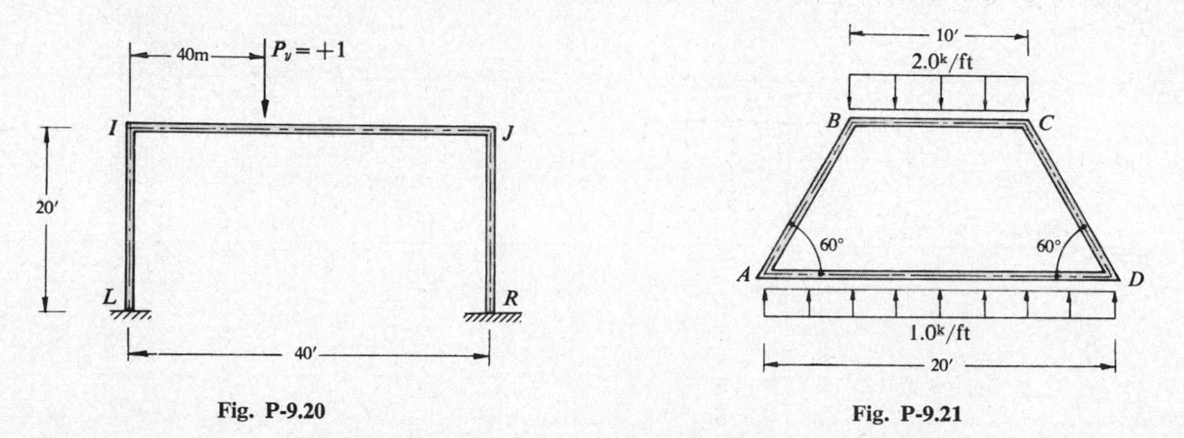

Fig. P-9.20

Fig. P-9.21

9.21. Analyze the closed ring of Fig. P-9.21 using (*9.10*) and the concept of neutral point. EI = constant.

9.22. Using (*9.15*) and the concept of neutral point, analyze the frame of Fig. P-9.22. EI = constant.

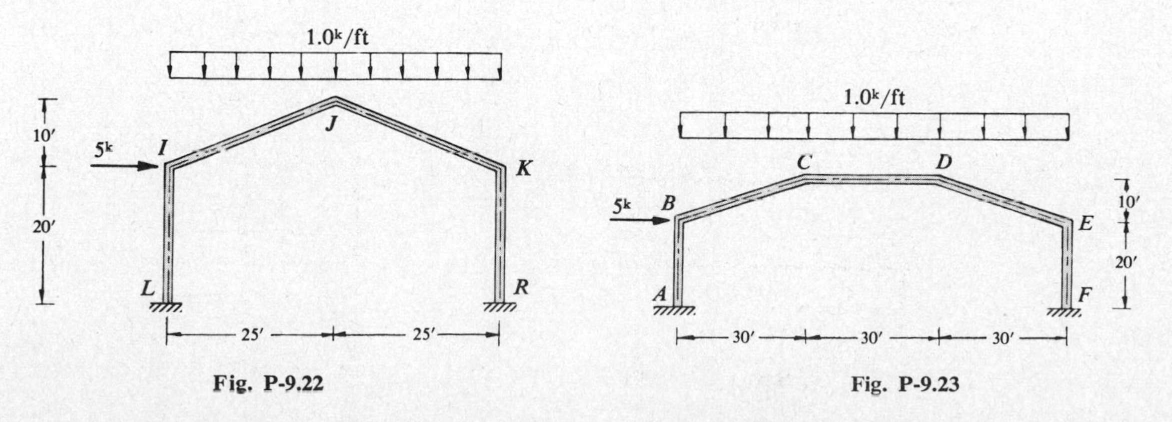

Fig. P-9.22

Fig. P-9.23

9.23. Using segmental elastic weights (*9.17*) and the conditions of compatibility (*9.16*), solve the frame of Fig. P-9.23 and compute the reactions. EI = constant.

9.24. Using the concept of neutral point for each panel and the procedure outlined in Sec. 9.8, analyze the two span frame of Fig. P-9.24. EI = constant.

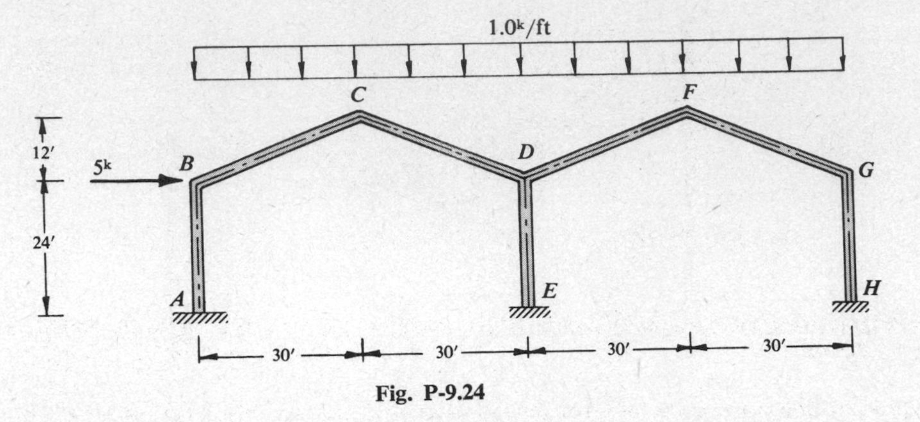

Fig. P-9.24

9.25. Use the concept of neutral point for each panel and solve the vierendeel girder shown in Fig. P-9.25.

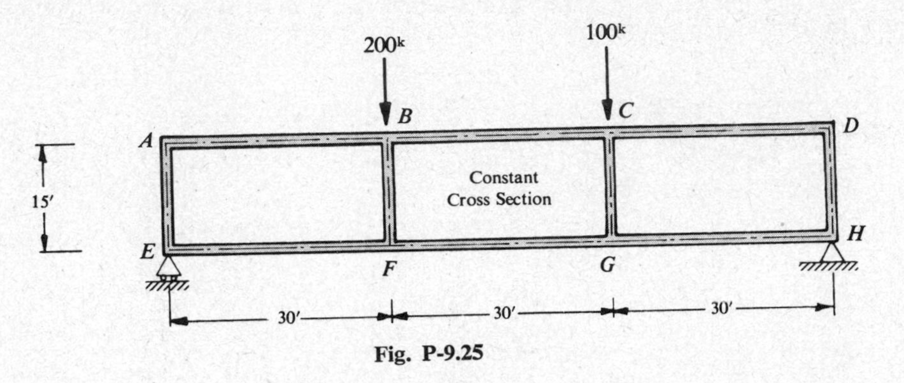

Fig. P-9.25

9.26. Solve the frame of Fig. P-9.26a for the redundants shown in Fig. b. Use (9.12) and consider flexural deformations only EI = constant.

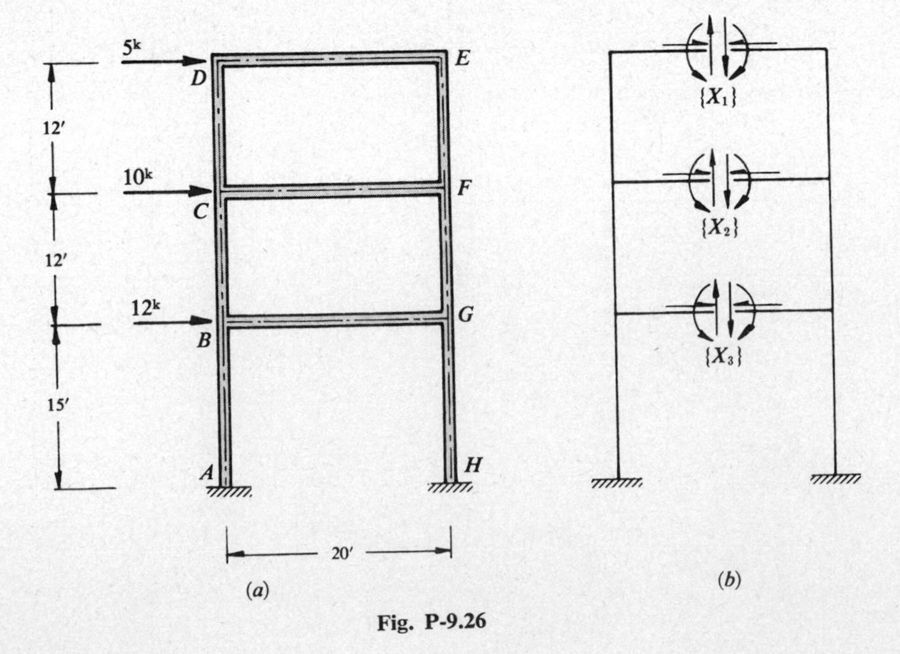

Fig. P-9.26

9.27. For the frame of Fig. P-9.27*a*, use the basic system of Fig. *b*, the complementary system of Fig. *c* and solve for the redundants. EI = constant.

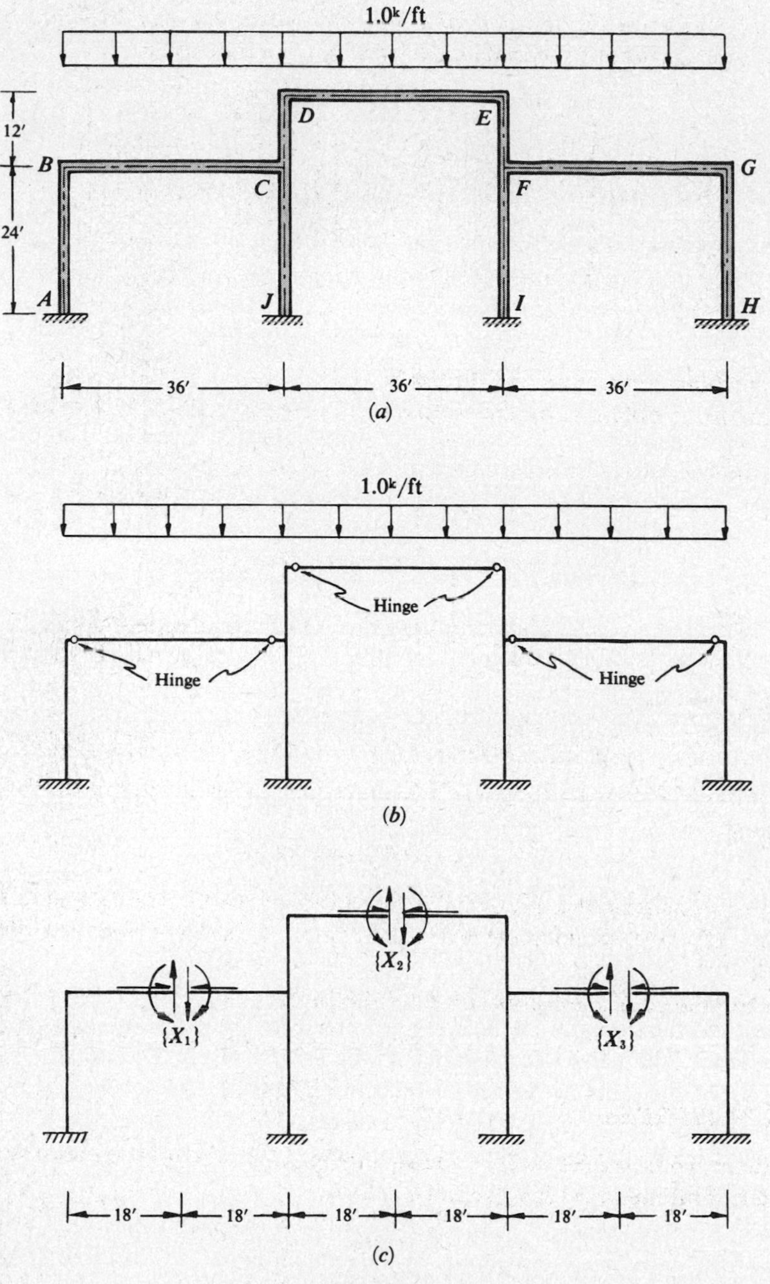

Fig. P-9.27

9.28. Compute the true stress vector (*9.33*) and the true displacement vector (*9.34*) for the frame of Problem 9.26.

Chapter 10

Stiffness Matrix

10.1 STIFFNESS METHOD

The stiffness method, frequently called the *displacement method* (or slope deflection method) is the third and last method of analysis introduced in this volume. Instead of working with the unknown stresses (or reactions), this method introduces *displacements* as the *unknown quantities*. Because the joints are the *reference points* of the structural topology, it is only logical (and also practical but not mandatory) to select the joint displacements for this purpose.

Since the displacements are the unknowns, the notion of static indeterminacy is replaced by the concept of *kinematic indeterminacy*, defined by the number of admissible, independent and unknown *joint displacements* (or selected displacements).

For a planar system of m bars, with j joints, s internal releases, c internal constraints and r reactive constraints, the *total number of admissible and independent joint displacements* (linear and angular) is

$$n = 3j + s - c - r \tag{10.1}$$

where the internal releases are special conditions (such as internal hinges, guides and/or hangers). In this equation, the *total number of joints* includes all internal joints, points of internal releases and constraints, and all points of supports.

Although the formulation is inverted, the conditions to be satisfied (static equilibrium and compatibility of deformation) remain the same. In order to meet these requirements, the given structure is again resolved into two component systems:

(*a*) *Basic System*, conceived by locking the ends of each member in the initial system, preventing their displacements (fixing the system), but retaining other causes, e.g. the applied loads and change in volume. The fixity of ends (joints) essentially isolates the structures into a system of fixed members (fixed end beams, fixed end arches and/or fixed end frames). Consequently the basic system is highly statically indeterminate.

(*b*) *Complementary System*, obtained from the initial system by removing the applied loads and volume changes, and introducing unknown (redundant) end deformations for each member, satisfying the natural constraints of the system (ends of members framed into a rigid joint undergo the same linear and angular displacement, ends of members connected by a mechanical hinge undergo the same linear displacement, initial free ends or fixed ends remain free and fixed respectively, etc.). Consequently, the complementary system is highly statically indeterminate.

The selection of these component systems is arbitrary provided that each one independently is in a *state of compatible deformation* (consistent with the remaining part of the same system) and is also *geometrically stable*.

10.2 STIFFNESS MATRIX

The end stress in each member of the component system must be a linear combination of joint displacements and applied loads.

In matrix form,

$$\sigma_{s0} = k_{s1}W_1 + k_{s2}W_2 + \cdots + k_{sm}W_m \tag{10.2}$$

and

$$\sigma_{s\Delta} = k_{si}\Delta_i + k_{sj}\Delta_j + \cdots + k_{sn}\Delta_n \tag{10.3}$$

where σ_{s0} = end stress vector at s of a given member in the basic system, [3 × 1], $\sigma_{s\Delta}$ = end stress vector at s of a given member in the complementary system, [3 × 1], $W_1, W_2, \ldots, W_m$ = load vectors at 1, 2,..., m respectively, [3 × 1], $\Delta_i, \Delta_j, \ldots, \Delta_n$ = redundant joint displacement vectors at $i, j, \ldots, n$ respectively, [3 × 1].

The new symbols $k_{s1}, k_{s2}, \ldots, k_{sm}$ represent [3 × 3] matrices of stiffness coefficients defining the stress vectors at s due to unit load vector at 1, 2,..., m respectively. Similarly, $k_{si}, k_{sj}, \ldots, k_{sn}$ represent again [3 × 3] matrices of stiffness coefficients defining the stress vectors at s due to unit displacement vector at $i, j, \ldots, n$ respectively. The notion of stiffness for coefficients of (*10.2*) is not correct since the cause is a unit load and not a unit displacement, but for the uniformity of formulation this designation is retained.

Similarly, the joint stress in the basic and complementary system defined as a joint load required to maintain the respective system in the state of static equilibrium and compatible deformation must also be a linear combination of the same causes.

In matrix form,

$$\begin{aligned} \sigma_{i0} &= k_{i1}W_1 + k_{i2}W_2 + \cdots + k_{im}W_m \\ \sigma_{j0} &= k_{j1}W_1 + k_{j2}W_2 + \cdots + k_{jm}W_m \\ &\cdots\cdots\cdots\cdots\cdots\cdots\cdots \\ \sigma_{n0} &= k_{n1}W_1 + k_{n2}W_2 + \cdots + k_{nm}W_m \end{aligned} \qquad (10.4)$$

and

$$\begin{aligned} \sigma_{i\Delta} &= k_{ii}\Delta_i + k_{ij}\Delta_j + \cdots + k_{in}\Delta_n \\ \sigma_{j\Delta} &= k_{ji}\Delta_i + k_{jj}\Delta_j + \cdots + k_{jn}\Delta_n \\ &\cdots\cdots\cdots\cdots\cdots\cdots\cdots \\ \sigma_{n\Delta} &= k_{ni}\Delta_i + k_{nj}\Delta_j + \cdots + k_{nn}\Delta_n \end{aligned} \qquad (10.5)$$

where $\sigma_{i0}, \sigma_{j0}, \ldots, \sigma_{n0}$ = joint stress vector in basic system at $i, j, \ldots, n$ respectively, [3 × 1], $\sigma_{i\Delta}, \sigma_{j\Delta}, \ldots, \sigma_{n\Delta}$ = joint stress vector in complementary system at $i, j, \ldots, n$ respectively, [3 × 1]. The remaining symbols represent the joint stiffness coefficient matrices [3 × 3] defining the joint stress vector at the respective joint due to a unit cause vector.

Equations (*10.4, 5*) in symbolic form are

$$\sigma_0 = sW \qquad \text{and} \qquad \sigma_\Delta = k\Delta \qquad (10.6)$$

where s and k are the *unit load and unit redundant stiffness matrices* of the basic and complementary system respectively.

10.3 CONDITIONS OF EQUILIBRIUM

The superposition of joint stress vectors σ_0 and σ_Δ must satisfy the *conditions of equilibrium*, namely the algebraic sum of joint stresses at $i, j, \ldots, n$ must either equal zero or equal the prescribed joint stress (or load). Thus

$$\sigma_0 + \sigma_\Delta = \sigma$$

and in terms of (*10.6*),

$$sW + k\Delta = \sigma \qquad (10.7)$$

Since there are n redundants and n equilibrium conditions,

$$\Delta = -k^{-1}[sW - \sigma] \qquad (10.8)$$

Equation (*10.7*) is called the *governing equation* (matrix) of the stiffness analysis. For the sign convention of loads, stresses and displacements, refer to Figs. 1-2 and 1-4 respectively.

The example of Fig. 10-1*a* illustrates the construction of (*10.7*) in which the joint displacements at i, j, k are selected as redundants. The fixed end beams of Fig. 10-1*b* form the basic system and the complementary system is shown in Fig. 10-1*c*. The superposition of the respective joint stress yields the governing equation (*10.7*) given for this case as

$$\underbrace{\begin{bmatrix} k_{ii} & k_{ij} & k_{ik} \\ k_{ji} & k_{jj} & k_{jk} \\ k_{ki} & k_{kj} & k_{kk} \end{bmatrix}}_{k} \underbrace{\begin{bmatrix} \Delta_i \\ \Delta_j \\ \Delta_k \end{bmatrix}}_{\Delta} + \underbrace{\begin{bmatrix} k_{i1} & k_{i2} \\ k_{j1} & k_{j2} \\ k_{k1} & k_{k2} \end{bmatrix}}_{s} \underbrace{\begin{bmatrix} W_1 \\ W_2 \end{bmatrix}}_{W} = 0$$

Obviously, in a general case some coefficients of k and s may equal zero.

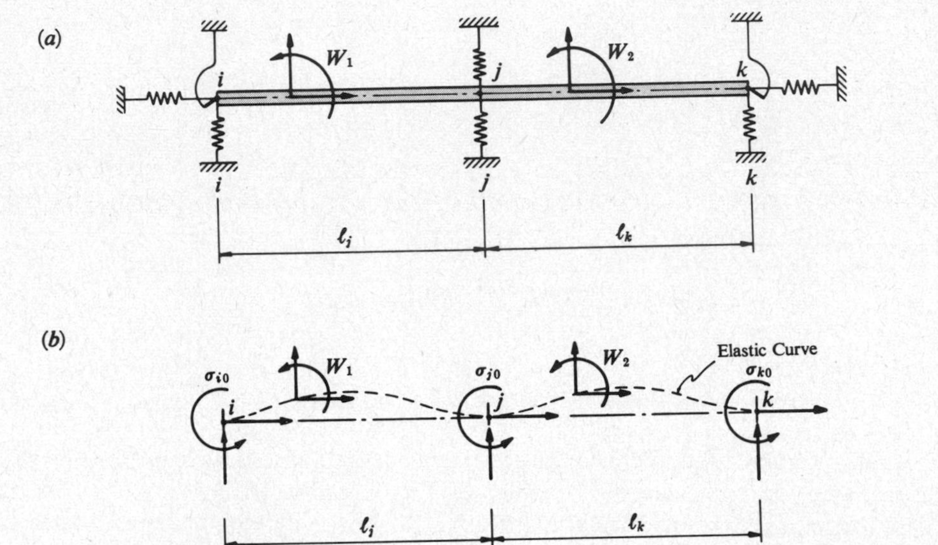

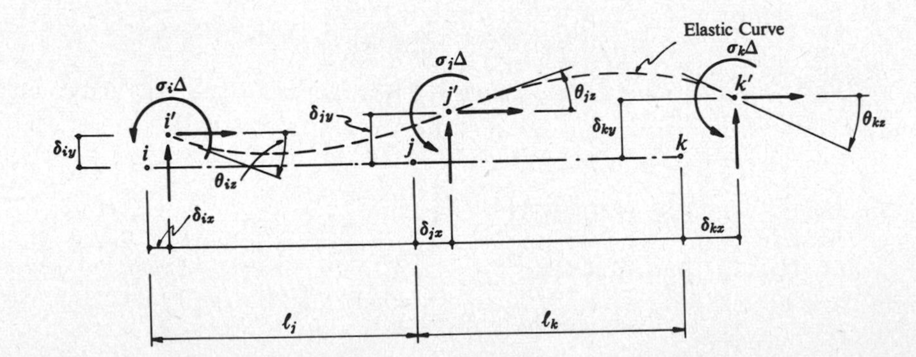

Fig. 10.1. Two Span Continuous Beam Elastically Restrained at i, j, k

10.4 CONSTRUCTION OF SYSTEM STIFFNESS MATRIX

The key to the solution is in this case the construction of matrices k and s, the coefficients of which are the joint stresses produced by unit redundants and unit loads respectively. This again can be accomplished by means of deformation geometry, virtual work or strain energy.

Regardless of the method used, the analytical expressions for the stiffness submatrices k_{aa} and k_{ab}, where $a = i, j, \ldots, n$ and $b = i, j, \ldots, n$ or $1, 2, \ldots, m$, can be obtained by the superposition of effects produced by unit causes, one at a time, when all other causes (joint displacements or loads) are suppressed.

10.5 SEGMENTAL STIFFNESS MATRIX

The construction of matrices k and s by the procedure outlined in Sec. 10.4 is always possible but not particularly convenient. For large complex structures it is advantageous to decompose the component systems into a series of segments, compute the stiffness matrices for each segment separately and then reassemble these segmental matrices into a system matrix equation (*10.7*).

(a) Segmental Stiffnesses, Bar of Arbitrary Shape

The *linear dependence of end stresses and end displacements* is given by the *state vector transport matrices* (*4.2*). Consequently these matrices provide a unique vehicle for the derivation of segmental stiffnesses. For the curved bar of Fig. 10-2, the lower submatrix equations of (*4.1*) give

$$\Delta_L{}^0 = b_L{}^0 + d^0_{LR}\sigma^0_{RL} + s^0_{LR}\Delta_R{}^0 \qquad \Delta_R{}^0 = b_R{}^0 - d^0_{RL}\sigma^0_{LR} + s^0_{RL}\Delta_L{}^0 \tag{10.9}$$

where σ^0_{RL}, σ^0_{LR} are the end stresses at R and L respectively and $\Delta_R{}^0$, $\Delta_L{}^0$ are the respective end displacements. The signs of these vectors are governed by (*1.16*). Then from (*10.9*),

$$\sigma^0_{RL} = \underbrace{-d^{(0)-1}_{LR}s^0_{LR}}_{k^0_{RR}}\Delta_R{}^0 + \underbrace{d^{(0)-1}_{LR}}_{k^0_{RL}}\Delta_L{}^0 \underbrace{- d^{(0)-1}_{LR}b_L{}^0}_{\sigma^0_{R0}} \qquad \sigma^0_{LR} = \underbrace{-d^{(0)-1}_{RL}}_{k^0_{LR}}\Delta_R{}^0 + \underbrace{d^{(0)-1}_{RL}s^0_{RL}}_{k^0_{LL}}\Delta_L{}^0 + \underbrace{d^{(0)-1}_{RL}b_R{}^0}_{\sigma^0_{L0}} \tag{10.10}$$

where k^0_{RR}, k^0_{RL}, k^0_{LR}, k^0_{RR} are the segmental stiffness submatrices [3 × 3], the coefficients of which are the end stresses due to respective unit displacement, and σ_{R0}, σ_{L0} are the end stress matrices [3 × 1] of the fixed end bar due to loads and/or volume change.

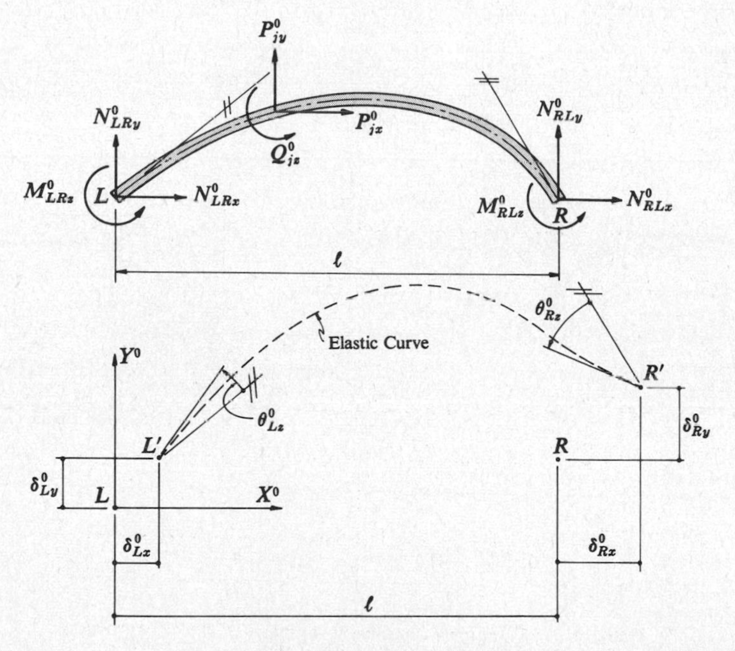

Fig. 10-2. Curved Bar

The assembly of (*10.10*) into one matrix equation leads to

$$\underbrace{\begin{bmatrix} \sigma^0_{RL} \\ \sigma^0_{LR} \end{bmatrix}}_{\sigma^0_{(LR)}} = \underbrace{\begin{bmatrix} k^0_{RR} & k^0_{RL} \\ k^0_{LR} & k^0_{LL} \end{bmatrix}}_{k^0_{(LR)}} \underbrace{\begin{bmatrix} \Delta_R{}^0 \\ \Delta_L{}^0 \end{bmatrix}}_{\Delta^0_{(LR)}} + \underbrace{\begin{bmatrix} \sigma^0_{R0} \\ \sigma^0_{L0} \end{bmatrix}}_{s^0_{(LR)}W^0_{(LR)}} \tag{10.11}$$

where $k^0_{(LR)}$ is the unit displacement segmental stiffness matrix, the coefficients of which are physically interpreted in Table 10-1. The load functions σ^0_{R0}, σ^0_{L0} are reactions of the fixed end bar.

Table 10-1. Segmental Stiffnesses, Curved Bar of Arbitrary Shape

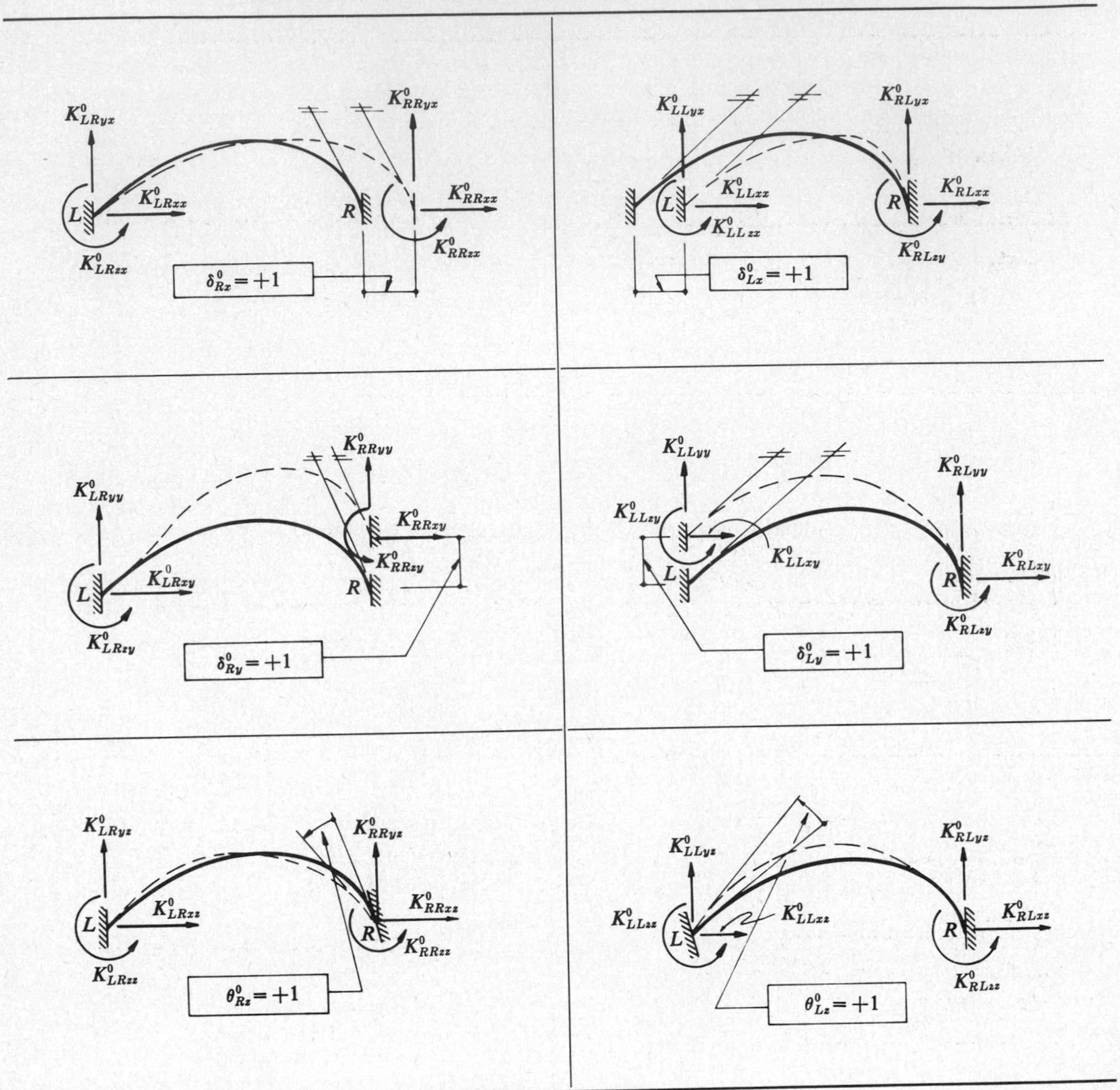

$\delta^0_{Rx} = +1$ $\delta^0_{Lx} = +1$

$\delta^0_{Ry} = +1$ $\delta^0_{Ly} = +1$

$\theta^0_{Rz} = +1$ $\theta^0_{Lz} = +1$

$$
k^0_{(LR)} = \left[\begin{array}{ccc|ccc}
K^0_{RRxx} & K^0_{RRxy} & K^0_{RRxz} & K^0_{RLxx} & K^0_{RLxy} & K^0_{RLxz} \\
K^0_{RRyx} & K^0_{RRyy} & K^0_{RRyz} & K^0_{RLyx} & K^0_{RLyy} & K^0_{RLyz} \\
K^0_{RRzx} & K^0_{RRzy} & K^0_{RRzz} & K^0_{RLzx} & K^0_{RLzy} & K^0_{RLzz} \\
\hline
K^0_{LRxx} & K^0_{LRxy} & K^0_{LRxz} & K^0_{LLxx} & K^0_{LLxy} & K^0_{LLxz} \\
K^0_{LRyx} & K^0_{LRyy} & K^0_{LRyz} & K^0_{LLyx} & K^0_{LLyy} & K^0_{LLyz} \\
K^0_{LRzx} & K^0_{LRzy} & K^0_{LRzz} & K^0_{LLzx} & K^0_{LLzy} & K^0_{LLzz}
\end{array}\right]
$$

Table 10-2. Segmental Stiffnesses, Straight Bar of Constant Cross Section

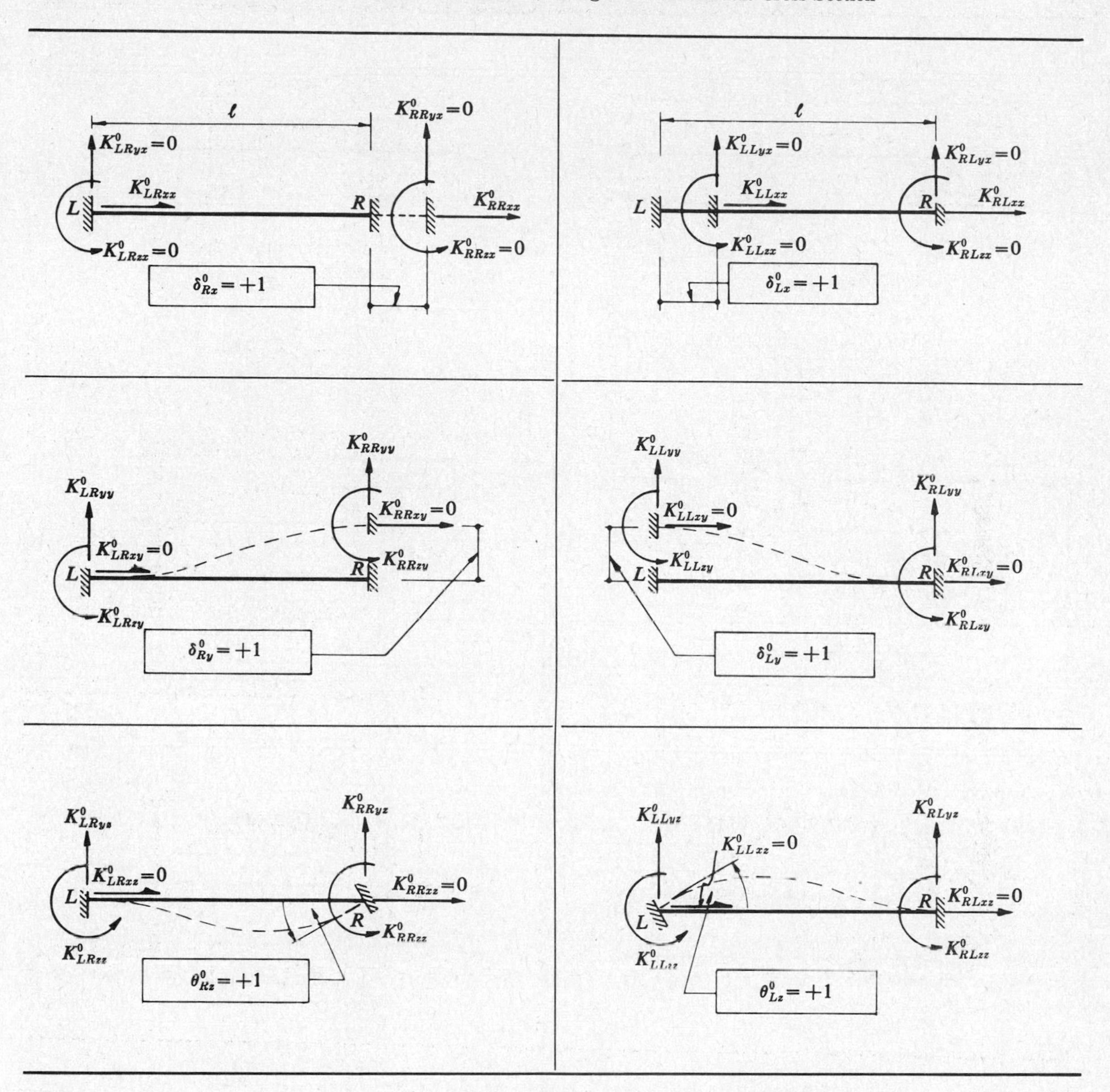

$$
k^0_{(LR)} = \left[\begin{array}{c|c|c|c|c|c}
\dfrac{EA}{l} & 0 & 0 & -\dfrac{EA}{l} & 0 & 0 \\ \hline
0 & \dfrac{12EI}{l^3} & -\dfrac{6EI}{l^2} & 0 & -\dfrac{12EI}{l^3} & -\dfrac{6EI}{l^2} \\ \hline
0 & -\dfrac{6EI}{l^2} & \dfrac{4EI}{l} & 0 & \dfrac{6EI}{l^2} & \dfrac{2EI}{l} \\ \hline
-\dfrac{EA}{l} & 0 & 0 & \dfrac{EA}{l} & 0 & 0 \\ \hline
0 & -\dfrac{12EI}{l^3} & \dfrac{6EI}{l^2} & 0 & \dfrac{12EI}{l^3} & \dfrac{6EI}{l^2} \\ \hline
0 & -\dfrac{6EI}{l^2} & \dfrac{2EI}{l} & 0 & \dfrac{6EI}{l^2} & \dfrac{4EI}{l}
\end{array}\right]
$$

Table 10-3. Fixed End Moments, Straight Bar of Constant Cross Section

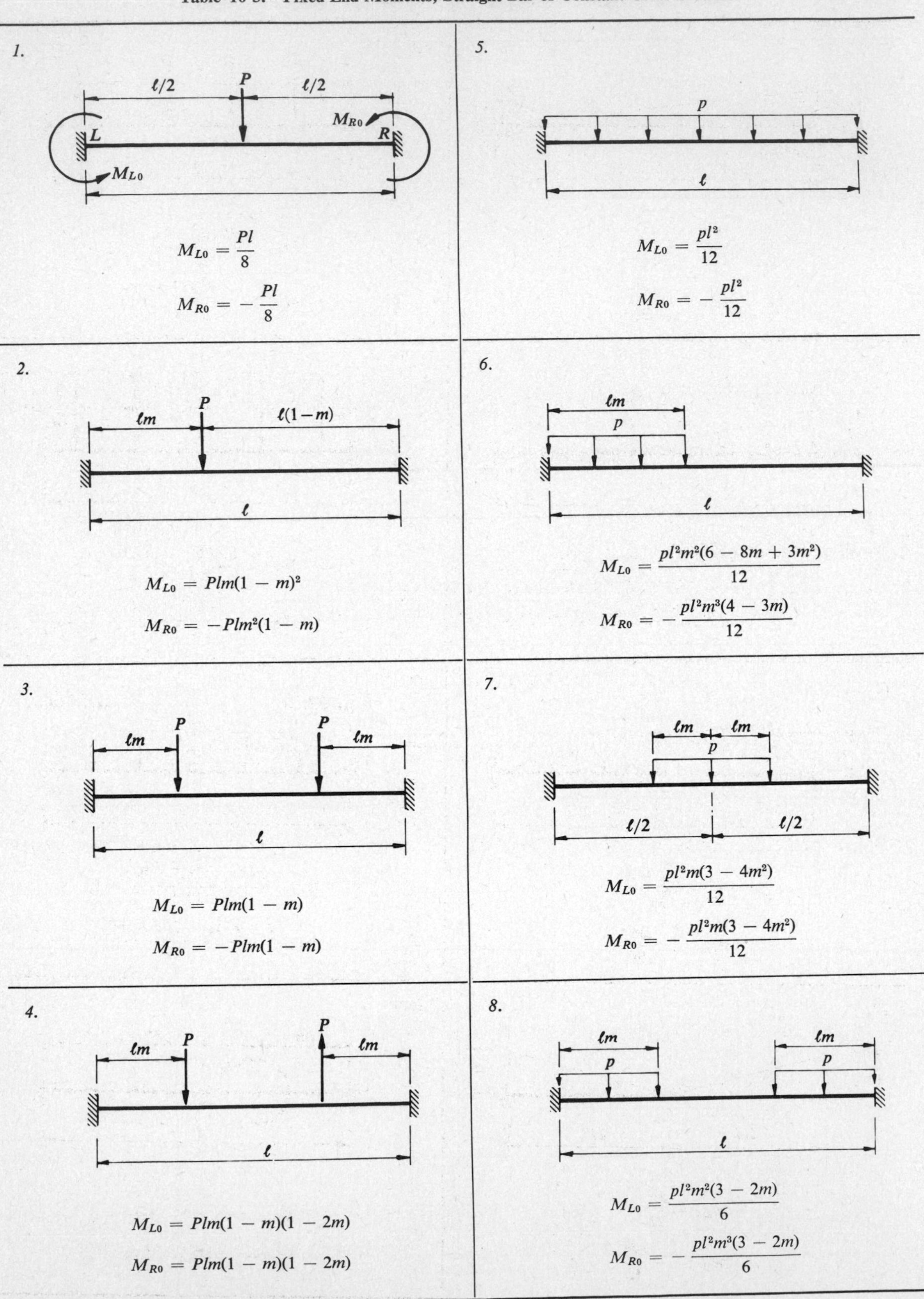

1.	$M_{L0} = \frac{Pl}{8}$	$M_{R0} = -\frac{Pl}{8}$
2.	$M_{L0} = Plm(1-m)^2$	$M_{R0} = -Plm^2(1-m)$
3.	$M_{L0} = Plm(1-m)$	$M_{R0} = -Plm(1-m)$
4.	$M_{L0} = Plm(1-m)(1-2m)$	$M_{R0} = Plm(1-m)(1-2m)$
5.	$M_{L0} = \frac{pl^2}{12}$	$M_{R0} = -\frac{pl^2}{12}$
6.	$M_{L0} = \frac{pl^2m^2(6-8m+3m^2)}{12}$	$M_{R0} = -\frac{pl^2m^3(4-3m)}{12}$
7.	$M_{L0} = \frac{pl^2m(3-4m^2)}{12}$	$M_{R0} = -\frac{pl^2m(3-4m^2)}{12}$
8.	$M_{L0} = \frac{pl^2m^2(3-2m)}{6}$	$M_{R0} = -\frac{pl^2m^3(3-2m)}{6}$

Table 10-3. (Cont'd.) Fixed End Moments, Straight Bar of Constant Cross Section

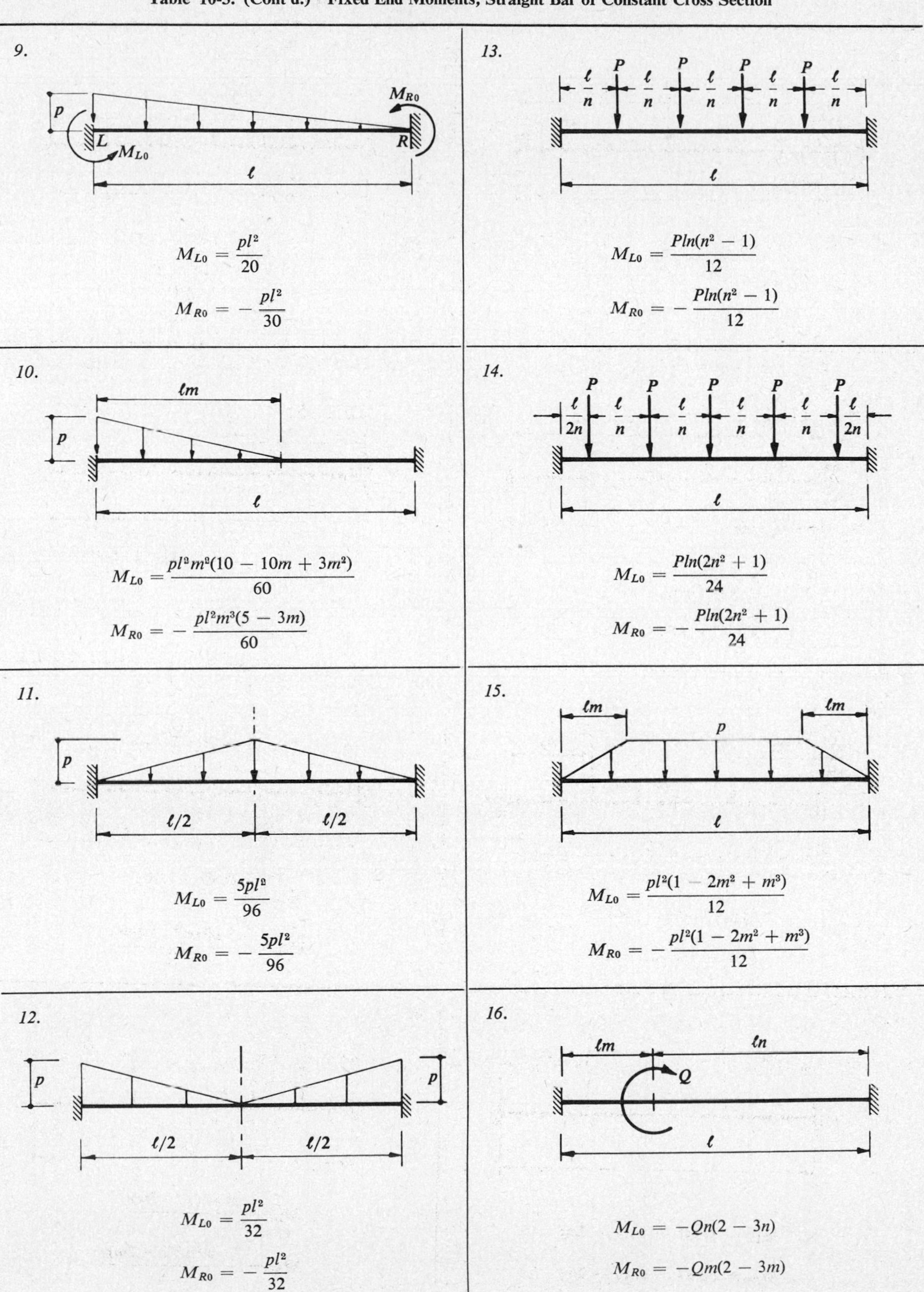

9.

$$M_{L0} = \frac{pl^2}{20}$$

$$M_{R0} = -\frac{pl^2}{30}$$

10.

$$M_{L0} = \frac{pl^2m^2(10 - 10m + 3m^2)}{60}$$

$$M_{R0} = -\frac{pl^2m^3(5 - 3m)}{60}$$

11.

$$M_{L0} = \frac{5pl^2}{96}$$

$$M_{R0} = -\frac{5pl^2}{96}$$

12.

$$M_{L0} = \frac{pl^2}{32}$$

$$M_{R0} = -\frac{pl^2}{32}$$

13.

$$M_{L0} = \frac{Pln(n^2 - 1)}{12}$$

$$M_{R0} = -\frac{Pln(n^2 - 1)}{12}$$

14.

$$M_{L0} = \frac{Pln(2n^2 + 1)}{24}$$

$$M_{R0} = -\frac{Pln(2n^2 + 1)}{24}$$

15.

$$M_{L0} = \frac{pl^2(1 - 2m^2 + m^3)}{12}$$

$$M_{R0} = -\frac{pl^2(1 - 2m^2 + m^3)}{12}$$

16.

$$M_{L0} = -Qn(2 - 3n)$$

$$M_{R0} = -Qm(2 - 3m)$$

Table 10-4. Influence Values M_{L0} and M_{R0}

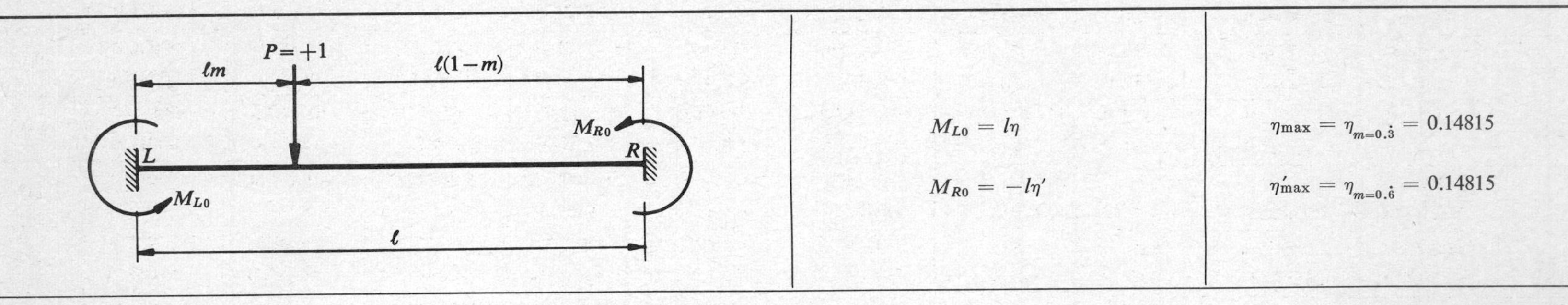

$$M_{L0} = l\eta \qquad M_{R0} = -l\eta'$$

$$\eta_{max} = \eta_{m=0.\dot{3}} = 0.14815 \qquad \eta'_{max} = \eta_{m=0.\dot{6}} = 0.14815$$

100 Point Table of Influence Values η and η'

m	0	1	2	3	4	5	6	7	8	9	m
0.0	0.00000 0.00000	0.00980 0.00010	0.01921 0.00039	0.02832 0.00087	0.03686 0.00154	0.04513 0.00237	0.05302 0.00338	0.06054 0.00456	0.06771 0.00589	0.07453 0.00737	0.0
0.1	0.08100 0.00900	0.08713 0.00977	0.09293 0.01267	0.09840 0.01470	0.10354 0.01686	0.10838 0.01912	0.11290 0.02150	0.11711 0.02399	0.12103 0.02657	0.12466 0.02924	0.1
0.2	0.12800 0.03200	0.13106 0.03484	0.13385 0.03775	0.13637 0.04073	0.13862 0.04378	0.04687 0.04687	0.14238 0.05003	0.14338 0.05322	0.14515 0.05645	0.14619 0.05971	0.2
0.3	0.14700 0.06300	0.14759 0.06630	0.14797 0.06960	0.14814 0.07296	0.14810 0.07630	0.14788 0.07962	0.14746 0.08294	0.14685 0.08625	0.14607 0.08953	0.14512 0.09278	0.3
0.4	0.14400 0.09600	0.14272 0.09918	0.14129 0.10231	0.13971 0.10539	0.13798 0.10842	0.13613 0.11137	0.13414 0.11426	0.13202 0.11708	0.12979 0.11981	0.12745 0.12245	0.4
0.5	0.12500 0.12500	0.12245 0.12745	0.11981 0.12979	0.11708 0.13202	0.11426 0.13414	0.11137 0.13616	0.10842 0.13798	0.10539 0.13971	0.10231 0.14129	0.09918 0.14272	0.5
0.6	0.09600 0.14400	0.09278 0.14512	0.08953 0.14607	0.08625 0.14685	0.08294 0.14746	0.07962 0.14788	0.07630 0.14810	0.07296 0.14814	0.06960 0.14797	0.06630 0.14759	0.6
0.7	0.06300 0.14700	0.05971 0.14619	0.05645 0.14515	0.05322 0.14388	0.05003 0.14328	0.04687 0.14063	0.04378 0.13862	0.04073 0.13637	0.03775 0.13385	0.03484 0.13106	0.7
0.8	0.03200 0.12800	0.02924 0.12466	0.02657 0.12103	0.02399 0.11711	0.02150 0.11290	0.01912 0.10838	0.01686 0.10354	0.01470 0.09840	0.01267 0.09293	0.00977 0.08713	0.8
0.9	0.00900 0.08100	0.00737 0.07453	0.00589 0.06771	0.00456 0.06054	0.00338 0.05302	0.00237 0.04513	0.00154 0.03686	0.00087 0.02832	0.00039 0.01921	0.00110 0.00980	0.9

Table 10-5. Influence Values M_{L0} and M_{R0}

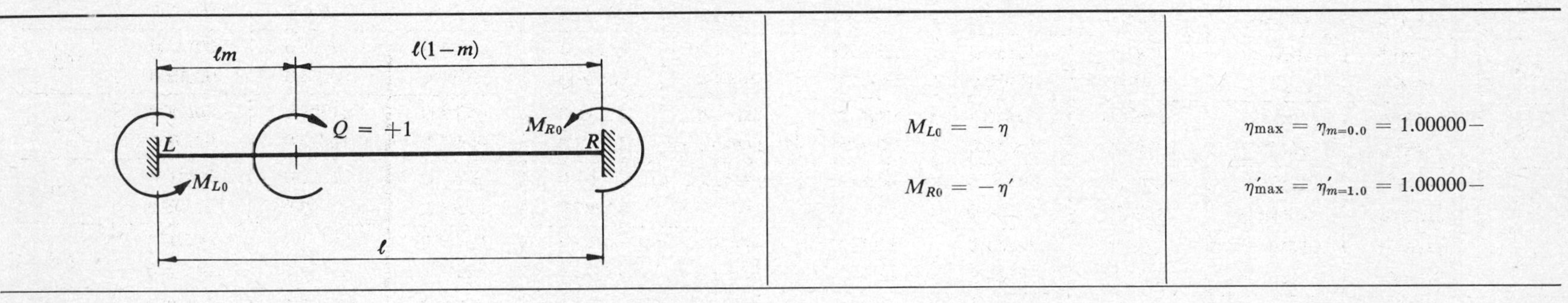

$M_{L0} = -\eta$

$M_{R0} = -\eta'$

$\eta_{max} = \eta_{m=0.0} = 1.00000-$

$\eta'_{max} = \eta'_{m=1.0} = 1.00000-$

100 Point Table of Influence Va ues Values η and η'

m	0	1	2	3	4	5	6	7	8	9	m
0.0	1.00000− 0.00000+	0.96030− 0.01970+	0.92120− 0.03880+	0.88270− 0.05730+	0.84480− 0.07520+	0.80750− 0.09250+	0.77080− 0.10920+	0.73470− 0.12530+	0.69920− 0.14080+	0.66430− 0.15570+	0.0
0.1	0.63000− 0.17000+	0.59630− 0.18370+	0.56320− 0.19680+	0.53070− 0.20930+	0.49880− 0.22120+	0.46750− 0.23250+	0.43680− 0.24320+	0.40670− 0.25330+	0.37720− 0.26280+	0.34830− 0.27170+	0.1
0.2	0.32000− 0.28000+	0.29230− 0.28770+	0.26520− 0.29480+	0.23870− 0.30130+	0.21280− 0.30720+	0.18750− 0.31250+	0.16280− 0.31720+	0.13870 − 0.32130+	0.11520− 0.32480+	0.09230− 0.32770+	0.2
0.3	0.07000− 0.33000+	0.04830− 0.33170+	0.02720− 0.33280+	0.00670− 0.33330+	0.01320+ 0.33320+	0.03250+ 0.33250+	0.05120+ 0.33120+	0.06930+ 0.32930+	0.08680+ 0.32680+	0.10370+ 0.32370+	0.3
0.4	0.12000+ 0.32000+	0.13570+ 0.31570+	0.15080+ 0.31080+	0.16530+ 0.30530+	0.17920+ 0.29920+	0.19250− 0.29250−	0.20520+ 0.28520+	0.21730+ 0.27730+	0.22880+ 0.26880+	0.23970+ 0.25970+	0.4
0.5	0.25000+ 0.25000+	0.25970+ 0.23970+	0.26880+ 0.22880+	0.27730+ 0.21730+	0.28520+ 0.20520+	0.29250+ 0.19250+	0.29920+ 0.17920+	0.30530+ 0.16530+	0.31080+ 0.15080+	0.31570+ 0.13570+	0.5
0 6	0.32000+ 0.12000+	0.32370+ 0.10370+	0.32680+ 0.08680+	0.32930+ 0.06930+	0.33120+ 0.05120+	0.33350+ 0.03250+	0.33320+ 0.01320+	0.33330+ 0.00670−	0.33280+ 0.02720−	0.33170+ 0.04830−	0.6
0.7	0.33000+ 0.07000−	0.32770+ 0.09230−	0.32480+ 0.11520−	0.32130+ 0.13870−	0.31720+ 0.16280−	0.31250+ 0.18750−	0.30720+ 0.21280−	0.30130+ 0.23870−	0.29480+ 0.26520−	0.28770+ 0.29230−	0.7
0.8	0.28000+ 0.32000−	0.27170+ 0.34830−	0.26280+ 0.37720−	0.25330+ 0.40670−	0.24320+ 0.43680−	0.23250+ 0.46750−	0.22120+ 0.49880−	0.20930+ 0.53070−	0.19680+ 0.56320−	0.18370+ 0.59630−	0 8
0.9	0.17000+ 0.63000−	0.15570+ 0.66430−	0.14080+ 0.69920−	0.12530+ 0.73470−	0.10920+ 0.77080−	0.09250+ 0.80750−	0.07520+ 0.84480−	0.05730+ 0.88270−	0.03880+ 0.92120−	0.01970+ 0.96030−	0.9

(b) Segmental Stiffnesses, Straight Bar of Constant Cross Section

If the axis of the bar is straight and the cross section is constant, the analytical expressions for the stiffness coefficients, introduced symbolically in Table 10-1, page 192, reduce to simple constants given in Table 10-2, page 193. Their physical interpretation is shown in the same table, where each unit displacement state corresponds to one column in the stiffness matrix $k_{(LR)}$ (Problem 10.1).

The load functions in (*10.11*) are the end stresses in the fixed end beam LR of Fig. 10-3, given as

$$\underbrace{\begin{bmatrix} N_{Rjx} \\ N_{Rjy} \\ M_{Rjz} \end{bmatrix}}_{\sigma_{Rj}} = \underbrace{\begin{bmatrix} -m & 0 & 0 \\ 0 & -m^2(1+2n) & -6mn/l \\ 0 & lm^2n & m(2-3m) \end{bmatrix}}_{s_{Rj}} \underbrace{\begin{bmatrix} P_{jx} \\ P_{jy} \\ Q_{jz} \end{bmatrix}}_{W_j}$$

$$\underbrace{\begin{bmatrix} N_{Ljx} \\ N_{Ljy} \\ M_{Ljz} \end{bmatrix}}_{\sigma_{Lj}} = \underbrace{\begin{bmatrix} -n & 0 & 0 \\ 0 & -n^2(1+2m) & 6mn/l \\ 0 & -lmn^2 & n(2-3n) \end{bmatrix}}_{s_{Lj}} \underbrace{\begin{bmatrix} P_{jx} \\ P_{jy} \\ Q_{jz} \end{bmatrix}}_{W_j}$$

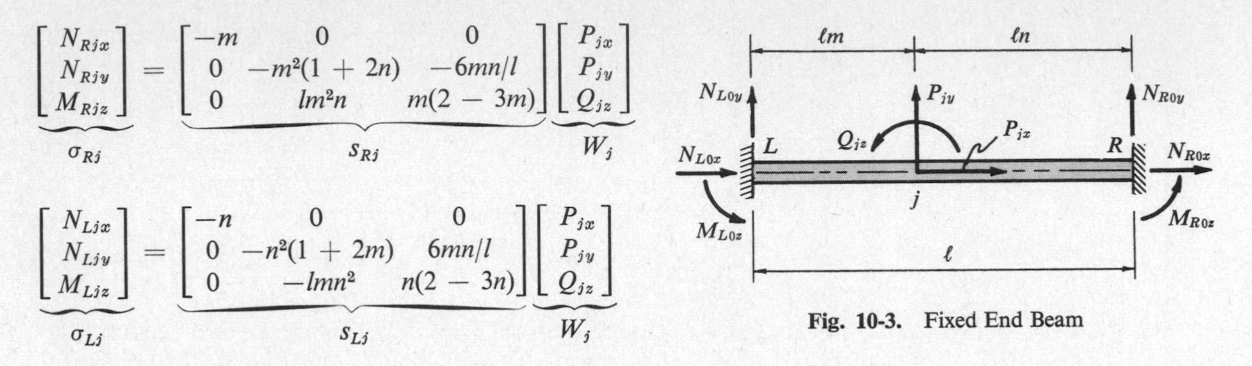

Fig. 10-3. Fixed End Beam

where s_{Rj} and s_{Lj} illustrate the meaning of unit load stiffnesses in (*10.2*) (Problem 10.2).

Similarly, the fixed end stresses due to temperature volume change are

$$\begin{bmatrix} N_{RTx} \\ N_{RTy} \\ M_{RTz} \end{bmatrix} = \begin{bmatrix} -\varepsilon_0 EA \\ 0 \\ -(\varepsilon_b - \varepsilon_t)\, EI/h \end{bmatrix}$$

$$\begin{bmatrix} N_{LTx} \\ N_{LTy} \\ M_{LTz} \end{bmatrix} = \begin{bmatrix} \varepsilon_0 EA \\ 0 \\ (\varepsilon_b - \varepsilon_t)\, EI/h \end{bmatrix}$$

where ϵ_b, ϵ_0, ϵ_t are thermal strains of the bottom, center and top of the cross section of depth. These strains are assumed to be positive, constant along l and linearly varying along h with $\epsilon_b > \epsilon_t$ (Problem 10.3).

Analytical expressions for fixed end moments due to particular load conditions are given in Table 10-3, pages 194-195. Influence lines for fixed end moments due to unit transverse force and unit couple are recorded in Tables 10-4, page 196, and 10-5, page 197, respectively.

10.6 GENERAL SEGMENTAL STIFFNESS MATRIX

A general case arises when the stresses and displacements at L and R are given in a specific system at each end (Fig. 10-4). Then (*4.2*) becomes a general state vector transport matrix and

$$\Delta_L{}^L = b_L{}^L + d_{LR}^{LR}\sigma_{RL}^R + s_{LR}^{LR}\Delta_R{}^R \qquad \Delta_R{}^R = b_R{}^R - d_{RL}^{RL}\sigma_{LR}^L + s_{RL}^{RL}\Delta_L{}^L \tag{10.12}$$

From these equations,

$$\sigma_{RL}^R = \underbrace{-d_{LR}^{LR)-1}s_{LR}^{LR}}_{k_{RR}^{RR}}\,\Delta_R{}^R + \underbrace{d_{LR}^{LR)-1}}_{k_{RL}^{RL}}\,\Delta_L{}^L \underbrace{-\,d_{LR}^{LR)-1}b_L{}^L}_{\sigma_{R0}^R}$$

$$\sigma_{LR}^L = \underbrace{-d_{RL}^{RL)-1}}_{k_{LR}^{LR}}\,\Delta_R{}^R + \underbrace{d_{RL}^{RL)-1}s_{RL}^{RL}}_{k_{LL}^{LL}}\,\Delta_L{}^L + \underbrace{d_{RL}^{RL)-1}b_R{}^R}_{\sigma_{L0}^L} \tag{10.13}$$

where k_{RR}^{RR}, k_{RL}^{RL}, k_{LR}^{LR}, k_{LL}^{LL} and σ_{R0}^{R}, σ_{L0}^{L} have the same meaning as their counterparts in (*10.10*), but are related to systems designated by their superscripts.

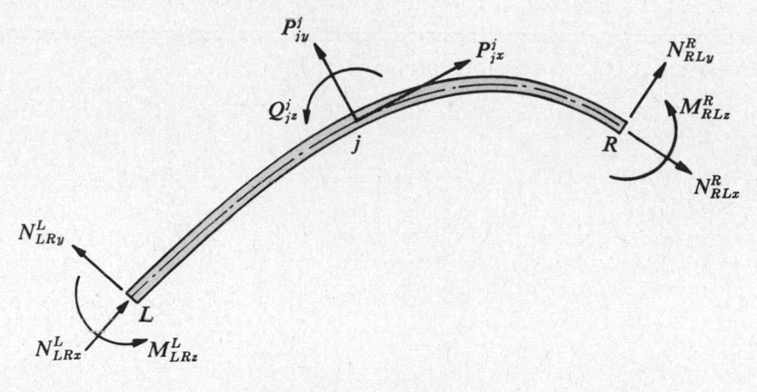

Fig. 10-4. Curved Bar

For the formulation of conditions of static equilibrium, the stress and displacement vectors must be transformed from their given systems to the reference system (to make possible the summation of stresses and also to express uniquely the unknown joint displacements). Thus

$$\sigma_{RL}^{0} = \underbrace{\omega^{0R}k_{RR}^{RR}\omega^{R0}}_{k_{RR}^{0}}\,\Delta_R^{\;0} + \underbrace{\omega^{0R}k_{RL}^{RL}\omega^{L0}}_{k_{RL}^{0}}\,\Delta_L^{\;0} + \underbrace{\omega^{0R}\sigma_{R0}^{R}}_{\sigma_{R0}^{0}}$$

$$\sigma_{LR}^{0} = \underbrace{\omega^{0L}k_{LR}^{LR}\omega^{R0}}_{k_{LR}^{0}}\,\Delta_R^{\;0} + \underbrace{\omega^{0L}k_{LL}^{LL}\omega^{L0}}_{k_{LL}^{0}}\,\Delta_L^{\;0} + \underbrace{\omega^{0L}\sigma_{L0}^{L}}_{\sigma_{L0}^{0}} \tag{10.14}$$

which can be written in matrix form as

$$\underbrace{\begin{bmatrix} \sigma_{RL}^{0} \\ \sigma_{LR}^{0} \end{bmatrix}}_{\sigma_{(LR)}^{0}} = \underbrace{\begin{bmatrix} \omega^{0R} & 0 \\ 0 & \omega^{0L} \end{bmatrix}}_{\pi^{0l}} \underbrace{\begin{bmatrix} k_{RR}^{RR} & k_{RL}^{RL} \\ k_{LR}^{LR} & k_{LL}^{LL} \end{bmatrix}}_{k_{(LR)}^{l}} \underbrace{\begin{bmatrix} \omega^{R0} & 0 \\ 0 & \omega^{L0} \end{bmatrix}}_{\pi^{l0}} \underbrace{\begin{bmatrix} \Delta_R^{\;0} \\ \Delta_L^{\;0} \end{bmatrix}}_{\Delta_{(LR)}^{0}} + \underbrace{\begin{bmatrix} \omega^{0R} & 0 \\ 0 & \omega^{0L} \end{bmatrix}}_{\pi^{0l}} \underbrace{\begin{bmatrix} \sigma_{R0}^{R} \\ \sigma_{L0}^{L} \end{bmatrix}}_{s_{(LR)}^{l}W_{(LR)}^{l}} \tag{10.15}$$

where π^{0l} and π^{l0} are the angular transport matrices furnishing the *congruent transformation*

$$k_{(LR)}^{0} = \pi^{0l}k_{(LR)}^{l}\pi^{l0} \tag{10.16}$$

and *preserving* the *symmetry* of the segmental stiffness matrix (Problem 10.4).

10.7 NEUTRAL POINT STIFFNESS MATRIX

For curved and bent bars of constant or variable cross section, the formulation of segmental stiffness matrices in terms of neutral point flexibilities offers some definite advantages. Considering the bar of Fig. 10-5*a* below and introducing positive support displacements $\Delta_R^{\;R}$ and $\Delta_L^{\;L}$ shown in Fig. 10-5*b*, the neutral point compatibility condition yields

$$\underbrace{-t_{RC}^{RC)T}\Delta_R^{\;R} + t_{LC}^{LC)T}\Delta_L^{\;L}}_{\Delta_C^{\;C}} = \underbrace{f_{CC}^{C}X_C^{\;C}}_{\Delta_{CX}^{C}} + \underbrace{l_{CC}^{C}W^C}_{\Delta_{CW}^{C}}$$

where $\Delta_C^{\;C}$ is the continuity gap at C created by $\Delta_R^{\;R}$ and $\Delta_L^{\;L}$.

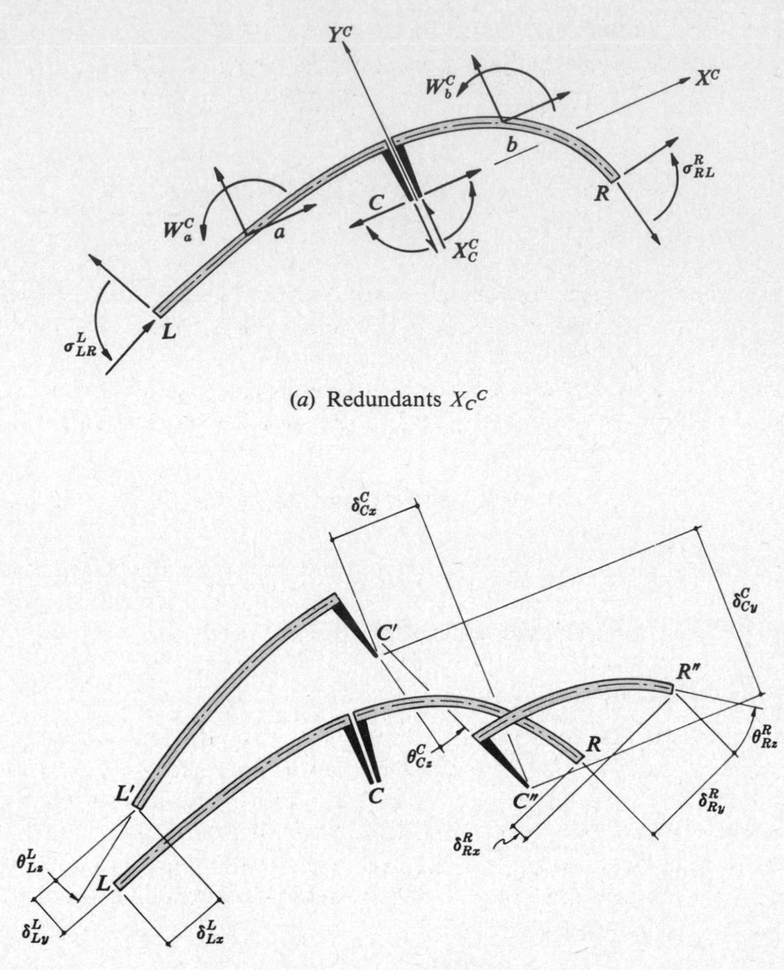

(*a*) Redundants $X_C{}^C$

(*b*) Rigid Body Motion $\Delta_L{}^L$, $\Delta_R{}^R$

Fig. 10-5. Neutral Point, Curved Bar

From this condition,

$$X_C{}^C = \underbrace{-f_{CC}^{C)-1} t_{RC}^{RC)T}}_{k_{CR}^{CR}} \Delta_R{}^R + \underbrace{f_{CC}^{C)-1} t_{LC}^{LC)T}}_{k_{CL}^{CL}} \Delta_L{}^L \underbrace{- f_{CC}^{C)-1} l_{CC}^{C} W^C}_{\sigma_{C0}^{C}} \tag{10.17}$$

where k_{CR}^{CR}, k_{CL}^{CL} are the neutral point stiffnesses due to unit displacement vector at R and L respectively and σ_{C0}^C are the neutral point stresses due to loads when $\Delta_R{}^R = \Delta_L{}^L = 0$.

10.8 GENERAL SLOPE-DEFLECTION EQUATION

The end stresses at R and L are obtained by transferring the effect of redundants and loads to the respective end. Thus by (*10.17*) and (*2.12*),

$$\begin{aligned} \sigma_{RL}^R &= \underbrace{t_{RC}^{RC} f_{CC}^{C)-1} t_{RC}^{RC)T}}_{k_{RR}^{RR}} \Delta_R{}^R - \underbrace{t_{RC}^{RC} f_{CC}^{C)-1} t_{LC}^{LC)T}}_{k_{RL}^{RL}} \Delta_L{}^L + \underbrace{t_{RC}^{RC} f_{CC}^{C)-1} l_{CC}^{C} W^C - t_{Rb}^{RC} W_b{}^C}_{\sigma_{R0}^R} \\ \sigma_{LR}^L &= \underbrace{-t_{LC}^{LC} f_{CC}^{C)-1} t_{RC}^{RC)T}}_{k_{LR}^{LR}} \Delta_R{}^R + \underbrace{t_{LC}^{LC} f_{CC}^{C)-1} t_{LC}^{LC)T}}_{k_{LL}^{LL}} \Delta_L{}^L \underbrace{- t_{LC}^{LC} f_{CC}^{C)-1} l_{CC}^{C} W^C - t_{La}^{LC} W_a{}^C}_{\sigma_{L0}^L} \end{aligned} \tag{10.18}$$

or

$$
\begin{aligned}
\sigma^{0}_{RL} &= \underbrace{\omega^{0R}k^{RR}_{RR}\omega^{R0}}_{k^{0}_{RR}}\,\Delta_{R}{}^{0} + \underbrace{\omega^{0R}k^{RL}_{RL}\omega^{L0}}_{k^{0}_{RL}}\,\Delta_{L}{}^{0} + \underbrace{\omega^{0R}\sigma^{R}_{R0}}_{\sigma^{0}_{R0}} \\
\sigma^{0}_{LR} &= \underbrace{\omega^{0L}k^{LR}\omega^{R0}}_{k^{0}_{LR}}\,\Delta_{R}{}^{0} + \underbrace{\omega^{0L}k^{LL}_{LL}\omega^{L0}}_{k^{0}_{LL}}\,\Delta_{L}{}^{0} + \underbrace{\omega^{0L}\sigma^{L}_{L0}}_{\sigma^{0}_{L0}}
\end{aligned}
\tag{10.19}
$$

where the last set of equations is stated in the reference system. The consistent correspondence of superscripts and subscripts offers continuous control and facilitates the symbolic writing of these transformations.

The algebraic construction of the near end stiffness matrices k^{RR}_{RR}, k^{LL}_{LL} and of the far end stiffness matrices k^{RL}_{RL}, k^{LR}_{LR} is greatly simplified, if prepared as shown in Tables 10-6 and 10-7 where

$$
\begin{aligned}
f^{C}_{Cxx} &= \int_{L}^{R} [\lambda_{sxx} + y^{2}\lambda_{szz}] = \bar{I}^{C}_{Cxx} \cong \int_{L}^{R} \frac{y^{2}\,ds}{EI} \\
f^{C}_{Cyy} &= \int_{L}^{R} [\lambda_{syy} + x^{2}\lambda_{szz}] = \bar{I}^{C}_{Cyy} \cong \int_{L}^{R} \frac{x^{2}\,ds}{EI} \\
f^{C}_{Czz} &= \int_{L}^{R} \lambda_{szz} \qquad\qquad\quad = \bar{A}^{C}_{Czz} \cong \int_{L}^{R} \frac{ds}{EI}
\end{aligned}
\tag{10.20}
$$

are the principal flexibilities at the neutral point known as the principal functions of the elastic area (Problem 10.5). The load functions σ^{R}_{R0} and σ^{L}_{L0} are the fixed end stresses due to loads and/or other causes (taking particular analytical form in each case). Segmental stiffness coefficients and fixed end stresses for the most common types of bars are given in Tables 10-8 to 10-15.

Equations (*10.13*) and (*10.14*) derived by (*4.2*), and their counterparts (*10.18*) and (*10.19*) derived by (*10.17*) and (*2.12*), represent identical relationships respectively known as the *general slope-deflection equations.*

Table 10-6. Segmental Stiffnesses in Terms of Elastic Area Functions, Unsymmetrical Bar

(*a*) *Component Matrices:*

$$
\underbrace{\begin{bmatrix} \cos\omega_{RC} & -\sin\omega_{RC} & 0 \\ \sin\omega_{RC} & \cos\omega_{RC} & 0 \\ 0 & 0 & 1 \end{bmatrix}}_{\omega^{RC}}
\underbrace{\begin{bmatrix} 1 & 0 & 0 \\ 0 & 1 & 0 \\ -y^{C}_{RC} & x^{C}_{RC} & 1 \end{bmatrix}}_{r^{C}_{RC}}
\underbrace{\begin{bmatrix} \frac{1}{\bar{I}^{C}_{Cxx}} & & \\ & \frac{1}{\bar{I}^{C}_{Cyy}} & \\ & & \frac{1}{\bar{A}^{C}_{Czz}} \end{bmatrix}}_{f^{C)-1}_{CC}}
\underbrace{\begin{bmatrix} 1 & 0 & 0 \\ 0 & 1 & 0 \\ -y^{C}_{LC} & x^{C}_{LC} & 1 \end{bmatrix}}_{r^{C}_{LC}}
\underbrace{\begin{bmatrix} \cos\omega_{LC} & -\sin\omega_{LC} & 0 \\ \sin\omega_{LC} & \cos\omega_{LC} & 0 \\ 0 & 0 & 1 \end{bmatrix}}_{\omega^{LC}}
$$

(*b*) *Matrix Products:*

$$
k^{RR}_{RR} = \underbrace{\omega^{RC}\,r^{C}_{RC}}_{t^{RC}_{RC}}\,f^{C)-1}_{CC}\,\underbrace{r^{C)T}_{RC}\,\omega^{RC)T}}_{t^{RC)T}_{RC}}
\qquad
k^{RL}_{RL} = \underbrace{-\omega^{RC}\,r^{C}_{RC}}_{-t^{RC}_{RC}}\,f^{C)-1}_{CC}\,\underbrace{r^{C)T}_{LC}\,\omega^{LC)T}}_{t^{LC)T}_{LC}}
$$

$$
k^{LR}_{LR} = \underbrace{-\omega^{LC}\,r^{C}_{LC}}_{-t^{LC}_{LC}}\,f^{C)-1}_{CC}\,\underbrace{r^{C)T}_{RC}\,\omega^{RC)T}}_{t^{RC)T}_{RC}}
\qquad
k^{LL}_{LL} = \underbrace{\omega^{LC}\,r^{C}_{LC}}_{t^{LC}_{LC}}\,f^{C)-1}_{CC}\,\underbrace{r^{C)T}_{LC}\,\omega^{LC)T}}_{t^{LC)T}_{LC}}
$$

Note: Positive angles ω_{RL} and ω_{LC} are measured counterclockwise from *R*- and *L*-Systems to *C*-System respectively.

Table 10-7. Segmental Stiffnesses in Terms of Elastic Area Functions, Symmetrical Bar

	$\delta^C_{Rx} = +1$	$\delta^C_{Ry} = +1$	$\theta^C_{Rz} = +1$	$\delta^C_{Lx} = +1$	$\delta^C_{Ly} = +1$	$\theta^C_{Lz} = +1$
N^C_{Rx}	$\dfrac{1}{\bar I_{Cxx}}$	0	$-\dfrac{\bar y}{\bar I_{Cxx}}$	$-\dfrac{1}{\bar I_{Cxx}}$	0	$\dfrac{\bar y}{\bar I_{Cxx}}$
N^C_{Ry}	0	$\dfrac{1}{\bar I_{Cyy}}$	$-\dfrac{\bar x}{\bar I_{Cyy}}$	0	$-\dfrac{1}{\bar I_{Cyy}}$	$-\dfrac{\bar x}{\bar I_{Cyy}}$
M^C_{Rz}	$-\dfrac{\bar y}{\bar I_{Cxx}}$	$-\dfrac{\bar x}{\bar I_{Cyy}}$	$\dfrac{1}{\bar A_{Czz}} + \dfrac{\bar y^2}{\bar I_{Cxx}} + \dfrac{\bar x^2}{\bar I_{Cyy}}$	$\dfrac{\bar y}{\bar I_{Cxx}}$	$\dfrac{\bar x}{\bar I_{Cyy}}$	$-\dfrac{1}{\bar A_{Czz}} - \dfrac{\bar y^2}{\bar I_{Cxx}} + \dfrac{\bar x^2}{\bar I_{Cyy}}$
N^C_{Lx}	$-\dfrac{1}{\bar I_{Cxx}}$	0	$\dfrac{\bar y}{\bar I_{Cxx}}$	$\dfrac{1}{\bar I_{Cxx}}$	0	$-\dfrac{\bar y}{\bar I_{Cxx}}$
N^C_{Ly}	0	$-\dfrac{1}{\bar I_{Cyy}}$	$\dfrac{\bar x}{\bar I_{Cyy}}$	0	$\dfrac{1}{\bar I_{Cyy}}$	$\dfrac{\bar x}{\bar I_{Cyy}}$
M^C_{Lz}	$\dfrac{y}{\bar I_{Cxx}}$	$-\dfrac{\bar x}{\bar I_{Cyy}}$	$-\dfrac{1}{\bar A_{Czz}} - \dfrac{\bar y^2}{\bar I_{Cxx}} + \dfrac{\bar x^2}{\bar I_{Cyy}}$	$-\dfrac{\bar y}{\bar I_{Cxx}}$	$\dfrac{\bar x}{\bar I_{Cyy}}$	$\dfrac{1}{\bar A_{Czz}} + \dfrac{\bar y^2}{\bar I_{Cxx}} + \dfrac{\bar x^2}{\bar I_{Cyy}}$

Note: $\bar x = x^C_{LC}$, $\bar y = y^C_{LC}$; for $\bar I_{Cxx}$, $\bar I_{Cyy}$, $\bar A_{Czz}$, refer to (*10.20*). The superscript C is omitted in all terms.

Table 10-8. Segmental Stiffnesses, Symmetrical Bent Bar of Constant Cross Section

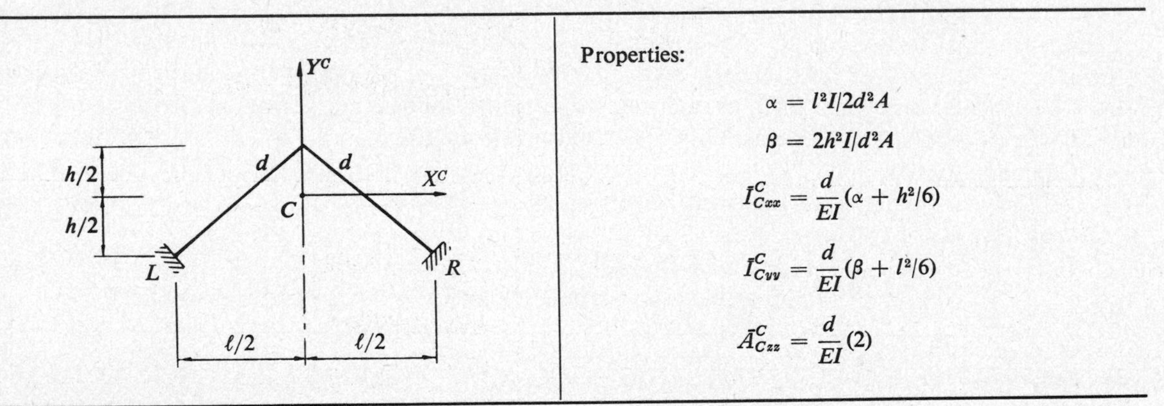

Properties:

$$\alpha = l^2 I/2d^2 A$$

$$\beta = 2h^2 I/d^2 A$$

$$\bar I^C_{Cxx} = \frac{d}{EI}(\alpha + h^2/6)$$

$$\bar I^C_{Cyy} = \frac{d}{EI}(\beta + l^2/6)$$

$$\bar A^C_{Czz} = \frac{d}{EI}(2)$$

Right End Stiffnesses ($\alpha \cong 0$, $\beta \cong 0$):

$$\frac{EI}{d}\Bigg[\underbrace{\begin{array}{c|c|c} 6/h^2 & 0 & -3/h \\ \hline 0 & 6/l^2 & -3/l \\ \hline -3/h & -3/l & 7/2 \end{array}}_{k^C_{RR}} \;\Bigg|\; \underbrace{\begin{array}{c|c|c} -6/h^2 & 0 & 3/h \\ \hline 0 & -6/l^2 & -3/l \\ \hline 3/h & 3/l & -1/2 \end{array}}_{k^C_{RL}}\Bigg]$$

Left End Stiffnesses ($\alpha \cong 0$, $\beta \cong 0$):

$$\frac{EI}{d}\Bigg[\underbrace{\begin{array}{c|c|c} -6/h^2 & 0 & 3/h \\ \hline 0 & -6/l^2 & 3/l \\ \hline 3/h & -3/l & -1/2 \end{array}}_{k^L_{LR}} \;\Bigg|\; \underbrace{\begin{array}{c|c|c} 6/h^2 & 0 & -3/h \\ \hline 0 & 6/l^2 & 3/l \\ \hline -3/h & 3/l & 7/3 \end{array}}_{k^C_{LL}}\Bigg]$$

Table 10-9. Fixed End Stresses, Symmetrical Bent Bar of Constant Cross Section ($\alpha \simeq 0, \beta \simeq 0$)

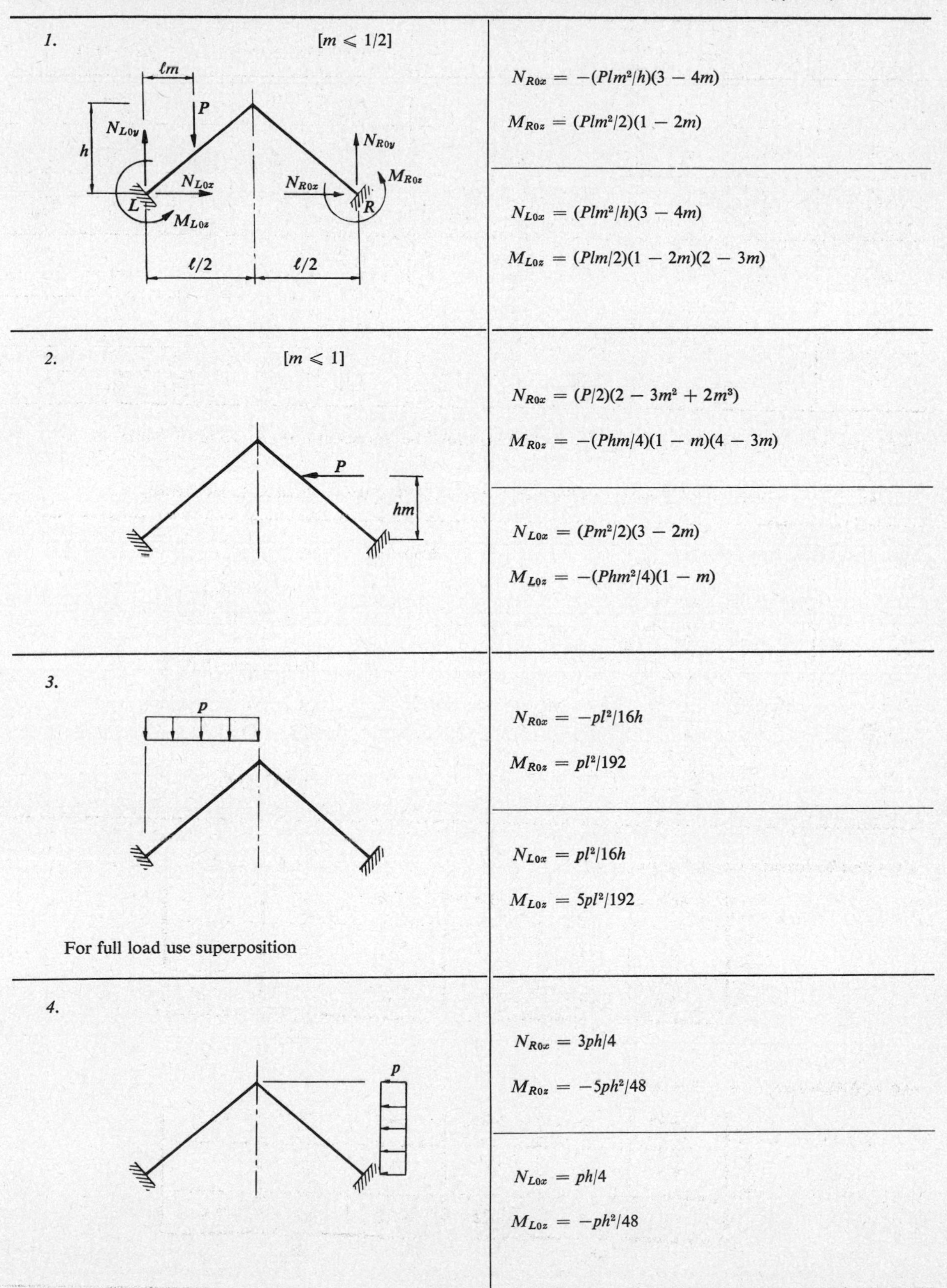

Case	Fixed end stresses
1. $[m \leqslant 1/2]$	$N_{R0x} = -(Plm^2/h)(3 - 4m)$ $M_{R0z} = (Plm^2/2)(1 - 2m)$ $N_{L0x} = (Plm^2/h)(3 - 4m)$ $M_{L0z} = (Plm/2)(1 - 2m)(2 - 3m)$
2. $[m \leqslant 1]$	$N_{R0x} = (P/2)(2 - 3m^2 + 2m^3)$ $M_{R0z} = -(Phm/4)(1 - m)(4 - 3m)$ $N_{L0x} = (Pm^2/2)(3 - 2m)$ $M_{L0z} = -(Phm^2/4)(1 - m)$
3. For full load use superposition	$N_{R0x} = -pl^2/16h$ $M_{R0z} = pl^2/192$ $N_{L0x} = pl^2/16h$ $M_{L0z} = 5pl^2/192$
4.	$N_{R0x} = 3ph/4$ $M_{R0z} = -5ph^2/48$ $N_{L0x} = ph/4$ $M_{L0z} = -ph^2/48$

Table 10-10. Segmental Stiffnesses, Symmetrical Parabolic Bar of Variable Cross Section

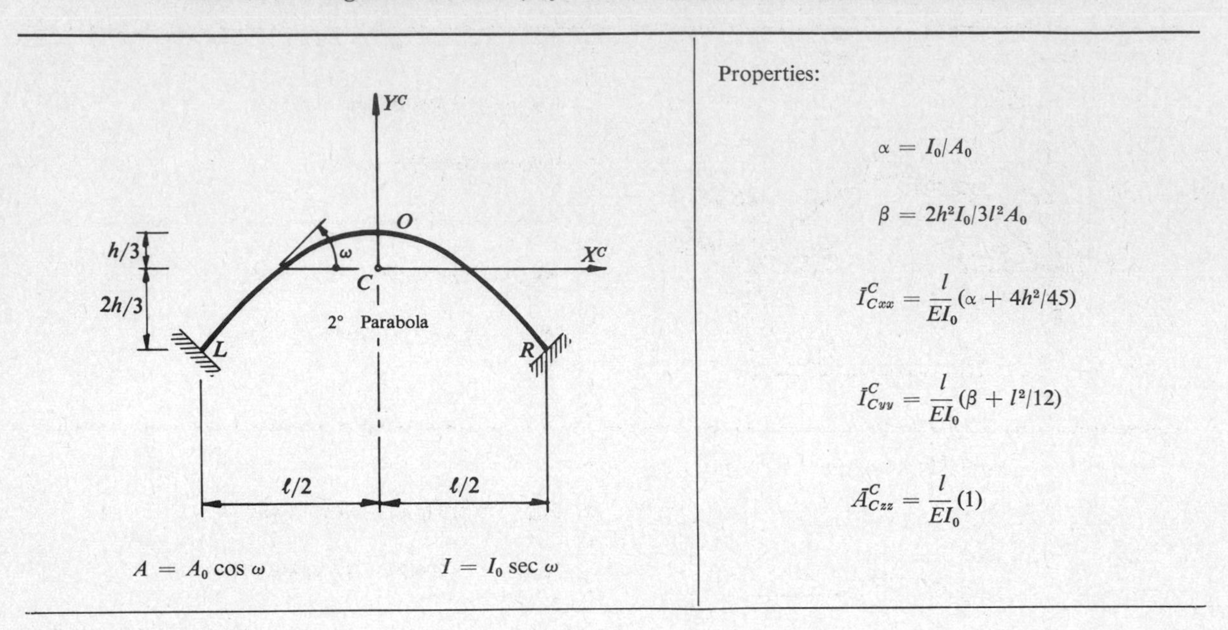

Properties:

$$\alpha = I_0/A_0$$

$$\beta = 2h^2 I_0/3l^2 A_0$$

$$\bar{I}^C_{Cxx} = \frac{l}{EI_0}(\alpha + 4h^2/45)$$

$$\bar{I}^C_{Cyy} = \frac{l}{EI_0}(\beta + l^2/12)$$

$$\bar{A}^C_{Czz} = \frac{l}{EI_0}(1)$$

$A = A_0 \cos \omega$ $\quad$ $I = I_0 \sec \omega$

Right End Stiffnesses ($\alpha \cong 0, \beta \cong 0$):

$$\frac{EI}{l}\Bigg[\underbrace{\begin{array}{c|c|c} 45/4h^2 & 0 & -15/2h \\ \hline 0 & 12/l^2 & -6/l \\ \hline -15/2h & -6/l & 9 \end{array}}_{k^C_{RR}} \Bigg| \underbrace{\begin{array}{c|c|c} -45/2h & 0 & 15/2h \\ \hline 0 & -12/l^2 & -6/l \\ \hline 15/2h & 6/l & -3 \end{array}}_{k^C_{RL}}\Bigg]$$

Left End Stiffnesses ($\alpha \cong 0, \beta \cong 0$):

$$\frac{EI}{l}\Bigg[\underbrace{\begin{array}{c|c|c} -45/4h^2 & 0 & 15/2h \\ \hline 0 & -12/l^2 & 6/l \\ \hline 15/2h & -6/l & -3 \end{array}}_{k^C_{LR}} \Bigg| \underbrace{\begin{array}{c|c|c} 45/4h^2 & 0 & -15/2h \\ \hline 0 & 12/l^2 & 6/l \\ \hline -15/2h & 6/l & 9 \end{array}}_{k^C_{LL}}\Bigg]$$

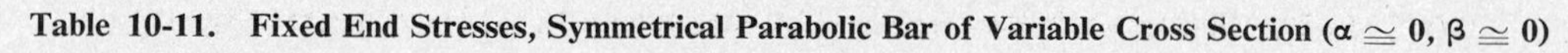

Table 10-11. Fixed End Stresses, Symmetrical Parabolic Bar of Variable Cross Section ($\alpha \simeq 0$, $\beta \simeq 0$)

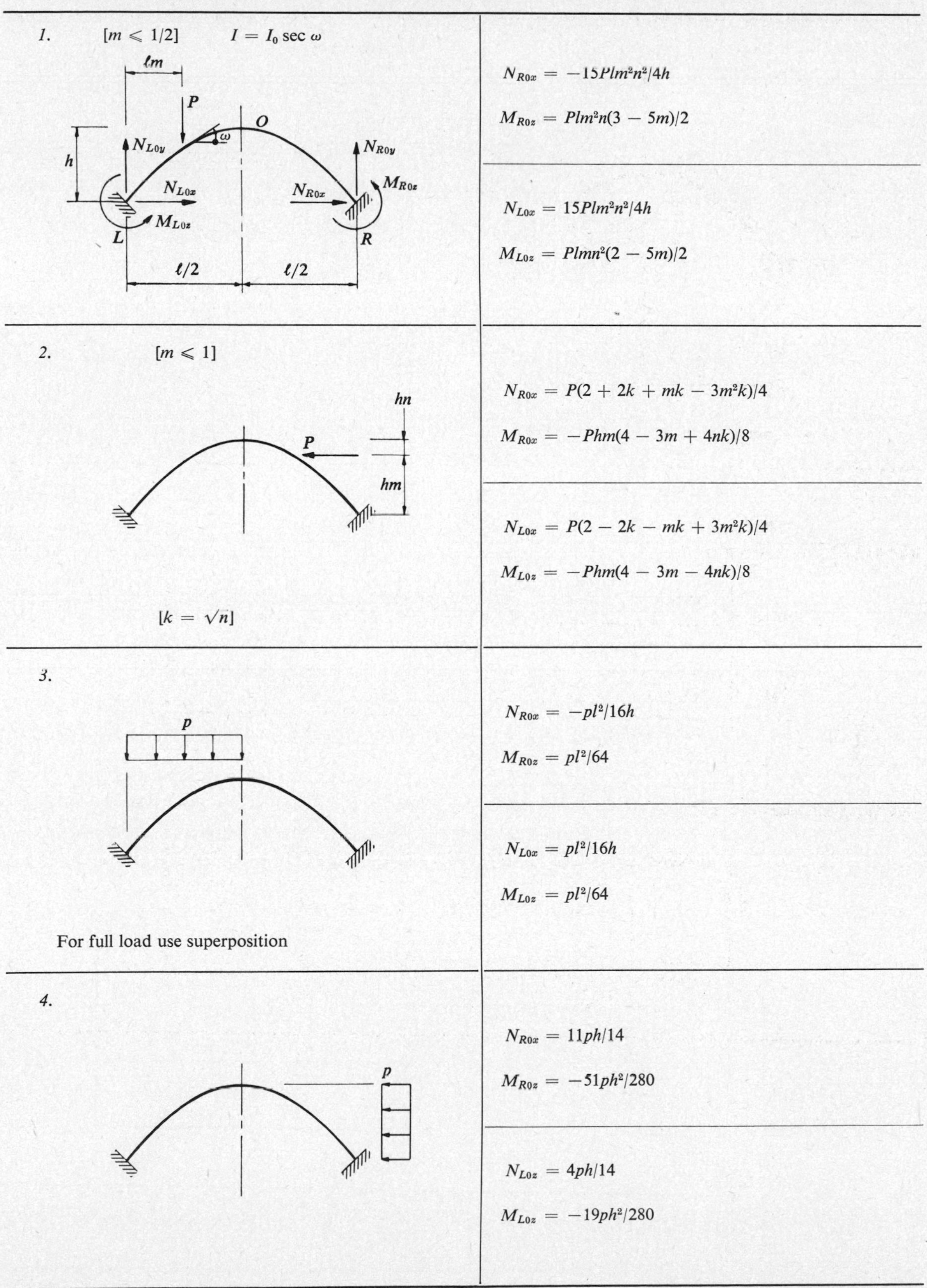

Case	Fixed end stresses
1. $[m \leqslant 1/2]$ $I = I_0 \sec \omega$	$N_{R0x} = -15Plm^2n^2/4h$ $M_{R0z} = Plm^2n(3 - 5m)/2$ $N_{L0x} = 15Plm^2n^2/4h$ $M_{L0z} = Plmn^2(2 - 5m)/2$
2. $[m \leqslant 1]$ $[k = \sqrt{n}]$	$N_{R0x} = P(2 + 2k + mk - 3m^2k)/4$ $M_{R0z} = -Phm(4 - 3m + 4nk)/8$ $N_{L0x} = P(2 - 2k - mk + 3m^2k)/4$ $M_{L0z} = -Phm(4 - 3m - 4nk)/8$
3. For full load use superposition	$N_{R0x} = -pl^2/16h$ $M_{R0z} = pl^2/64$ $N_{L0x} = pl^2/16h$ $M_{L0z} = pl^2/64$
4.	$N_{R0x} = 11ph/14$ $M_{R0z} = -51ph^2/280$ $N_{L0x} = 4ph/14$ $M_{L0z} = -19ph^2/280$

Table 10-12. Segmental Stiffnesses, Symmetrical Circular Bar of Constant Cross Section

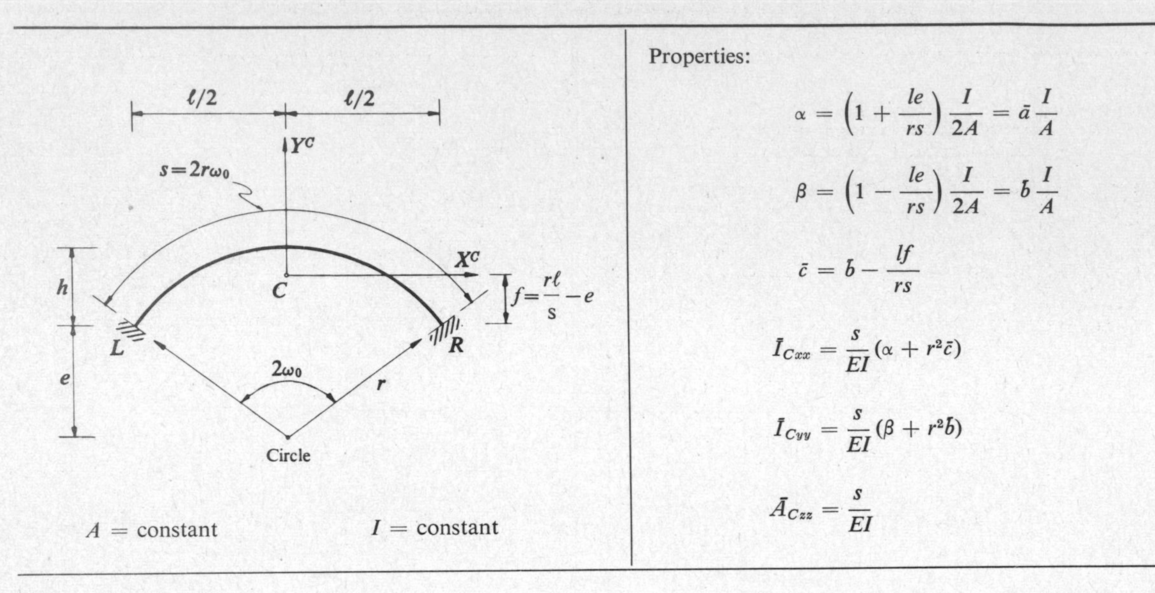

Properties:

$$\alpha = \left(1 + \frac{le}{rs}\right)\frac{I}{2A} = \bar{a}\,\frac{I}{A}$$

$$\beta = \left(1 - \frac{le}{rs}\right)\frac{I}{2A} = \bar{b}\,\frac{I}{A}$$

$$\bar{c} = \bar{b} - \frac{lf}{rs}$$

$$\bar{I}_{Cxx} = \frac{s}{EI}(\alpha + r^2\bar{c})$$

$$\bar{I}_{Cyy} = \frac{s}{EI}(\beta + r^2\bar{b})$$

$$\bar{A}_{Czz} = \frac{s}{EI}$$

Right End Stiffnesses ($\alpha \cong 0, \beta \cong 0$):

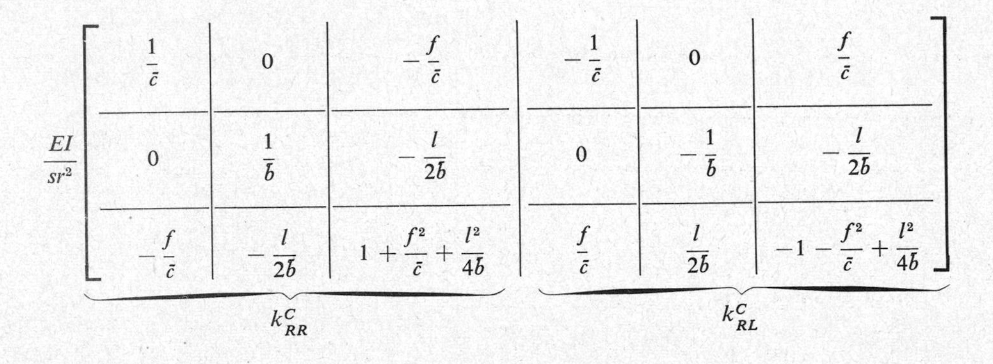

$$\frac{EI}{sr^2}\underbrace{\left[\begin{array}{ccc|ccc} \frac{1}{\bar{c}} & 0 & -\frac{f}{\bar{c}} & -\frac{1}{\bar{c}} & 0 & \frac{f}{\bar{c}} \\ 0 & \frac{1}{\bar{b}} & -\frac{l}{2\bar{b}} & 0 & -\frac{1}{\bar{b}} & -\frac{l}{2\bar{b}} \\ -\frac{f}{\bar{c}} & -\frac{l}{2\bar{b}} & 1+\frac{f^2}{\bar{c}}+\frac{l^2}{4\bar{b}} & \frac{f}{\bar{c}} & \frac{l}{2\bar{b}} & -1-\frac{f^2}{\bar{c}}+\frac{l^2}{4\bar{b}} \end{array}\right]}_{k^C_{RR}\qquad\qquad k^C_{RL}}$$

Left End Stiffnesses ($\alpha \cong 0, \beta \cong 0$):

$$\frac{EI}{sr^2}\underbrace{\left[\begin{array}{ccc|ccc} -\frac{1}{\bar{c}} & 0 & \frac{f}{\bar{c}} & \frac{1}{\bar{c}} & 0 & -\frac{f}{\bar{c}} \\ 0 & -\frac{1}{\bar{b}} & \frac{l}{2\bar{b}} & 0 & \frac{1}{\bar{b}} & \frac{l}{2\bar{b}} \\ \frac{f}{\bar{c}} & -\frac{l}{2\bar{b}} & -1-\frac{f^2}{\bar{c}}+\frac{l^2}{4\bar{b}} & -\frac{f}{\bar{c}} & \frac{l}{2\bar{b}} & 1+\frac{f^2}{\bar{c}}+\frac{l^2}{4\bar{b}} \end{array}\right]}_{k^C_{LR}\qquad\qquad k^C_{LL}}$$

Table 10-13. Fixed End Stresses, Uniformly Distributed Load
Symmetrical Circular Bar of Constant Cross Section ($\alpha \simeq 0$, $\beta \simeq 0$)

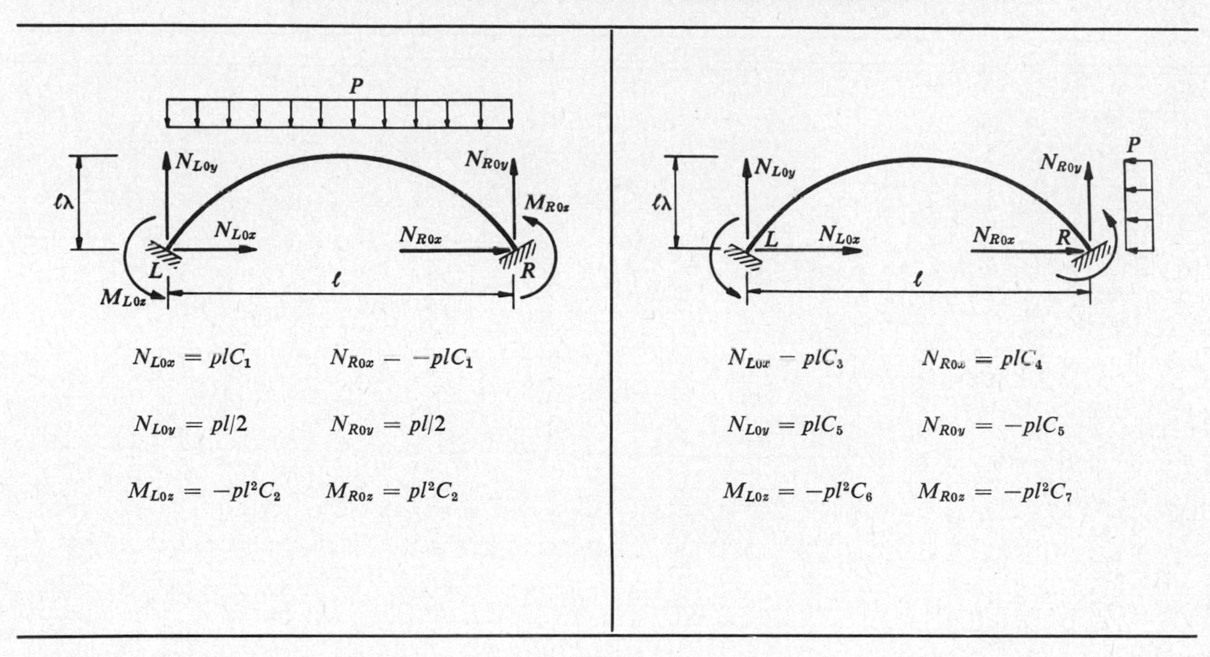

Stress Coefficients*

λ	C_1	C_2	C_3	C_4	C_5	C_6	C_7	λ
0.10	1.2584	0.001,230	0.021,43	0.078,57	0.002,480	0.000,689	0.001,831	0.10
0.12	1.0507	0.001,680	0.025,67	0.094,33	0.003,559	0.000,994	0.002,647	0.12
0.14	0.9027	0.002,224	0.030,10	0.109,90	0.004,825	0.001,377	0.003,598	0.14
0.16	0.7924	0.002,898	0.034,44	0.125,56	0.006,274	0.001,817	0.004,709	0.16
0.18	0.7069	0.003,659	0.038,75	0.141,25	0.007,899	0.002,320	0.005,981	0.18
0.20	0.6388	0.004,507	0.043,11	0.156,89	0.009,696	0.002,900	0.007,404	0.20
0.22	0.5833	0.005,439	0.047,46	0.172,54	0.011,660	0.003,551	0.008,989	0.22
0.24	0.5372	0.006,452	0.051,83	0.188,17	0.013,784	0.004,282	0.010,734	0.24
0.26	0.4983	0.007,549	0.056,22	0.203,78	0.016,062	0.005,094	0.012,643	0.26
0.28	0.4652	0.008,725	0.060,62	0.219,38	0.018,488	0.005,994	0.014,719	0.28
0.30	0.4366	0.009,981	0.065,04	0.234,96	0.021,054	0.006,983	0.016,963	0.30
0.32	0.4117	0.011,315	0.069,47	0.250,53	0.023,755	0.008,065	0.019,380	0.32
0.34	0.3898	0.012,726	0.073,91	0.266,09	0.026,583	0.009,245	0.021,972	0.34
0.36	0.3705	0.014,213	0.078,37	0.281,63	0.029,533	0.010,527	0.024,740	0.36

*Source: John I. Parcel and Robert B. B. Moorman, "Analysis of Statically Indeterminate Structures," John Wiley & Sons, Inc., New York, 1955, pp. 416–417, *by permission*.

Table 10-14. Fixed End Stresses, Vertical Concentrated Load
Symmetrical Circular Bar of Constant Cross Section ($\alpha \cong 0$, $\beta \cong 0$)

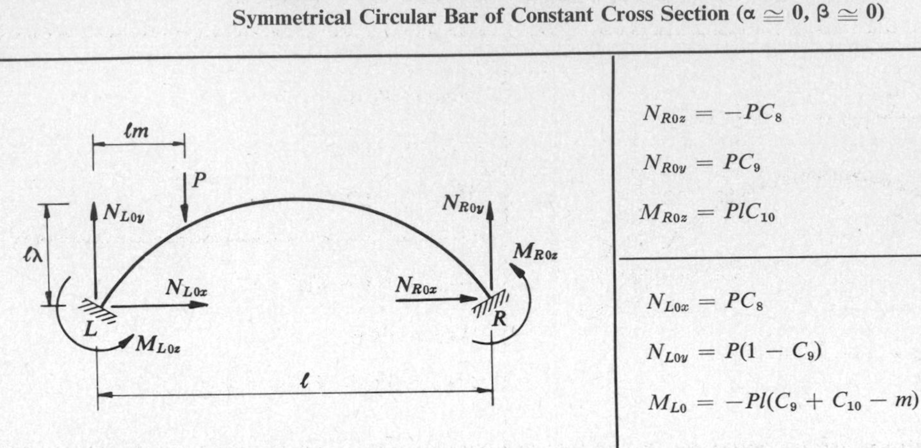

$$N_{R0x} = -PC_8$$

$$N_{R0y} = PC_9$$

$$M_{R0z} = PlC_{10}$$

$$N_{L0x} = PC_8$$

$$N_{L0y} = P(1 - C_9)$$

$$M_{L0} = -Pl(C_9 + C_{10} - m)$$

Stress Coefficients*

	λ \ m	0.1	0.2	0.3	0.4	0.5	0.6	0.7	0.8	0.9
C_8	0.1	0.3193	0.9944	1.6817	2.1850	2.3678	2.1850	1.6817	0.9944	0.3193
	0.2	0.1706	0.5099	0.8466	1.0826	1.1668	1.0826	0.8466	0.5099	0.1706
	0.3	0.1305	0.3628	0.5778	0.7304	0.7742	0.7304	0.5778	0.3628	0.1305
	0.4	0.1178	0.2935	0.4443	0.5432	0.5774	0.5432	0.4443	0.2935	0.1178
	0.5	0.1150	0.2523	0.3638	0.4348	0.4591	0.4348	0.3638	0.2523	0.1150
C_9	0.1	0.0286	0.1053	0.2176	0.3529	0.5000	0.6471	0.7824	0.8947	0.9714
	0.2	0.0307	0.1100	0.2226	0.3562	0.5000	0.6438	0.7774	0.8000	0.9693
	0.3	0.0348	0.1178	0.2305	0.3610	0.5000	0.6390	0.7695	0.8822	0.9652
	0.4	0.0416	0.1287	0.2406	0.3669	0.5000	0.6331	0.7594	0.8713	0.9584
	0.5	0.0510	0.1423	0.2522	0.3735	0.5000	0.6265	0.7478	0.8577	0.9490
C_{10}	0.1	0.0121	0.0341	0.0491	0.0503	0.0341	0.0032	−0.0331	−0.0604	−0.0592
	0.2	0.0131	0.0351	0.0500	0.0507	0.0354	0.0069	−0.0272	−0.0548	−0.0561
	0.3	0.0155	0.0386	0.0532	0.0554	0.0404	0.0165	−0.0162	−0.0435	−0.0496
	0.4	0.0197	0.0431	0.0571	0.0585	0.0471	0.0254	−0.0021	−0.0281	−0.0394
	0.5	0.0241	0.0479	0.0617	0.0639	0.0553	0.0375	+0.0139	−0.0097	−0.0237

* Source: James Michalos, "Theory of Structural Analysis and Design," The Ronald Press Company, New York, 1958, p. 288, *by permission.*

Table 10-15. Fixed End Stresses, Horizontal Concentrated Load
Symmetrical Circular Bar of Constant Cross Section ($\alpha \cong 0$, $\beta \cong 0$)

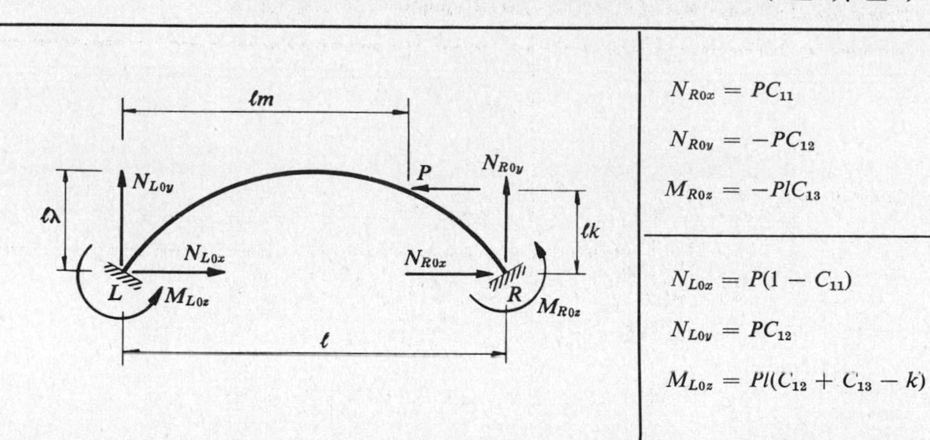

$$N_{ROx} = PC_{11}$$
$$N_{ROy} = -PC_{12}$$
$$M_{ROz} = -PlC_{13}$$

$$N_{LOx} = P(1 - C_{11})$$
$$N_{LOy} = PC_{12}$$
$$M_{LOz} = Pl(C_{12} + C_{13} - k)$$

Stress Coefficients*

	λ \ m	0.1	0.2	0.3	0.4	0.5	0.6	0.7	0.8	0.9
	0.1	0.1167	0.2720	0.4218	0.4911	0.5000	0.5089	0.5782	0.7280	0.8833
	0.2	0.1291	0.3174	0.4403	0.4923	0.5000	0.5077	0.5597	0.6826	0.8709
C_{11}	0.3	0.1630	0.3450	0.4524	0.4939	0.5000	0.5061	0.5476	0.6550	0.8370
	0.4	0.2110	0.3777	0.4639	0.4955	0.5000	0.5045	0.5361	0.6223	0.7890
	0.5	0.2696	0.4075	0.4733	0.4967	0.5000	0.5033	0.5267	0.5925	0.7304
	0.1	0.0101	0.0313	0.0531	0.0687	0.0744	0.0687	0.0531	0.0313	0.0101
	0.2	0.0230	0.0662	0.1074	0.1355	0.1454	0.1355	0.1074	0.0662	0.0230
C_{12}	0.3	0.0435	0.1072	0.1624	0.1982	0.2105	0.1982	0.1624	0.1072	0.0435
	0.4	0.0724	0.1539	0.2161	0.2552	0.2682	0.2552	0.2161	0.1539	0.0724
	0.5	0.1145	0.2037	0.2673	0.3055	0.3183	0.3055	0.2673	0.2037	0.1145
	0.1	0.0045	0.0084	0.0124	0.0133	0.0127	0.0140	0.0188	0.0250	0.0222
	0.2	0.0099	0.0223	0.0277	0.0281	0.0272	0.0293	0.0366	0.0463	0.0466
C_{13}	0.3	0.0191	0.0377	0.0452	0.0457	0.0447	0.0471	0.0558	0.0690	0.0720
	0.4	0.0350	0.0578	0.0663	0.0667	0.0658	0.0681	0.0768	0.0911	0.1003
	0.5	0.0581	0.0822	0.0905	0.0915	0.0908	0.0927	0.1002	0.1140	0.1272

* Source: James Michalos, "Theory of Structural Analysis and Design, "The Ronald Press Company, New York, 1958, p. 290, *by permission.*

Solved Problems

SEGMENTAL STIFFNESSES, STRAIGHT BAR

10.1. Derive by means of the general transport matrix (*4.2*) the unit displacement stiffness coefficients given in Table 10-2.

Equations (*10.9, 10*) are derived directly from (*4.2*). The required stiffness coefficients are contained in the following sub-matrices:

$$\overset{0}{k}_{RR} = -\overset{0)-1}{d}_{LR}\overset{0}{s}_{LR} \qquad \overset{0}{k}_{RL} = \overset{0)-1}{d}_{LR}$$

$$\overset{0}{k}_{LR} = -\overset{0)-1}{d}_{RL} \qquad \overset{0}{k}_{LL} = \overset{0)-1}{d}_{RL}\overset{0}{s}_{RL}$$

From (*4.5*),

$$\overset{0}{d}_{LR} = -\sum_L^R \overset{0}{s}_{Ls}\overset{0}{\lambda}_s\overset{0}{t}_{sR} = -\sum_L^R \overset{0)T}{r}_{sL}\overset{0}{\lambda}_s\overset{0}{r}_{sR}$$

$$= -\sum_L^R \begin{bmatrix} 1 & 0 & 0 \\ 0 & 1 & -x \\ 0 & 0 & 1 \end{bmatrix}\begin{bmatrix} \lambda_{xx} & 0 & 0 \\ 0 & 0 & 0 \\ 0 & 0 & \lambda_{zz} \end{bmatrix}\begin{bmatrix} 1 & 0 & 0 \\ 0 & 1 & 0 \\ 0 & x' & 1 \end{bmatrix}$$

$$= -\sum_L^R \begin{bmatrix} \lambda_{xx} & 0 & 0 \\ 0 & xx'\lambda_{zz} & -x\lambda_{zz} \\ 0 & x'\lambda_{zz} & \lambda_{zz} \end{bmatrix} = -\begin{bmatrix} l/AE & 0 & 0 \\ 0 & -l^3/6EI & -l^2/2EI \\ 0 & l^2/2EI & l/EI \end{bmatrix}$$

where $\lambda_{xx} = ds/AE$, $\lambda_{zz} = ds/EI$, $\lambda_{xy} = \lambda_{yx} \simeq 0 = \lambda_{yy}$ and $x' = l - x$.
Similarly,

$$\overset{0}{d}_{RL} = \sum_L^R \overset{0}{s}_{Rs}\overset{0}{\lambda}_s\overset{0}{t}_{sL} = \sum_L^R \overset{0)T}{r}_{sR}\overset{0}{\lambda}_s\overset{0}{r}_{sL}$$

$$= \sum_L^R \begin{bmatrix} 1 & 0 & 0 \\ 0 & 1 & x' \\ 0 & 0 & 1 \end{bmatrix}\begin{bmatrix} \lambda_{xx} & 0 & 0 \\ 0 & 0 & 0 \\ 0 & 0 & \lambda_{zz} \end{bmatrix}\begin{bmatrix} 1 & 0 & 0 \\ 0 & 1 & 0 \\ 0 & -x & 1 \end{bmatrix} = \begin{bmatrix} l/AE & 0 & 0 \\ 0 & -l^3/6EI & l^2/2EI \\ 0 & -l^2/2EI & l/EI \end{bmatrix}$$

From these,

$$\overset{0)-1}{d}_{LR} = \begin{bmatrix} -EA/l & 0 & 0 \\ 0 & -12EI/l^3 & -6EI/l^2 \\ 0 & 6EI/l^2 & 2EI/l \end{bmatrix} \quad \text{and} \quad \overset{0)-1}{d}_{RL} = \begin{bmatrix} EA/l & 0 & 0 \\ 0 & 12EI/l^3 & -6EI/l^2 \\ 0 & 6EI/l^2 & -2EI/l \end{bmatrix}$$

Also noting that

$$\overset{0}{s}_{LR} = \overset{0)T}{r}_{RL} = \begin{bmatrix} 1 & 0 & 0 \\ 0 & 1 & -l \\ 0 & 0 & 1 \end{bmatrix} \quad \text{and} \quad \overset{0}{s}_{RL} = \overset{0)T}{r}_{LR} = \begin{bmatrix} 1 & 0 & 0 \\ 0 & 1 & l \\ 0 & 0 & 1 \end{bmatrix}$$

and substituting in the stiffness sub-matrices expressions mentioned above, the stiffness matrix shown in Table 10-2 can be easily derived.

10.2. Using the unit load flexibility coefficients of Table 5-1, derive the unit load stiffness coefficients introduced in Sec. 10.5*b*.

Considering the cantilever bar of Table 5-1 as the basic system, the deformation condition for the bar shown in Fig. 10-3 is

$$\Delta_R{}^0 = lW + f\sigma_R{}^0 = 0$$

where from Table 5-1

$$l = \begin{bmatrix} D_{RP} & 0 & 0 \\ 0 & C_{RP} & B_{RQ} \\ 0 & B_{RP} & A_{RQ} \end{bmatrix} = \begin{bmatrix} a/EA & 0 & 0 \\ 0 & a^2(3s-a)/6EI & a(2s-a)/2EI \\ 0 & a^2/2EI & a/EI \end{bmatrix}$$

and
$$f = \begin{bmatrix} D_{RR} & 0 & 0 \\ 0 & C_{RR} & B_{RR} \\ 0 & B_{RR} & A_{RR} \end{bmatrix} = \begin{bmatrix} s/EA & 0 & 0 \\ 0 & s^3/3EI & s^2/2EI \\ 0 & s^2/2EI & s/EI \end{bmatrix}$$

Hence

$$\sigma_R{}^0 = -f^{-1}lW$$

which becomes after substitution of $f^{-1} = \begin{bmatrix} EA/s & 0 & 0 \\ 0 & 12EI/s^3 & -6EI/s^2 \\ 0 & -6EI/s^2 & 4EI/s \end{bmatrix}$ and l from above,

$$\begin{bmatrix} N_{Rjx} \\ N_{Rjy} \\ M_{Rjz} \end{bmatrix} = \begin{bmatrix} -m & 0 & 0 \\ 0 & -m^2(1+2n) & -6mn/l \\ 0 & lm^2n & m(2-3m) \end{bmatrix} \begin{bmatrix} P_{jx} \\ P_{jy} \\ Q_{jz} \end{bmatrix}$$

where $m = a/l$, $n = 1 - m$, $l = s$.

Also, $\sigma_L{}^0$ can simply be obtained from the statical equilibrium condition $\sigma_L{}^0 + r^0_{LR}\sigma_R{}^0 + r^0_{Lj}W^0 = 0$. Thus

$$\sigma_L{}^0 = \begin{bmatrix} N_{Ljx} \\ N_{Ljy} \\ M_{Ljz} \end{bmatrix} = \begin{bmatrix} -n & 0 & 0 \\ 0 & -n^2(1+2m) & 6mn/l \\ 0 & -lmn^2 & n(2-3n) \end{bmatrix} \begin{bmatrix} P_{jx} \\ P_{jy} \\ Q_{jz} \end{bmatrix}$$

10.3. Using the Virtual Forces Method, derive the end stresses due to temperature change introduced in Sec. 10.5*b*.

The flexibilities in Table 5-1 for a cantilever bar are a direct result of the Virtual Forces Method. Conceiving the bar to be a basic cantilever system, the deformation condition for the constrained bar subjected to temperature volume change is

$$f\sigma_R{}^0 + \Delta^{(T)} = 0$$

Therefore

$$\sigma_R{}^0 = -f^{-1}\Delta^{(T)} \qquad \Delta^{(T)} = \begin{bmatrix} l\epsilon_0 \\ (\epsilon_b - \epsilon_t)l^2/2h \\ (\epsilon_b - \epsilon_t)l/h \end{bmatrix}$$

and f^{-1} is the same as in Problem 10.2. Hence

$$\sigma_R{}^0 = \begin{bmatrix} N_{RTx} \\ N_{RTy} \\ M_{RTz} \end{bmatrix} = \begin{bmatrix} -\epsilon_0 EA \\ 0 \\ -(\epsilon_b - \epsilon_t)EI/h \end{bmatrix}$$

$\sigma_L{}^0$ is obtained from statics of the bar.

$$\sigma_L{}^0 = \begin{bmatrix} N_{LTx} \\ N_{LTy} \\ M_{LTz} \end{bmatrix} = \begin{bmatrix} \epsilon_0 EA \\ 0 \\ (\epsilon_b - \epsilon_t)EI/h \end{bmatrix}$$

SEGMENTAL STIFFNESSES, BENT BAR

10.4. Using (*10.18*), compute the stiffness coefficients k_{RR}^{RR}, k_{RL}^{RL}, k_{LR}^{LR}, k_{LL}^{LL} for the bent bar of Fig. P-10.4. Assume EI = constant and consider only the flexural deformations.

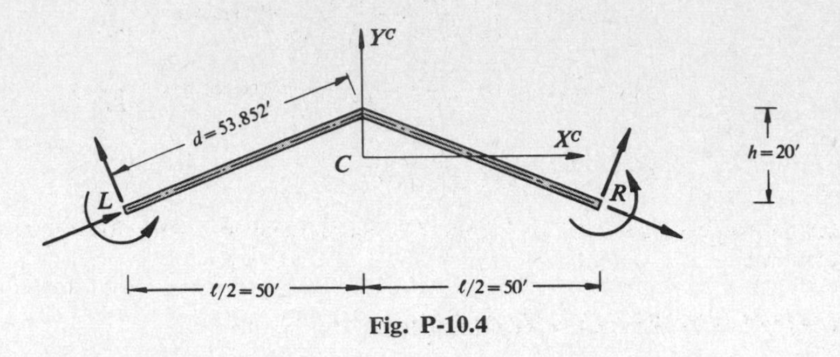

Fig. P-10.4

The neutral point for a symmetrical bent bar of constant cross section such as shown in Fig. P-10.4 is at $x = l/2$, $y = h/2$ with respect to the left end. The principal flexibilities at the neutral point can be computed as explained in Sec. 8.7 or by using (*10.20*). Thus for

$$\bar{I}_{Cxx}^{C} = \int_L^R \frac{y^2 ds}{EI} = \frac{h^2 d}{6EI}, \qquad \bar{I}_{Cyy}^{C} = \int_L^R \frac{x^2 ds}{EI} = \frac{l^2 d}{6EI} \qquad \text{and} \qquad \bar{A}_{Czz}^{C} = \int_L^R \frac{ds}{EI} = \frac{2d}{EI},$$

$$f_{CC}^{C} = \frac{1}{6EI}\begin{bmatrix} h^2 d & 0 & 0 \\ 0 & l^2 d & 0 \\ 0 & 0 & 12d \end{bmatrix} \qquad \text{and} \qquad f_{CC}^{C)-1} = 6EI\begin{bmatrix} 1/h^2 d & 0 & 0 \\ 0 & 1/l^2 d & 0 \\ 0 & 0 & 1/12d \end{bmatrix}$$

in which $l = 100'$, $h = 20'$ and $d = 53.85'$.

From (*10.18*),

$$k_{RR}^{RR} = t_{RC}^{RC} f_{CC}^{C)-1} t_{RC}^{RC)T} \qquad k_{RL}^{RL} = -t_{RC}^{RC} f_{CC}^{C)-1} t_{LC}^{LC)T}$$

$$k_{LR}^{LR} = -t_{LC}^{LC} f_{CC}^{C)-1} t_{RC}^{RC)T} \qquad k_{LL}^{LL} = t_{LC}^{LC} f_{CC}^{C)-1} t_{LC}^{LC)T}$$

$$t_{RC}^{RC} = \omega^{RC} r_{RC}^{C} = \begin{bmatrix} 0.928 & -0.371 & 0 \\ 0.371 & 0.928 & 0 \\ 0 & 0 & 1 \end{bmatrix}\begin{bmatrix} 1 & 0 & 0 \\ 0 & 1 & 0 \\ -10 & -50 & 1 \end{bmatrix} = \begin{bmatrix} 0.928 & -0.371 & 0 \\ 0.371 & 0.928 & 0 \\ -10 & -50 & 1 \end{bmatrix}$$

where $\omega_{RC} = -21.8°$. Similarly,

$$t_{LC}^{LC} = \omega^{LC} r_{LC}^{C} = \begin{bmatrix} 0.928 & 0.371 & 0 \\ -0.371 & 0.928 & 0 \\ -10 & 50 & 1 \end{bmatrix}$$

in which $\omega_{LC} = +21.8°$. Substituting these values and their transposes in proper places,

$$k_{RR}^{RR} = \frac{EI}{10^4}\begin{bmatrix} 2.414 & 0.921 & -23.782 \\ 0.921 & 0.479 & -15.504 \\ -23.782 & -15.504 & 649.9 \end{bmatrix} \qquad k_{RL}^{RL} = \frac{EI}{10^4}\begin{bmatrix} -2.383 & 0.997 & 27.916 \\ -0.997 & 0.287 & 5.164 \\ 27.916 & -5.164 & -92.85 \end{bmatrix}$$

$$k_{LR}^{LR} = \frac{EI}{10^4}\begin{bmatrix} -2.383 & -0.997 & 27.916 \\ 0.997 & 0.287 & -5.164 \\ 27.916 & 5.164 & -92.85 \end{bmatrix} \qquad k_{LL}^{LL} = \frac{EI}{10^4}\begin{bmatrix} 2.414 & -0.921 & -23.782 \\ -0.921 & 0.479 & 15.504 \\ -23.782 & 15.504 & 649.9 \end{bmatrix}$$

10.5. Compute the principal flexibilities at the neutral point of the bent bar of Table 10-8 and prepare by means of Table 10-7 the segmental stiffness matrix given in Table 10-8.

The neutral point of the bent bar is located on the axis of symmetry at $y_{AC} = -h/2$.
Using (*10.20*), the principal flexibilities at the neutral point are

$$f^C_{Cxx} = \bar{I}^C_{Cxx} = \int_L^R \frac{y^2\,ds}{EI} = \frac{2}{EI}\int_{-h/2}^{h/2} y^2\,dy/\sin\theta = \frac{h^2 d}{6EI}$$

$$f^C_{Cyy} = \bar{I}^C_{Cyy} = \int_L^R \frac{x^2\,ds}{EI} = \frac{2}{EI}\int_0^{l/2} x^2\,dx/\cos\theta = \frac{l^2 d}{6EI}$$

$$f^C_{Czz} = \bar{A}^C_{Czz} = \int_L^R \frac{ds}{EI} = \frac{2d}{EI}$$

Substituting the above values and $\bar{y} = h/2$ and $\bar{x} = l/2$ in Table 10-7, the stiffness values given in Table 10-8 can be readily verified.

SEGMENTAL STIFFNESSES, CURVED BAR

10.6. Using Engesser's Theorem II, derive the general slope-deflection equation (*10.19*) for a symmetrical parabolic bar given in Table 10-10.

To derive the general slope deflection equations of the bar given in Table 10-10, consider the bar of Fig. 10-2 with its imposed end deformation and consider the left end forces as redundants, $N^0_{LRx} = X_1$, $N^0_{LRy} = X_2$ and $M^0_{LRz} = X_3$. Then according to Engesser's Theorem II,

$$\frac{\partial U_s}{\partial X_i} = \frac{\partial U_R}{\partial X_i} \qquad i = 1, 2, 3.$$

where the strain energy $U_s = \int M_x{}^2 ds/2EI_s = \int M_x{}^2 dx/2EI_c$, $M_x = -X_1 y + X_2 x - X_3 + BM_x$, BM_x = moment at a section due to applied loads.

The work of reactions

$$U_R = N^0_{LRx}\,\delta^0_{LX} + N^0_{LRy}\,\delta^0_{Ly} + M^0_{LRz}\,\theta^0_{Lz} + N^0_{RLx}\,\delta^0_{Rx} + N^0_{RLy}\,\delta^0_{Ry} + M^0_{RLz}\,\theta^0_{Rz}$$

where, in terms of the redundants, the end reactions are

$$N^0_{LRx} = X_1 \qquad N^0_{RLx} = X_1 + BN^0_{RLx}$$

$$N^0_{LRy} = X_2 \qquad N^0_{RLy} = -X_2 + BN^0_{RLy}$$

$$M^0_{LRz} = X_3 \qquad M^0_{RLz} = X_2 l - X_3 + BM^0_{RLz}$$

where BN^0_{RLx}, BN^0_{RLy} and BM^0_{RLz} are the reactions at R induced by applied loads.
Applying Engesser's Theorem II and reducing gives

$$\begin{bmatrix} \bar{I}_{xx} & -\bar{I}_{xy} & \overline{SA}_{xx} \\ -\bar{I}_{yx} & \bar{I}_{yy} & -\overline{SA}_{yy} \\ \overline{SA}_{xx} & -\overline{SA}_{yy} & \bar{A} \end{bmatrix} \begin{bmatrix} X_1 \\ X_2 \\ X_3 \end{bmatrix} + \begin{bmatrix} -\overline{M}_{xx} \\ \overline{M}_{yy} \\ -\overline{W}_{zz} \end{bmatrix} = \begin{bmatrix} \delta_{Lx} - \delta_{Rx} \\ \delta^0_{Ly} - \delta^0_{Ry} + l\theta^0_{Rz} \\ \theta^0_{Lz} - \theta^0_{Rz} \end{bmatrix}$$

where for the given bar the elastic properties are

$$\bar{I}_{xx} = \int \frac{y^2\,ds}{EI_x} = \int_0^l \frac{y^2\,dx}{EI_c} = \frac{8lh^2}{15EI_c}, \qquad \bar{I}_{yy} = \int \frac{x^2\,ds}{EI_s} = \int_0^l \frac{x^2\,dx}{EI_c} = \frac{l^3}{3EI_c}$$

$$\bar{I}_{xy} = \bar{I}_{yx} = \int \frac{xy\,ds}{EI_s} = \int_0^l \frac{xy\,dx}{EI_c} = \frac{hl^2}{3EI_c}, \qquad \bar{A} = \int \frac{ds}{EI_s} = \int_0^l \frac{dx}{EI_c} = \frac{l}{EI_c}$$

$$\overline{SA}_{xx} = \int \frac{y\,ds}{EI_s} = \int_0^l \frac{y\,dx}{EI_c} = \frac{2lh}{3EI_c}, \qquad \overline{SA}_{yy} = \int \frac{x\,ds}{EI_s} = \int_0^l \frac{x\,dx}{EI_c} = \frac{l^2}{2EI_c}$$

and

$$\overline{M}_{xx} = \int_0^l \frac{BM_x y\,dx}{EI_c}, \qquad \overline{M}_{yy} = \int \frac{BM_x x\,dx}{EI_c} \quad \text{and} \quad \overline{W}_{zz} = \int_0^l \frac{BM_x\,dx}{EI_c}$$

are the load functions.

Substituting these values, the redundants and then the end forces can be solved for in terms of end deformations and loads — which constitute the slope deflection equations desired. The stiffness values given in Table 10-10 can be obtained, and for any specific load condition as given in Table 10-11 the fixed end stress values can be easily verified.

It may be noted that a choice of the redundants at the elastic center will greatly simplify their solution, which can then be transferred to the ends; however, the same results are to be expected.

INFLUENCE LINES

10.7. Derive the analytical expressions for the fixed end moments in a straight bar acted upon by an applied moment Q (Table 10-3, Case 16) and compute a 100 point table of influence values η and η' (Table 10-5). Also sketch the influence lines for M_{L0} and M_{R0}.

The fixed end moment values desired are already derived in Problem 10.2 as load functions and had also been introduced in Sec. 10.5*b*. Using proper sign to match the direction of Q given in Case *16*, Table 10-3,

$$M_{L0} = -Qn(2-3n) \qquad M_{R0} = -Qm(2-3m)$$

Defining as in Table 10-5 $M_{L0} = -Q\eta$ and $M_{R0} = -Q\eta'$,

$$\eta = n(2-3n) = (1-m)(3m-1) \text{ and } \eta' = m(2-3m)$$

which are tabulated for $m = 0$ to 1 in increments of 0.01 (Table 10-5). The influence lines for M_{L0} and M_{R0} are sketched in Fig. P-10.7.

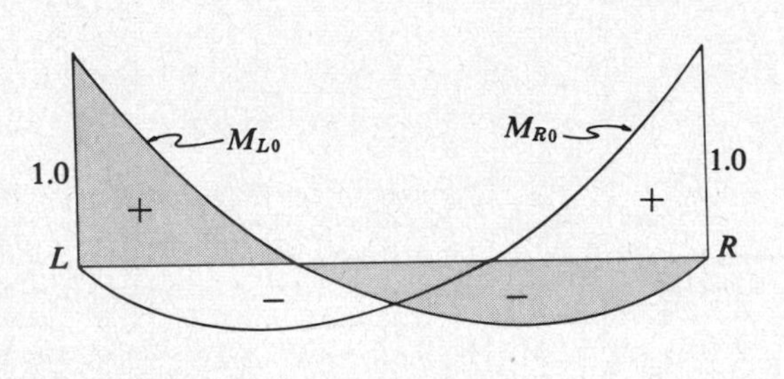

Fig. P-10.7

10.8. Derive the analytical expressions for the fixed end thrust and moments in a symmetrical parabolic arch acted upon by a vertical concentrated load (Table 10-11, Case 1) and prepare a 100 point table of influence values η, η' and μ such that $M_{L0} = (Pl)\,\eta_m$, $M_{R0} = (Pl)\,\eta_m'$, $N_{L0x} = -N_{R0x} = (Pl/h)\,\mu_m$.

For the simple arch of Table 8-4 as a basic structure, the deformation condition for the arch of Table 10-11 is

$$\Delta = f\sigma + lW = 0$$

where

$$\Delta = \{\Delta_{Rx}, \theta_{Rz}, \theta_{Lz}\} \qquad \sigma = \{N_{Rx}, M_{Rz}, M_{Lz}\}$$

Matrix f is given in Table 8-4 and elements of matrix l were derived in Problem 8.6. Thus

$$\sigma = -f^{-1}lW$$

and for a vertical load only,

$$l = \{G_{RV}, F_{RV}, F_{LV}\}$$

Substituting,

$$f^{-1} = \frac{EI_c}{l}\begin{bmatrix} 90/8h^2 & -15/2h & -15/2h \\ -15/2h & 9 & 3 \\ -15/2h & 3 & 9 \end{bmatrix} \quad \text{and} \quad l = \frac{1}{EI_c}\begin{bmatrix} -ah(l^3 - 2la^2 + a^3)/3l^2 \\ -a(l^2 - a^2)/6l \\ -a(2l^2 - 3la + a^2)/6l \end{bmatrix}$$

and adjusting signs for N_{Rx}, M_{Lz} and for the unit downward vertical load, the required values finally become

$$\begin{bmatrix} N_{L0x} = -N_{R0x} \\ M_{R0} \\ M_{L0} \end{bmatrix} = \begin{bmatrix} \mu_m Pl/h \\ \eta_m' Pl \\ \eta_m Pl \end{bmatrix} = \begin{bmatrix} (15m^2n^2/4)(Pl/h) \\ (m^2n(3-5m)/2)Pl \\ (mn^2(2-5m)/2)Pl \end{bmatrix}$$

wherein $m = a/l$, $n = 1 - m$. The 100 point table for the influence coefficient is given below (Table P-10.8).

Table P-10.8. Coefficients μ, η and η'

m	0	1	2	3	4	5	6	7	8	9	*m*
0.0	0.00000+ 0.00000+ 0.00000+	0.00037+ 0.00015+ 0.00956+	0.00144+ 0.00057+ 0.01825+	0.00553+ 0.00124+ 0.02611+	0.00553+ 0.00215+ 0.03318+	0.00846+ 0.00327+ 0.03948+	0.01193+ 0.00457+ 0.04506+	0.01589 + 0.00604+ 0.04995+	0.02031+ 0.00765+ 0.05417+	0.02515+ 0.00940+ 0.05776+	0.0
0.1	0.03037+ 0.01125+ 0.06075+	0.03594+ 0.01319+ 0.06317+	0.04182+ 0.01521+ 0.06505+	0.04797+ 0.01728+ 0.06642+	0.05436+ 0.01938+ 0.06730+	0.06096+ 0.02152+ 0.06773+	0.06774+ 0.02365+ 0.06774+	0.07466+ 0.02579+ 0.06734+	0.08170+ 0.02790+ 0.06657+	0.08882+ 0.02997+ 0.06545+	0.1
0.2	0.09600+ 0.03200+ 0.06400+	0.10321+ 0.03397+ 0.06225+	0.11042+ 0.03586+ 0.06023+	0.11762+ 0.03768+ 0.05796+	0.12476+ 0.03940+ 0.05545+	0.13184+ 0.04102+ 0.05273+	0.13882+ 0.04252+ 0.04983+	0.14568+ 0.04390+ 0.04676+	0.15241+ 0.04516+ 0.04355+	0.15898+ 0.04628+ 0.04020+	0.2
0.3	0.16537+ 0.04725+ 0.03675+	0.17157+ 0.04807+ 0.03321+	0.17756+ 0.04874+ 0.02959+	0.18332+ 0.04925+ 0.02592+	0.18883+ 0.04959+ 0.02222+	0.19409+ 0.04977+ 0.01848+	0.19907+ 0.04977+ 0.01475+	0.20376+ 0.04959+ 0.01101+	0.20815+ 0.04924+ 0.00730+	0.21224+ 0.04871+ 0.00363+	0.3
0.4	0.21600+ 0.04800+ 0.00000+	0.21943+ 0.04711+ 0.00357−	0.22253+ 0.04604+ 0.00706+	0.22528+ 0.04479+ 0.01048−	0.22767+ 0.04337+ 0.01380−	0.22971+ 0.04177+ 0.01702−	0.23138+ 0.03999+ 0.02012−	0.23269+ 0.03805+ 0.02310−	0.23363+ 0.03594+ 0.02596−	0.23419+ 0.03367+ 0.02868−	0.4
0.5	0.23438+ 0.03125+ 0.03125−	0.23419+ 0.02868+ 0.03367−	0.23363+ 0.02596+ 0.03594−	0.23269+ 0.02310+ 0.03805−	0.23138+ 0.02012+ 0.03999−	0.22971+ 0.01702+ 0.04177−	0.22767+ 0.01380+ 0.04337−	0.22528+ 0.01048+ 0.04479−	0.22253+ 0.00706+ 0.04604−	0.21943+ 0.00357+ 0.04711−	0.5
0.6	0.21600+ 0.00000+ 0.04800−	0.21224+ 0.00363− 0.04871−	0.20815+ 0.00730− 0.04924−	0.20376+ 0.01101− 0.04959−	0.19907+ 0.01475− 0.04977−	0.19409+ 0.01848− 0.04977+	0.18883+ 0.02222− 0.04959−	0.18332+ 0.02592− 0.04925−	0.17756+ 0.02959− 0.04874−	0.17157+ 0.03321− 0.04807−	0.6
0.7	0.16537+ 0.03675− 0.04725−	0.15898+ 0.04020− 0.04628−	0.15241+ 0.04355− 0.04516−	0.14568+ 0.04676− 0.04390−	0.13882+ 0.04983− 0.04252−	0.13184− 0.05273− 0.04102−	0.12476+ 0.05545− 0.03940−	0.11762+ 0.05796− 0.03768−	0.11042+ 0.06023− 0.03586−	0.10321+ 0.06225− 0.03397−	0.7
0.8	0.09600+ 0.06400− 0.03200−	0.08882+ 0.06545− 0.02997−	0.08170+ 0.06657− 0.02790−	0.07466+ 0.06734− 0.02579−	0.06774+ 0.06774− 0.02365−	0.06096− 0.06773− 0.02152−	0.05436+ 0.06730− 0.01938−	0.04797+ 0.06642− 0.01728−	0.04182+ 0.06505− 0.01521−	0.03594+ 0.06317− 0.01319−	0.8
0.9	0.03037+ 0.06075− 0.01125−	0.02515+ 0.05776− 0.00940−	0.02031+ 0.05417− 0.00765−	0.01589+ 0.04995− 0.00604−	0.01193+ 0.04506− 0.00457−	0.00846+ 0.03948− 0.00327−	0.00553+ 0.03318− 0.00215−	0.00318+ 0.02611− 0.00124−	0.00144+ 0.01825− 0.00057−	0.00037+ 0.00956− 0.00015−	0.9

Supplementary Problems

10.9. Using the superposition of causes and the Moment Area Method, derive the unit displacement stiffness coefficients of Table 10-2.

10.10. Using the Virtual Forces Method, derive the stiffness matrix of Table 10-12.

10.11. Consider the basic system of Fig. P-10.11 and derive the stiffness matrix for σ^0_{12} and σ^0_{21} in terms of displacements $\Delta_L{}^0$ and $\Delta_R{}^0$. Assume the axis of the symmetrical bar to be a 2° parabola and $I = I_0 \sec \omega$ and $A = A_0 \cos \omega$. Consider axial and flexural deformations.

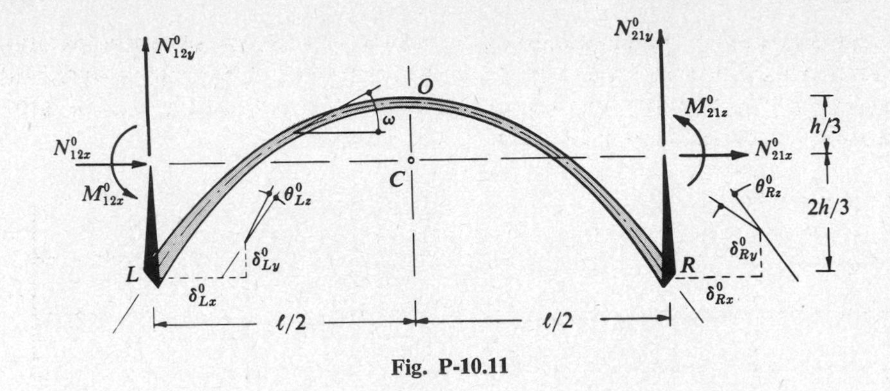

Fig. P-10.11

10.12. Transfer the results of Problem 10.11 to L and R and reduce to the matrix given in Table 10-10.

10.13. Verify the values of $\bar{I}^C_{Cxx}$, $\bar{I}^C_{Cyy}$ and $\bar{A}^C_{Czz}$ for the symmetrical bent bar shown in Table 10-8, and then using Table 10-7 verify the segmental stiffnesses of the bent bar given in Table 10-8.

10.14. Verify the fixed end stresses of the symmetrical parabolic bar for the load condition shown in Case 1, Table 10-11, using the expressions for σ^0_{R0} and σ^0_{L0} obtained in (*10.18, 19*).

10.15. Compute the stiffness values k^0_{RR}, k^0_{LL}, k^0_{LR} and k^0_{RL} for the straight bar of variable section of Fig. P-10.15, using (*10.18*) and the results of Problem 6.17.

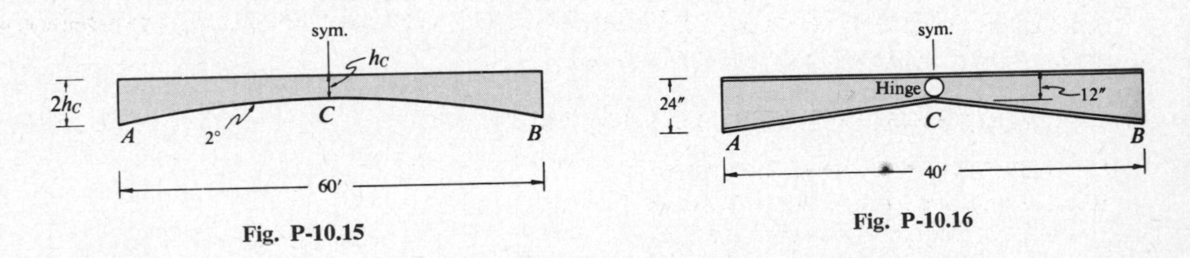

Fig. P-10.15 **Fig. P-10.16**

10.16. Using the results of Problem 6.5 and (*10.18*), compute the stiffness k^0_{RR}, k^0_{LL}, k^0_{LR} and k^0_{RL} of the wedged bar of variable depth shown in Fig. P-10.16. (Hint: Construct f^C_{CC} for (*10.18*) using only the applicable flexibilities.)

10.17. Using the segmental flexibilities of a constant section cantilever bar and (*10.18*), compute the stiffness k^0_{RR}, k^0_{LL}, k^0_{LR} and k^0_{RL} and the fixed end stresses σ^0_{R0} and σ^0_{L0} of the bent wedged bar shown in Fig. P-10.17.

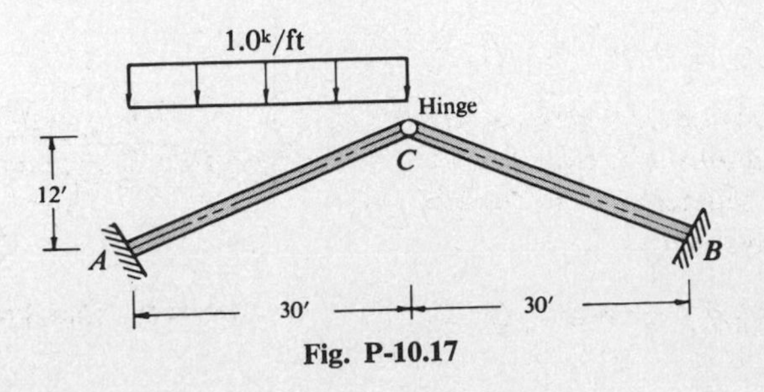

Fig. P-10.17

Chapter 11

Complex Frame

11.1 SYSTEM

Rigid frames, formed by polygonal rings in such a way that the classification introduced in Fig. 9-1 does not apply, are called *complex frames*. Their most typical characteristics are *offset columns* (Fig. 11-1*a*), *offset girders* (Fig. 11-1*c*), internal *ties* and/or *braces* (Fig. 11-1*b*). If certain parts of such frames are trusses, the designation of *composite complex frame* or *truss frame* is used.

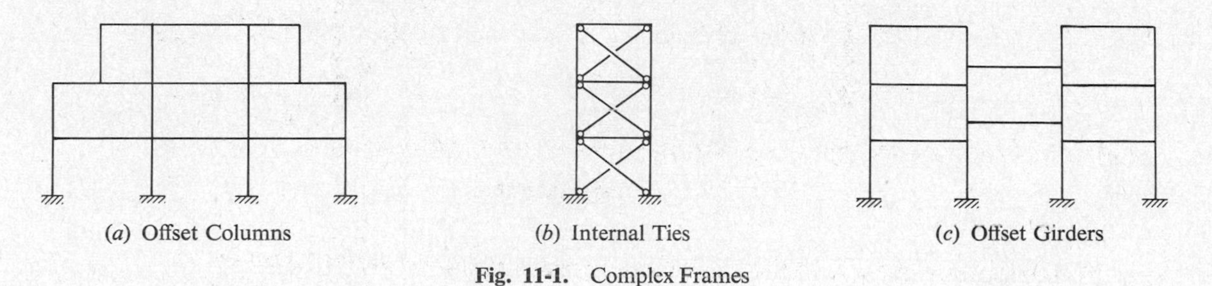

Fig. 11-1. Complex Frames

11.2 ANALYSIS

As the complexity of the frame increases, the application of the general flexibility method becomes more involved. Specifically, the selection of basic and complementary systems requires more judgement and the calculation of flexibility coefficients becomes more laborious. In such cases, the *general stiffness method*, outlined in the preceding chapter, offers some advantages. Although the prime object of this chapter is the systematic development of this latter method for analyzing complex frames, the same procedure is applicable in the analysis of continuous beams, arches and frames of all kinds. The extension of this method to truss analysis is shown in Chapter 12.

11.3 SEGMENTAL STIFFNESS MATRIX CHAIN

Similarly, as in the flexibility analysis, the system stiffness matrix for a multisegment bar or ring is constructed from the segmental stiffness matrices discussed in the preceding chapter.

Considering the cantilever bent bar $0m$ of Fig. 11-2, the *condition of static equilibrium* at the intermediate joint j (any joint) requires that

$$\sigma_{ji}^{0} + \sigma_{jk}^{0} = W_j^{0} \qquad (11.1)$$

This condition expressed in terms of the *slope-deflection equations* (*10.10*), written for the right end of segment ij and the left end of segment jk, becomes

$$k_{ji}^{0}\Delta_i^{0} + k_j^{0}\Delta_j^{0} + k_{jk}^{0}\Delta_k^{0} = W_j^{0} \qquad (11.2)$$

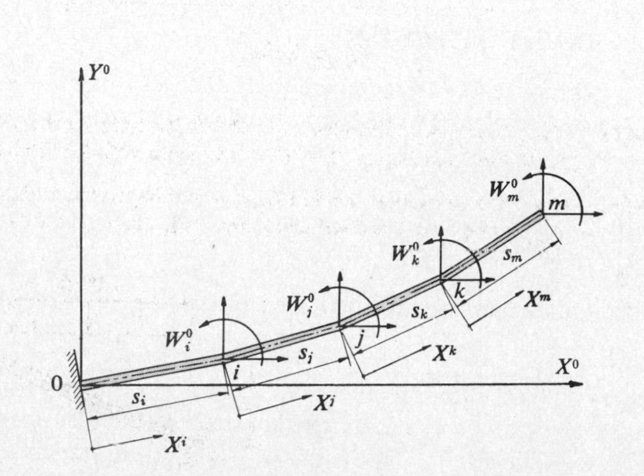

Fig. 11-2. Cantilever Bent Bar, Loads at Joints

where Δ_i^0, Δ_j^0, Δ_k^0 are the unknown *joint displacement vectors* at *i*, *j*, *k* respectively and

$$k_j^0 = k_{jj,i}^0 + k_{jj,k}^0 \tag{11.3}$$

Equation (*11.2*) is known as the *general three-displacement equation*, which can be used as a recurrent formula for the construction of the system stiffness matrix given below:

$$\begin{bmatrix} k_m^0 & k_{mk}^0 & & \\ k_{km}^0 & k_k^0 & k_{kj}^0 & \\ & k_{jk}^0 & k_j^0 & k_{ji}^0 \\ & & k_{ij}^0 & k_i^0 \end{bmatrix} \begin{bmatrix} \Delta_m^0 \\ \Delta_k^0 \\ \Delta_j^0 \\ \Delta_i^0 \end{bmatrix} = \begin{bmatrix} W_m^0 \\ W_k^0 \\ W_j^0 \\ W_i^0 \end{bmatrix}$$

or symbolically

$$K^0 \Delta^0 = W^0 \tag{11.4}$$

where K^0 is the *system stiffness matrix* (Problem 11.1).

The same result is obtained by the overlapping of segmental stiffness matrices $k_{(km)}^0$, $k_{(jk)}^0$, $k_{(ij)}^0$.

$K^0 =$ 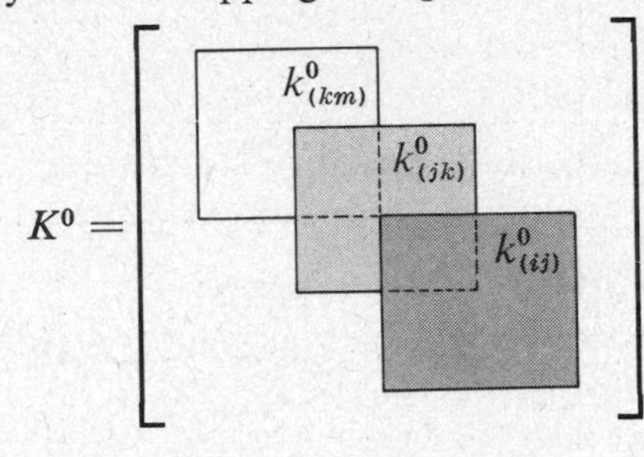

where by (*10.15*)

$$k_{(km)}^0 = \pi^{0m} k_{(km)}^m \pi^{m0}; \qquad k_{(jk)}^0 = \pi^{0k} k_{(jk)}^k \pi^{k0}; \qquad k_{(ij)}^0 = \pi^{0j} k_{(ij)}^j \pi^{j0}$$

Since by (*5.18*), $\Delta^0 = \Phi^0 W^0$, the system stiffness matrix K^0 is the inverse of the system flexibility matrix Φ^0 and vice versa.

$$K^0 \Phi^0 = \Phi^0 K^0 = I \tag{11.5}$$

The effect of intermediate loads or other causes is included in (*11.4*) by adding the joint effect vector $\sigma^0 = \{\sigma_{m0}^0, \sigma_{k0}^0, \sigma_{j0}^0, \sigma_{i0}^0\}$ where each term is the sum of fixed end stresses due to these causes at the respective joint.

Thus the completely *general form* of (*11.4*) becomes

$$K^0 \Delta^0 + \sigma^0 = W^0 \tag{11.6}$$

11.4 JOINT STIFFNESS

If more than two members meet at the joint (Fig. 11-3), the joint equilibrium equation must include the end stresses of all members involved. Thus at *j*,

$$\sigma_{ji}^0 + \sigma_{jr}^0 + \sigma_{jk}^0 = W_j^0 \tag{11.7}$$

with

$$k_{jj,i}^0 + k_{jj,r}^0 + k_{jj,k}^0 = k_j^0 \tag{11.8}$$

and

$$\sigma_{j0,i}^0 + \sigma_{j0,r}^0 + \sigma_{j0,k}^0 = \sigma_{j0}^0 \tag{11.9}$$

The equilibrium equation written similarly as (*11.2*) becomes

$$k_{ji}^0 \Delta_i^0 + k_j^0 \Delta_j^0 + k_{jk}^0 \Delta_k^0 + \sigma_{j0}^0 = W_j^0 \tag{11.10}$$

where k_j^0 is the joint stiffness (*11.8*) and σ_{j0} is the fixed joint stress due to loads and/or other causes.

The system stiffness matrix constructed for this structure, using (*11.10*) recurrently, is formally identical to K^0 in (*11.4*). The matrices forming the principal diagonal of K^0 are the joint stiffness matrices, representing the joint stress vectors of respective joints caused by the corresponding joint displacement vector when the remaining joints are fixed (Problem 11.2).

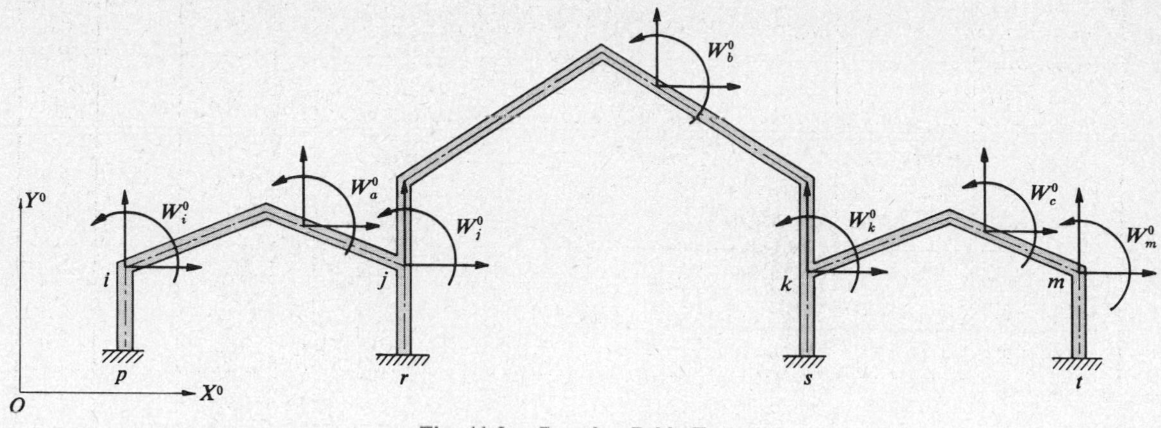

Fig. 11-3. Complex Gable Frame

11.5 ELASTIC CONSTRAINTS

If the joint constraints or support constraints are elastic springs, such as those shown in Fig. 11-4, the joint stiffness must include the spring stiffness.

Thus at j,

$$k_j^{\,0} = k^0_{jj,i} + k^0_{jj,\Delta} + k^0_{jj,k} \tag{11.11}$$

where

$$k^0_{jj,\Delta} = \text{Diag.}[K^0_{jj,\Delta x}\,,\ K^0_{jj,\Delta y}\,,\ K^0_{jj,\theta z}] \tag{11.12}$$

is the spring stiffness matrix at j, the coefficients of which are the stresses required to produce a unit displacement of the spring at j.

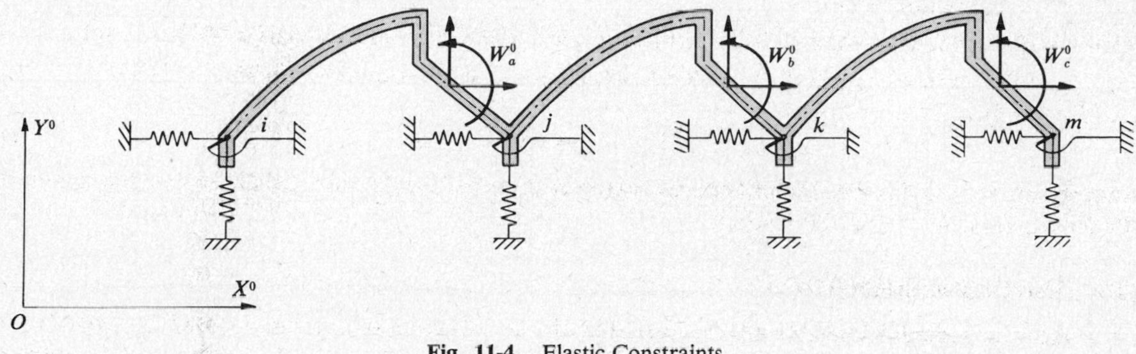

Fig. 11-4. Elastic Constraints

The end stiffnesses $K^0_{ii,p}$, $K^0_{jj,r}$, $K^0_{kk,s}$, $K^0_{mm,t}$ in Fig. 11-3 are essentially spring stiffness matrices of the respective columns. Since the point of action is the top of the column and not the neutral point, some or all off-diagonal terms in these matrices are nonzero, whereas the spring stiffness matrix is by definition given only by the principal values (Problem 11.3).

11.6 INTERMEDIATE HINGE

If the continuity or fixity (in a case of support) is interrupted by a mechanical hinge, the unit displacement stiffness matrix and fixed end stress expressions due to loads or other causes must be modified for the affected member. These modifications derived by their definitions are given for a straight bar of constant cross section with a hinge at C (arbitrary position) in Tables 11-1 and 11-2 respectively. Since the analytical expressions are in algebraic form, they are also valid for the hinged end, thus giving modifications for the propped end beam (or column). For the left end hinge, $u = 0$, $a = 0$, $v = +1$, $b = l$; and for the right end hinge, $u = +1$, $a = l$, $v = 0$, $b = 0$.

Similar modifications for a symmetrical bent bar and a symmetrical parabolic bar with a hinge at the crown are given in Tables 11-3, 11-4 and 11-5, 11-6 respectively (Problem 11.5).

Table 11-1. Segmental Stiffnesses, Straight Bar with a Hinge, Constant Cross Section

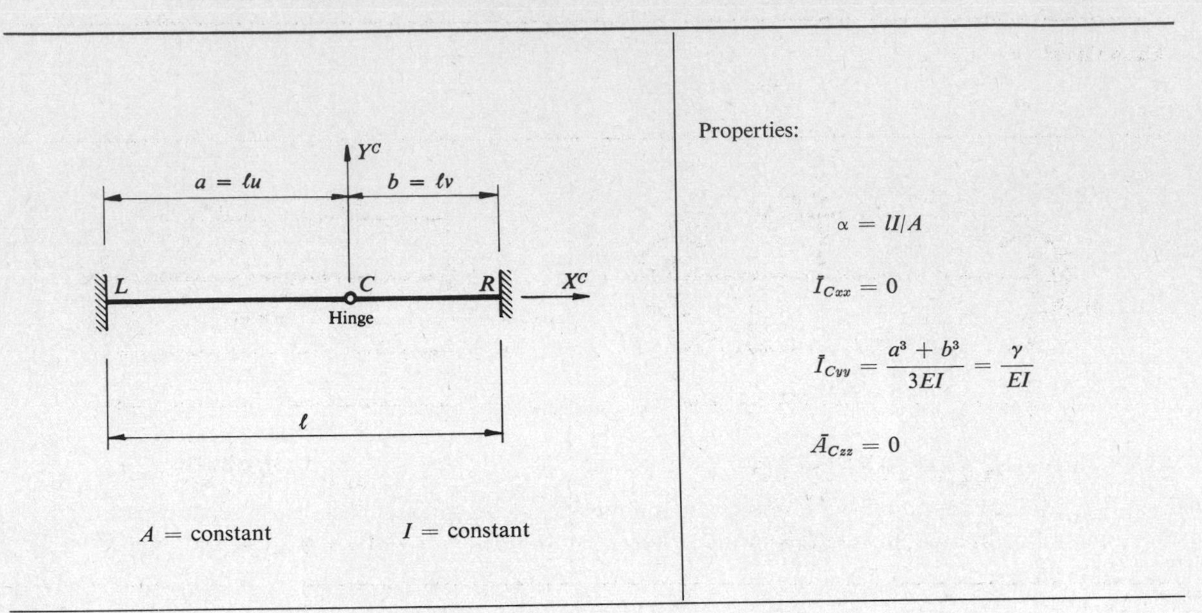

Properties:

$$\alpha = lI/A$$

$$\bar{I}_{Cxx} = 0$$

$$\bar{I}_{Cyy} = \frac{a^3 + b^3}{3EI} = \frac{\gamma}{EI}$$

$$\bar{A}_{Czz} = 0$$

Right End Stiffnesses:

$$\frac{EI}{\gamma}\left[\begin{array}{ccc|ccc} \gamma/\alpha & 0 & 0 & -\gamma/\alpha & 0 & 0 \\ 0 & 1 & -b & 0 & -1 & -a \\ 0 & -b & b^2 & 0 & b & ab \end{array}\right]$$

$$\underbrace{\qquad\qquad}_{k^C_{RR}} \qquad \underbrace{\qquad\qquad}_{k^C_{RL}}$$

Left End Stiffnesses:

$$\frac{EI}{\gamma}\left[\begin{array}{ccc|ccc} -\gamma/\alpha & 0 & 0 & \gamma/\alpha & 0 & 0 \\ 0 & -1 & b & 0 & 1 & a \\ 0 & -a & ab & 0 & a & a^2 \end{array}\right]$$

$$\underbrace{\qquad\qquad}_{k^C_{LR}} \qquad \underbrace{\qquad\qquad}_{k^C_{LL}}$$

Table 11-2. Fixed End Moments, Straight Bar with a Hinge, Constant Cross Section

Equivalents: $u + v = 1$

$m + n = u$ $\quad \lambda = 1 - 3uv$

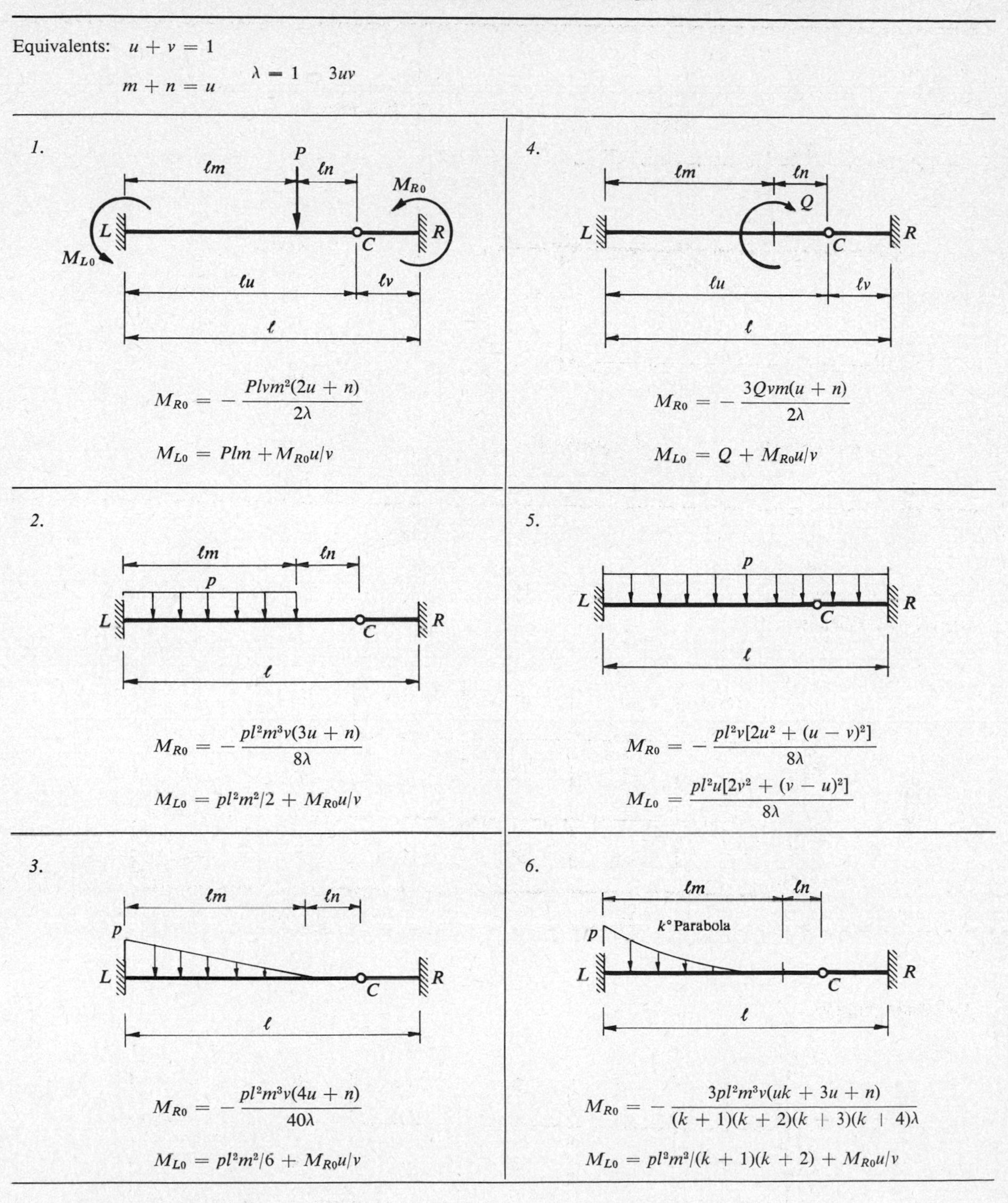

1.

$$M_{R0} = -\frac{Plvm^2(2u + n)}{2\lambda}$$

$$M_{L0} = Plm + M_{R0}u/v$$

2.

$$M_{R0} = -\frac{pl^2m^3v(3u + n)}{8\lambda}$$

$$M_{L0} = pl^2m^2/2 + M_{R0}u/v$$

3.

$$M_{R0} = -\frac{pl^2m^3v(4u + n)}{40\lambda}$$

$$M_{L0} = pl^2m^2/6 + M_{R0}u/v$$

4.

$$M_{R0} = -\frac{3Qvm(u + n)}{2\lambda}$$

$$M_{L0} = Q + M_{R0}u/v$$

5.

$$M_{R0} = -\frac{pl^2v[2u^2 + (u - v)^2]}{8\lambda}$$

$$M_{L0} = \frac{pl^2u[2v^2 + (v - u)^2]}{8\lambda}$$

6.

$$M_{R0} = -\frac{3pl^2m^3v(uk + 3u + n)}{(k + 1)(k + 2)(k + 3)(k + 4)\lambda}$$

$$M_{L0} = pl^2m^2/(k + 1)(k + 2) + M_{R0}u/v$$

7. Difference in temperature:

$$M_{L0} = \frac{3EI(\epsilon_{Tb} - \epsilon_{Tt})\,u(u - v)}{2h\lambda} \qquad M_{R0} = \frac{3EI(\epsilon_{Tb} - \epsilon_{Tt})\,v(u - v)}{2h\lambda}$$

where h = section depth

ϵ_{Tt}, ϵ_{Tb} = thermal strain at top and bottom of the beam respectively

Table 11-3. Segmental Stiffnesses, Symmetrical Bent Bar with a Hinge, Constant Cross Section

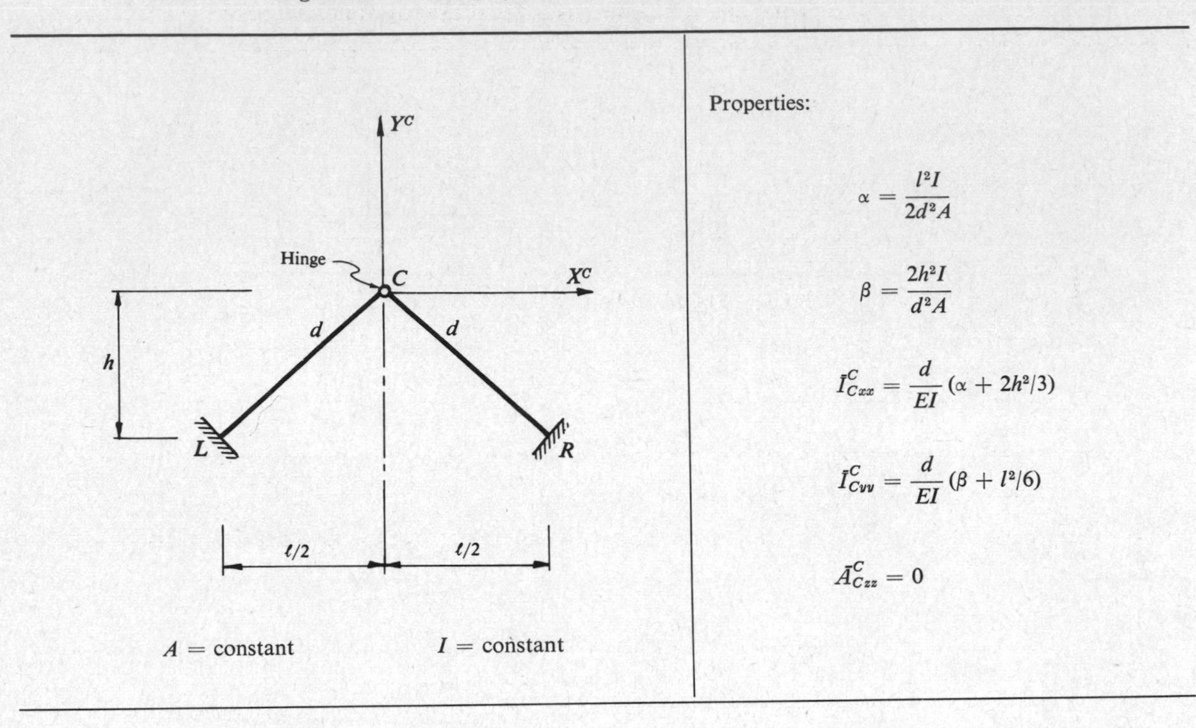

Properties:

$$\alpha = \frac{l^2 I}{2d^2 A}$$

$$\beta = \frac{2h^2 I}{d^2 A}$$

$$\bar{I}^C_{Cxx} = \frac{d}{EI}(\alpha + 2h^2/3)$$

$$\bar{I}^C_{Cyy} = \frac{d}{EI}(\beta + l^2/6)$$

$$\bar{A}^C_{Czz} = 0$$

Right End Stiffnesses ($\alpha \cong 0, \beta \cong 0$):

$$\frac{EI}{d}\left[\begin{array}{ccc|ccc} 3/2h^2 & 0 & -3/2h & -3/2h^2 & 0 & 3/2h \\ 0 & 6/l^2 & -3/l & 0 & -6/l^2 & -3/l \\ -3/2h & -3/l & 3 & 3/2h & 3/l & 0 \end{array}\right]$$

$$\underbrace{\qquad\qquad}_{k^C_{RR}} \qquad \underbrace{\qquad\qquad}_{k^C_{RL}}$$

Left End Stiffnesses ($\alpha \cong 0, \beta \cong 0$):

$$\frac{EI}{d}\left[\begin{array}{ccc|ccc} -3/2h^2 & 0 & 3/2h & 3/2h^2 & 0 & -3/2h \\ 0 & -6/l^2 & 3/l & 0 & 6/l^2 & 3/l \\ 3/2h & -3/l & 0 & -3/2h & 3/l & 3 \end{array}\right]$$

$$\underbrace{\qquad\qquad}_{k^C_{LR}} \qquad \underbrace{\qquad\qquad}_{k^C_{LL}}$$

Table 11-4. Fixed End Stresses ($\alpha \cong 0$, $\beta \cong 0$)
Symmetrical Bent Bar with a Hinge, Constant Cross Section

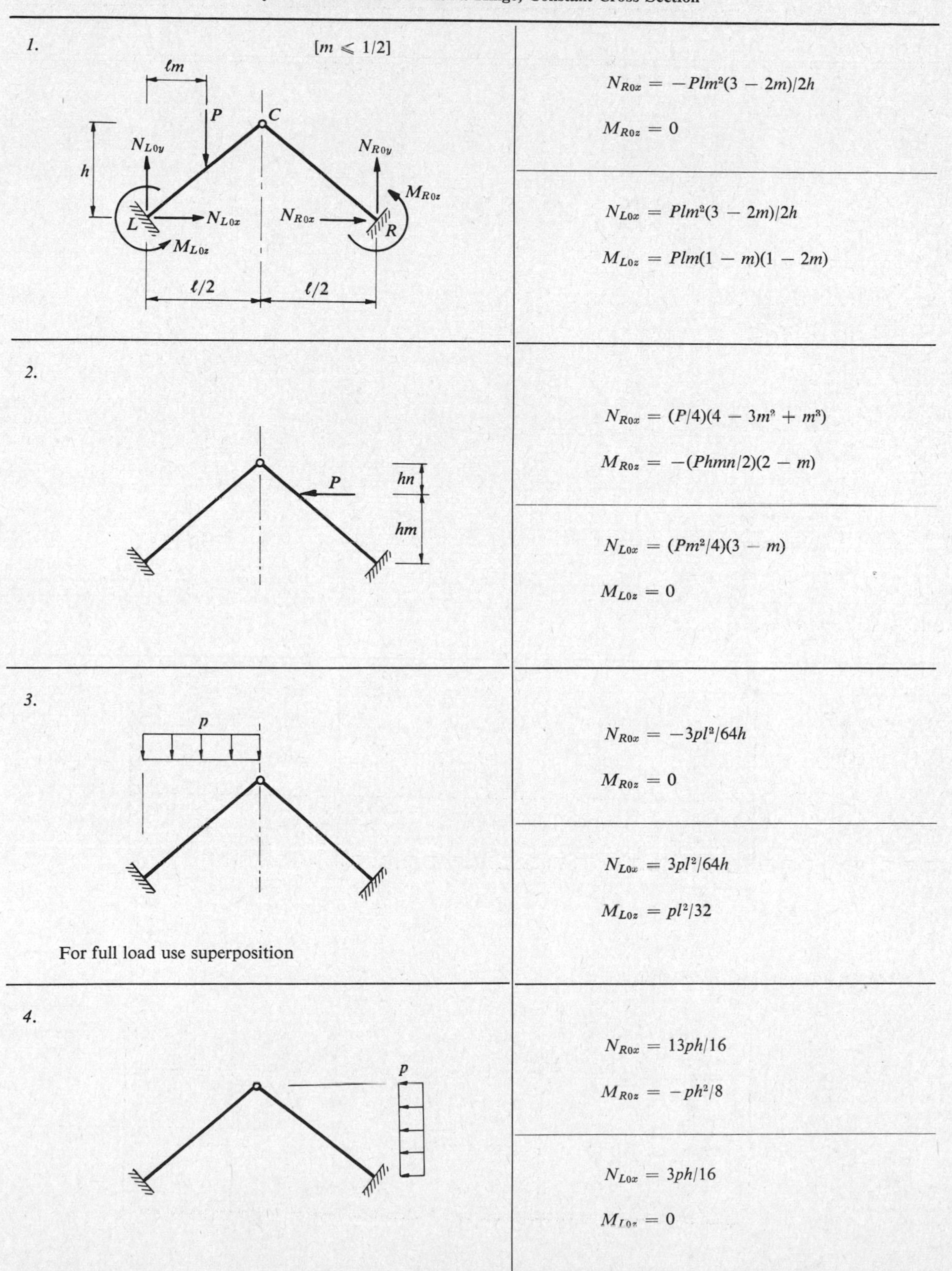

Case	Fixed end stresses
1. $[m \leqslant 1/2]$	$N_{R0x} = -Plm^2(3-2m)/2h$ $M_{R0z} = 0$ $N_{L0x} = Plm^2(3-2m)/2h$ $M_{L0z} = Plm(1-m)(1-2m)$
2.	$N_{R0x} = (P/4)(4 - 3m^2 + m^3)$ $M_{R0z} = -(Phmn/2)(2-m)$ $N_{L0x} = (Pm^2/4)(3-m)$ $M_{L0z} = 0$
3. For full load use superposition	$N_{R0x} = -3pl^2/64h$ $M_{R0z} = 0$ $N_{L0x} = 3pl^2/64h$ $M_{L0z} = pl^2/32$
4.	$N_{R0x} = 13ph/16$ $M_{R0z} = -ph^2/8$ $N_{L0x} = 3ph/16$ $M_{L0z} = 0$

Table 11-5. Segmental Stiffnesses
Symmetrical Parabolic Bar with a Hinge, Variable Cross Section

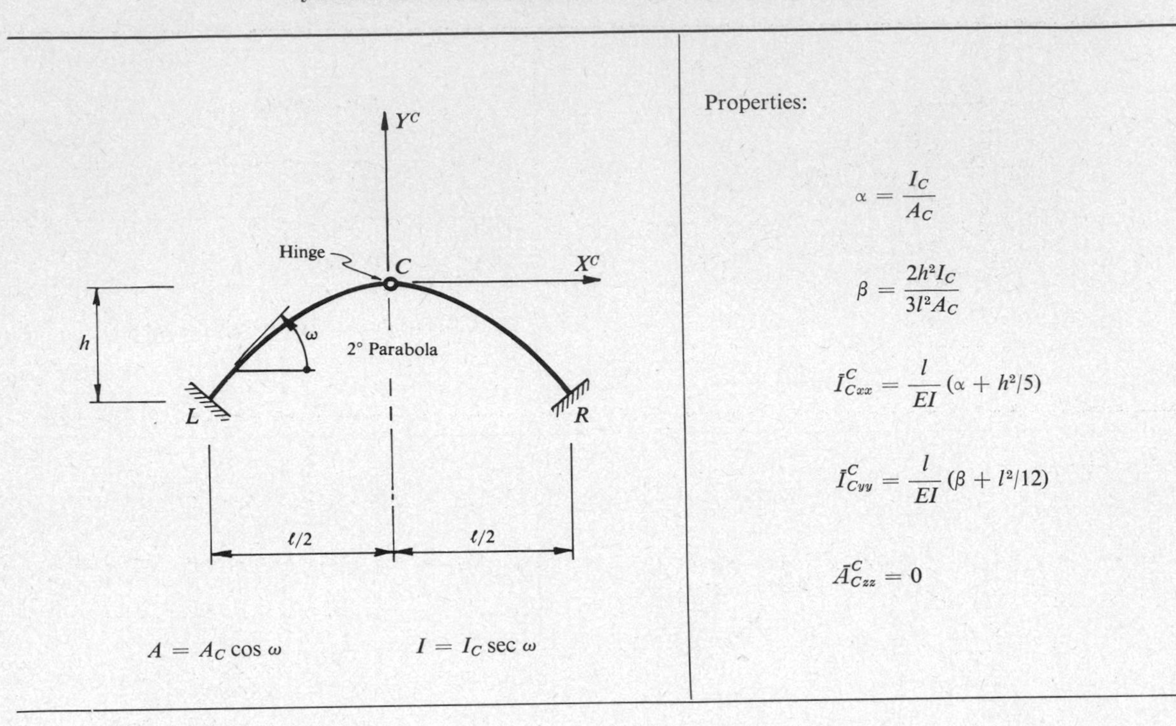

$A = A_C \cos \omega$ $\qquad I = I_C \sec \omega$

Properties:

$$\alpha = \frac{I_C}{A_C}$$

$$\beta = \frac{2h^2 I_C}{3l^2 A_C}$$

$$\bar{I}^C_{Cxx} = \frac{l}{EI}(\alpha + h^2/5)$$

$$\bar{I}^C_{Cyy} = \frac{l}{EI}(\beta + l^2/12)$$

$$\bar{A}^C_{Czz} = 0$$

Right End Stiffnesses ($\alpha \cong 0, \beta \cong 0$):

$$\frac{EI}{l}\left[\underbrace{\begin{array}{c|c|c} 5/h^2 & 0 & -5/h \\ \hline 0 & 12/l^2 & -6/l \\ \hline -5/h & -6/l & 8 \end{array}}_{k^C_{RR}} \;\middle|\; \underbrace{\begin{array}{c|c|c} -5/h^2 & 0 & 5/h \\ \hline 0 & -12/l^2 & -6/l \\ \hline 5/h & 6/l & -2 \end{array}}_{k^C_{RL}}\right]$$

Left End Stiffnesses ($\alpha \cong 0, \beta \cong 0$):

$$\frac{EI}{l}\left[\underbrace{\begin{array}{c|c|c} -5/h^2 & 0 & 5/h \\ \hline 0 & -12/l^2 & 6/l \\ \hline 5/h & -6/l & -2 \end{array}}_{k^C_{LR}} \;\middle|\; \underbrace{\begin{array}{c|c|c} 5/h^2 & 0 & -5/h \\ \hline 0 & 12/l^2 & 6/l \\ \hline -5/h & 6/l & 8 \end{array}}_{k^C_{LL}}\right]$$

Table 11-6. Fixed End Stresses ($\alpha \simeq 0$, $\beta \simeq 0$)
Symmetrical Parabolic Bar with a Hinge, Variable Cross Section

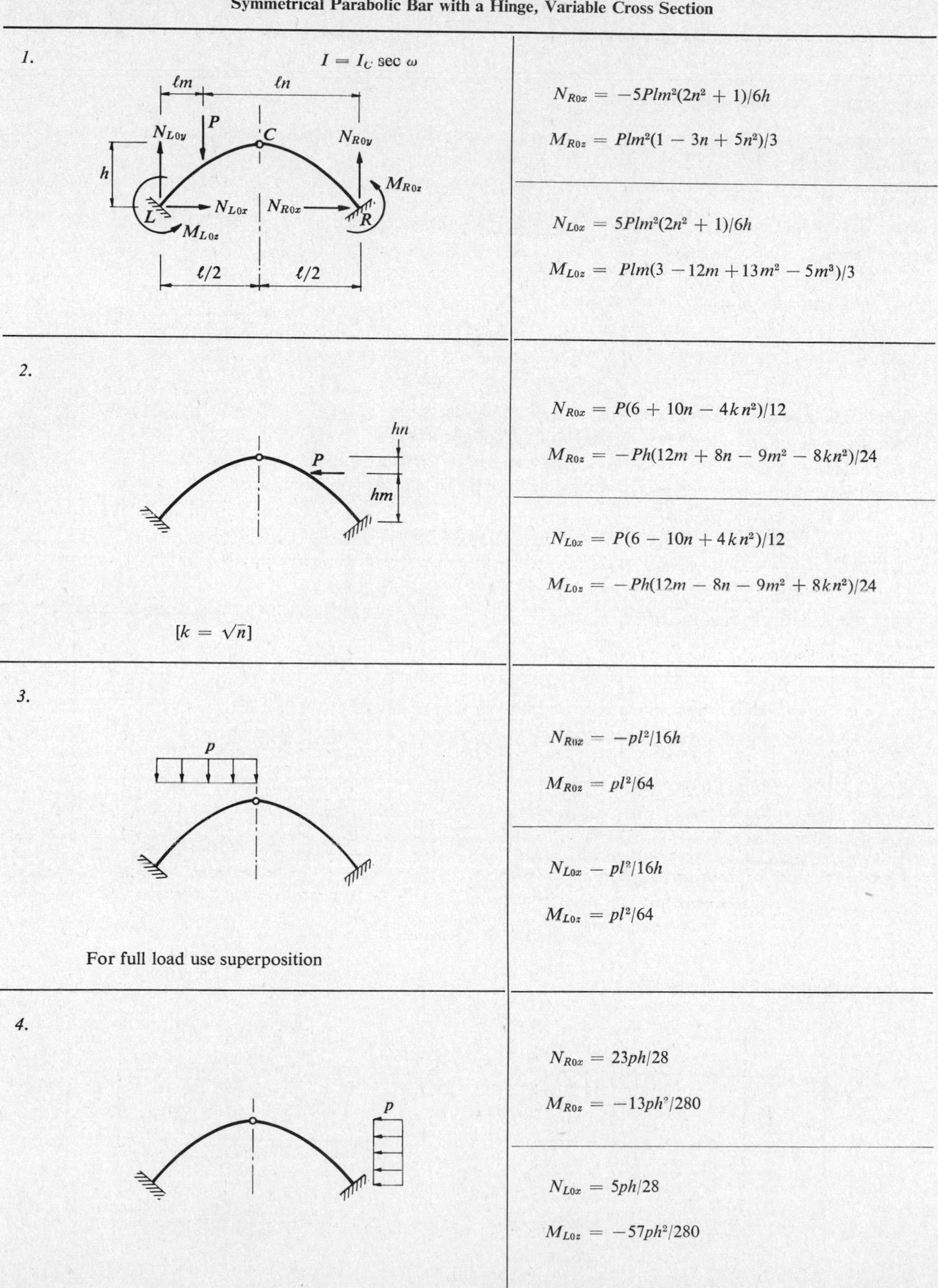

1. $I = I_C \sec \omega$	$N_{R0x} = -5Plm^2(2n^2 + 1)/6h$ $M_{R0z} = Plm^2(1 - 3n + 5n^2)/3$ $N_{L0x} = 5Plm^2(2n^2 + 1)/6h$ $M_{L0z} = Plm(3 - 12m + 13m^2 - 5m^3)/3$
2. $[k = \sqrt{n}]$	$N_{R0x} = P(6 + 10n - 4kn^2)/12$ $M_{R0z} = -Ph(12m + 8n - 9m^2 - 8kn^2)/24$ $N_{L0x} = P(6 - 10n + 4kn^2)/12$ $M_{L0z} = -Ph(12m - 8n - 9m^2 + 8kn^2)/24$
3. For full load use superposition	$N_{R0x} = -pl^2/16h$ $M_{R0z} = pl^2/64$ $N_{L0x} = pl^2/16h$ $M_{L0z} = pl^2/64$
4.	$N_{R0x} = 23ph/28$ $M_{R0z} = -13ph^2/280$ $N_{L0x} = 5ph/28$ $M_{L0z} = -57ph^2/280$

11.7 SYMMETRY AND ANTISYMMETRY

Two other important modifications of the stiffness matrices follow from the symmetry or antisymmetry of the member end displacements.

(a) Symmetrical End Displacements

If $\delta_{Rx} = -\delta_{Lx}$, $\delta_{Ry} = \delta_{Ly}$, $\theta_{Rz} = -\theta_{Lz}$, then the slope-deflection equation (*10.10*) of the right end reduces to

$$\sigma_{RL} = (k_{RR} - k_{RL}i)\,\Delta_R + \sigma_{R0} \tag{11.13}$$

where $i = \text{Diag.}\,[+1, -1, +1]$ and $(k_{RR} - k_{RL}i)$ is the *modified stiffness matrix* of the right end due to the symmetry of end displacements.

(b) Antisymmetrical End Displacements

If $\delta_{Rx} = \delta_{Lx}$, $\delta_{Ry} = -\delta_{Ly}$, $\theta_{Rz} = \theta_{Lz}$, then the slope-deflection equation of the right end reduces to

$$\sigma_{RL} = (k_{RR} + k_{RL}i)\,\Delta_R + \sigma_{R0} \tag{11.14}$$

where i has the same meaning as in the case of symmetry and $(k_{RR} + k_{RL}i)$ is the *modified stiffness matrix* of the right end due to the antisymmetry of end displacements.

The coefficients of the modified stiffness matrices for a symmetrical bar of arbitrary shape and for a straight bar of constant cross section are given in Table 11-7 (Problem 11.6).

Table 11-7. Modified Stiffness Matrices

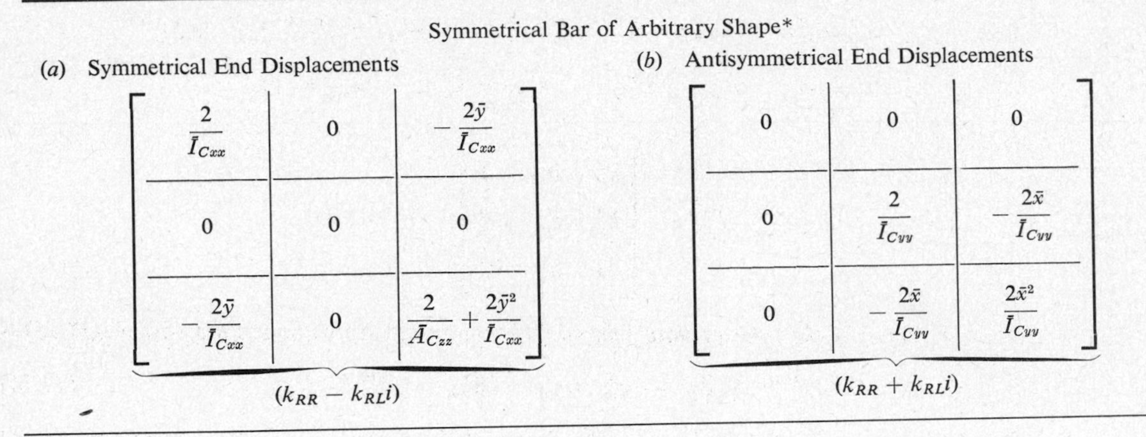

Symmetrical Bar of Arbitrary Shape*

(*a*) Symmetrical End Displacements

$$\underbrace{\begin{bmatrix} \dfrac{2}{\bar{I}_{Cxx}} & 0 & -\dfrac{2\bar{y}}{\bar{I}_{Cxx}} \\ 0 & 0 & 0 \\ -\dfrac{2\bar{y}}{\bar{I}_{Cxx}} & 0 & \dfrac{2}{\bar{A}_{Czz}} + \dfrac{2\bar{y}^2}{\bar{I}_{Cxx}} \end{bmatrix}}_{(k_{RR} - k_{RL}i)}$$

(*b*) Antisymmetrical End Displacements

$$\underbrace{\begin{bmatrix} 0 & 0 & 0 \\ 0 & \dfrac{2}{\bar{I}_{Cyy}} & -\dfrac{2\bar{x}}{\bar{I}_{Cyy}} \\ 0 & -\dfrac{2\bar{x}}{\bar{I}_{Cyy}} & \dfrac{2\bar{x}^2}{\bar{I}_{Cyy}} \end{bmatrix}}_{(k_{RR} + k_{RL}i)}$$

Straight Bar of Constant Cross Section

(*a*) Symmetrical End Displacements

$$\underbrace{\begin{bmatrix} \dfrac{2EA}{l} & 0 & 0 \\ 0 & 0 & 0 \\ 0 & 0 & \dfrac{2EI}{l} \end{bmatrix}}_{(k_{RR} - k_{RL}i)}$$

(*b*) Antisymmetrical End Displacements

$$\underbrace{\begin{bmatrix} 0 & 0 & 0 \\ 0 & \dfrac{24EI}{l^3} & -\dfrac{12EI}{l^2} \\ 0 & -\dfrac{12EI}{l^2} & \dfrac{6EI}{l} \end{bmatrix}}_{(k_{RR} + k_{RL}i)}$$

*Note: $\bar{x} = x^C_{LC}$, $\bar{y} = y^C_{LC}$; for $\bar{I}_{Cxx}$, $\bar{I}_{Cyy}$, $\bar{A}_{Czz}$ refer to (10.20). The superscript C is omitted in all terms.

11.8 VARIABLE CROSS SECTION

If the cross section of the bar varies, the analytical expressions for the coefficients of the unit displacement stiffness matrix and for the fixed end stresses due to loads and other causes become more involved. Since the components of these expressions are the respective unit stress flexibilities and/or unit load flexibilities, these flexibility coefficients are calculated first by one of the methods outlined in Chapter 6 and then inserted as numerical constants in the respective stiffness expression (Problems 11.7 and 11.8).

11.9 GROUP STIFFNESS MATRIX

For bars of polygonal shape and frames with a large number joints, it serves to an advantage to introduce the concept of *group stiffness*, which is functionally similar to the group flexibility derived in Sec. 9.3.

(a) Single Branch Group

The stiffness matrix for the planar bar LR consisting of segments Li, ij, jk, kR can be prepared by Table 10-6 or more conveniently by the recurrent use of (*11.10*) in terms of the segmental stiffnesses. By the latter,

$$\begin{bmatrix} k^0_{RR,m} & k^0_{Rm} & \\ k^0_{mR} & k_m{}^0 & k^0_{mL} \\ & k^0_{Lm} & k^0_{LL,m} \end{bmatrix} \begin{bmatrix} \Delta_R{}^0 \\ \Delta_m{}^0 \\ \Delta_L{}^0 \end{bmatrix} + \begin{bmatrix} \sigma^0_{R0,m} \\ \sigma^0_{m0} \\ \sigma^0_{L0,m} \end{bmatrix} = \begin{bmatrix} \sigma^0_{RL} \\ W_m{}^0 \\ \sigma^0_{LR} \end{bmatrix} \tag{11.15}$$

where

$$\Delta_m{}^0 = \{\Delta_k{}^0, \Delta_j{}^0, \Delta_i{}^0\}, \qquad \sigma^0_{m0} = \{\sigma^0_{k0}, \sigma^0_{j0}, \sigma^0_{i0}\}, \qquad W_m{}^0 = \{W_k{}^0, W_j{}^0, W_i{}^0\},$$

$$k^0_{Rm} = k^0_{Rk}, \qquad k^0_{mR} = k^0_{kR}, \qquad k^0_{Lm} = k^0_{Li}, \qquad k^0_{mL} = k^0_{iL}$$

and

$$k_m{}^0 = \begin{bmatrix} k_k{}^0 & k^0_{kj} & 0 \\ k^0_{jk} & k_j{}^0 & k^0_{ji} \\ 0 & k^0_{ij} & k_i{}^0 \end{bmatrix}$$

The *displacement vector of the intermediate joints i, j, k* computed from the second row of (*11.15*) is

$$\Delta_m{}^0 = -k_m^{0)-1} k^0_{mR} \Delta_R{}^0 - k_m^{0)-1}(\sigma^0_{m0} - W_m{}^0) - k_m^{0)-1} k^0_{mL} \Delta_L{}^0 \tag{11.16}$$

and the *slope-deflection equations* of LR given by the first and third row of (*11.15*) in terms of (*11.16*) become

$$\sigma^0_{RL} = \underbrace{(k^0_{RR,m} - k^0_{Rm} k_m^{0)-1} k^0_{mR})}_{k^0_{RR}} \Delta_R{}^0 - \underbrace{k^0_{Rm} k_m^{0)-1} k^0_{mL}}_{k^0_{RL}} \Delta_L{}^0 + \underbrace{\sigma^0_{R0,m} - k^0_{Rm} k_m^{0)-1}(\sigma^0_{m0} - W_m{}^0)}_{\sigma^0_{R0}}$$

$$\sigma^0_{LR} = \underbrace{-k^0_{Lm} k_m^{0)-1} k^0_{mR}}_{k^0_{LR}} \Delta_R{}^0 + \underbrace{(k^0_{LL,m} - k^0_{Lm} k_m^{0)-1} k^0_{mL})}_{k^0_{LL}} \Delta_L{}^0 + \underbrace{\sigma^0_{L0,m} - k^0_{Lm} k_m^{0)-1}(\sigma^0_{m0} - W_m{}^0)}_{\sigma^0_{L0}} \tag{11.17}$$

where the unit displacement coefficients k^0_{RR}, k^0_{RL}, k^0_{LR}, k^0_{RR} are the *group stiffnesses* and the load functions σ^0_{R0}, σ^0_{L0} are the *group fixed end stresses* (due to these loads), all related to R and L when i, j, k are free to displace (Problem 11.9).

(b) Multibranch Group

The technique of eliminating some unknowns and developing the stiffness matrix in terms of stresses due to certain unit displacements of the system leads to the *generalized group stiffness matrix* concept.

In order to obtain this matrix, let the system matrix (*11.10*) written for a complex frame of general configuration be given in the following partitioned form:

$$\begin{bmatrix} k_S{}^0 & k_{SM}^0 \\ k_{MS}^0 & k_M{}^0 \end{bmatrix}\begin{bmatrix} \Delta_S{}^0 \\ \Delta_M{}^0 \end{bmatrix} + \begin{bmatrix} \sigma_{S0,M}^0 \\ \sigma_{M0}^0 \end{bmatrix} = \begin{bmatrix} \sigma_{SM}^0 \\ W_M{}^0 \end{bmatrix} \tag{11.18}$$

from which

$$\Delta_M{}^0 = -k_M^{0)-1} k_{MS}^0 \Delta_S{}^0 - k_M^{0)-1}(\sigma_{M0}^0 - W_M{}^0) \tag{11.19}$$

and

$$\sigma_{SM}^0 = \underbrace{(k_S{}^0 - k_{SM}^0 k_M^{0)-1} k_{MS}^0)}_{k_{SS}^0} \Delta_S{}^0 + \underbrace{\sigma_{S0,M}^0 - k_{SM}^0 k_M^{0)-1}(\sigma_{M0}^0 - W_M{}^0)}_{\sigma_{S0}^0} \tag{11.20}$$

where k_{SS}^0 is the *multibranch group stiffness matrix* and σ_{S0}^0 is the *multibranch group fixed end stress vector* due to loads (or other causes) (Problem 11.10).

11.10 GENERAL METHOD

Joint equilibrium equations in terms of the segmental stiffnesses and fixed end stresses due to primary and secondary causes developed in this chapter for particular structures are only special forms of the general stiffness method, applicable to structures of all kinds. The underlying principles of this method and the procedure of application have been discussed in the first part of Chapter 10; the formulation of this procedure in terms of segmental matrices is introduced here as a *final summary and conclusion of the stiffness analysis*.

(1) *Component Systems.* The degree of kinematic indeterminacy of the initial system is determined by (*10.1*) and the initial system is resolved into a basic system and complementary system, the definitions and qualifications of which are given in Sec. 10.1.

(2) *Basic System.* By locking (fixing) the initial system at selected points and retaining applied loads, the basic system and its load vector $W = \{W_a, W_b, ..., W_m\}$ are defined. The joint stress vector required to produce the locking of joints is

$$\sigma_W = jsW = K_W W \tag{11.21}$$

where K_W is the *unit load system stiffness matrix*. For the construction of this matrix, the basic structure is resolved in a series of segments ($a, b, ..., m$), the segmental or group stiffnesses of which are given by (*10.19*) or (*11.17*).

The diagonal assembly of these segmental matrices, known as the *unit load segmental stiffness chain*, is

$$s = \begin{bmatrix} s_a & & & & \\ & s_b & & & \\ & & \cdot & & \\ & & & \cdot & \\ & & & & s_m \end{bmatrix} \tag{11.22}$$

where all diagonal terms are [6×3] matrices and all off-diagonal terms are zero. This form of construction, of course, allows only one load vector per segment.

The transfer of the effect of W from the fixed end of segments to the respective joint ($i, j, ..., p$) is accomplished by the *general transfer matrix j*,

$$\begin{array}{cccc} s_a W_a = +1 & s_b W_b = +1 & \cdots & s_m W_m = +1 \\ \downarrow & \downarrow & & \downarrow \end{array}$$

$$j = \begin{bmatrix} j_{ia} & j_{ib} & \cdots & j_{im} \\ j_{ja} & j_{jb} & \cdots & j_{jm} \\ \cdots & \cdots & \cdots & \cdots \\ j_{pa} & j_{pb} & \cdots & j_{pm} \end{bmatrix} \tag{11.23}$$

where each of these columns consists of p (3×6) matrices of influence values caused by the respective fixed end unit stress vector, which precludes that only one load vector acts in each segment.

With

$$K_W = js \tag{11.24}$$

known, the *joint stress vector* σ_W is determined. In practice, however, this transformation is rarely performed by multiplication. All that is required is the sum of fixed end stresses due to loads at the reference joints and this can be done directly.

(3) *Complementary System.* By removing the applied loads from the initial system and introducing unknown (redundant) displacements of joints satisfying the natural constraints of the initial system, the complementary system and its redundant displacement vector $\Delta = \{\Delta_i, \Delta_j, ..., \Delta_p\}$ are defined. The joint stress vector at $i, j,..., p$ is

$$\sigma_\Delta = jkj^{)T}\Delta = K_\Delta \Delta \tag{11.25}$$

where K_Δ is the *unit displacement system stiffness matrix*. For the construction of this matrix, the complementary structure is resolved in a series of segments $(a, b,..., m)$, the segmental or group stiffnesses of which are given again by (*10.19*) or (*11.17*).

The diagonal assembly of these matrices, known as the *unit displacement segmental stiffness chain* is

$$k = \begin{bmatrix} k_a & & & \\ & k_b & & \\ & & \cdot & \\ & & & \cdot \\ & & & & k_m \end{bmatrix} \tag{11.26}$$

where all diagonal terms are (6×6) matrices and all off-diagonal terms are zero.

The transfer of the effect of Δ from the points of action to the respective segments $(a, b,..., m)$ is accomplished by the transpose of the general transfer matrix j.

The matrix product $kj^{)T}\Delta$ gives the end stress vector due to Δ at $a, b,..., m$, the effect of which must be transferred back to the joints $i, j,..., p$.

The general joint transfer matrix j produces the necessary vehicle, making

$$K_\Delta = jkj^{)T} \tag{11.27}$$

With K_Δ known, σ_Δ becomes a linear combination of the computed coefficients of K_Δ and the unknown components of Δ. The congruent transformation (*11.27*) is rarely necessary. Laying out the segmental matrices diagonally like a deck of cards with overlapping corners and summing the overlapping terms yields the same result (Sec. 11.3).

(4) *Secondary Effects.* The joint stress vector in the basic structure due to secondary causes such as volume change, prestressing, etc., is determined in resultant form or can be obtained by superposition of transferred segmental effects as

$$\sigma_T = j\{\sigma_{aT}, \sigma_{bT}, ..., \sigma_{mT}\} \tag{11.28}$$

where $\sigma_{aT}, \sigma_{bT}, ..., \sigma_{mT}$ are the *segmental fixed end stress matrices due to these secondary causes.*

Similarly as in steps (2) and (3), the same result is obtained by summing the fixed end stresses at the respective joints.

(5) *Governing Equation.* The superposition of joint stress vectors σ_W, σ_T and σ_Δ must satisfy the condition of equilibrium, namely, the algebraic sum of joint stresses at $i, j,..., p$ must either equal zero or equal the prescribed joint stress (joint load). Thus

$$\sigma_W + \sigma_T + \sigma_\Delta = \sigma$$

and in terms of (*11.21*) and (*11.25*)

$$K_\Delta \Delta + K_W W + \sigma_T = \sigma \tag{11.29}$$

Since there are p redundant vectors and p matrix equilibrium equations,

$$\Delta = -K_\Delta^{)-1}[K_W W + \sigma_T - \sigma] \tag{11.30}$$

If $\sigma_T = 0$, (*11.30*) in terms of (*11.24*) and (*11.25*) becomes

$$\Delta = -[jkj^{)T}]^{-1}[jsW - \sigma] \tag{11.31}$$

If the loads act at the segment boundaries, (*11.31*) reduces to the *standard form*

$$\Delta = [jkj^{)T}]^{-1}\, W = K_{\Delta}^{)-1} W \tag{11.32}$$

which occurs in the literature in *three different forms*:

Argyris[1]: $U = [a_1^{)T} k a_1]^{-1}\, R$

Gallagher[2]: $\Delta = [a^{)T} k a]^{-1}\, p$

Prezemieniecki[3]: $U = [A^{)T} k A]^{-1}\, P$

Although the symbols differ, their physical *meaning is the same.*

(6) *Stress Vector.* With the redundants known, the *true stress vector* at $a, b, \ldots, m$ due to loads in segments is

$$\sigma = kj^{)T}\Delta + sW = \underbrace{[s - kj^{)T} K_{\Delta}^{)-1} K_W]}_{A}\, W \tag{11.33}$$

where A is the *true unit load system transfer matrix* in the initial system.

(7) *Displacement Vector.* Similarly, the *true displacement vector* at $a, b, \ldots, m$ in terms of (*11.30*) is

$$\Delta = \underbrace{-K_{\Delta}^{)-1} K_W}_{\Phi}\, W \tag{11.34}$$

where Φ is the *true unit load system flexibility matrix* in the initial system.

Again as in Sec. 9.9, once the true stress vector and the true displacement vectors are known, the objective of the analysis is accomplished (Problem 11.11).

11.11 GENERAL PROPERTIES

The general procedure described in the preceding section deals with *three classes of basic matrices*,

(*a*) state vector W, σ, Δ,

(*b*) transfer matrices $j_W = j_\Delta = j$,

(*c*) stiffness chain matrices k, s,

and *two system matrices* K_W, K_Δ.

The coefficients of stiffness matrices of all kinds exhibit certain *characteristic properties* useful in their construction.

(1) *Symmetry*:

By Maxwell-Mohr's Theorem, $k_{ij} = k_{ji}^{)T}$ and consequently all stiffness matrices (elemental, segmental, group and system) are symmetrical, which reduces the number of coefficients to be determined.

(2) *Positive Definiteness*:

Since the stress due to a unit displacement of the same line of action cannot act against the direction of the cause, the principal diagonal coefficients (direct stiffnesses) cannot be negative.

(3) *Superposition of Coefficients*:

Since the stress due to a unit displacement is the sum of component stresses, each stiffness can be treated as a set of parallel springs.

---

[1] J. H. Argyris, "Recent Advances in Matrix Methods of Structural Analysis," Macmillan Company, New York, 1964.

[2] R. H. Gallagher, "A Correlation Study of Methods of Matrix Structural Analysis," Macmillan Company, New York, 1964.

[3] J. S. Prezemieniecki, "Theory of Matrix Structural Analysis," McGraw-Hill Book Company, New York, 1968.

Solved Problems

SYSTEM STIFFNESS MATRIX

11.1. Construct the system stiffness matrix K^0 for the frame shown in Fig. P-11.1 and set up the equilibrium equation (*11.4*). $A/I = 2\ \text{ft}^{-2}$ for all bars.

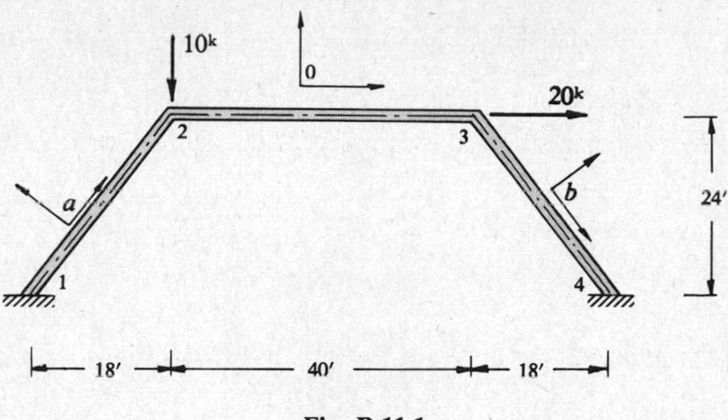

Fig. P-11.1

The system has six independent joint displacements, $\Delta^0 = \{\Delta_2^0, \Delta_3^0\}$. The system stiffness matrix

$$K^0 = \begin{bmatrix} k_2^0 & k_{23}^0 \\ k_{32}^0 & k_3^0 \end{bmatrix}$$

where

$$k_2^0 = k_{22,1}^0 + k_{22,3}^0, \qquad k_3^0 = k_{33,2}^0 + k_{33,4}^0$$

$$k_{22,1}^0 = \omega^{0a} k_{22,1}^a \omega^{a0} = \frac{EI}{30^3}\begin{bmatrix} 0.6 & -0.8 & 0 \\ 0.8 & 0.6 & 0 \\ 0 & 0 & 1 \end{bmatrix}\begin{bmatrix} 2(30)^2 & 0 & 0 \\ 0 & 12 & -6(30) \\ 0 & -6(30) & 4(30)^2 \end{bmatrix}\begin{bmatrix} 0.6 & 0.8 & 0 \\ -0.8 & 0.6 & 0 \\ 0 & 0 & 1 \end{bmatrix}$$

$$= \frac{EI}{30^3}\begin{bmatrix} 655.7 & 858.2 & 144 \\ 858.2 & 1{,}156.3 & -108 \\ 144 & -108 & 3{,}600 \end{bmatrix} \qquad \text{where} \quad \omega_{a0} = \sin^{-1} 0.8$$

Similarly,

$$k_{33,4}^0 = \omega^{0b} k_{33,4}^b \omega^{b0} = \frac{EI}{30^3}\begin{bmatrix} 655.7 & -858.2 & 144 \\ -858.2 & 1{,}156.3 & 108 \\ 144 & 108 & 3{,}600 \end{bmatrix} \qquad \text{where} \quad \omega_{b0} = -\sin^{-1} 0.8$$

Also,

$$k_{22,3}^0 = \frac{EI}{40^3}\begin{bmatrix} 2(40)^2 & 0 & 0 \\ 0 & 12 & 6(40) \\ 0 & 6(40) & 4(40)^2 \end{bmatrix}, \qquad k_{33,2}^0 = \frac{EI}{40^3}\begin{bmatrix} 2(40)^2 & 0 & 0 \\ 0 & 12 & -6(40) \\ 0 & -6(40) & 4(40)^2 \end{bmatrix}$$

$$k_{23}^0 = \frac{EI}{40^3}\begin{bmatrix} -2(40)^2 & 0 & 0 \\ 0 & -12 & 6(40) \\ 0 & -6(40) & 2(40)^2 \end{bmatrix} = k_{32}^{0)T}$$

Substitution of these submatrices gives K^0.

The equilibrium equation is as shown in (*11.4*) with $W = \{0, -10, 0, 20, 0, 0\}$.

11.2. Construct the system stiffness matrix K^0 and set up the equilibrium equation matrix (*11.6*) for the frame shown in Fig. P-11.2. $(A/I)_{girder} = 2\ \text{ft}^{-2}$ and $(A/I)_{column} = 3\ \text{ft}^{-2}$.

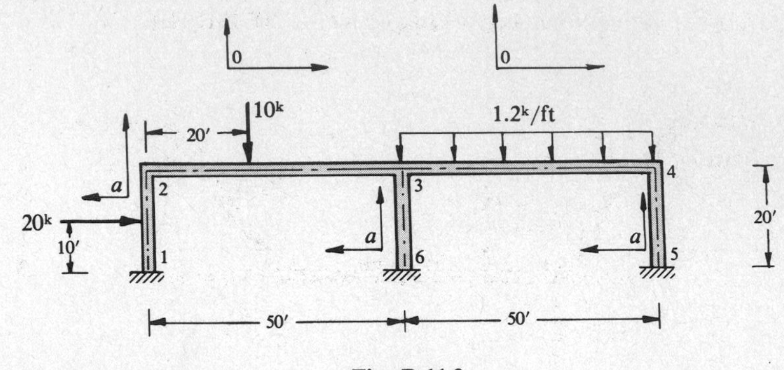

Fig. P-11.2

The basic equation to be set up is

$$K^0\Delta^0 + \sigma^0 = W^0 \tag{1}$$

in which the system stiffness matrix

$$K^0 = \begin{bmatrix} k_2^0 & k_{23}^0 & 0 \\ k_{32}^0 & k_3^0 & k_{34}^0 \\ 0 & k_{43}^0 & k_4^0 \end{bmatrix} \quad \text{where} \quad k_2^0 = k_{22,1}^0 + k_{22,3}^0, \quad k_3^0 = k_{33,2}^0 + k_{33,6}^0 + k_{33,4}^0, \quad k_4^0 = k_{44,3}^0 + k_{44,5}^0$$

and

$$\Delta^0 = \{\Delta_2^0, \Delta_3^0, \Delta_4^0\}$$

Now

$$k_{22,1}^0 = k_{33,6}^0 = k_{44,5}^0 = \omega^{0a} k_{22,1}^a \omega^{a0} = \frac{EI}{20^3}\begin{bmatrix} 12 & 0 & 120 \\ 0 & 1{,}200 & 0 \\ 120 & 0 & 1{,}600 \end{bmatrix} \quad \text{where} \quad \omega_{a0} = 90°$$

$$k_{22,3}^0 = k_{33,4}^0 = \frac{EI}{50^3}\begin{bmatrix} 2(50)^2 & 0 & 0 \\ 0 & 12 & 6(50) \\ 0 & 6(50) & 4(50)^2 \end{bmatrix}$$

$$k_{33,2}^0 = k_{44,3}^0 = \frac{EI}{50^3}\begin{bmatrix} 2(50)^2 & 0 & 0 \\ 0 & 12 & -6(50) \\ 0 & -6(50) & 4(50)^2 \end{bmatrix}$$

$$k_{23}^0 = k_{34}^0 = \frac{EI}{50^3}\begin{bmatrix} -2(50)^2 & 0 & 0 \\ 0 & -12 & 6(50) \\ 0 & -6(50) & 2(50)^2 \end{bmatrix} = k_{32}^{0)T} = k_{43}^{0)T}$$

The joint effect vector

$$\sigma^0 = \{\sigma_{20}^0, \sigma_{30}^0, \sigma_{40}^0\}$$

where

$$\sigma_{20}^0 = \sigma_{20,1}^0 + \sigma_{20,3}^0 = \omega^{0a}\sigma_{20,1}^a + \sigma_{20,3}^0 = \begin{bmatrix} 0 & -1 & 0 \\ 1 & 0 & 0 \\ 0 & 0 & 1 \end{bmatrix}\begin{bmatrix} 0 \\ 10 \\ -50 \end{bmatrix} + \begin{bmatrix} 0 \\ 6.48 \\ 72 \end{bmatrix} = \begin{bmatrix} -10 \\ 6.48 \\ 22 \end{bmatrix}$$

and similarly

$$\sigma_{30}^0 = \sigma_{30,2}^0 + \sigma_{30,6}^0 + \sigma_{30,4}^0 = \{0, 33.52, 202\} \qquad \sigma_{40}^0 = \sigma_{40,3}^0 + \sigma_{40,5}^0 = \{0, 30, -250\}$$

For the given frame, $W^0 = 0$.

Substitution of the established values in (*1*) gives the required matrix equation.

ELASTIC CONSTRAINTS

11.3. Set up the system stiffness matrix K^0 for the system 1234 shown in Fig. P-11.3. $A/I = 2\text{ ft}^{-2}$ for all bars. Use $EI = 450 \times 10^3\text{ k-ft}^2$, $k_{1\Delta x} = k_{2\Delta x} = k_{3\Delta x} = k_{4\Delta x} = 200\text{ k/ft}$, $k_{1\Delta y} = k_{2\Delta y} = k_{3\Delta y} = k_{4\Delta y} = 200\text{ k/ft}$ and $k_{1\theta z} = k_{2\theta z} = k_{3\theta z} = k_{4\theta z} = 20 \times 10^3\text{ k-ft/rad}$.

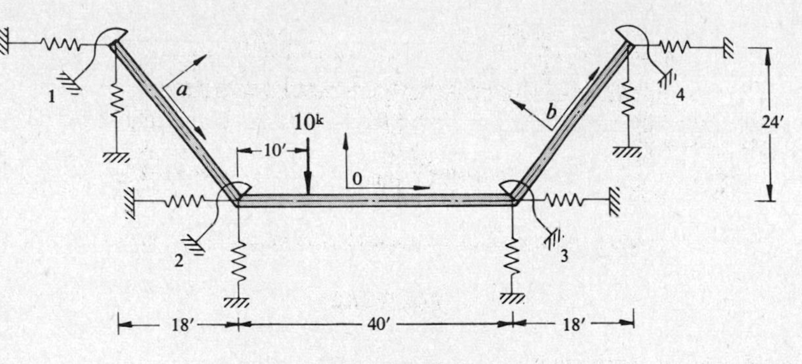

Fig. P-11.3

The system stiffness matrix

$$K^0 = \begin{bmatrix} k_1^0 & k_{12}^0 & 0 & 0 \\ k_{21}^0 & k_2^0 & k_{23}^0 & 0 \\ 0 & k_{32}^0 & k_3^0 & k_{34}^0 \\ 0 & 0 & k_{43}^0 & k_4^0 \end{bmatrix}$$

where $k_1^0 = k_{11,2}^0 + k_{11,\Delta}^0$, $k_2^0 = k_{22,1}^0 + k_{22,\Delta}^0 + k_{22,3}^0$, $k_3^0 = k_{33,2}^0 + k_{33,\Delta}^0 + k_{33,4}^0$, $k_4^0 = k_{44,3}^0 + k_{44,\Delta}^0$. Some values computed in Problem 11.1 can be used here too. Thus

$$k_{11,2}^0 = \omega^{0a} k_{11,2}^a \omega^{a0} = \frac{EI}{30^3}\begin{bmatrix} 655.7 & -858.2 & 144 \\ -858.2 & 1{,}156.3 & 108 \\ 144 & 108 & 3{,}600 \end{bmatrix}$$

$$k_{44,3}^0 = \omega^{0b} k_{44,3}^b \omega^{b0} = \frac{EI}{30^3}\begin{bmatrix} 655.7 & 858.2 & 144 \\ 858.2 & 1{,}156.3 & -108 \\ 144 & -108 & 3{,}600 \end{bmatrix}$$

$$k_{22,3}^0 = \frac{EI}{40^3}\begin{bmatrix} 3{,}200 & 0 & 0 \\ 0 & 12 & 240 \\ 0 & 240 & 6{,}400 \end{bmatrix}, \qquad k_{33,2}^0 = \frac{EI}{40^3}\begin{bmatrix} 3{,}200 & 0 & 0 \\ 0 & 12 & -240 \\ 0 & -240 & 6{,}400 \end{bmatrix}$$

Additionally,

$$k_{22,1}^0 = \omega^{0a} k_{22,1}^a \omega^{a0} = \frac{EI}{30^3}\begin{bmatrix} 655.7 & -858.2 & -144 \\ -858.2 & 1{,}156.3 & -108 \\ -144 & -108 & 3{,}600 \end{bmatrix}$$

$$k_{33,4}^0 = \omega^{0b} k_{33,4}^b \omega^{b0} = \frac{EI}{30^3}\begin{bmatrix} 655.7 & 858.2 & -144 \\ 858.2 & 1{,}156.3 & 108 \\ -144 & 108 & 3{,}600 \end{bmatrix}$$

and

$$k_{jj,\Delta}^0 = \begin{bmatrix} 200 & 0 & 0 \\ 0 & 200 & 0 \\ 0 & 0 & 20{,}000 \end{bmatrix} \qquad j = 1, 2, 3, 4$$

INTERMEDIATE HINGE

11.4. Set up the equilibrium matrix equation for the frame shown in Fig. P-11.4 using modified stiffnesses discussed in Sec. 11.6. Use $(A/I)_{\text{girder}} = 2\text{ ft}^{-2}$, $(A/I)_{\text{column}} = 1\text{ ft}^{-2}$.

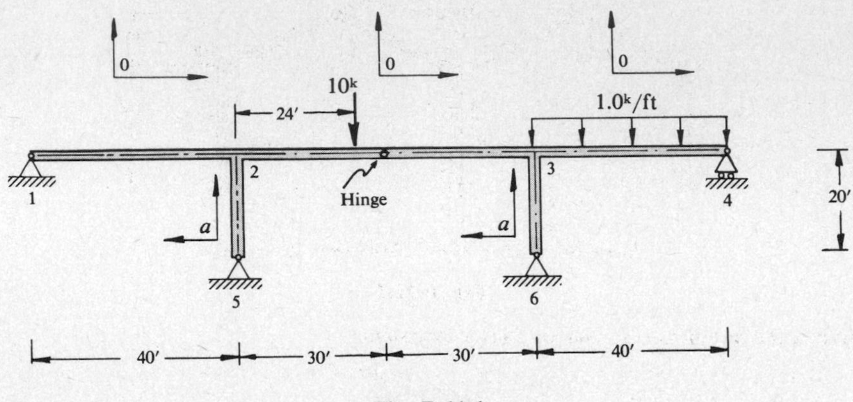

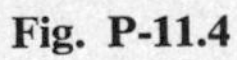
Fig. P-11.4

Modified stiffnesses for members 12, 52 and 63 for left end hinges, for member 34 for a right end hinge and for member 23 for a intermediate hinge are computed using Table 11-1 and appropriate values of parameters a and b. Also, if there are no displacements Δ_x or Δ_y at the support hinges, the problem can be formulated using simpler system stiffness matrix

$$K^0 = \begin{bmatrix} k_2{}^0 & k_{23}^0 \\ k_{32}^0 & k_3{}^0 \end{bmatrix}$$

where $k_2{}^0 = k_{22,1}^0 + k_{22,5}^0 + k_{22,3}^0$, $k_3{}^0 = k_{33,2}^0 + k_{33,6}^0 + k_{33,4}^0$, all modified, and

$$\Delta^0 = \{\Delta_2{}^0, \Delta_3{}^0\}.$$

Now

$$k_{22,1}^0 = \frac{3EI}{40^3}\begin{bmatrix} (2)40^2/3 & 0 & 0 \\ 0 & 1 & -40 \\ 0 & -40 & 40^2 \end{bmatrix}, \qquad k_{33,4}^0 = \frac{3EI}{40^3}\begin{bmatrix} (2)40^2/3 & 0 & 0 \\ 0 & 1 & 40 \\ 0 & 40 & 40^2 \end{bmatrix}$$

$$k_{22,5}^0 = \omega^{0a}{}^a k_{22,5}\omega^{a0} = \frac{3EI}{20^3}\begin{bmatrix} 1 & 0 & 20 \\ 0 & 20^2/3 & 0 \\ 20 & 0 & 20^2 \end{bmatrix} = k_{33,6}^0 \quad \text{and} \quad \omega_{a0} = 90^\circ$$

$$k_{22,3}^0 = \frac{12EI}{60^3}\begin{bmatrix} (2)60^2/12 & 0 & 0 \\ 0 & 1 & 30 \\ 0 & 30 & 60^2/4 \end{bmatrix}, \qquad k_{33,2}^0 = \frac{12EI}{60^3}\begin{bmatrix} (2)60^2/12 & 0 & 0 \\ 0 & 1 & -30 \\ 0 & -30 & 60^2/4 \end{bmatrix}$$

Also,

$$k_{23}^0 = \frac{12EI}{60^3}\begin{bmatrix} -(2)60^2/12 & 0 & 0 \\ 0 & -1 & 30 \\ 0 & -30 & 60^2/4 \end{bmatrix} = k_{32}^{0)T}$$

The equilibrium matrix equation is $K^0\Delta^0 + \sigma^0 = W^0$ in which $W^0 = 0$ for the given system and $\sigma^0 = \{\sigma_{20}^0, \sigma_{30}^0\}$ wherein $\sigma_{20}^0 = \sigma_{20,1}^0 + \sigma_{20,5}^0 + \sigma_{20,3}^0 = \sigma_{20,3}^0$ and $\sigma_{30}^0 = \sigma_{30,2}^0 + \sigma_{30,6}^0 + \sigma_{30,4}^0 = \sigma_{30,2}^0 + \sigma_{30,4}^0$. These values are obtained by using Table 11-2, Cases 1 and 2. Thus

$$\sigma_{20}^0 = \{0, 6.48, 134.4\} \quad \text{and} \quad \sigma_{30}^0 = \{0, 28.52, 94.4\}$$

11.5. Solve the frame shown in Fig. P-11.5 for the end stresses in various members. EI = constant and $A/I = 2\ \text{ft}^{-2}$ for all bars.

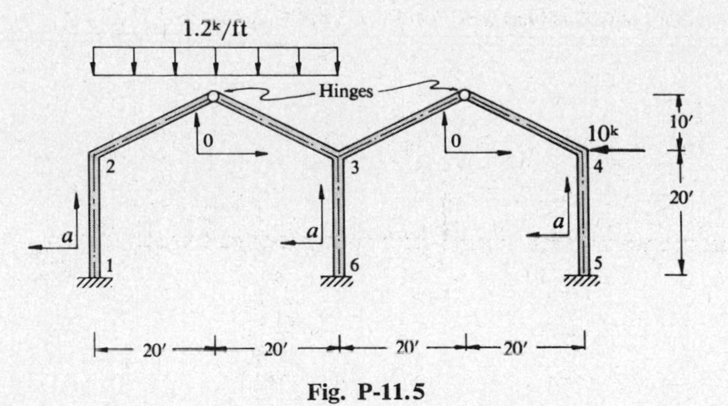

Fig. P-11.5

The basic equilibrium matrix equation for the system is

$$K^0\Delta^0 + \sigma^0 = W^0$$

in which $\Delta^0 = \{\Delta_2^0, \Delta_3^0, \Delta_4^0\}$

$$K^0 = \begin{bmatrix} k_2^0 & k_{23}^0 & 0 \\ k_{32}^0 & k_3^0 & k_{34}^0 \\ 0 & k_{43}^0 & k_4^0 \end{bmatrix} \quad \text{wherein } k_2^0 = k_{22,1}^0 + k_{22,3}^0,\ k_3^0 = k_{33,2}^0 + k_{33,6}^0 + k_{33,4}^0,\ k_4^0 = k_{44,3}^0 + k_{44,5}^0$$

$\sigma^0 = \{\sigma_{20}^0, \sigma_{30}^0, \sigma_{40}^0\}$ such that $\sigma_{20}^0 = \sigma_{20,1}^0 + \sigma_{20,3}^0$, $\sigma_{30}^0 = \sigma_{30,2}^0 + \sigma_{30,6}^0 + \sigma_{30,4}^0$, $\sigma_{40}^0 = \sigma_{40,3}^0 + \sigma_{40,5}^0$

$W^0 = \{W_2^0, W_3^0, W_4^0\}$.

For the given system, $\sigma_{20,1}^0 = 0 = \sigma_{30,6}^0 = \sigma_{30,4}^0 = \sigma_{40,3}^0 = \sigma_{40,5}^0$.

Using Table 11-4, $\sigma_{20,3}^0 = \{18, 24, 60\}$ and $\sigma_{30,2}^0 = \{-18, 24, -60\}$.

Also, $W_2^0 = 0 = W_3^0$ and $W_4^0 = \{-10, 0, 0\}$.

Now,

$$k_{22,1}^0 = k_{33,6}^0 = k_{44,5}^0 = \omega^{0a}k_{22,1}^a\omega^{a0} = \frac{EI}{20^3}\begin{bmatrix} 12 & 0 & 120 \\ 0 & 800 & 0 \\ 120 & 0 & 1{,}600 \end{bmatrix} \quad \text{wherein } \omega_{a0} = 90^\circ$$

From Table 11-3,

$$k_{22,3}^0 = k_{33,4}^0 = \frac{EI}{22.36\ (40)^2}\begin{bmatrix} 24 & 0 & -240 \\ 0 & 6 & 120 \\ -240 & 120 & 4{,}800 \end{bmatrix}, \quad k_{33,2}^0 = k_{44,3}^0 = \frac{EI}{22.36\ (40)^2}\begin{bmatrix} 24 & 0 & -240 \\ 0 & 6 & -120 \\ -240 & -120 & 4{,}800 \end{bmatrix}$$

$$k_{23}^0 = k_{34}^0 = \frac{EI}{22.36\ (40)^2}\begin{bmatrix} -24 & 0 & 240 \\ 0 & -6 & 120 \\ 240 & -120 & 0 \end{bmatrix} = k_{32}^{0)T} = k_{43}^{0)T}$$

Substituting in the equilibrium matrix equation and solving,

$$\Delta_2^0 = \frac{1}{EI}\{-8{,}152, -249, -38.2\},\ \Delta_3^0 = \frac{1}{EI}\{+3{,}039, -243, 305.9\},\ \Delta_4^0 = \frac{1}{EI}\{-4{,}349, 11.9, 61.9\}$$

Using these values and the member stress equation (*10.11*), the following values are obtained.

$$\sigma_{23}^0 = -\sigma_{21}^0 = \{12.8, 24.9, 129.9\}, \quad \sigma_{32}^0 = \{-12.8, 23.1, -94.0\}$$

$$\sigma_{34}^0 = \{3.65, 1.19, -12.7\}, \quad \sigma_{43}^0 = \{-3.65, -1.19, 60.4\}$$

$$\sigma_{63}^0 = \{-9.15, 24.3, 76.2\}, \quad \sigma_{36}^0 = \{9.15, -24.29, 106.8\}$$

$$\sigma_{54}^0 = \{6.36, -1.19, -66.6\}, \quad \sigma_{45}^0 = \{-6.35, 1.19, -60.4\}$$

$$\sigma_{12}^0 = \{12.8, 24.9, -126.1\}$$

SYMMETRY AND ANTISYMMETRY

11.6. Formulate the equilibrium matrix equation for the 3-span continuous frame shown in Fig. P-11.6, using modified stiffnesses as discussed in Sec. 11.7. $(A/I)_{\text{column}} = 2\ \text{ft}^{-2}$.

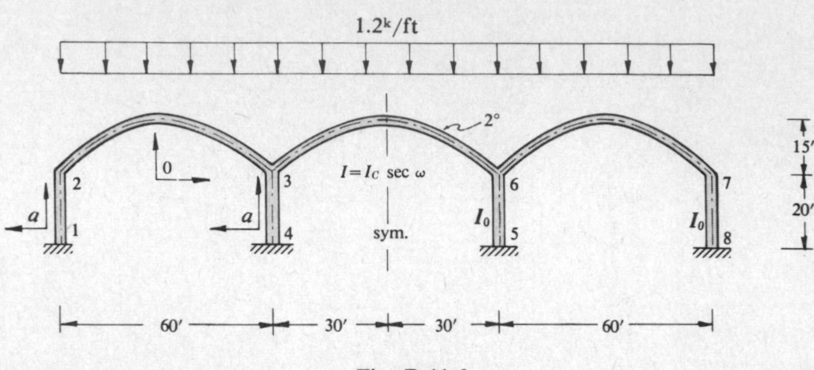

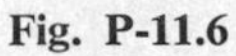

Fig. P-11.6

For reasons of symmetry of the frame and of the loads, only half of the frame need be analyzed. For the left half of the system, in the equilibrium equation $K^0\Delta^0 + \sigma^0 = W^0$ we have

$$\Delta^0 = \{\Delta_2^0, \Delta_3^0\}, \qquad W^0 = 0$$

$$K^0 = \begin{bmatrix} k_2^0 & k_{23}^0 \\ k_{32}^0 & k_3^0 \end{bmatrix} \quad \text{in which} \quad k_2^0 = k_{22,1}^0 + k_{22,3}^0, \quad k_3^0 = k_{33,2}^0 + k_{33,4}^0 + k_{33,6}^0 \ \text{modified}$$

$$\sigma^0 = \{\sigma_{20}^0, \sigma_{30}^0\} \quad \text{where} \quad \sigma_{20}^0 = \sigma_{22,1}^0 + \sigma_{22,3}^0, \quad \sigma_{30}^0 = \sigma_{33,2}^0 + \sigma_{33,4}^0 + \sigma_{33,6}^0$$

$$\sigma_{22,1}^0 = \sigma_{33,4}^0 = 0$$

$$k_{22,1}^0 = k_{33,4}^0 = \omega^{0a} k_{22,1}^a \omega^{a0} = \frac{EI}{20^3}\begin{bmatrix} 12 & 0 & 120 \\ 0 & 800 & 0 \\ 120 & 0 & 1{,}600 \end{bmatrix} \quad \text{for } \omega_{a0} = 90°$$

From Table 10-10,

$$k_{22,3}^0 = k_{33,6}^0 = \frac{EI}{60^2}\begin{bmatrix} 3 & 0 & -30 \\ 0 & 0.2 & 6 \\ -30 & 6 & 540 \end{bmatrix}$$

$$k_{33,2}^0 = k_{66,3}^0 = \frac{EI}{60^2}\begin{bmatrix} 3 & 0 & -30 \\ 0 & 0.2 & -6 \\ -30 & -6 & 540 \end{bmatrix}$$

$$k_{23}^0 = k_{36}^0 = \frac{EI}{60^2}\begin{bmatrix} -3 & 0 & 30 \\ 0 & -0.2 & 6 \\ 30 & -6 & -180 \end{bmatrix} = k_{32}^{0)T} = k_{63}^{0)T}$$

$$k_{33,6}^0\,(\text{modified}) = k_{33,6}^0 - k_{36}^0 i = \frac{EI}{60^2}\begin{bmatrix} 6 & 0 & -60 \\ 0 & 0 & 0 \\ -60 & 0 & 720 \end{bmatrix}$$

Using Table 10-11,

$$\sigma_{22,3}^0 = \sigma_{33,6}^0 = \{36, 36, 0\} \quad \text{and} \quad \sigma_{33,2}^0 = \{-36, 36, 0\}$$

These values can now be substituted in the equilibrium equation.

VARIABLE CROSS SECTION

11.7. Relate the stiffness values of a straight bar of variable cross section to its segmental flexibilities of Table 6-4.

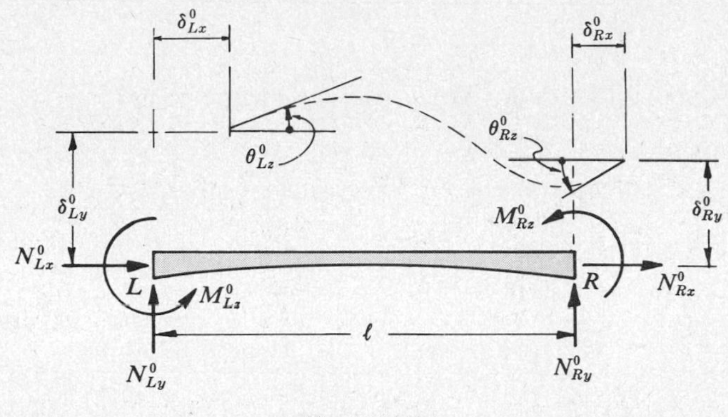

Fig. P-11.7a

A straight bar of variable cross section, with imposed end forces, end deformations and applied loads is considered (Fig. P-11.7). If the basic system of such a bar is considered to be a simple beam shown in Table 6-4, considering N^0_{Rx}, M^0_{Rz} and M^0_{Lz} as redundants, the following deformation compatibility equations can be established by superposition, in terms of the flexibilities of Table 6-4.

$$E_{RR}N^0_{Rx} = \delta^0_{Rx} - \delta^0_{Lx} - E_{RP}$$

$$F_{LL}M^0_{Lz} - F_{LR}M^0_{Rz} = (\delta^0_{Ly} - \delta^0_{Ry})/l + \theta^0_{Lz} + \tau_{LR}$$

$$F_{RR}M_{Rz} - F_{RL}M^0_{Lz} = (\delta^0_{Ly} - \delta^0_{Ry})/l + \theta^0_{Rz} - \tau_{RL}$$

The three redundants N^0_{Rx}, M^0_{Rz} and M^0_{Lz} can be solved for from above, in terms of imposed deformations and unit stress and load flexibilities of the bar. The remaining three reactive elements on the bar, N^0_{Lx}, N^0_{Ly} and N^0_{Ry} can then be solved by statics. These six force values related in matrix form to the six end deformations and loads, are shown in Fig. P-11.7*b* below. Comparison with the matrix in Table 10-1 gives the stiffness coefficients in terms of flexibilities of a simple bar. $D = F_{LL}F_{RR} - F^2_{LR}$ and BR_{Lx}, BR_{Ly} and BR_{Ry} are the reactions of the basic structure due to the applied load.

11.8. Using the results of Problem 11.7 compute the stiffness coefficients for the members of the frame shown in Fig. P-11.8. Then compute the influence lines for N^0_{1x} and M^0_{2z} for the unit load shown. $A_0/I_0 = 8\ \text{ft}^{-2}$.

Using the procedure explained in Chapter 6, the following simple beam flexibility coefficients are obtained for bars 12 and 23 of the given frame.

For bar 12,

$$F_{11} = 0.1931\frac{s}{EI_0} = \frac{5.793}{EI_0}$$

$$F_{22} = 0.0681\frac{s}{EI_0} = \frac{2.043}{EI_0}$$

$$F_{12} = F_{21} = 0.0569\frac{s}{EI_0} = \frac{1.707}{EI_0}$$

$$E_{22} = 0.69315\frac{s}{EA_0} = \frac{20.7945}{EA_0}$$

For bar 23,

$$F_{22} = F_{33} = 0.1607\frac{s}{EI_0} = \frac{9.642}{EI_0}$$

$$F_{23} = F_{32} = 0.1116\frac{s}{EI_0} = \frac{6.696}{EI_0}$$

$$E_{33} = 0.7854\frac{s}{EA_0} = \frac{47.124}{EA_0}$$

$$\begin{bmatrix} N^0_{Rx} \\ N^0_{Ry} \\ M^0_{Rz} \\ N^0_{Lx} \\ N^0_{Ly} \\ M^0_{Lz} \end{bmatrix} = \begin{bmatrix} \frac{1}{E_{RR}} & 0 & 0 & -\frac{1}{E_{RR}} & 0 & 0 \\ 0 & \frac{(F_{LL}+F_{RR}+2F_{LR})}{Dl^2} & -\frac{(F_{LL}+F_{LR})}{Dl} & 0 & \frac{-(F_{LL}+F_{LR}+2F_{LR})}{Dl^2} & -\frac{(F_{RR}+F_{LR})}{Dl} \\ 0 & -\frac{(F_{LL}+F_{LR})}{Dl} & \frac{F_{LL}}{D} & 0 & \frac{(F_{LL}+F_{LR})}{Dl} & \frac{F_{LR}}{D} \\ -\frac{1}{E_{RR}} & 0 & 0 & \frac{1}{E_{RR}} & 0 & 0 \\ 0 & \frac{-(F_{LL}+F_{LR}+2F_{LR})}{Dl^2} & \frac{(F_{LL}+F_{LR})}{Dl} & 0 & \frac{(F_{LL}+F_{RR}+2F_{LR})}{Dl^2} & \frac{(F_{RR}+F_{LR})}{Dl} \\ 0 & \frac{-(F_{RR}+F_{LR})}{Dl} & \frac{F_{LR}}{D} & 0 & \frac{(F_{RR}+F_{LR})}{Dl} & \frac{F_{RR}}{D} \end{bmatrix} \begin{bmatrix} \delta^0_{Rx} \\ \delta^0_{Ry} \\ \theta^0_{Rz} \\ \delta^0_{Lx} \\ \delta^0_{Ly} \\ \theta^0_{Lz} \end{bmatrix} + \begin{bmatrix} -\frac{E_{RP}}{E_{RR}} \\ BR_{Ry} - \frac{1}{Dl}[(F_{LR}+F_{RR})\tau_{LR} - (F_{LL}+F_{LR})\tau_{RL}] \\ \frac{(F_{LR}\tau_{LR} - F_{LL}\tau_{RL})}{D} \\ BR_{Lx} + \frac{E_{RP}}{E_{RR}} \\ BR_{Ly} + \frac{1}{Dl}[(F_{LR}+F_{RR})\tau_{LR} - (F_{LL}+F_{LR})\tau_{RL}] \\ \frac{(F_{RR}\tau_{LR} - F_{LR}\tau_{RL})}{D} \end{bmatrix}$$

Fig. P-11.7b

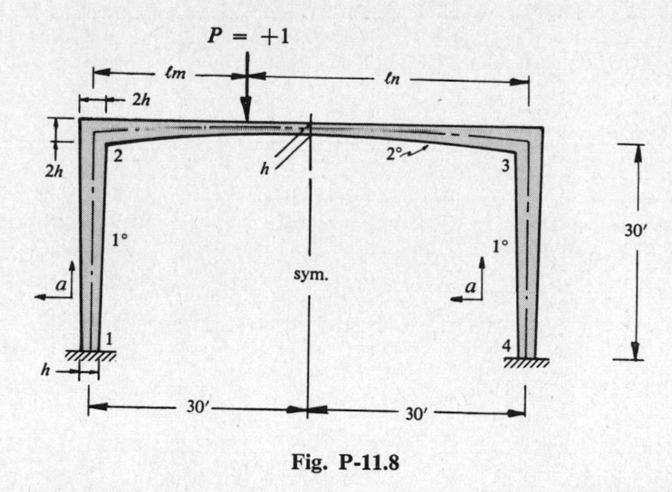

Fig. P-11.8

Substituting in the results of Problem 11.7, reducing and transforming to the 0-system gives

$$k^0_{22,1} = k^0_{33,4} = \frac{EI_0}{30^2}\begin{bmatrix} 1.261 & 0 & 25.22 \\ 0 & 346.2 & 0 \\ 25.22 & 0 & 584.4 \end{bmatrix}, \qquad k^0_{12} = k^0_{43} = \frac{EI_0}{30^2}\begin{bmatrix} -1.261 & 0 & -25.22 \\ 0 & -346.2 & 0 \\ 12.61 & 0 & 172.2 \end{bmatrix}$$

$$k^0_{22,3} = \frac{EI_0}{60^2}\begin{bmatrix} 611.2 & 0 & 0 \\ 0 & 0.6789 & 20.367 \\ 0 & 20.367 & 721.2 \end{bmatrix}, \qquad k^0_{33,2} = \frac{EI_0}{60^2}\begin{bmatrix} 611.2 & 0 & 0 \\ 0 & 0.6789 & -20.367 \\ 0 & -20.367 & 721.2 \end{bmatrix}$$

$$k^0_{23} = \frac{EI_0}{60^2}\begin{bmatrix} -611.2 & 0 & 0 \\ 0 & -0.6789 & 20.367 \\ 0 & -20.367 & 500.8 \end{bmatrix} = k^{0)T}_{32}$$

In the governing equilibrium equation $K^0\Delta^0 + \sigma^0 = W^0$,

$$W^0 = 0, \qquad \Delta^0 = \{\Delta_2^0, \Delta_3^0\}$$

$$K^0 = \begin{bmatrix} k_2^{\ 0} & k^0_{23} \\ k^0_{32} & k_3^{\ 0} \end{bmatrix} \quad \text{in which} \quad k_2^{\ 0} = k^0_{22,1} + k^0_{22,3}, \quad k_3^{\ 0} = k^0_{33,2} + k^0_{33,4}$$

and

$$\sigma^0 = \{\sigma_2^0, \sigma_3^0\} = \{\sigma^0_{20,3}, \sigma^0_{30,2}\}$$

Again using the results of Problem 11.7 and the flexibilities established above, for the given vertical load,

$$\sigma^0_{20,3} = \frac{1}{60^2}\{0,\ 60^2 n + 20.367(\tau_{23} - \tau_{32})\,EI_0,\ (721.2\tau_{23} - 500.8\tau_{32})\,EI_0\}$$

and

$$\sigma^0_{30,2} = \frac{1}{60^2}\{0,\ 60^2 m - 20.367(\tau_{23} - \tau_{32})\,EI_0,\ (500.8\tau_{23} - 721.2\tau_{32})\,EI_0\}$$

τ_{23} and τ_{32} are computed for the variable section beam 23 for $m = 0$ to 1 in increments of 0.1 and are as follows:

m	0.0	0.1	0.2	0.3	0.4	0.5	0.6	0.7	0.8	0.9	1.0
$EI_0\tau_{23}$	0	55.08	102.96	138.96	159.12	160.56	144.36	115.20	79.20	39.96	0
$EI_0\tau_{32}$	0	39.96	79.20	115.20	144.36	160.56	159.12	138.96	102.96	55.08	0

Upon substitution of these values, the governing equilibrium equation is solved for Δ^0; and substituting appropriate values in the force deformation relations for bar 12, the influence values for N_{1x}^0 and M_{2z}^0 are obtained as follows:

m	0.0	0.1	0.2	0.3	0.4	0.5	0.6	0.7	0.8	0.9	1.0
N_{1x} k	0	0.115	0.220	0.307	0.366	0.387	0.366	0.307	0.220	0.115	0
M_{25} k-ft	0	−3.19	−5.93	−7.94	−9.01	−8.98	−7.97	−6.27	−4.26	−2.13	0

GROUP STIFFNESS MATRIX

11.9. Compute the group stiffness k_{RR}^0, k_{RL}^0, k_{LR}^0, k_{LL}^0 and the group fixed end stresses σ_{R0}^0 and σ_{L0}^0 for the frame shown in Fig. P-11.9. $A/I = 2\text{ ft}^{-2}$ for all bars.

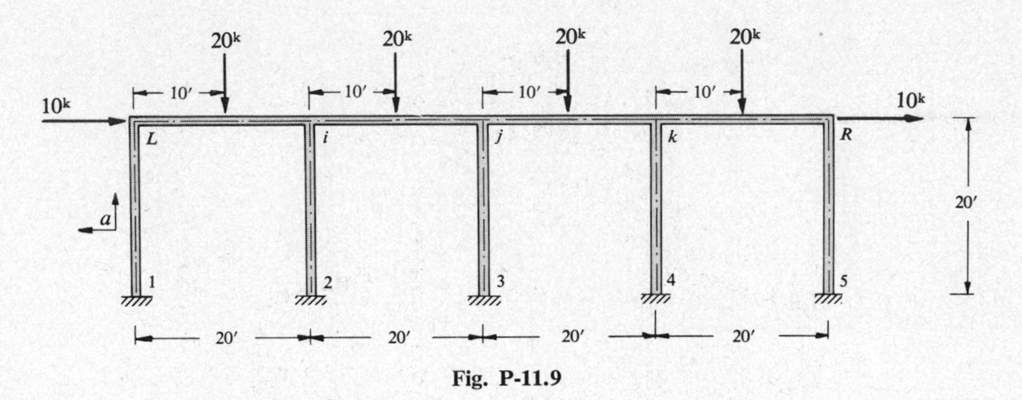

Fig. P-11.9

The member properties are established first.

$$k_{LL,i}^0 = k_{ii,j}^0 = k_{jj,k}^0 = k_{kk,R}^0 = \frac{EI}{20^3}\begin{bmatrix} 800 & 0 & 0 \\ 0 & 12 & 120 \\ 0 & 120 & 1{,}600 \end{bmatrix}$$

$$k_{ii,L}^0 = k_{jj,i}^0 = k_{kk,j}^0 = k_{RR,k}^0 = \frac{EI}{20^3}\begin{bmatrix} 800 & 0 & 0 \\ 0 & 12 & -120 \\ 0 & -120 & 1{,}600 \end{bmatrix}$$

$$k_{Li}^0 = k_{ij}^0 = k_{jk}^0 = k_{kR}^0 = \frac{EI}{20^3}\begin{bmatrix} -800 & 0 & 0 \\ 0 & -12 & 120 \\ 0 & -120 & 800 \end{bmatrix} = k_{iL}^{0)T} = k_{ji}^{0)T} = k_{kj}^{0)T} = k_{Rk}^{0)T}$$

$$k_{LL,1}^0 = k_{ii,2}^0 = k_{jj,3}^0 = k_{kk,4}^0 = k_{RR,5}^0 = \omega^{0a} k_{LL,1}^a \omega^{a0} = \frac{EI}{20^3}\begin{bmatrix} 12 & 0 & 120 \\ 0 & 800 & 0 \\ 120 & 0 & 1{,}600 \end{bmatrix}$$

for $\omega_{a0} = 90°$. Also,

$$\sigma_{L0,i}^0 = \sigma_{i0,j}^0 = \sigma_{j0,k}^0 = \sigma_{k0,R}^0 = \{0,\ 10,\ 50\}$$

$$\sigma_{i0,L}^0 = \sigma_{j0,i}^0 = \sigma_{k0,j}^0 = \sigma_{R0,k}^0 = \{0,\ 10,\ -50\}$$

Thus

$$\sigma_{i0} = \sigma_{j0} = \sigma_{k0} = \{0,\ 20,\ 0\}$$

$$W_i^0 = W_j^0 = W_k^0 = 0 \quad \text{and} \quad W_L^0 = W_R^0 = \{10,\ 0,\ 0\}$$

Using these values (*11.15*) is constructed; and computing and inserting $k_m^{0)-1}$ in (*11.16*) and (*11.17*), the following group stiffnesses and group fixed end stresses are obtained.

$$\overset{0}{k}_{RR} = \frac{EI}{20^3}\begin{bmatrix} 220.1 & 2.067 & 106.2 \\ 2.067 & 808.7 & -97.67 \\ 106.2 & -97.67 & 3{,}045.5 \end{bmatrix} \qquad \overset{0}{k}_{RL} = \frac{EI}{20^3}\begin{bmatrix} -194.1 & -0.565 & -3.817 \\ 0.565 & 0.066 & 0.419 \\ -3.817 & -0.419 & -2.655 \end{bmatrix}$$

$$\overset{0}{k}_{LR} = \frac{EI}{20^3}\begin{bmatrix} -194.1 & 0.565 & -3.817 \\ -0.565 & 0.066 & -0.419 \\ -3.817 & 0.419 & -2.655 \end{bmatrix} \qquad \overset{0}{k}_{LL} = \frac{EI}{20^3}\begin{bmatrix} 220.1 & -2.067 & 106.2 \\ -2.067 & 808.7 & 97.67 \\ 106.2 & 97.67 & 3{,}045.5 \end{bmatrix}$$

$$\overset{0}{\sigma}_{R0} = \{0.0375,\ 10.22,\ -52.45\} \qquad \overset{0}{\sigma}_{L0} = \{-0.0375,\ 10.22,\ 52.45\}$$

11.10. Set up the equilibrium matrix equation for the frame shown in Fig. P-11.10 using the group stiffnesses for group A and group stiffnesses for group B modified for symmetry and respective group fixed end stresses. Assume $A/I = 1$ ft^{-2} for all bars.

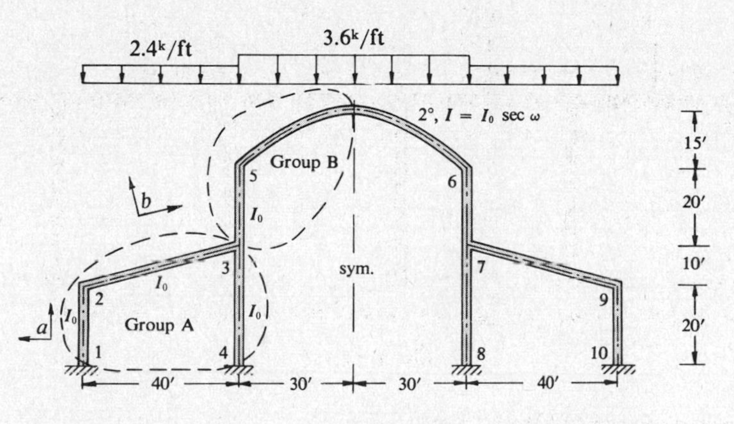

Fig. P-11.10

For group A, from the equilibrium equation

$$\begin{bmatrix} k_3{}^0 & \overset{0}{k}_{32} \\ \overset{0}{k}_{23} & k_2{}^0 \end{bmatrix}\begin{bmatrix} \Delta_3{}^0 \\ \Delta_2{}^0 \end{bmatrix} + \begin{bmatrix} \overset{0}{\sigma}_{30,2} \\ \overset{0}{\sigma}_{20} \end{bmatrix} = \begin{bmatrix} W_3{}^0 \\ W_2{}^0 \end{bmatrix} \qquad \text{in which} \quad k_3{}^0 = \overset{0}{k}_{33,2} + \overset{0}{k}_{33,4}, \quad k_2{}^0 = \overset{0}{k}_{22,3} + \overset{0}{k}_{22,1}$$

$\Delta_2{}^0$ will be eliminated to obtain the group stiffnesses and the group fixed end stresses. In the equation above,

$$\overset{0}{k}_{33,4} = \omega^{0a}\overset{a}{k}_{33,4}\omega^{a0} = \frac{EI}{30^3}\begin{bmatrix} 12 & 0 & 180 \\ 0 & 900 & 0 \\ 180 & 0 & 3{,}600 \end{bmatrix}$$

Similarly,

$$\overset{0}{k}_{22,1} = \frac{EI}{20^3}\begin{bmatrix} 12 & 0 & 120 \\ 0 & 400 & 0 \\ 120 & 0 & 1{,}600 \end{bmatrix} \qquad \overset{0}{k}_{22,3} = \omega^{0b}\overset{b}{k}_{22,3}\omega^{b0} = \frac{EI}{41(23^3)}\begin{bmatrix} 1{,}600.8 & 397.1 & -60.0 \\ 397.1 & 111.26 & 240.0 \\ -60.0 & 240.0 & 6{,}799.7 \end{bmatrix}$$

$$\overset{0}{k}_{33,2} = \frac{EI}{41(23^3)}\begin{bmatrix} 1{,}600.8 & 397.1 & 60.0 \\ 397.1 & 111.26 & -240.0 \\ 60.0 & -240.0 & 6{,}799.7 \end{bmatrix} \qquad \overset{0}{k}_{23} = \frac{EI}{41(23^3)}\begin{bmatrix} -1{,}600.8 & -397.1 & -60.0 \\ -397.1 & -111.26 & 240.0 \\ 60.0 & 240.0 & 3{,}399.8 \end{bmatrix} = k_{32}^{0)T}$$

$$\overset{0}{\sigma}_{30,2} = \{0,\ 48,\ -320\}, \qquad \overset{0}{\sigma}_{20} = \{0,\ 48,\ 320\}, \qquad W_3{}^0 = 0 = W_2{}^0$$

Then as per (*11.20*) the group stiffness

$$k^0_{33,A} = (k_3^{\;0} - k^0_{32}k_2^{0)-1}k^0_{23}) = \frac{EI}{10^4}\begin{bmatrix} 11.58 & 3.53 & 43.52 \\ 3.53 & 336.0 & -35.73 \\ 43.52 & -35.73 & 2{,}215.1 \end{bmatrix}$$

and the group fixed end stress vector

$$\sigma^0_{30,A} = (\sigma^0_{30,2} - k^0_{32}k_2^{0)-1}\sigma^0_{20}) = \{-15.33, 48.39, -377.6\}$$

For group *B*, modified stiffnesses for the bar 56 will be used and $\Delta_5{}^0$ eliminated from

$$\begin{bmatrix} k_3{}^0 & k^0_{35} \\ k^0_{53} & k_5{}^0 \end{bmatrix}\begin{bmatrix} \Delta_3{}^0 \\ \Delta_5{}^0 \end{bmatrix} + \begin{bmatrix} \sigma^0_{30,5} \\ \sigma^0_{50} \end{bmatrix} = \begin{bmatrix} W_3{}^0 \\ W_5{}^0 \end{bmatrix} \qquad \text{in which} \quad k_3{}^0 = k^0_{33,5}, \quad k_5{}^0 = k^0_{55,3} + k^0_{55,6} \quad \text{(modified)}$$

In the equation above,

$$k^0_{33,5} = \frac{EI}{20^3}\begin{bmatrix} 12 & 0 & -120 \\ 0 & 400 & 0 \\ -120 & 0 & 1{,}600 \end{bmatrix} \qquad k^0_{55,3} = \frac{EI}{20^3}\begin{bmatrix} 12 & 0 & 120 \\ 0 & 400 & 0 \\ 120 & 0 & 1{,}600 \end{bmatrix}$$

$$k^0_{35} = \frac{EI}{20^3}\begin{bmatrix} -12 & 0 & -120 \\ 0 & -400 & 0 \\ 120 & 0 & 800 \end{bmatrix} = k_{53}^{0)T} \qquad k^0_{55,6}\,\text{(modified)} = \frac{EI}{60^2}\begin{bmatrix} 6 & 0 & -60 \\ 0 & 0 & 0 \\ -60 & 0 & 720 \end{bmatrix}$$

$$\sigma^0_{30,5} = \{0, 0, 0\}, \qquad \sigma^0_{50} = \{108, 108, 0\}, \qquad W_3{}^0 = 0 = W_5{}^0$$

The modified group stiffness therfore becomes

$$k^0_{33,B} = (k_3{}^0 - k^0_{35}k_5^{0)-1}k^0_{53}) = \frac{EI}{10^4}\begin{bmatrix} 1.65 & 0 & -36.36 \\ 0 & 0 & 0 \\ -36.26 & 0 & 997.8 \end{bmatrix}$$

and the modified group fixed end stress vector

$$\sigma^0_{30,B} = -k^0_{35}k_5^{0)\,-1}\sigma^0_{50} = \{53.4, 108.0, -526.9\}$$

The solution for the entire system is then obtained from

$$(k^0_{33,A} + k^0_{33,B})\,\Delta_3{}^0 + (\sigma^0_{30,A} + \sigma^0_{30,B}) = 0$$

GENERAL METHOD

11.11. Using the general method described in Sec. 11.10, solve the frame shown in Fig. P-11.11. State the true unit load system transfer matrix A and the true unit load system flexibility matrix Φ. Use $A/I = 1$ ft^{-2} for all bars.

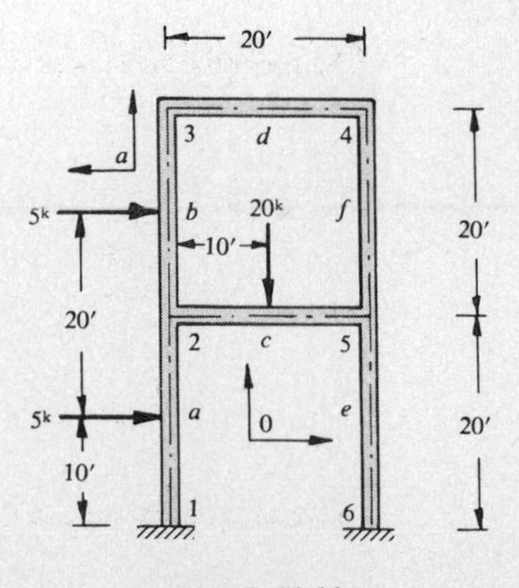

Fig. P-11.11

The system has six members, a through f, and 12° of kinematic indeterminacy in the four joints 2, 3, 4 and 5. The load vector $W = \{W_{ax}, W_{bx}, W_{cy}\}_{3\times1} = \{5, 5, -20\}$. Only the applicable part of the unit load segmental stiffness chain, s, is used. Thus retaining only the first, fourth and the eighth columns of s gives

$$s = \begin{bmatrix} s_a & 0 & 0 \\ 0 & s_b & 0 \\ 0 & 0 & s_c \\ 0 & 0 & 0 \\ 0 & 0 & 0 \\ 0 & 0 & 0 \end{bmatrix}_{36\times9} \rightarrow [s]_{36\times3} \quad \text{as shown below}$$

$$
s = \left[\begin{array}{c|c|c}
-0.5 & 0 & 0 \\
0 & 0 & 0 \\
-2.5 & 0 & 0 \\
-0.5 & 0 & 0 \\
0 & 0 & 0 \\
2.5 & 0 & 0 \\
\hline
0 & -0.5 & \\
0 & 0 & 0 \\
0 & -2.5 & 0 \\
0 & -0.5 & 0 \\
0 & 0 & 0 \\
0 & 2.5 & 0 \\
\hline
0 & 0 & 0 \\
0 & 0 & -0.5 \\
0 & 0 & 2.5 \\
0 & 0 & 0 \\
0 & 0 & -0.5 \\
0 & 0 & -2.5 \\
\hline
0 & 0 & 0 \\
0 & 0 & 0 \\
0 & 0 & 0 \\
0 & 0 & 0 \\
0 & 0 & 0 \\
0 & 0 & 0 \\
0 & 0 & 0 \\
0 & 0 & 0 \\
0 & 0 & 0 \\
0 & 0 & 0 \\
0 & 0 & 0 \\
0 & 0 & 0 \\
0 & 0 & 0 \\
0 & 0 & 0 \\
0 & 0 & 0 \\
0 & 0 & 0 \\
0 & 0 & 0 \\
0 & 0 & 0
\end{array}\right]_{36\times3}
$$

The general transfer matrix j is

$$
j = \left[\begin{array}{c|c|c|c|c|c|c|c|c|c|c|c}
I & 0 & 0 & I & 0 & I & 0 & 0 & 0 & 0 & 0 & 0 \\
\hline
0 & 0 & I & 0 & 0 & 0 & 0 & I & 0 & 0 & 0 & 0 \\
\hline
0 & 0 & 0 & 0 & 0 & 0 & I & 0 & 0 & 0 & I & 0 \\
\hline
0 & 0 & 0 & 0 & I & 0 & 0 & 0 & I & 0 & 0 & I
\end{array}\right]_{12\times36}
$$

in which each submatrix is (3×3).

The unit displacement segmental stiffness chain k is as shown in (*11.26*) for members a through f and

$$k_a = \frac{EI}{20^3}\begin{bmatrix} 12 & 0 & 120 & -12 & 0 & 120 \\ 0 & 400 & 0 & 0 & -400 & 0 \\ 120 & 0 & 1{,}600 & -120 & 0 & 800 \\ -12 & 0 & -120 & 12 & 0 & -120 \\ 0 & -400 & 0 & 0 & 400 & 0 \\ 120 & 0 & 800 & -120 & 0 & 1{,}600 \end{bmatrix}_{6\times 6}, \quad k_c = \frac{EI}{20^3}\begin{bmatrix} 400 & 0 & 0 & -400 & 0 & 0 \\ 0 & 12 & -120 & 0 & -12 & -120 \\ 0 & -120 & 1{,}600 & 0 & 120 & 800 \\ -400 & 0 & 0 & 400 & 0 & 0 \\ 0 & -12 & 120 & 0 & 12 & 120 \\ 0 & -120 & 800 & 0 & 120 & 1{,}600 \end{bmatrix}_{6\times 6}$$

with $k_b = k_e = k_f = k_a$ and $k_d = k_c$.

With these values established, K_Δ and K_W can be computed. Also computing $K)_\Delta^{-1}$ from *(11.33)* and *(11.34)* the true unit load system transfer matrix A and the true unit load system flexibility matrix Φ are computed.

$$A = \begin{bmatrix} -0.2066 & 0.4501 & 0.0802 \\ 0.1081 & 0.8785 & 0.5000 \\ 0.3978 & 3.103 & 1.070 \\ -0.7934 & -0.4501 & -0.0802 \\ -0.1081 & -0.8785 & -0.5000 \\ 5.469 & 5.899 & 0.5331 \\ 0.0247 & -0.2245 & 0.0535 \\ 0.0134 & 0.2020 & 0 \\ 0.2100 & 1.477 & 0.1777 \\ -0.0247 & -0.7752 & -0.0535 \\ -0.0134 & -0.2020 & 0 \\ 0.2834 & 4.027 & 0.8926 \\ -0.2313 & -0.3252 & 0.0267 \\ 0.0947 & 0.6764 & -0.5000 \\ -1.213 & -6.399 & 1.963 \\ 0.2313 & 0.3252 & -0.0267 \\ -0.0947 & -0.6764 & -0.5000 \\ -0.6813 & -7.130 & -1.963 \\ 0.0247 & -0.2248 & 0.0535 \\ 0.0134 & 0.2020 & 0 \\ -0.0583 & -2.564 & 0.1777 \\ -0.0247 & 0.2248 & -0.0535 \\ -0.0134 & -0.2020 & 0 \\ -0.2100 & -1.477 & -0.1777 \\ 0.2066 & 0.5499 & -0.0802 \\ -0.1081 & -0.8785 & 0.5000 \\ 1.765 & 4.467 & -1.070 \\ -0.2066 & -0.5499 & 0.0802 \\ 0.1081 & 0.8785 & -0.5000 \\ 2.368 & 6.532 & -0.5331 \\ -0.0247 & 0.2248 & -0.0535 \\ -0.0134 & -0.2020 & 0 \\ 0.0583 & 2.564 & -0.1777 \\ 0.0247 & -0.2248 & 0.0535 \\ 0.0134 & 0.2020 & 0 \\ -0.5517 & 1.932 & -0.8926 \end{bmatrix}_{36\times 3}$$

$$\Phi = \frac{1}{EI}\begin{bmatrix} 202.7 & 579.6 & -.267 \\ 2.163 & 17.57 & 10.0 \\ -0.714 & -27.96 & 5.371 \\ 240.8 & 1{,}077.3 & -0.535 \\ 2.431 & 21.61 & 10.0 \\ -1.449 & -3.461 & -1.777 \\ 241.3 & 1{,}072.8 & 0.535 \\ -2.431 & -21.61 & 10.0 \\ 0.068 & -14.33 & 1.777 \\ 198.1 & 573.1 & 0.267 \\ -2.163 & -17.57 & 10.0 \\ -6.033 & -20.65 & -5.371 \end{bmatrix}_{12\times 3}$$

The true stress vector $\sigma = AW$ and the true displacement vector $\Delta = \Phi W$ are finally computed.

$$\sigma = \begin{bmatrix} -0.386 \\ -5.067 \\ -3.903 \\ -4.614 \\ 5.067 \\ 46.18 \\ -2.071 \\ 1.077 \\ 4.881 \\ -2.929 \\ -1.077 \\ 3.702 \\ -3.316 \\ 13.86 \\ -77.32 \\ 3.316 \\ 6.144 \\ 0.202 \\ -2.071 \\ 1.077 \\ -16.67 \\ 2.071 \\ -1.077 \\ -4.881 \\ 5.386 \\ -14.93 \\ 52.56 \\ -5.386 \\ 14.93 \\ 55.16 \\ 2.071 \\ -1.077 \\ 16.67 \\ -2.071 \\ 1.077 \\ 24.75 \end{bmatrix}_{36\times 1} \qquad \Delta = \frac{1}{EI}\begin{bmatrix} 3{,}917 \\ -101.3 \\ -250.8 \\ 6{,}601 \\ -79.8 \\ 11.0 \\ 6{,}560 \\ -320.2 \\ -106{,}9 \\ 3{,}851 \\ -298.7 \\ -26.0 \end{bmatrix}_{12\times 1}$$

Supplementary Problems

11.12. Construct the system stiffness matrix for the frame shown in Fig. P-11.12 and formulate the equilibrium matrix equation (*11.6*) for the same. All bars have the same section and $A/I = 2\ \text{ft}^{-2}$.

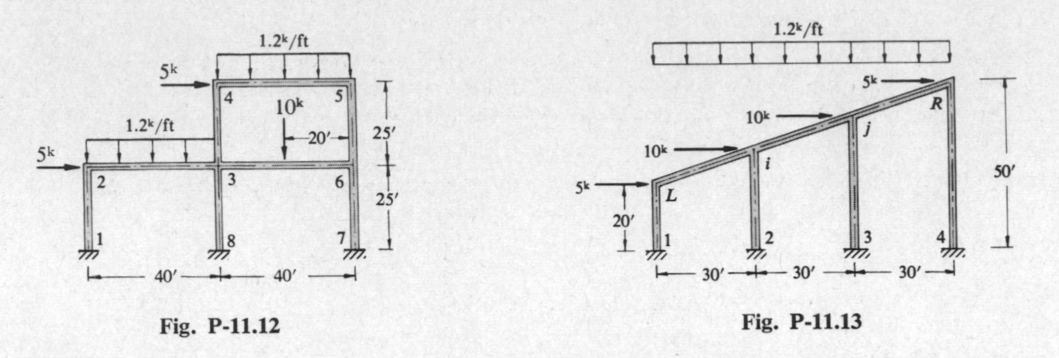

Fig. P-11.12

Fig. P-11.13

11.13. Construct the system stiffness matrix for the frame shown in Fig. P-11.13 and forumlate the equilibrium matrix equation (*11.6*). Use EI = constant and $A/I = 3\ \text{ft}^{-2}$.

11.14. Using the results of Prob. 11.1, compute the final end stresses in all members of the frame shown in Fig. P-11.1.

11.15. Use the results of Prob. 11.2 to compute the final end stresses for all bars of the frame shown in Fig. P-11.2.

11.16. Set up the equilibrium matrix equation (*11.6*) for the frame shown in Fig. P-9.13*a*.

11.17. Compute the axial forces and maximum bending moments in members 52 and 63 of the frame shown in Fig. P-11.17. EI = constant, $A/I = 1\ \text{ft}^{-2}$.

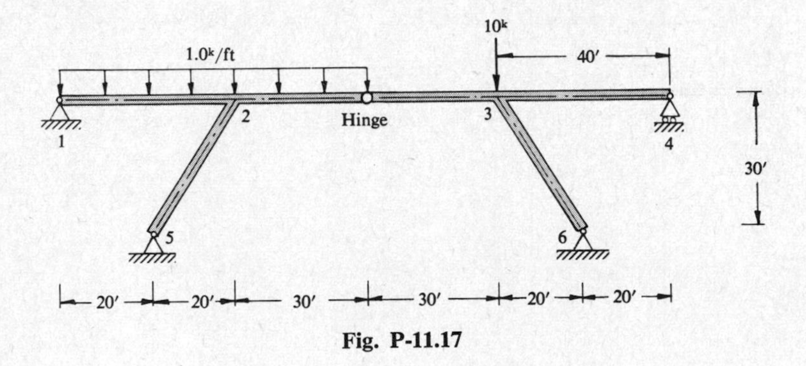

Fig. P-11.17

11.18. Solve the three span gable frame shown in Fig. P-11.18 by resolving into cases of symmetry and antisymmetry and using modified stiffness discussed in Sec. 11.7. $A/I = 2\ \text{ft}^{-2}$ for all bars.

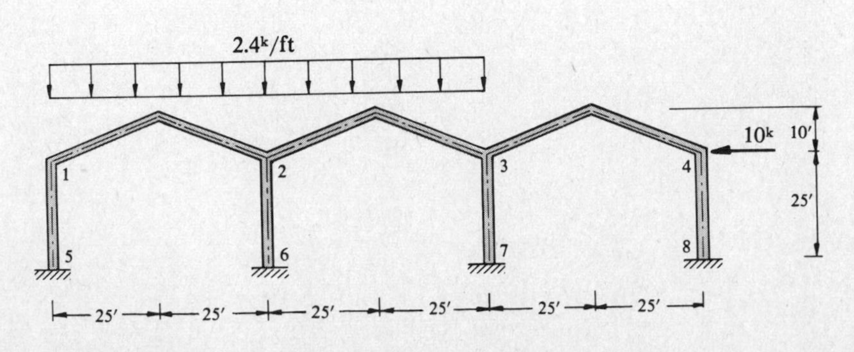

Fig. P-11.18

11.19. Verify that for a constant section bar, the stiffness matrix developed in Problem 11.7 reduces to the one shown in Table 10-2.

11.20. Verify the results of Prob. 10.4 by computing k_{RR}^{RR}, k_{RL}^{RL}, k_{LR}^{LR}, k_{LL}^{LL} using the procedure explained in Sec. 11.9*a*.

11.21. Following the procedure discussed in Sec. 11.9*b*, compute the group stiffnesses k_{RR}^{0}, k_{RL}^{0}, k_{LR}^{0} and k_{LL}^{0} and the group fixed end stresses σ_{R0}^{0} and σ_{L0}^{0} for the group *LijR*32 of the frame shown in Fig. P-11.2. Then show the reduced equilibrium matrix equation for the frame, using these values.

11.22. Using the general stiffness method (Sec. 11.10), compute the true stress vector and the true displacement vector for the frame shown in Fig. P-11.22. State the true unit load system transfer matrix A and the true unit load system flexibility matrix Φ. All bars have the same cross section and $A/I = 1\ \text{ft}^{-2}$.

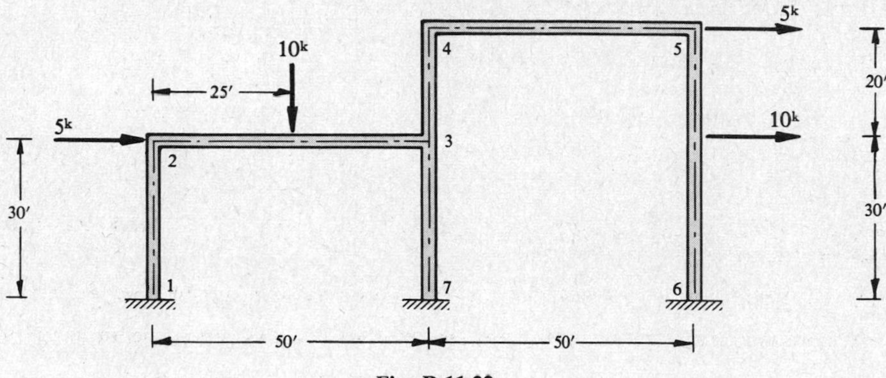

Fig. P-11.22

Chapter 12

Planar Truss

12.1 SYSTEM

A *truss* is a system of straight bars joined together at their ends to form a rigid framework. Essentially all trusses are three-dimensional structures, which in many cases can be decomposed into *planar trusses*, with loads and reactions acting in their plane.

For the analysis, the real planar truss is replaced by a *mathematical model* called the *ideal planar truss*, subject to the simplifying assumptions introduced before (Sec. I-4.1).

According to their *shapes*, planar trusses are classified as *single span* or *continuous*, *compound* or *complex* (Fig. 12-1). If the joint connections are furnished with heavy gusset plates, the system ceases to be a truss and becomes a rigid frame. Finally, if flexural members are combined with truss members, the system is called a *truss frame* (Fig. 12-2).

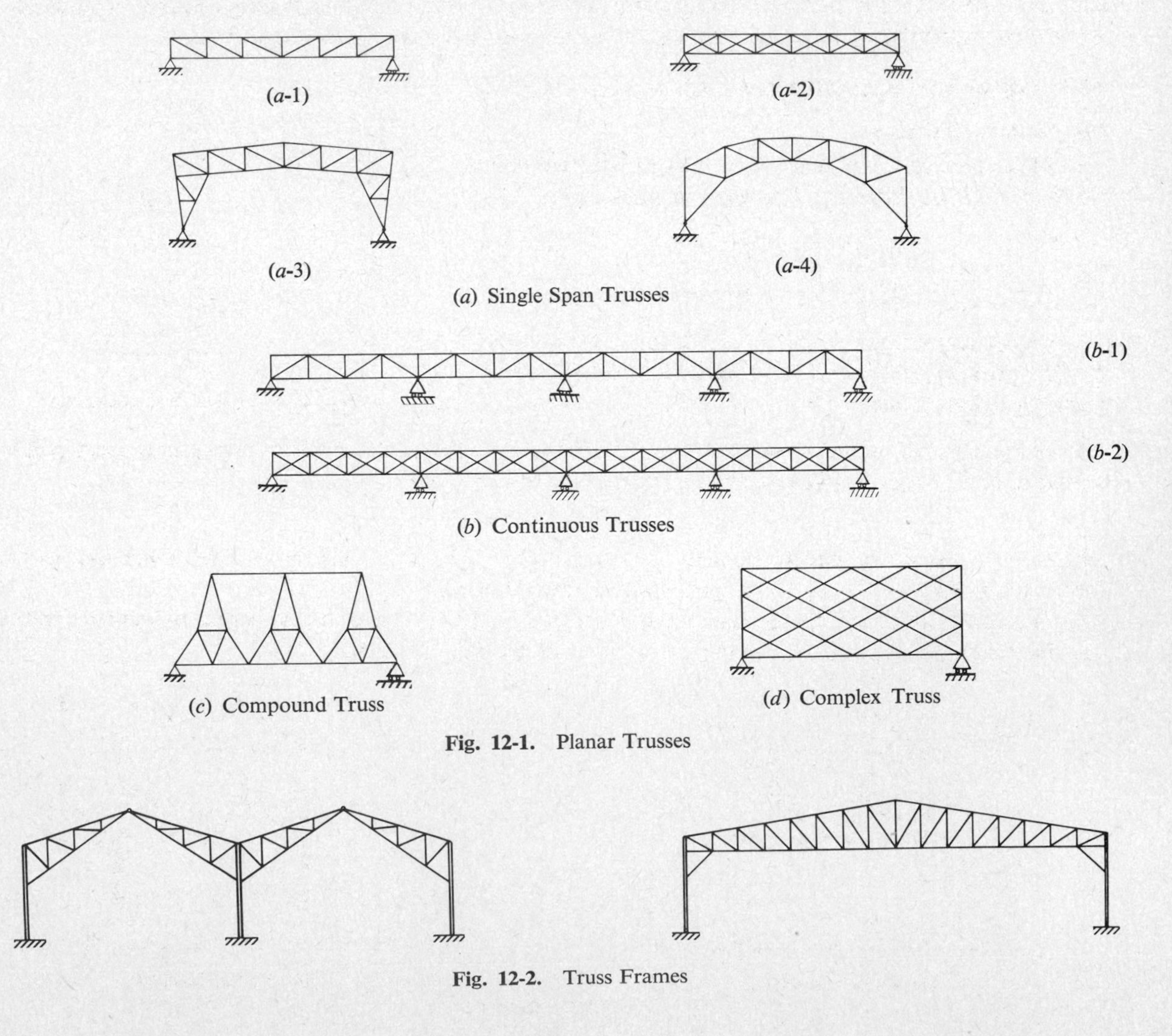

Fig. 12-1. Planar Trusses

Fig. 12-2. Truss Frames

In general, trusses are statically indeterminate systems. If the truss is in a state of static equilibrium, each of its members and joints must be in the same state. Thus for a pin-connected truss, the total number of independent *conditions of static equilibrium* is

$$e = m + 2j \tag{12.1}$$

where m = number of members (bars), j = number of joints.

Since there are two unknown end stresses in each bar and r unknown reactions at the supports, the number of *redundants* is

$$n_F = 2m + r - e = m + r - 2j > 0 \tag{12.2}$$

If $n_F = 0$ the truss is statically determinate, and if $n_F < 0$ the truss is statically overdeterminate and unsuitable to carry loads (Definition I-4.4).

Kinematically, the total number of admissible, independent *joint displacements* (linear) is

$$n_K = 2j - r \tag{12.3}$$

The total number of joints in (*12.1*, *12.2* and *12.3*) includes all internal joints and all points of supports.

12.2 ANALYSIS

Since the planar truss is essentially a planar frame whose joints are assumed to be frictionless hinges, the flexibility method and stiffness method developed in Chapters 9 and 11 respectively are directly applicable. Because this truss (by definition) is a system of straight bars (segments) with loads applied only at joints, the construction of the system flexibility matrix or system stiffness matrix in terms of the respective segmental matrices is particularly simple and is the object of this chapter.

12.3 GENERAL FLEXIBILITY METHOD

(a) Joint Equilibrium

Each joint of the planar truss must satisfy two conditions of static equilibrium. Considering joint j (Fig. 12-3),

$$\begin{aligned} \sum \alpha^{0s}_{jsx} N^s_{js} + P^0_{jx} &= 0 \\ \sum \alpha^{0s}_{jsy} N^s_{js} + P^0_{jy} &= 0 \end{aligned} \tag{12.4}$$

where s = far joint $i, k, \ldots$, N^s_{js} = axial force (stress) in bar js, $\alpha^{os}_{jx} = \cos \omega_{js}$, $\alpha^{os}_{jy} = \sin \omega_{js}$ and ω_{js} is the member slope given by truss geometry.

Fig. 12-3. Loads and Stresses at j

For a *statically determinate truss* with j joints and m bars, the relation between m axial forces, r reactions and j loads is given symbolically in terms of (*12.4*) as

$$\alpha^{0s} \sigma^s + P^0 = 0 \tag{12.5}$$

where α^{0s} = matrix of direction coefficients α^{os}_{jsx}, α^{os}_{jsy}, $[2j \times (m + r)]$, σ^s = axial force and reactive force vector, $[(m + r) \times 1]$, P^0 = joint load vector, $[2j \times 1]$.

The construction of α^{0s} for the simple truss of Fig. 12-4 is given below where for convenience the reactive forces are represented by the axial forces in *auxiliary bars* $0A$, $2B$, $2C$.

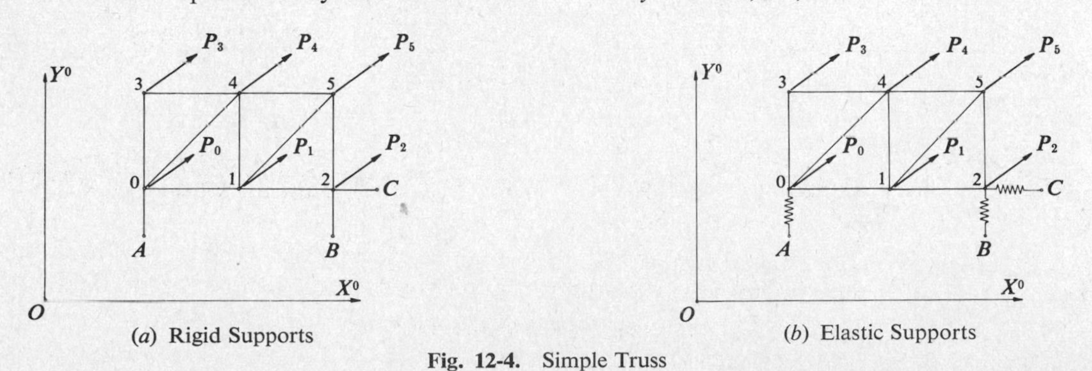

(*a*) Rigid Supports (*b*) Elastic Supports

Fig. 12-4. Simple Truss

$$\left[\begin{array}{cc|cc|cc|ccc|ccc}
\alpha_{01x} & & & & \alpha_{04x} & & \alpha_{03x} & & & \alpha_{0Ax} & & \\
\alpha_{10x} & \alpha_{12x} & & & & \alpha_{15x} & & \alpha_{14x} & & & & \\
& \alpha_{21x} & & & & & & & \alpha_{25x} & & \alpha_{2Bx} & \alpha_{2Cx} \\
\hline
& & \alpha_{34x} & & & & \alpha_{30x} & & & & & \\
& & \alpha_{43x} & \alpha_{45x} & \alpha_{40x} & & & \alpha_{41x} & & & & \\
& & & \alpha_{54x} & & \alpha_{51x} & & & \alpha_{52x} & & & \\
\hline
\alpha_{01y} & & & & \alpha_{04y} & & \alpha_{03y} & & & \alpha_{0Ay} & & \\
\alpha_{10y} & \alpha_{12y} & & & & \alpha_{15y} & & \alpha_{14y} & & & & \\
& \alpha_{21y} & & & & & & & \alpha_{25y} & & \alpha_{2By} & \alpha_{2Cy} \\
\hline
& & \alpha_{34y} & & & & \alpha_{30y} & & & & & \\
& & \alpha_{43y} & \alpha_{45y} & \alpha_{40y} & & & \alpha_{41y} & & & & \\
& & & \alpha_{54y} & & \alpha_{51y} & & & \alpha_{52y} & & &
\end{array}\right]
\left[\begin{array}{c}
N_{01} \\ N_{12} \\ N_{34} \\ \hline N_{45} \\ N_{04} \\ N_{15} \\ \hline N_{03} \\ N_{14} \\ N_{25} \\ \hline N_{0A} \\ N_{2B} \\ N_{2C}
\end{array}\right]
= -
\left[\begin{array}{c}
P_{0x} \\ P_{1x} \\ P_{2x} \\ \hline P_{3x} \\ P_{4x} \\ P_{5x} \\ \hline P_{0y} \\ P_{1y} \\ P_{2y} \\ \hline P_{3y} \\ P_{4y} \\ P_{5y}
\end{array}\right]$$

This formulation of the joint equilibrium conditions has many characteristics facilitating the matrix construction:

(1) α^{0s} is formed by submatrices of special nature and shape.

$$\alpha^{0s} = \begin{bmatrix} \alpha_{BBx} & 0 & \alpha_{BDx} & \alpha_{BVx} & \alpha_{BRx} \\ 0 & \alpha_{TTx} & \alpha_{TDx} & \alpha_{TVx} & 0 \\ \alpha_{BBy} & 0 & \alpha_{BDy} & \alpha_{BVy} & \alpha_{BRy} \\ 0 & \alpha_{TTy} & \alpha_{TDy} & \alpha_{TVy} & 0 \end{bmatrix} \qquad (12.6)$$

where the subscript T, B, D, V, R identifies the top, bottom, diagonal, vertical, reactive force direction coefficients.

(2) α_x-, and α_y-matrices are identical in the arrangement and have identical subscripts.

(3) For each α_{ijx} and α_{ijy} there is α_{jix} and α_{jiy} in the same column.

By (*12.5*),

$$\sigma^s = -\alpha^{0s)-1}P^0 = q_P^{s0}P^0 \qquad (12.7)$$

where $-\alpha^{0s)-1} = q_P^{s0}$ is the general transfer matrix whose coefficients are the axial forces due to unit loads (Problems 12.3, 4).

(b) Joint Displacements

Once the general transfer matrix is available, the construction of the *system flexibility matrix* Φ^0 and the computation of the joint *displacement vector* δ^0 follow the well-established pattern of Chapter 9.

$$\delta_P{}^0 = \underbrace{q_P^{s0)T}\Lambda_P{}^s q_P^{s0}}_{\Phi^0}\, P^0 \qquad (12.8)$$

where

$$\Lambda_P{}^s = \begin{bmatrix} \Lambda^1_{(01)} & & & & & \\ & \Lambda^2_{(12)} & & & & \\ & & \ddots & & & \\ & & & \Lambda^A_{(0A)} & & \\ & & & & \Lambda^B_{(2B)} & \\ & & & & & \Lambda^C_{(2C)} \end{bmatrix} \qquad (12.9)$$

is the *segmental flexibility chain* consisting of a diagonal of coefficients $\Lambda^j_{(ij)}$. For the real bars, this coefficient equals $s_{ij}/A_{ij}E$, where s_{ij} = bar length and A_{ij} = area of its cross section. For the rigid supports of Fig. 12-4*a*, $\Lambda^A_{(0A)} = \Lambda^B_{(2B)} = \Lambda^C_{(2C)} = 0$. For the elastic supports of Fig. 12-4*b*, $\Lambda^A_{(0A)}$, $\Lambda^B_{(2B)}$, $\Lambda^C_{(2C)}$ equal the respective spring flexibilities (given values) (Problem 12.5).

(c) Redundants

The *statically indeterminate truss* of Fig. 12-5*a* is again resolved into the complementary system of Fig. 12-5*b* and the basic system of Fig. 12-5*c*, the definitions and qualifications of which are given in Sec. 5.1 and Sec. 9.9. Whereas in beams, arches and frames this resolution is achieved by cutting the initial system at certain points, in trusses the same is accomplished by removing a certain number of bars. The selection of component systems introduced herein is typical but not exclusive.

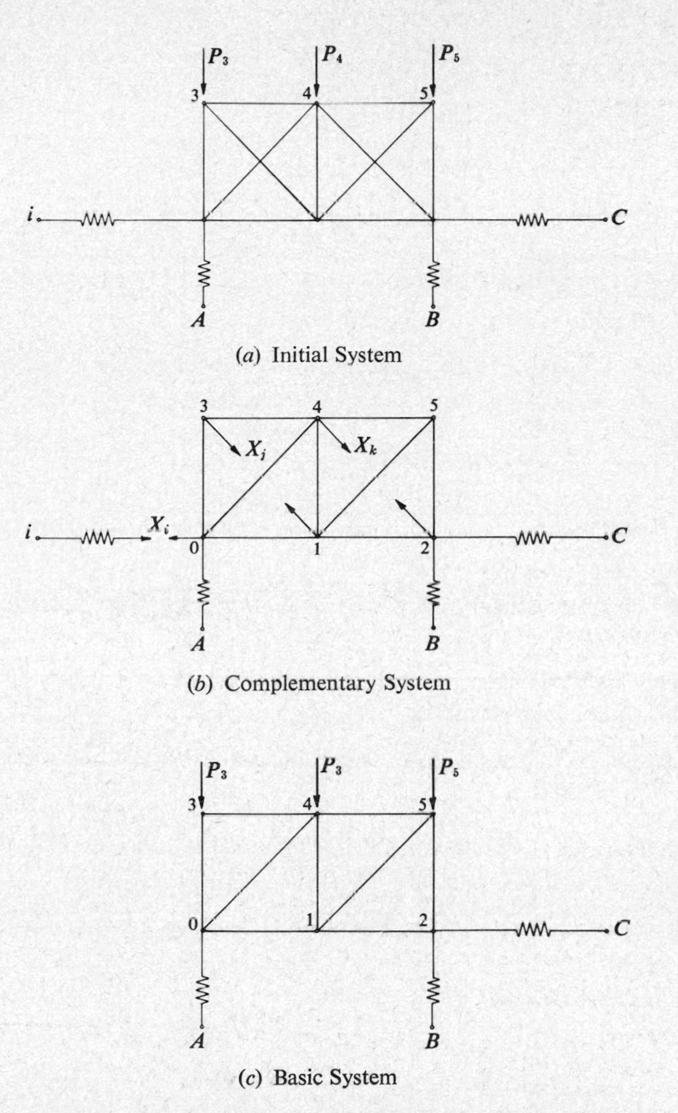

Fig. 12-5. Statically Indeterminate Truss on Elastic Supports

Following the general procedure of Sec. 9.9, the displacement vectors at these releases in the complementary and basic system are respectively

$$\delta_X = \underbrace{q_X^{)T} \Lambda q_X}_{\Phi_X} X \tag{12.10}$$

$$\delta_P = \underbrace{q_X^{)T} \Lambda q_P}_{\Phi_P} P \tag{12.11}$$

where

$$\Lambda = \text{Diag.}[\Lambda_{(01)}, \Lambda_{(12)}, ..., \Lambda_{(0A)}, \Lambda_{(2B)}, \Lambda_{(2C)}, \Lambda_{(xi)}, \Lambda_{(xj)}, \Lambda_{(xk)}] = \text{Diag.}[\Lambda_{(0)}, \Lambda_{(x)}] \qquad (12.12, 13)$$

is the segmental flexibility chain and

$$q_X = \begin{array}{c} \begin{array}{ccc} X_i = +1 & X_j = +1 & X_k = +1 \\ \downarrow & \downarrow & \downarrow \end{array} \\ \left[\begin{array}{ccc} q_{(01)i} & q_{(01)j} & q_{(01)k} \\ q_{(12)i} & q_{(12)j} & q_{(12)k} \\ \cdots & \cdots & \cdots \\ q_{(0A)i} & q_{(0A)j} & q_{(0A)k} \\ \cdots & \cdots & \cdots \\ 1 & 0 & 0 \\ 0 & 1 & 0 \\ 0 & 0 & 1 \end{array}\right] \end{array} \qquad q_P = \begin{array}{c} \begin{array}{ccc} P_3 = +1 & P_4 = +1 & P_5 = +1 \\ \downarrow & \downarrow & \downarrow \end{array} \\ \left[\begin{array}{ccc} q_{(01)3} & q_{(01)4} & q_{(01)5} \\ q_{(12)3} & q_{(12)4} & q_{(12)5} \\ \cdots & \cdots & \cdots \\ q_{(0A)3} & q_{(0A)4} & q_{(0A)5} \\ \cdots & \cdots & \cdots \\ 0 & 0 & 0 \\ 0 & 0 & 0 \\ 0 & 0 & 0 \end{array}\right] \end{array} \qquad (12.14, 15)$$

are the general transfer matrices whose coefficients are the axial forces due to unit redundants and unit loads respectively. The superscripts are omitted in all terms.

Combining (*12.10*) and (*12.11*), the *compatibility condition* of the initial system yields

$$\delta_X + \delta_P = \Phi_X X + \Phi_P P = 0 \qquad (12.16)$$

where Φ_X is the *unit stress redundant system flexibility matrix* and Φ_P is the *unit load system flexibility matrix*.

By (*12.16*),

$$X = -\Phi_X^{)-1}\Phi_P P \qquad (12.17)$$

The *true stress vector* $\sigma = \{\sigma_{01}, \sigma_{12}, ..., \sigma_{0A}, \sigma_{0B}, \sigma_{0C}, \sigma_i, \sigma_j, \sigma_k\}$ in terms of (*12.17*) is

$$\sigma = q_P P + q_X X = \underbrace{[q_P - q_X \Phi_X^{)-1}\Phi_P]}_{B} P \qquad (12.18)$$

where B is the *true unit load transfer matrix* in the initial system.

Similarly, the *true displacement vector* $\delta = \{\delta_{0x}, \delta_{1x}, \delta_{2x}, ..., \delta_{0y}, \delta_{1y}, \delta_{2y}, ...\}$ is

$$\delta = q_W^{)T}\Lambda BP = \underbrace{[q_W^{)T}\Lambda q_P - \Phi_W^{)T}\Phi_X^{)-1}\Phi_P]}_{\Phi} P \qquad (12.19)$$

where $q_W^{)T}$ is the transpose of the complete general transfer matrix of (*12.6*) and Φ is the *true unit load system flexibility matrix* in the initial system (Problem 12.6).

(d) Secondary Effects

The effect of volume change is introduced in the analysis by the secondary effect displacement vector δ_T. Thus for the *statically determinate truss* (*12.8*),

$$\delta_T = q_W^{)T}\Delta_T \qquad (12.20)$$

where Δ_T is a column vector of linear thermal deformations.

Similarly for the *statically indeterminate truss* (*12.17*),

$$X = -\Phi_X^{)-1}\delta_T \qquad (12.21)$$

where δ_T is given by (*12.20*).

12.4 GENERAL STIFFNESS METHOD

(a) Segmental Stiffness Matrix

The relation between the end displacements δ^0_{Rx}, δ^0_{Ry}, δ^0_{Lx}, δ^0_{Ly} and the end forces N^0_{RLx}, N^0_{RLy}, N^0_{LRx}, N^0_{LRy} of a truss member LR in Fig. 12-6 are given by the *reduced slope-deflection equations* (*10.19*), where by definition $M^0_{RLz} = 0$, $M^0_{LRz} = 0$, $\sigma^0_{R0} = 0$, $\sigma^0_{L0} = 0$. The stiffnesses of these equations are interpreted physically and given analytically in Table 12-1 (Problem 12.7).

Symbolically,

$$N^0_{RL} = k^0_{RR}\delta_R{}^0 + k^0_{RL}\delta_L{}^0 \qquad (12.22)$$
$$N^0_{LR} = k^0_{LR}\delta_R{}^0 + k^0_{LL}\delta_L{}^0$$

where
$$N^0_{RL} = \{N^0_{RLx}\,,\ N^0_{RLy}\},$$
$$N^0_{LR} = \{N^0_{LRx}\,,\ N^0_{LRy}\},$$
$$\delta_R{}^0 = \{\delta^0_{Rx}\,,\ \delta^0_{Ry}\},$$
$$\delta_L{}^0 = \{\delta^0_{Lx}\,,\ \delta^0_{Ly}\}.$$

Segments a and b are *directed segments* (they have a sign) given as

$$a = x_R{}^0 - x_L{}^0 \quad \text{and} \quad b = y_R{}^0 - y_L{}^0 \qquad (12.23)$$

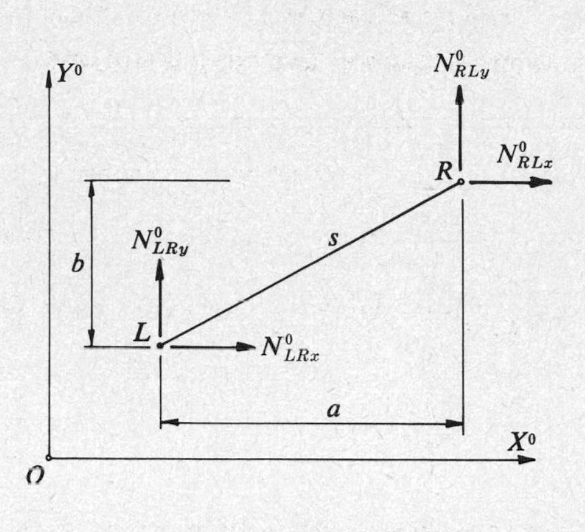

Fig. 12-6. Bar LR

Table 12-1. Segmental Stiffnesses, Truss Member

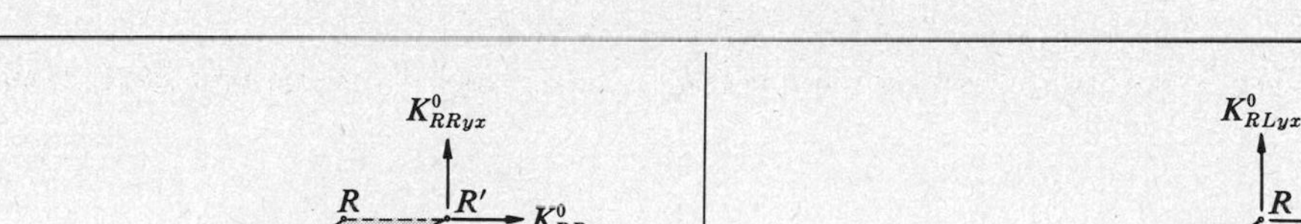

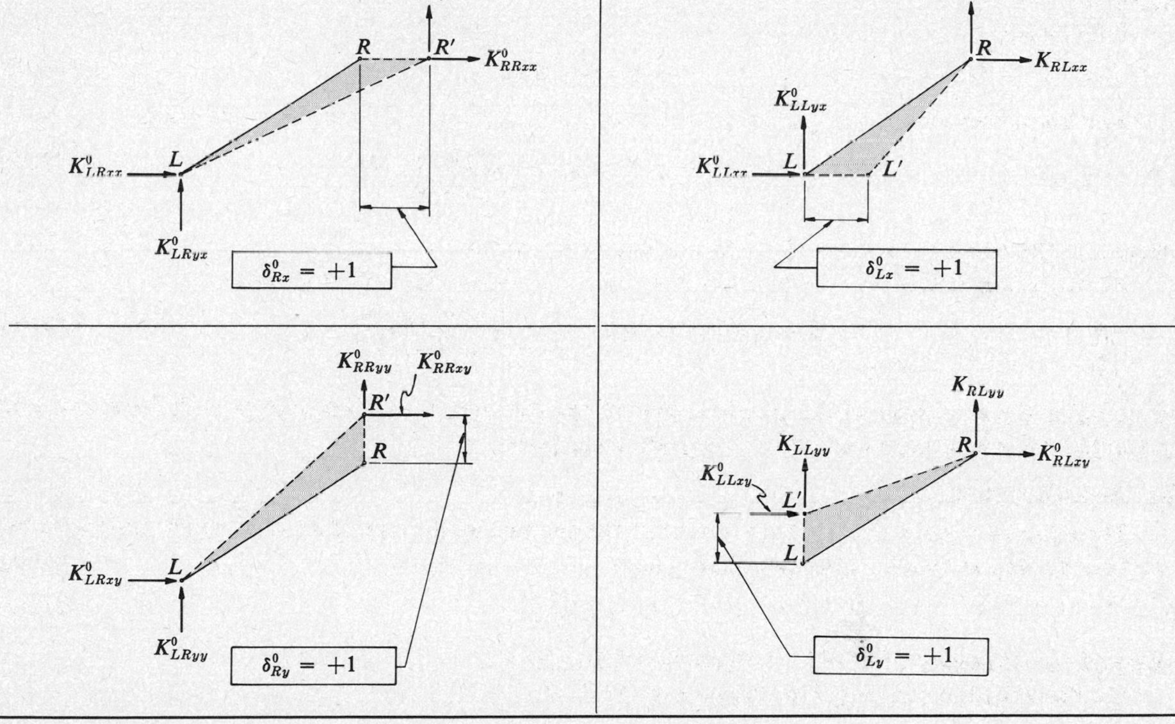

Right End Stiffnesses:

$$\underbrace{\frac{EA}{s^3}\begin{bmatrix} a^2 & ab \\ ab & b^2 \end{bmatrix}}_{k^0_{RR}} \underbrace{\begin{bmatrix} -a^2 & -ab \\ -ab & -b^2 \end{bmatrix}}_{k^0_{RL}}$$

Left End Stiffnesses:

$$\underbrace{\frac{EA}{s^3}\begin{bmatrix} -a^2 & -ab \\ -ab & -b^2 \end{bmatrix}}_{k^0_{LR}} \underbrace{\begin{bmatrix} a^2 & ab \\ ab & b^2 \end{bmatrix}}_{k^0_{LL}}$$

(b) Joint Equilibrium Equation

Once the segmental stiffness matrices are available for all members of a given truss and the admissible joint displacement vectors are introduced as the unknowns of the analysis, the joint equilibrium equations become formally identical to those developed for a hinge in a rigid frame.

At the joint j (any joint) of Fig. 12-7,

$$N_{j1}^0 + N_{j2}^0 + N_{j3}^0 + N_{j4}^0 + N_{j5}^0 = P_j{}^0 \tag{12.24}$$

and in terms of (*12.22*),

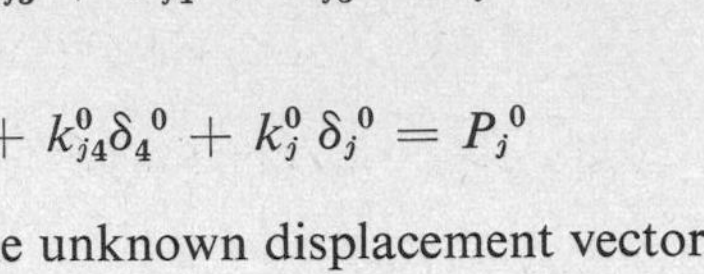

$$k_{j2}^0\delta_2{}^0 + k_{j3}^0\delta_3{}^0 + k_{j4}^0\delta_4{}^0 + k_j^0\,\delta_j{}^0 = P_j{}^0 \tag{12.25}$$

where $P_j{}^0$= joint load at j, $\delta_2{}^0$, $\delta_3{}^0$, $\delta_4{}^0$, $\delta_j{}^0$ are the unknown displacement vectors at 2, 3, 4, j respectively and

$$k_j{}^0 = k_{jj,1}^0 + k_{jj,2}^0 + k_{jj,3}^0 + k_{jj,4}^0 + k_{jj,5}^0 \tag{12.26}$$

Fig. 12-7. Planar Truss

(c) System Stiffness Matrix

Equation (*12.24*) can be used as a recurrent formula for the construction of the system stiffness matrix given below,

$$\begin{bmatrix} k_2{}^0 & k_{23}^0 & 0 & k_{2j}^0 \\ k_{32}^0 & k_3{}^0 & k_{34}^0 & k_{3j}^0 \\ 0 & k_{43}^0 & k_4{}^0 & k_{4j}^0 \\ k_{j2}^0 & k_{j3}^0 & k_{j4}^0 & k_j{}^0 \end{bmatrix} \begin{bmatrix} \delta_2{}^0 \\ \delta_3{}^0 \\ \delta_4{}^0 \\ \delta_j{}^0 \end{bmatrix} = \begin{bmatrix} P_2{}^0 \\ P_3{}^0 \\ P_4{}^0 \\ P_j{}^0 \end{bmatrix}$$

or symbolically

$$K^0\delta^0 = P^0 \tag{12.27}$$

where K^0 is the *system stiffness matrix*.

The same result is obtained by the overlapping of segmental stiffness matrices (Sec. 11.3) or by means of the general transfer matrix j (Sec. 11.10) (Problem 12.8).

(d) Secondary Effects

As in the analysis of rigid frame, the fixed end forces due to secondary effects are summed at each joint and are included in (*12.27*) as the secondary effect vector $N_T{}^0$. For $P_j{}^0 = 0$,

$$\delta^0 = -K^{0)-1}N_T{}^0 \tag{12.28}$$

(e) Joint Displacement Vector

By (*12.27*), the joint displacement vector is

$$\delta^0 = \underbrace{K^{0)-1}}_{\Phi^0}\,P^0 \tag{12.29}$$

where Φ^0 is the *true unit load system flexibility matrix*.

(f) Axial Stress Vector

With the redundants known, the *true stress in each member* is given by the general expression

$$\sigma_{RL}^{s} = \frac{EA}{s^2} [(\delta_{Rx}^0 - \delta_{Lx}^0)\, a + (\delta_{Ry}^0 - \delta_{Ly}^0)\, b] \tag{12.30}$$

Equation (*12.30*) can be used as a recurrent formula for the construction of the *true stress vector*

$$\sigma^s = k^s j^{0s)T} \delta^0 = A^{s0} P^0 \tag{12.31}$$

where A is the *true unit load system transfer matrix* in the initial system (Problems 12.9, 10, 11).

Solved Problems

CLASSIFICATION

12.1. Classify the trusses of Fig. 12-1 according to (*12.2*) as statically determinate or indeterminate. If applicable, determine the number of redundants.

Case	m	r	j	Number of Redundants $n_F = m + r - 2j$	Classification of the Truss
a-1	25	3	14	$25 + 3 - 28 = 0$	Determinate
a-2	31	3	14	$31 + 3 - 28 = 6$	Indeterminate
a-3	37	4	20	$37 + 4 - 40 = 1$	Indeterminate
a-4	25	4	14	$25 + 4 - 28 = 1$	Indeterminate
b-1	65	6	34	$65 + 6 - 68 = 3$	Indeterminate
b-2	81	6	34	$81 + 6 - 68 = 19$	Indeterminate
c	29	3	16	$29 + 3 - 32 = 0$	Determinate
d	26	3	14	$26 + 3 - 28 = 1$	Indeterminate

12.2. Determine the number of joint displacements for the trusses of Fig. 12-1 according to (*12.3*).

Case	j	r	Number of Joint Displacements $n_K = 2j - r$
a-1	14	3	$28 - 3 = 25$
a-2	14	3	$28 - 3 = 25$
a-3	20	4	$40 - 4 = 36$
a-4	14	4	$28 - 4 = 24$
b-1	34	6	$68 - 6 = 62$
b-2	34	6	$68 - 6 = 62$
c	16	3	$32 - 3 = 29$
d	14	3	$28 - 3 = 25$

GENERAL FLEXIBILITY METHOD

12.3. Construct the direction coefficients matrix α^{0s} for the planar truss of Fig. P-12.3*a*.

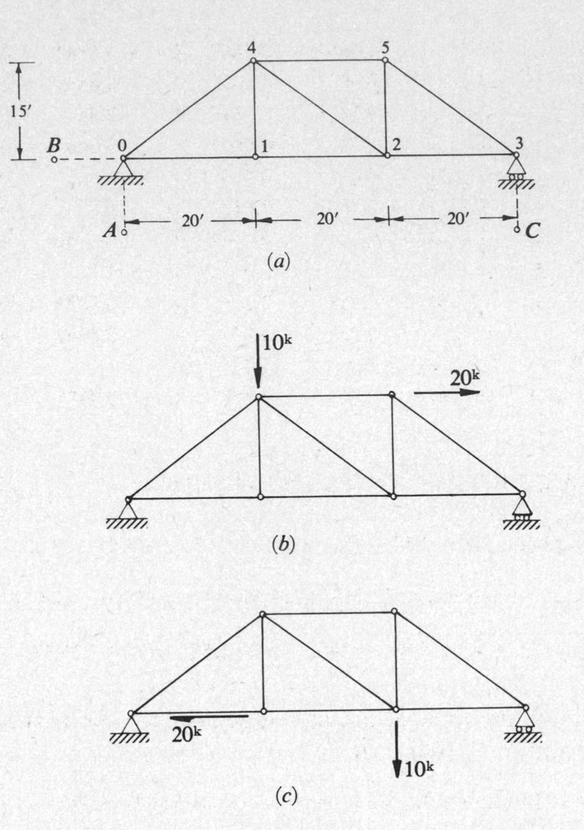

Fig. P-12.3

Following the procedure explained in Sec. 12.3, α^{0s} is constructed for $N^s = \{N^s_{01}, N^s_{12}, N^s_{23}, N^s_{45}, N^s_{04}, N^s_{24}, N^s_{35}, N^s_{14}, N^s_{25}, N^s_{0A}, N^s_{0B}, N^s_{3C}\}$ and $P^0 = \{P^0_{0x}, \ldots, P^0_{5x}, P^0_{0y}, \ldots, P^0_{5y}\}$.

$$
\alpha^{0s} = \begin{bmatrix}
1 & & & & 0.8 & & & & & 0 & -1 & \\
-1 & 1 & & & & & & 0 & & & & \\
 & -1 & 1 & & & -0.8 & & & 0 & & & \\
 & & -1 & & & & -0.8 & & & & & 0 \\
 & & & 1 & -0.8 & 0.8 & & 0 & & & & \\
 & & & -1 & & & 0.8 & & 0 & & & \\
\hline
0 & & & & 0.6 & & & & & -1 & 0 & \\
0 & 0 & & & & & & 1 & & & & \\
 & 0 & 0 & & & 0.6 & & & 1 & & & \\
 & & 0 & & & & 0.6 & & & & & -1 \\
 & & & 0 & -0.6 & -0.6 & & -1 & & & & \\
 & & & 0 & & & -0.6 & & -1 & & &
\end{bmatrix}
$$

Only the pertinent elements are shown, the remaining elements being zero.

12.4. Using the results of the preceding problem, compute the general transfer matrix q_P^{s0} and by (*12.7*) determine the bar stresses for the load conditions given in Fig. P-12.3*b*, *c*.

$$q_P^{s0} = -\alpha^{0s)-1} = \begin{bmatrix} 0 & 1.0 & 1.0 & 1.0 & 0.6667 & 0.6667 & 0 & -0.8889 & 0.4444 & 0 & -0.8889 & -0.4444 \\ 0 & 0 & 1.0 & 1.0 & 0.6667 & 0.6667 & 0 & -0.8889 & -0.4444 & 0 & -0.8889 & -0.4444 \\ 0 & 0 & 0 & 1.0 & 0.3333 & 0.3333 & 0 & -0.4444 & -0.8889 & 0 & -0.4444 & -0.8889 \\ 0 & 0 & 0 & 0 & -0.3333 & 0.6667 & 0 & 0.4444 & 0.8889 & 0 & 0.4444 & 0.8889 \\ 0 & 0 & 0 & 0 & 0.4167 & 0.4167 & 0 & 1.1111 & 0.5556 & 0 & 1.1111 & 0.5556 \\ 0 & 0 & 0 & 0 & -0.4167 & -0.4167 & 0 & 0.5556 & -0.5556 & 0 & 0.5556 & -0.5556 \\ 0 & 0 & 0 & 0 & -0.4167 & -0.4167 & 0 & 0.5556 & 1.1111 & 0 & 0.5556 & 1.1111 \\ 0 & 0 & 0 & 0 & 0 & 0 & 0 & -1.0 & 0 & 0 & 0 & 0 \\ 0 & 0 & 0 & 0 & 0.25 & 0.25 & 0 & -0.3333 & -0.6667 & 0 & -0.3333 & 0.3333 \\ 0 & 0 & 0 & 0 & 0.25 & 0.25 & 1.0 & 0.6667 & 0.3333 & 0 & 0.6667 & 0.3333 \\ 1.0 & 1.0 & 1.0 & 1.0 & 1.0 & 1.0 & 0 & 0 & 0 & 0 & 0 & 0 \\ 0 & 0 & 0 & 0 & -0.25 & -0.25 & 0 & 0.3333 & 0.6667 & 1.0 & 0.3333 & 0.6667 \end{bmatrix}$$

Then for $P^0 = \{0, 0, 0, 0, 0, 20, 0, 0, 0, 0, -10, 0\}$ of Fig. 12.3*b*,

$$N^s = q_P^{s0} P^0 = \{22.22, 22.22, 11.11, 8.89, -2.78, -13.89, -13.89, 0, 8.33, -1.67, 20.0, -8.33\}$$

where N^s is the vector given in Problem 12.3. Similarly for $P^0 = \{0, -20, 0, 0, 0, 0, 0, 0, -10, 0, 0, 0\}$ of Fig. 12.3*c*,

$$N^s = q_P^{s0} P^0 = \{-15.56, 4.44, 8.89, -8.89, -5.56, 5.56, -11.11, 0, 6.67, -3.33, -20.0, -6.67\}$$

12.5. Using (*12.8*), compute the joint displacement vectors for the trusses of Fig. P-12.3*b*, *c*. Assume $E = 30 \times 10^6$ psi and $A = 10$ in^2 for all bars.

The segmental flexibility chain $\Lambda_P{}^s$ (*12.9*) for the truss of Fig. P-12.3*a* is

$$\Lambda_P{}^s = \frac{1}{AE} \text{Diag. } \{20, 20, 20, 20, 25, 25, 25, 15, 15, 0, 0, 0\} \quad \text{and} \quad AE = 30 \times 10^4 \text{ k-ft}^2/\text{ft}^2.$$

The system flexibility matrix $\phi^0 = q_P^{0s)T} \Lambda_P{}^s q_P^{s0}$ is constructed using q_P^{s0} computed in Problem 12.4. The displacement vectors then are computed using (*12.8*).

For the loads shown in Fig. P-12.3*b*,

$$\delta_P{}^0 = 10^{-3}\{0, 1.48, 2.96, 3.70, 3.00, 3.59, 0, -4.38, -2.50, 0, -4.38, -2.08\}$$

in feet units and for those shown in Fig. *c*,

$$\delta_P{}^0 = 10^{-3}\{0, -1.04, -0.74, -0.15, -0.015, -0.61, 0, -0.75, -2.49, 0, -0.75, -2.16\}$$

where $\delta_P{}^0 = \{\delta^0_{0x}, \delta^0_{1x}, \ldots, \delta^0_{5x}, \delta^0_{0y}, \delta^0_{1y}, \ldots, \delta^0_{5y}\}$.

12.6. Compute the true stress vectors (*12.18*) and the true displacement vectors (*12.19*) for the trusses shown in Fig. P-12.6*b*, *c* below. Assume *AE* for the redundant bar to be the same as for other bars.

For these statically indeterminate trusses the redundant force X in member 15 is first solved for from the compatibility condition (*12.16*).

The general transfer matrix q_X is established by statics:

$$q_X = \{0, -0.8, 0, -0.8, 0, -0.8, 0, 1, 0, -0.6, -0.6, 0, 0, 0, 1\}_{13\times 1}$$

The general transfer matrix q_P (13×12) is the same as in Prob. 12.4 with the thirteenth row consisting of zeros added to it.

The segmental flexibility chain Λ becomes (13×13) and is the same as before, with the thirteenth diagonal element equal to 25 added to it.

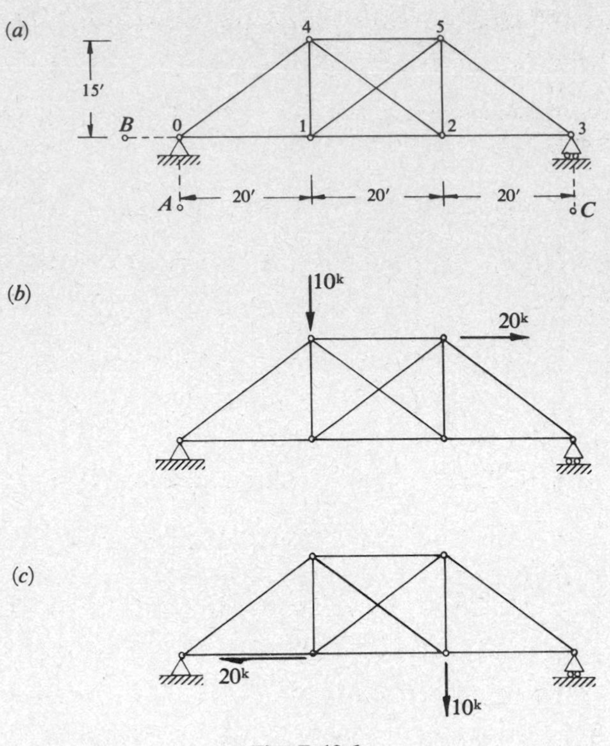

Fig. P-12.6

Substituting these values, Φ_X and Φ_P (*12.10, 11*) arc computed. From (*12.17*) then, the value of the redundant force $X = 10.648^k$ for the truss of Fig. P-12.6*b* and $X = -1.736^k$ for the truss of Fig. P-12.6*c*. The true stress vectors (*12.18*) for the two cases respectively are

$$N^s = \{22.22, 13.70, 11.11, 0.37, -2.78, -3.24, -13.89, -6.39, 1.94, -1.67, 20.00, -8.33, 10.65\}_{13\times1}$$

$$N^s = \{-15.56, 5.83, 8.89, -7.50, -5.56, 3.82, -11.11, 1.04, 7.71, -3.33, -20,00, -6.67, -1.74\}_{13\times1}$$

The true displacement vectors (*12.19*) are respectively

$$\delta^0 = 10^{-3}\{0, 1.48, 2.40, 3.14, 2.36, 2.38, 0, -3.21, -3.03, 0, -3.53, -2.93\}_{13\times1} \text{ in feet units}$$

$$\delta^0 = 10^{-3}\{0, -1.04, -0.65, -0.06, 0.09, -0.41, 0, -0.94, -2.40, 0, -0.89, -2.02\}_{13\times1}$$

GENERAL STIFFNESS METHOD

12.7. By the Virtual Forces Method, derive the segmental stiffnesses for the bar *LR* given in Table 12-1.

For the first case ($\delta^0_{Rx} = +1$) shown in Table 12-1 let there be a unit virtual force $\bar{P}_{Rx} = +1$ applied at *R*. This unit force generates the following external and internal virtual forces as a result of statical conditions:

$$\bar{P}_{Ry} = \frac{b}{a}(1), \qquad \bar{P}_{Lx} = -\bar{P}_{Rx} = -1, \qquad \bar{P}_{Ly} = -\bar{P}_{Ry} = -\frac{b}{a} \qquad \text{and} \qquad \bar{N} = \frac{s}{a}(1)$$

For this case then equating the external virtual work to the internal virtual work,

$$(1)(1) = \int_0^s \frac{\bar{N}N\,d\xi}{AE} = \int_0^s \left(\frac{s}{a}\right)\left(\frac{s}{a}K^0_{RRxx}\right)\frac{d\xi}{AE} = \frac{s^3}{a^2}\frac{K^0_{RRxx}}{AE}$$

wherein K^0_{RRxx}, K^0_{RRyx}, K^0_{LRxx}, K^0_{LRyx} are the real external forces and the real internal force $N = (s/a)\,K^0_{RRxx}$.

Thus $K^0_{RRxx} = (a^2/s^3)AE$, and the other real external forces being related to K^0_{RRxx} by statical relations are therefore

$$K^0_{RRyx} = \frac{b}{a}K^0_{RRxx} = \frac{ab}{s^3}AE = -K^0_{LRyx}, \qquad K^0_{LRxx} = -K^0_{RRxx} = -\frac{a^2}{s^3}AE$$

The remaining values can be obtained in a similar manner.

12.8. Using the segmental stiffnesses, construct the system stiffness matrix K^0 for the truss of Fig. P-12.3*a*. $E = 30 \times 10^6$ psi and $A = 10$ in^2 for all bars.

In the system equilibrium matrix equation $K^0\delta^0 = P^0$, for $\delta^0 = \{\delta^0_{1x}, \delta^0_{1y}, \delta^0_{2x}, \delta^0_{2y}, \delta^0_{3x}, \delta^0_{4x}, \delta^0_{4y}, \delta^0_{5x}, \delta^0_{5y}\}_{9\times1}$ the system stiffness matrix K^0 is

$$K^0 = \begin{bmatrix} k_1^0 & k_{12}^0 & & k_{14}^0 & \\ k_{21}^0 & k_2^0 & k_{23x}^0 & k_{24}^0 & k_{25}^0 \\ & k_{3x2}^0 & k_{3x}^0 & & k_{3x5}^0 \\ k_{41}^0 & k_{42}^0 & & k_4^0 & k_{45}^0 \\ & k_{52}^0 & k_{53x}^0 & k_{54}^0 & k_5^0 \end{bmatrix} \quad \text{in which} \quad \begin{cases} k_1^0 = k_{11,0}^0 + k_{11,2}^0 + k_{11,4}^0 & (2\times2) \\ k_2^0 = k_{22,1}^0 + k_{22,4}^0 + k_{22,3}^0 + k_{22,5}^0 & (2\times2) \\ k_{3x}^0 = k_{33,2x}^0 + k_{33,5x}^0 & (1\times1) \\ k_4^0 = k_{44,0}^0 + k_{44,1}^0 + k_{44,2}^0 + k_{44,5}^0 & (2\times2) \\ k_5^0 = k_{55,4}^0 + k_{55,2}^0 + k_{55,3}^0 & (2\times2) \end{cases}$$

and k^0_{23x} (2×1), k^0_{32x} (1×2), k^0_{3x5} (1×2) and k^0_{53x} (2×1) are partitions of k^0_{23}, k^0_{32}, k^0_{35} and k^0_{53} related to δ^0_{3x} only.

Using Table 12-1,

$$k^0_{11,0} = \frac{EA}{20^3}\begin{bmatrix} 400 & 0 \\ 0 & 0 \end{bmatrix} = k^0_{22,1} = k^0_{33,2} = k^0_{55,4} = k^0_{11,2} = k^0_{22,3} = k^0_{44,5}$$

$$k^0_{12} = k^0_{21} = k^0_{23} = k^0_{32} = k^0_{45} = k^0_{54} = -k^0_{11,0}$$

$$k^0_{44,0} = \frac{EA}{25^3}\begin{bmatrix} 400 & 300 \\ 300 & 225 \end{bmatrix}$$

$$k^0_{44,2} = \frac{EA}{25^3}\begin{bmatrix} 400 & -300 \\ -300 & 225 \end{bmatrix} = k^0_{55,3} = k^0_{22,4} = k^0_{33,5} = -k^0_{24} = -k^0_{42} = -k^0_{35} = -k^0_{53}$$

$$k^0_{11,4} = \frac{EA}{15^3}\begin{bmatrix} 0 & 0 \\ 0 & 225 \end{bmatrix} = k^0_{22,5} = k^0_{44,1} = k^0_{55,2} = -k^0_{14} = -k^0_{41} = -k^0_{52} = -k^0_{25}$$

Also from the above matrices,

$$k^0_{33,2x} = \frac{EA}{20^3}[400], \qquad k^0_{33,5x} = \frac{EA}{25^3}[400], \qquad k^0_{23x} = \frac{EA}{20^3}\begin{bmatrix} -400 \\ 0 \end{bmatrix} = k^{0)T}_{3x2}, \qquad k^0_{53x} = \frac{EA}{25^3}\begin{bmatrix} -400 \\ 300 \end{bmatrix} = k^{0)T}_{3x5}$$

Substitution of these matrices gives K^0, with $EA = 30 \times 10^4$ k-ft^2/ft^2.

12.9. Using (*12.29*), compute the true joint displacement vectors for the trusses of Fig. P-12.3*b*, *c*. Also compute the bar stresses and compare the results with those of Problems 12.4, 5.

By (*12.29*), $$\delta^0 = K^{0)-1}P^0$$

Inverting K^0 obtained in Problem 12.8 and post-multiplying by the respective load vectors for the trusses shown in Fig. P-12.3*b*, *c*,

$$P^0 = \{0, 0, 0, 0, 0, -10, 0, 20, 0\}_{9\times1} \quad \text{and} \quad P^0 = \{-20, 0, 0, -10, 0, 0, 0, 0, 0\}_{9\times1}$$

the following joint displacement vectors are obtained:

$$\delta^0 = 10^{-3}\{1.48, -4.38, 2.96, -2.50, 3.70, 3.00, -4.38, 3.59, -2.08\}$$

$$\delta^0 = 10^{-3}\{-1.04, -0.75, -0.74, -2.49, -0.15, -0.015, -0.75, -0.61, -2.16\}$$

The bar stresses computed using (*12.30*) are as follows:

Case	N_{10}	N_{21}	N_{32}	N_{54}	N_{40}	N_{42}	N_{53}	N_{41}	N_{52}
Fig. 12-3*b*	22.22	22.22	11.11	8.89	−2.78	−13.89	−13.89	0	8.33
Fig. 12-3*c*	−15.56	4.44	8.89	−8.89	−5.56	5.56	−11.11	0	6.67

These values of stresses and displacements can be verified to be the same as those computed in Problems 12.4 and 12.5.

12.10. Reconstruct the system stiffness matrix K^0 of Problem 12.8 to accommodate the redundant bar 51 of the trusses of Fig. 12.6*b*, *c* and compute the respective joint displacement vectors.

The system stiffness matrix K^0 of Problem 12.8 will be modified by the inclusion of the stiffness submatrices $k^0_{55,1}$, $k^0_{11,5}$, k^0_{15} and k^0_{51} of the redundant bar 51. The new matrix K^0 is as follows:

$$K^0 = \begin{bmatrix} k_1^0 & k_{12}^0 & & k_{14}^0 & k_{15}^0 \\ k_{21}^0 & k_2^0 & k_{23x}^0 & k_{24}^0 & k_{25}^0 \\ & k_{3x2}^0 & k_{3x}^0 & & k_{3x5}^0 \\ k_{41}^0 & k_{42}^0 & & k_4^0 & k_{45}^0 \\ k_{51}^0 & k_{52}^0 & k_{53x}^0 & k_{54}^0 & k_5^0 \end{bmatrix}$$

all values of the previous matrix remaining the same except $k_1^0 = k^0_{11,0} + k^0_{11,2} + k^0_{11,4} + k^0_{11,5}$ and $k_5^0 = k^0_{55,4} + k^0_{55,2} + k^0_{55,3} + k^0_{55,1}$. Also

$$k^0_{55,1} = k^0_{11,5} = -k^0_{15} = -k^0_{51} = k^0_{44,0} = \frac{EA}{25^3}\begin{bmatrix} 400 & 300 \\ 300 & 225 \end{bmatrix}$$

The joint displacement vectors for the trusses shown in Fig. P-12.6*b*, *c* are computed using (*12.29*) and the respective load vectors. Thus

$$\delta^0 = 10^{-3}\{1.48, -3.21, 2.40, -3.03, 3.14, 2.36, -3.53, 2.38, -2.93\} \text{ for Fig. } b$$

and $$\delta^0 = 10^{-3}\{-1.04, -0.94, -0.65, -2.40, -0.06, 0.09, -0.89, -0.41, -2.02\} \text{ for Fig. } c$$

Comparison of these values with those of Problem 12.9 shows the stiffening effect of the redundant bar.

12.11. Using the results of Problem 12.10, compute the true stress vectors in the trusses of Fig. P-12.6*b*, *c*.

Using the displacement values computed in Problem 12.10 in (*12.30*), the following bar stresses are computed.

Case	N_{10}	N_{21}	N_{32}	N_{54}	N_{40}	N_{51}	N_{42}	N_{53}	N_{41}	N_{52}
Fig. 12-6*b*	22.22	13.70	11.11	0.37	−2.78	10.65	−3.24	−13.89	−6.39	1.94
Fig. 12-6*c*	−15.56	5.83	8.89	−7.50	−5.56	−1:74	3.82	−11.11	1.04	7.71

Comparison with the stresses obtained in Problem 12.9 shows the effect of the redundant bar in redistributing the stresses.

Supplementary Problems

12.12. For the trusses shown in Fig. P-12.12, determine the classification, the number of redundants, if any, and the number of admissible joint displacements.

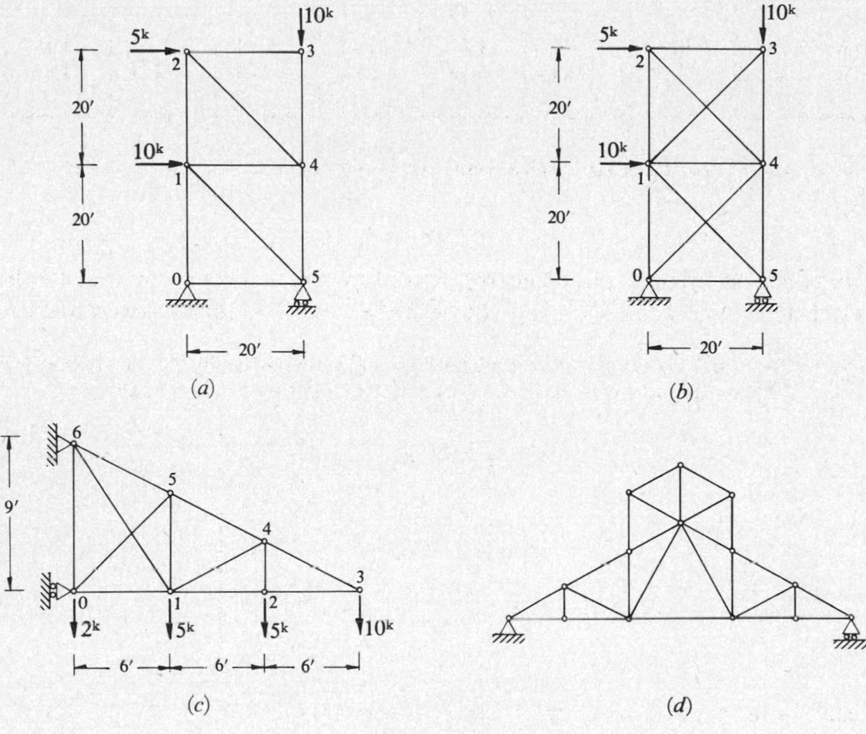

Fig. P-12.12

12.13. Using the general flexibility method, determine the bar stresses and joint displacements for the truss shown in Fig. P-12.12*a*. $EA = 30 \times 10^4$ k-ft²/ft² for all bars.

12.14. Analyze the truss of Fig. P-12.12*b* for bar stresses and joint displacements by the general flexibility method. Consider the bars 13 and 04 redundants and use $EA = 30 \times 10^4$ k-ft²/ft² for all bars.

12.15. Compute the redundant force in bar 16 of the truss of Fig. P-12.12*c* by (*12.17*). $EA = 15 \times 10^4$ k-ft²/ft² for all bars.

12.16. Solve the truss of Fig. P-12.12*a* by the general stiffness method and compare the results with those of Problem 12.13. $EA = 30 \times 10^4$ k-ft²/ft² for all bars.

12.17. Show the modification necessary to be made in the system stiffness matrix K^0 of the truss of Fig. P-12.12*a* to obtain the system stiffness matrix K^0 of the truss shown in Fig. P-12.12*b*. Then compute the redundant forces in bars 13 and 04 and the true bar stresses in the truss of Fig. *b*.

12.18. Compute the true unit load system transfer matrix A^{s0} of (*12.31*) for the truss shown in Fig. P-12.12*c*.

Answers to Supplementary Problems

Forces are given in kips, moments in k-feet, coordinates, segments, lengths, depths, widths and deflections in feet, and rotations in radians, unless stated otherwise.

CHAPTER 2

2.9. $\sigma_E^0 = \{-3.33, 5.0, 0\}$, $\sigma_A^0 = \{6.67, 5.0, 0\}$

2.10. $\sigma_4^4 = \{-4.472, 2.236, 0\}$, $\sigma_3^3 = \{0, 5, 50\}$

$\sigma_2^3 = \{0, 5, 150\}$, $\sigma_2^2 = \{-13.416, -6.708, 150\}$

$\sigma_1^1 = \{-13.416, -6.708, 0\}$

2.11.

$$t_{ij}^{ij} = \begin{bmatrix} \cos\theta & \sin\theta & 0 \\ -\sin\theta & \cos\theta & 0 \\ R(\cos\theta - 1) & R\sin\theta & 1 \end{bmatrix}$$

Hence for

	$\theta = 30°$	$\theta = 45°$	$\theta = 60°$
$t_{ij}^{ij} =$	$\begin{bmatrix} 0.866 & 0.5 & 0 \\ -0.5 & 0.866 & 0 \\ -0.134R & 0.5R & 1 \end{bmatrix}$	$\begin{bmatrix} 0.707 & 0.707 & 0 \\ -0.707 & 0.707 & 0 \\ -0.293R & 0.707R & 1 \end{bmatrix}$	$\begin{bmatrix} 0.5 & 0.866 & 0 \\ -0.866 & 0.5 & 0 \\ -0.5R & 0.866R & 1 \end{bmatrix}$

2.12. $M_{max} = 128$ at $x = 12$

2.13. $R_R = 9.0,\ R_L = 11.0,\ M_i = 42.5,\ M_j = 60.0,\ M_k = 65.0$

CHAPTER 3

3.11. $\Delta_{Bx}^0 = 31379/EI + 162/EA$

3.12. $\Delta_{4x}^0 = 69814/EI$

3.13. $\Delta = \dfrac{1}{EI}\{0, 1533, 2936, 4083, 4868, 5208, 5052, 4387, 3251, 1737, 0\}$

3.14. $\Delta_1 = 1823/EI,\ \Delta_2 = 3073/EI,\ \Delta_3 = 3750/EI,\ \Delta_4 = 1224/EI$

CHAPTER 4

4.9. For the uniformly distributed load,

$$a_L^0 = \{0, -wl, -wl^2/2\}, \qquad a_R^0 = \{0, wl, -wl^2/2\}$$

$$b_L^0 = \frac{1}{EI}\{whl^3/10, -wl^4/24, wl^3/6\}, \qquad b_R^0 = \frac{1}{EI}\{-whl^3/10, -wl^4/24, -wl^3/6\}$$

4.10.

$$\hat{T}^0_{LR} = \begin{bmatrix} 1 & 0 & 0 & 0 & 0 & 0 & 0 \\ 0 & 1 & 0 & 0 & 0 & 0 & 0 \\ 0 & 0 & 1 & 0 & 0 & 0 & 0 \\ 0 & 0 & 60 & 1 & 0 & 0 & 0 \\ 0 & -3102/EI & -11633/EI & -387.7/EI & 1 & 0 & 0 \\ 0 & 11633/EI & 38774/EI & 1939/EI & 0 & 1 & -60 \\ 0 & -387.7/EI & -1939/EI & -64.62/EI & 0 & 0 & 1 \end{bmatrix}$$

$$\hat{T}^0_{RL} = \begin{bmatrix} 1 & 0 & 0 & 0 & 0 & 0 & 0 \\ 0 & 1 & 0 & 0 & 0 & 0 & 0 \\ 0 & 0 & 1 & 0 & 0 & 0 & 0 \\ 0 & 0 & -60 & 1 & 0 & 0 & 0 \\ 0 & 3102/EI & -11633/EI & 387.7/EI & 1 & 0 & 0 \\ 0 & 11633/EI & -38774/EI & 1939/EI & 0 & 1 & 60 \\ 0 & 387.7/EI & -1939/EI & 64.62/EI & 0 & 0 & 1 \end{bmatrix}$$

4.11. $M_i = -104.9, \; M_j = -90.6, \; M_k = -67.04, \; M_l = -48.9$

4.12. $\hat{H}^0_{12} = \{1, -1.087, -8.726, -16.30, 0, 0, -81.506/EI\}$

$\hat{H}^0_{54} = \{1, -0.328, -0.975, 5.85, 0, 0, 0\}$

4.13. $\sigma^0_A = \{-36.17, -44.69, 342.9\}, \quad \sigma^0_F = \{-41.17, 45.31, 415.0\}$

4.14. $\hat{H}^0_{BD} = \{1, -18.42, -29.46, -171.3, -12520/EI, -354/EI, -245/EI\}$

$\hat{H}^0_{GD} = \{1, -16.95, 30.21, -203.0, 19630/EI, -363/EI, -9.1/EI\}$

CHAPTER 5

5.13. $\{X_i, X_j, X_k\} = \{-1.768, -2.131, 18.787\}$

5.14. $\{X_i, \ldots, X_n\} = \{5.678, 3.908, 3.602, 0.901, -0.692, -10.299\}$

5.15. $\{X_i, X_j, X_k\} = \{30.09, 48.44, 76.16\}$

5.16. $\{\Delta_i, \Delta_j, \Delta_k\} = 10^{-2}\{0, -2.913, -0.532, 0, -9.690, -0.785, 0, -18.05, -0.861\}$

5.17. $\Delta^0_k = \{-187.2/EA + 158106/EI, -574.8/EA - 339785/EI, -13058/EI\}$

5.18.

$$\begin{bmatrix} \Delta^0_0 \\ \Delta^0_i \\ \Delta^0_j \\ \Delta^0_k \\ \Delta^0_m \end{bmatrix} = \frac{10^3}{EI} \begin{bmatrix} \{0, & 0, & -5.366\} \\ \{0, & -59.09, & -4.070\} \\ \{0, & -91.94, & 0.176\} \\ \{0, & -55.68, & 4.016\} \\ \{0, & 0, & 4.952\} \end{bmatrix}$$

5.19.

$$\begin{bmatrix} \Delta_0^0 \\ \Delta_1^0 \\ \Delta_2^0 \\ \Delta_3^0 \end{bmatrix} = \frac{10}{EI} \begin{bmatrix} \{0, & 0, & -37.60\} \\ \{0, & -252.0, & 5.00\} \\ \{0, & 0, & 17.60\} \\ \{0, & 51.00, & 0.93\} \end{bmatrix}$$

5.20. $\Delta_4^0 = \frac{1}{EI}\{69814, 0, 1662\}$

5.21. $\Delta_2^0 = \frac{1}{EI}\{545.4, -64.38, -7.958\}$

CHAPTER 6

6.17. $A_{RR} = \frac{s}{EI_R} Q_0, \quad B_{RR} = \frac{s^2}{EI_R} Q_1, \quad C_{RR} = \frac{s^3}{EI_R} Q_2, \quad D_{RR} = \frac{s}{EA_R} R_0$

For $\omega = +1$, $A_{RR} = 0.5445s/EI_R$, $B_{RR} = 0.1875s^2/EI_R$

$C_{RR} = 0.0982s^3/EI_R$, $D_{RR} = 0.7854s/EA_R$

6.18.

	$k = 0.5$	$k = 1.0$
A_{RR}	$5.5216s/EI_L$	$3.0s/EI_L$
B_{RR}	$2.0s^2/EI_L$	$1.0s^2/EI_L$
C_{RR}	$1.0264s^3/EI_L$	$0.5445s^3/EI_L$
D_{RR}	$1.6932s/EA_L$	$1.3863s/EA_L$

6.19.

	$k = 0.0$	$k = 0.5$
E_{RR}	$0.6932s/EA_L$	$0.8466s/EA_L$
F_{RR}	$0.0681s/EI_L$	$0.1283s/EI_L$
$F_{RL} = F_{LR}$	$0.0569s/EI_L$	$0.1217s/EI_L$
F_{LL}	$0.1931s/EI_L$	$0.3158s/EI_L$

6.20.

	$k = 0.0$	$k = 0.5$
E_{RR}	$0.7854s/EA_L$	$0.8927s/EA_L$
F_{RR}	$0.0982s/EI_L$	$0.1689s/EI_L$
$F_{RL} = F_{LR}$	$0.0893s/EI_L$	$0.1391s/EI_L$
F_{LL}	$0.2677s/EI_L$	$0.3251s/EI_L$

6.21. $E_{RR} = 0.8453s/EA_L$, $F_{RR} = 0.0768s/EI_L$

$F_{RL} = F_{LR} = 0.603s/EI_L$, $F_{LL} = 0.1969s/EI_L$

6.25. $E_{RR} = 0.7854s/EA_C$, $F_{RR} = F_{LL} = 0.1607s/EI_C$, $F_{LR} = F_{RL} = 0.1116s/EI_C$

6.31. $F_{LL} = 0.1781s/EI_C$, $F_{RR} = 0.1505s/EI_C$, $F_{LR} = F_{RL} = 0.1169s/EI_C$

6.32.

$$f^0_{kk} = \frac{1}{EI}\begin{bmatrix} 1925.5 & -3751.8 & -132.6 \\ -3751.8 & 10357.4 & 465.3 \\ -132.6 & 465.3 & 29.01 \end{bmatrix}$$

CHAPTER 7

7.15. $\{M_i, M_j, M_k\} = \{-51.37, -42.76, -67.85\}$

7.16. $\{M_j, M_k, M_l\} = \{-5.00, -8.55, -11.21\}$

7.17. $\{M_1, M_2\} = \{-386.3, -154.8\}$

7.18. (*a*) $EI\,10^{-2}\{10.26, -7.69, 3.85\}$; (*b*) $EI\,10^{-4}\{33.57, -134.3, 503.5\}$

7.19. $\{M_i, M_j\} = \{-150.8, -194.1\}$

7.20. Influence values for M_1 for load position at every tenth of a span length:

Stations	1–10	11–20	21–30
	−1.604	−2.837	0.770
	−3.103	−5.168	1.444
	−4.356	−6.727	1.965
	−5.269	−7.331	2.271
	−5.703	−6.952	2.329
	−5.562	−5.810	2.152
	−4.813	−4.278	1.779
	−3.536	−2.719	1.267
	−1.885	−1.278	0.655
	0	0	0

7.21. $\{M_{21}, M_{23}, M_{32}, M_{34}\} = \{-210.1, -227.6, -153.7, -56.26\}$

7.22. $\{M_{12}, M_{21}, M_{23}, M_{32}, M_{34}, M_{43}, M_{45}, M_{54}\} = \{-16.30, -21.23, -7.88, -6.47, -18.97, -22.23, -11.70, 5.85\}$

7.23. $\{M_i, M_j\} = \{-44.37, 85.42\}$

CHAPTER 8

8.21. $R^0_L = \{20, 32.5, 100\}$, $R^0_R = \{-20, 7.5, 100\}$

8.22. $R^0_L = \{16.18, 12.5, 0\}$, $R^0_R = \{-16.18, 17.5, 0\}$
$\theta^0_{Lz} = 657.7/EI$, $\theta^0_{Rz} = 505.2/EI$

8.23. $f_{LLzz} = l/9EI_c$

8.24. $R_L^0 = \{81.7, 50, 0\}, \quad R_R^0 = \{-81.7, 50, 0\}$

8.25.

$$[f] = \frac{l}{EI_c}\begin{bmatrix} \alpha/4h^2 + 2/15 & -\alpha/2h^2 + 1/15 & \alpha/4h^2 - 1/30 \\ -\alpha/2h^2 + 1/15 & \alpha/h^2 + 8/15 & -\alpha/2h^2 + 1/15 \\ \alpha/4h^2 - 1/30 & -\alpha/2h^2 + 1/15 & \alpha/4h^2 + 2/15 \end{bmatrix}$$

8.26.

$$\begin{bmatrix} N_{Rx} \\ N_{Ry} \\ M_{Rz} \end{bmatrix} = \begin{bmatrix} -15m^2(1-m)^2 \\ m^2(3-2m^2) \\ 50m^2(1-m)(3-5m) \end{bmatrix}$$

8.28. $R_A^0 = \{2.714, 7.941, 87.78\}, \quad R_E^0 = \{-2.714, 2.059, 29.87\}$

CHAPTER 9

9.17.

Case	(*a*)	(*b*)	(*c*)	(*d*)	(*e*)	(*f*)
n	5	8	1	1	5	24

9.18.

$$f^s_{RR,L} = \frac{100}{3EI}\begin{bmatrix} 640 & 720 & 36 \\ 720 & 1600 & 48 \\ 36 & 48 & 2.4 \end{bmatrix}$$

9.19.

$$l^s_{RR,L} = \frac{-800}{3EI}\begin{bmatrix} 30m(1+2m) \\ 40m(3+3m-m^2) \\ 3m(1+m) \end{bmatrix}$$

9.20.

$$R_R^0 = \begin{bmatrix} -1.2m(1-m) \\ 0.25m(3+3m-2m^2) \\ m(1-m)(13+10m) \end{bmatrix}$$

9.21. $X_C = \{-3.553, 0, 38.33\}$

9.22. $X_C = \{18.328, 0, 203.62\}$

9.23. $R_A^0 = \{36.17, 44.69, -342.9\}, \quad R_F^0 = \{-41.17, 45.31, 415.0\}$

9.24. $X_1 = \{-18.41, 0.552, 293.2\}, \quad X_2 = \{-16.93, 0.193, 281.4\}$

9.25. $X_1 = \{-162.7, -83.33, 1250.0\}, \quad X_2 = \{-278.3, 16.67, 2250.0\}, \quad X_3 = \{-134.2, 66.67, 1000.0\}$

9.26. $X_1 = \{-2.5, 2.534, 0\}, \quad X_2 = \{-5.0, 6.258, 0\}, \quad X_3 = \{-6.0, 10.909, 0\}$

9.27. $X_1 = \{-5.036, 0.522, -87.53\}$, $X_2 = \{-2.395, 0, -80.95\}$, $X_3 = \{-5.036, -0.522, -87.53\}$

9.28. $\Delta = \frac{1}{EI}\{13156, 11038, 6525\}$.

The true stress vector can be verified using the results of Problem 9.26.

CHAPTER 10

10.15.

$$\left[\begin{array}{c|c} k_{RR}^0 & k_{RL}^0 \\ \hline k_{LR}^0 & k_{LL}^0 \end{array}\right] = \frac{EI_c}{l}\left[\begin{array}{ccc|ccc} 1.273A_c/I_c & 0 & 0 & -1.273A_cI_c & 0 & 0 \\ 0 & 40.758/l^2 & -20.379/l & 0 & -40.758/l^2 & -20.379/l \\ 0 & -20.379/l & 12.03 & 0 & 20.379/l & 8.349 \\ \hline -1.273A_c/I_c & 0 & 0 & 1.273A_c/I_c & 0 & 0 \\ 0 & -40.758/l^2 & 20.379/l & 0 & 40.758/l^2 & 20.379/l \\ 0 & -20.379/l & 8.349 & 0 & 20.379/l & 12.03 \end{array}\right]$$

10.16.

$$\left[\begin{array}{c|c} k_{RR}^0 & k_{RL}^0 \\ \hline k_{LR}^0 & k_{LL}^0 \end{array}\right] = \frac{E}{10^3}\left[\begin{array}{ccc|ccc} 1204.7 & 0 & 0 & -1204.7 & 0 & 0 \\ 0 & 1.2142 & -24.284 & 0 & -1.2142 & -24.284 \\ 0 & -24.284 & 485.69 & 0 & 24.284 & 485.69 \\ \hline -1204.7 & 0 & 0 & 1204.7 & 0 & 0 \\ 0 & -1.2142 & 24.284 & 0 & 1.2142 & 24.284 \\ 0 & -24.284 & 485.69 & 0 & 24.284 & 485.69 \end{array}\right]$$

10.17. See Tables 11-3 and 11-4.

CHAPTER 11

11.14.

$$\begin{bmatrix} \sigma_{12}^0 \\ \sigma_{21}^0 \\ \sigma_{23}^0 \\ \sigma_{32}^0 \\ \sigma_{34}^0 \\ \sigma_{43}^0 \end{bmatrix} = \begin{bmatrix} \{-6.288, & 4.485, & 121.1\} \\ \{6.288, & -4.485, & 110.6\} \\ \{-6.288, & -5.515, & -110.6\} \\ \{6.288, & 5.515, & -110.0\} \\ \{13.712, & -5.515, & 110.0\} \\ \{-13.712, & 5.515, & 119.8\} \end{bmatrix}$$

11.15.

$$\begin{bmatrix} \Delta_2^0 \\ \Delta_3^0 \\ \Delta_4^0 \end{bmatrix} = \frac{1}{EI}\begin{bmatrix} \{2223, & -30.03, & -94.13\} \\ \{2021, & -239.4, & -737.3\} \\ \{1618, & -197.2, & 911.8\} \end{bmatrix} \qquad \begin{aligned} \sigma_{12}^0 &= \{-11.92, 4.50, 73.93\} \\ \sigma_{63}^0 &= \{8.03, 35.91, -43.41\} \\ \sigma_{54}^0 &= \{-16.11, 29.59, 115.46\} \end{aligned}$$

11.17. $N_{25}^2 = -62.11$, $M_{25}^2 = -49.95$, $N_{36}^6 = -22.0$, $M_{36}^6 = 82.36$

11.18. Total deformations:

$$\begin{bmatrix} \Delta_1^0 \\ \Delta_2^0 \\ \Delta_3^0 \\ \Delta_4^0 \end{bmatrix} = \frac{10^3}{EI}\begin{bmatrix} \{-30.71, & -0.747, & -0.341\} \\ \{-6.436, & -1.530, & 0.193\} \\ \{16.89, & -0.729, & 0.814\} \\ \{5.907, & 0.0063, & -0.560\} \end{bmatrix}$$

11.21. Reduced equilibrium matrix equation:

$$\frac{EI}{10^3}\left[\begin{array}{ccc|ccc} 30.165 & 9.458 & 13.825 & -28.358 & -9.419 & -0.535 \\ 9.458 & 153.43 & 4.844 & -9.457 & -3.159 & 0 \\ 13.825 & 4.844 & 315.48 & 0.152 & -0.128 & 1.757 \\ \hline -28.358 & -9.457 & 0.152 & 28.64 & 9.531 & 2.442 \\ -9.419 & -3.159 & -0.128 & 9.531 & 63.484 & -5.103 \\ -0.535 & 0 & 1.757 & 2.442 & -5.103 & 194.23 \end{array}\right]\left[\begin{array}{c} \Delta_L^0 \\ \hline \Delta_R^0 \end{array}\right]$$

$$+\left[\begin{array}{c} -9.955 \\ 14.770 \\ 91.783 \\ \hline -9.951 \\ 14.873 \\ -93.063 \end{array}\right] = \left[\begin{array}{c} 5.0 \\ 0 \\ 0 \\ \hline 5.0 \\ 0 \\ 0 \end{array}\right]$$

11.22. True displacement vector:

$$\{\Delta^0\} = \{\Delta_2^0, \Delta_3^0, \Delta_4^0, \Delta_5^0\} = \{263.1, -0.289, -9.851, 263.1, -2.098, -7.04, 461.4, -1.689, -8.036, 465.0, -1.022, -0.455\}10^2/EI$$

CHAPTER 12

12.12.

Case	Classification	Number of redundants n_F	Number of joint displacements n_K
(*a*)	Determinate	0	9
(*b*)	Indeterminate	2	9
(*c*)	Indeterminate	1	11
(*d*)	Indeterminate	1	25

12.13. $\sigma^s = \{N_{01}, N_{12}, N_{54}, N_{43}, N_{23}, N_{14}, N_{05}, N_{24}, N_{15}, N_{0x}, N_{0y}, N_{5y}\}$

$= \{20.0, 5.0, -15.0, -10.0, 0, 5.0, 15.0, -7.07, -21.21, 15.0, 20.0, -30.0\}$

$\delta_P^0 = 10^{-3}\{0, 5.16, 9.10, 9.10, 5.49, 1.0, 0, 1.33, 1.67, -1.67, -1.0, 0\}$

12.14. $\sigma^s = \{13.10, 4.25, -21.90, -10.75, -7.49, -2.65, 8.10, -6.01, -11.45, 15.0, 20.0, -30.0, 1.06, 9.76\}$

$\delta^0 = 10^{-3}\{0, 2.94, 6.18, 6.13, 2.76, 0.54, 0, 0.873, 1.16, -2.18, -1.46, 0\}$

12.15. $X = 6.42$

12.16. Same as for Problem 12.13.

12.17. $N_{13}^s = 1.06$, $N_{04}^s = 9.76$

Selected References and Bibliography

Chapter 1. PRINCIPLES OF ANALYSIS

1.01. Argyris, J. H. and S. Kelsey, *Energy Theorems and Structural Analysis,* Butterworth, London, 1960.

1.02. Asplund, S. O., *Structural Mechanics, Classical and Matrix Methods,* Prentice-Hall, Englewood Cliffs, 1966.

1.03. Au, T., *Elementary Structural Mechanics,* Prentice-Hall, Englewood Cliffs, 1963.

1.04. Hoff, N. J., *Analysis of Structures,* Wiley, New York, 1956.

1.05. Laursen, H. I., *Structural Analysis,* McGraw-Hill, New York, 1969.

1.06. Maugh, L. C., *Statically Indeterminate Structures,* 2nd ed., Wiley, New York, 1964.

1.07. Oden, J. T., *Mechanics of Elastic Structures,* McGraw-Hill, New York, 1967.

1.08. Rubinstein, M. F., *Structural Systems—Statics, Dynamics and Stability,* Prentice-Hall, Englewood Cliffs, 1970.

1.09. Timoshenko, S. P., *History of Strength of Materials,* McGraw-Hill, New York, 1953.

1.10. Timoshenko, S. P., and D. H. Young, *Theory of Structures,* 2nd ed., McGraw-Hill, New York, 1965.

1.11. Tuma, J. J., *Theory and Problems of Structural Analysis,* Schaum's Outline Series, McGraw-Hill, New York, 1969.

1.12. Venkatraman, B. and S. A. Patel, *Structural Mechanics with Introduction to Elasticity and Plasticity,* McGraw-Hill, New York, 1970.

Chapter 2. STATIC VECTOR

2.1. Asplund, S. O., *Structural Mechanics, Classical and Matrix Methods,* Prentice-Hall, Englewood Cliffs, 1966, pp. 246–261.

2.2. Hall, A. S. and R. W. Woodhead, *Frame Analysis,* 2nd ed., Wiley, New York, 1967, pp. 69–83.

2.3. Newmark, N. M., *Numerical Procedure for Computing Deflection, Moments and Buckling Loads,* Trans. ASCE, Vol. 108, 1943, p. 1161.

Chapter 3. DEFORMATION VECTOR

3.1. Clough, R. W., *Matrix Analysis of Beams,* Proc. ASCE, Journal of the Engineering Mechanics Division, Vol. 84, No. EM1, January 1958, Paper 1494.

3.2. Godden, W. G., *Numerical Analysis of Beam and Column Structures,* Prentice-Hall, Englewood Cliffs, 1965, pp. 1–59.

3.3. Hall, A. S. and R. W. Woodhead, *Frame Analysis,* 2nd ed., Wiley, New York, 1967, pp. 29–33.

Chapter 4. TRANSPORT MATRIX

4.1. Livesley, R. K., *Matrix Methods of Structural Analysis*, Pergamon Press, Oxford, 1964, pp. 177–198.

4.2. Pestel, E. C. and F. A. Leckie, *Matrix Methods of Elastostatics*, McGraw-Hill, New York, 1963, pp. 130–191.

4.3. Tuma, J. J., *Theory and Problems of Structural Analysis*, Schaum's Outline Series, McGraw-Hill, New York, 1969, pp. 138–161.

Chapter 5. FLEXIBILITY MATRIX

5.1. Gere, J. M. and W. Weaver, Jr., *Analysis of Framed Structures*, Van Nostrand, Princeton, N. J., 1965, pp. 41–120.

5.2. Hall, A. S. and R. W. Woodhead, *Frame Analysis*, 2nd ed., Wiley, New York, 1967, pp. 85–105.

5.3. Michalos, J., *Theory of Structural Analysis and Design*, Ronald Press, New York, 1959, pp. 20–24.

5.4. Tuma, J. J., *Flexibilities, Vol. I*, School of Civil Engineering Research Publication No. 9, Oklahoma State University, Stillwater, Oklahoma, 1961.

Chapter 6. VARIABLE CROSS SECTION

6.1. Boecker, H. C., J. E. French, T. L. Lassley, J. T. Oden, H. S. Yu, and J. J. Tuma, *Flexibilities, Vol. III*, School of Civil Engineering Research Publication No. 11, Oklahoma State University, Stillwater, Oklahoma, 1963.

6.2. Chu, S. L., *Beam Constants by the String Polygon Method*, School of Civil Engineering Research Publication No. 16, Oklahoma State University, Stillwater, Oklahoma, 1963.

6.3. Gere, J. M., *Moment Distribution*, Van Nostrand, Princeton, N. J., 1963, pp. 104–131.

6.4. *Handbook of Frame Constants*, Portland Cement Association, Chicago, 1947, pp. 24–31.

6.5. Lassley, T. L., S. E. French, and J. J. Tuma, *Analysis of Continuous Beam Bridges, Vol. II*, School of Civil Engineering Research Publication No. 4, Oklahoma State University, Stillwater, Oklahoma, 1959.

6.6. Tuma, J. J., S. E. French, and T. L. Lassley, *Analysis of Continuous Beam Bridges, Vol. I*, School of Civil Engineering Research Publication No. 3, Oklahoma State University, Stillwater, Oklahoma, 1959.

Chapter 7. CONTINUOUS BEAM

7.1. Benscoter, S. U., *Matrix Analysis of Continuous Beams*, Trans. ASCE., Vol. 112, 1947, p. 1109.

7.2. Clough, R. W., *Matrix Analysis of Beams*, Proc. ASCE, Journal of the Engineering Mechanics Division, Vol. 84, No. EM1, January 1958, Paper 1494.

7.3. Munshi, R. K., *Analysis of Prestressed Concrete Continuous Beams by the Carry-Over Moment Method*, M. S. Thesis, Oklahoma State University Library, Stillwater, Oklahoma, 1961.

7.4. Tuma, J. J., *Analysis of Continuous Beams by Carry-Over Moments*, Proc. ASCE, Journal of the Structural Division, Vol. 84, No. ST5, Sept. 1958, Paper 1762.

7.5. Tuma, J. J. and K. S. Havner, *Analysis of Continuous Beams on Elastic Supports by Carry-Over Moments*, School of Civil Engineering Research Publication No. 7, Oklahoma State University, Stillwater, Oklahoma, 1959.

Chapter 8. ELASTIC ARCH

8.1. Cross, H., *Column Analogy,* University of Illinois Engineering Experiment Station Bulletin No. 203, Urbana, Illinois, 1930.

8.2. Grinter, L. E., *Theory of Modern Steel Structures, Vol. II,* rev. ed., Macmillan, New York, 1949, pp. 239–303.

8.3. Maugh, L. C., *Statically Indeterminate Structures,* 2nd ed., Wiley, New York, 1964, pp. 288–335.

8.4. Parcel, J. I., and R. B. B. Moorman, *Analysis of Statically Indeterminate Structures,* Wiley, New York, 1955, pp. 457-501.

Chapter 9. RIGID FRAME

9.1. Argyris, J. H., *Recent Advances in Matrix Methods of Structural Analysis,* Macmillan, New York, 1964, pp. 1–32.

9.2. Denke, P. H., *A General Digital Computer Analysis of Statically Indeterminate Structures,* Agard Structures and Materials Panel Meeting, Aachen, Germany, 1959.

9.3. Gallagher, R. H., *A Correlation Study of Methods of Matrix Structural Analysis,* Macmillan, New York, 1964, pp. 5–11.

9.4. Griffiths, J. O., *Single Span Rigid Frames in Steel,* American Institute of Steel Construction, Inc., New York, 1948, pp. 18–19, 24–25.

9.5. Michalos, J., *Theory of Structural Analysis and Design,* Ronald Press, New York, 1958, pp. 197–234.

9.6. Przemieniecki, J. S., *Theory of Matrix Structural Analysis,* McGraw-Hill, New York, 1968, pp. 192–230.

9.7. Timoshenko, S. P. and D. H. Young, *Theory of Structures,* 2nd ed., McGraw-Hill, New York, 1965, pp. 510–516.

9.8. Tuma, J. J., *Theory and Problems of Structural Analysis,* Schaum's Outline Series, McGraw-Hill, New York, 1969, pp. 208–217.

9.9. Tuma, J. J. and J. T. Oden, *String Polygon Analysis of Frames with Straight Members,* Proc. ASCE, Journal of the Structural Division, Vol. 87, No. ST7, October 1961, Paper 2956, p. 61.

Chapter 10. STIFFNESS MATRIX

10.1. Carman, D. C. and J. J. Tuma, *Preliminary Analysis of Continuous Curved Girder Frames,* Proc. ASCE, Journal of the Structural Division, Vol. 90, No. ST4, August 1964, Paper 4012.

10.2. Fowler, K. T., *Slope Deflection Equations for Curved Members,* Trans. ASCE, Vol. 116, 1951, pp. 125–143.

10.3. Gere, J. M. and W. Weaver, Jr., *Analysis of Framed Structures,* Van Nostrand, Princeton, N. J., 1965, pp. 41–120.

10.4. Gillespie, J. W. and J. J. Tuma, *Preliminary Analysis of Continuous Gable Frames,* Proc. ASCE, Journal of the Structural Division, Vol. 86, No. ST4, April 1960, Paper 2444.

10.5. Michalos, J., *Theory of Structural Analysis and Design,* Ronald Press, New York, 1958, pp. 234–252, 288–291.

10.6. Parcel, J. I. and R. B. B. Moorman, *Analysis of Statically Indeterminate Structures,* Wiley, New York, 1955, pp. 408–430.

10.7. Tuma, J. J., K. S. Havner and F. Hedges, *Analysis of Frames with Curved and Bent Members,* Proc. ASCE, Journal of the Structural Division, Vol. 84, No. ST5, Sept. 1958, Paper 1764.

Chapter 11. COMPLEX FRAME

11.1. Argyris, J. H., *Recent Advances in Matrix Methods of Structural Analysis,* Macmillan, New York, 1964, pp. 40–86.

11.2. Gallagher, R. H., *A Correlation Study of Methods of Matrix Structural Analysis,* Macmillan, New York, 1964, pp. 11–15.

11.3. Martin, C. A., *Application of a Digital Computer to the Solution of Slope Deflection Equations for Rigid Frames and Truss-Frames,* M. S. Thesis, Oklahoma State University Library, Stillwater, Oklahoma, 1958.

11.4. Przemieniecki, J. S., *Matrix Structural Analysis of Substructures,* AIAA Journal, No. 1, January 1963, pp. 138–147.

Chapter 12. PLANAR TRUSS

12.1. Martin, H. C., *Introduction to Matrix Methods of Structural Analysis,* McGraw-Hill, New York, 1966, pp. 28–60.

12.2. Timoshenko, S. P. and D. H. Young, *Theory of Structures,* 2nd ed., McGraw-Hill, New York, 1965, pp. 491–500.

12.3. Tuma, J. J., *Analysis of Continuous Trusses by Carry-Over Moments,* Proc. ASCE, Vol. 85, No. ST10, December 1959, Paper 2314.

12.4. Wang, C. K., *Matrix Methods of Structural Analysis,* International Textbook, Scranton, Pa., 1966, pp. 34–55, 139–155.

INDEX